The ARRL
Operating
Manual
For Radio Amateurs

Tenth Edition

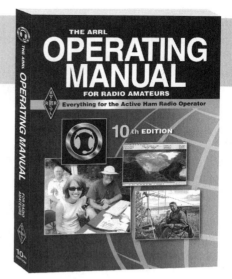

Cover Info: Clockwise from lower right, Stu, WØSTU, uses a dual band 2-meter/ 70 cm antenna to enjoy VHF contesting in the great outdoors (photo by Danny Oldfield, NØOLD); a Field Day "Get On the Air" station (photo by Dick Orander, KD4ISC); *Sat32PC* software tracking the Fuji-OSCAR 29 satellite.

Back cover: Several PSK31 signals in a *DigiPan* waterfall display.

Editor
Mark J. Wilson, K1RO

Editorial Assistant
Maty Weinberg, KB1EIB

Cover Design
Sue Fagan, KB1OKW

Production
Michelle Bloom, WB1ENT
Jodi Morin, KA1JPA
Nancy G. Hallas, W1NCY
David F. Pingree, N1NAS
Carol Michaud, KB1QAW
Becky R. Schoenfeld, W1BXY

Published by:
ARRL

the national association for Amateur Radio™
Newington, CT 06111 USA

P9-CJJ-751

Table of Contents

Foreword

Talking to friends. Serving your community. Chasing DX. Adding a new band. Trying a new mode. Working a contest. Having fun with radio. Does any of this sound appealing? If so, you've come to the right place.

Amateur Radio offers a stunning variety of on-air operating activities to try. Once you have your license in hand and have mastered the basics, what else can you try? The 10th edition of the *ARRL Operating Manual* is here to show you some of the many different activities in the world of Amateur Radio. Each chapter jumps into a different aspect of ham radio, but all of the chapters describe things you can do with your gear. In some cases you may need to pick up another radio, antenna or accessory, but in many cases you already have the hardware needed to get started.

Each chapter in the edition has been prepared and revised by experienced hams who are active on the air. They have "been there, done that" and are happy to share what they have learned so that you can get involved too.

Your station isn't a museum display. It's there to be used and is just waiting for a chance to reach out and contact someone. So what are you waiting for? Get on the air, stretch your comfort zone a bit and see what Amateur Radio has to offer.

David Sumner, K1ZZ
Chief Executive Officer
Newington, Connecticut
September 2012

About the ARRL

The seed for Amateur Radio was planted in the 1890s, when Guglielmo Marconi began his experiments in wireless telegraphy. Soon he was joined by dozens, then hundreds, of others who were enthusiastic about sending and receiving messages through the air—some with a commercial interest, but others solely out of a love for this new communications medium. The United States government began licensing Amateur Radio operators in 1912.

By 1914, there were thousands of Amateur Radio operators—hams—in the United States. Hiram Percy Maxim, a leading Hartford, Connecticut inventor and industrialist, saw the need for an organization to band together this fledgling group of radio experimenters. In May 1914 he founded the American Radio Relay League (ARRL) to meet that need.

Today ARRL, with approximately 155,000 members, is the largest organization of radio amateurs in the United States. The ARRL is a not-for-profit organization that:
- promotes interest in Amateur Radio communications and experimentation
- represents US radio amateurs in legislative matters, and
- maintains fraternalism and a high standard of conduct among Amateur Radio operators.

At ARRL headquarters in the Hartford suburb of Newington, the staff helps serve the needs of members. ARRL is also International Secretariat for the International Amateur Radio Union, which is made up of similar societies in 150 countries around the world.

ARRL publishes the monthly journal *QST* and an interactive digital version of *QST*, as well as newsletters and many publications covering all aspects of Amateur Radio. Its headquarters station, W1AW, transmits bulletins of interest to radio amateurs and Morse code practice sessions. The ARRL also coordinates an extensive field organization, which includes volunteers who provide technical information and other support services for radio amateurs as well as communications for public-service activities. In addition, ARRL represents US amateurs with the Federal Communications Commission and other government agencies in the US and abroad.

Membership in ARRL means much more than receiving *QST* each month. In addition to the services already described, ARRL offers membership services on a personal level, such as the Technical Information Service—where members can get answers by phone, email or the ARRL website, to all their technical and operating questions.

Full ARRL membership (available only to licensed radio amateurs) gives you a voice in how the affairs of the organization are governed. ARRL policy is set by a Board of Directors (one from each of 15 Divisions). Each year, one-third of the ARRL Board of Directors stands for election by the full members they represent. The day-to-day operation of ARRL HQ is managed by an Executive Vice President and his staff.

No matter what aspect of Amateur Radio attracts you, ARRL membership is relevant and important. There would be no Amateur Radio as we know it today were it not for the ARRL. We would be happy to welcome you as a member! (An Amateur Radio license is not required for Associate Membership.) For more information about ARRL and answers to any questions you may have about Amateur Radio, write or call:

ARRL — the national association for Amateur Radio®
225 Main Street
Newington CT 06111-1494
Voice: 860-594-0200
Fax: 860-594-0259
E-mail: **hq@arrl.org**
Internet: **www.arrl.org**

Prospective new amateurs call (toll-free):
800-32-NEW HAM (800-326-3942)
You can also contact us via e-mail at **newham@arrl.org**
or check out the ARRL website at **www.arrl.org**

ARRL Member Services

 **Get Involved**
www.arrl.org/get-involved

 **Join or Renew**
www.arrl.org/join

 **Donate**
www.arrl.org/donate

 **Shop**
www.arrl.org/shop

Membership Benefits

Your ARRL membership includes *QST* magazine, plus dozens of other services and resources to help you **Get Started**, **Get Involved** and **Get On the Air**. ARRL members enjoy Amateur Radio to the fullest!

Members-Only Web Services

Create an online ARRL Member Profile, and get access to ARRL members-only Web services. Visit **www.arrl.org/myARRL** to register.

- **New *QST* Digital Edition – www.arrl.org/qst**
  All ARRL members can access the online digital edition of *QST*. Enjoy enhanced content, convenient access and a more interactive experience.

- ***QST* Archive and Periodicals Search – www.arrl.org/qst**
  Browse ARRL's extensive online *QST* archive (1915-2011). A searchable index for *QEX* and *NCJ* is also available.

- **Free E-Newsletters**
  Subscribe to a variety of ARRL E-newsletters and e-mail announcements: ham radio news, radio clubs, public service, contesting and more!

- **Product Review Archive – www.arrl.org/qst**
  Search for, and download, *QST* Product Reviews published from 1980 to present.

- **E-Mail Forwarding Service**
  E-mail sent to your arrl.net address will be forwarded to any e-mail account you specify.

- **Customized ARRL.org home page**
  Customize your home page to see local ham radio events, clubs and news.

- **ARRL Member Directory**
  Connect with other ARRL members via a searchable online Member Directory. Share profiles, photos and more with members who have similar interests.

ARRL Technical Information Service — www.arrl.org/tis

Get answers on a variety of technical and operating topics through ARRL's Technical Information Service. ARRL Lab experts and technical volunteers can help you overcome hurdles and answer all your questions.

ARRL as an Advocate — www.arrl.org/regulatory-advocacy

ARRL supports legislation and regulatory measures that preserve and protect access to Amateur Radio Service frequencies. Members may contact the **ARRL Regulatory Information Branch** for information on FCC rules; problems with antenna, tower and zoning restrictions; and reciprocal licensing procedures for international travelers.

ARRL Group Benefit Programs* — www.arrl.org/benefits

- **ARRL "Special Risk" Ham Radio Equipment Insurance Plan**
  Insurance is available to protect you from loss or damage to your station, antennas and mobile equipment by lightning, theft, accident, fire, flood, tornado, and other natural disasters.

- **The ARRL Visa Signature® Card**
  Every purchase supports ARRL programs and services.

- **MetLife® Auto, Home, Renters, Boaters, Fire Insurance and Banking Products**
  ARRL members may qualify for up to a 10% discount on home or auto insurance.

  * ARRL Group Benefit Programs are offered by third parties through contractual arrangements with ARRL. The programs and coverage are available in the US only. Other restrictions may apply.

Programs

Public Service — www.arrl.org/public-service
Amateur Radio Emergency Service® – **www.arrl.org/ares**
Emergency Communications Training – **www.arrl.org/emcomm-training**

Radiosport
Awards – **www.arrl.org/awards**
Contests – **www.arrl.org/contests**
QSL Service – **www.arrl.org/qsl**
Logbook of the World – **www.arrl.org/lotw**

Community
Radio Clubs (ARRL-affiliated clubs) – **www.arrl.org/clubs**
Hamfests and Conventions – **www.arrl.org/hamfests**
ARRL Field Organization – **www.arrl.org/field-organization**

Licensing, Education and Training
Find a License Exam Session – **www.arrl.org/exam**
Find a Licensing Class – **www.arrl.org/class**
ARRL Continuing Education Program – **www.arrl.org/courses-training**
Books, Software and Operating Resources – **www.arrl.org/shop**

Quick Links and Resources
QST – ARRL members' journal – **www.arrl.org/qst**
QEX – A Forum for Communications Experimenters – **www.arrl.org/qex**
NCJ – National Contest Journal – **www.arrl.org/ncj**
Support for Instructors – **www.arrl.org/instructors**
Support for Teachers – **www.arrl.org/teachers**
ARRL Volunteer Examiner Coordinator (ARRL VEC) – **www.arrl.org/vec**
Public and Media Relations – **www.arrl.org/media**
Forms and Media Warehouse – **www.arrl.org/forms**
FCC License Renewal – **www.arrl.org/fcc**
Foundation, Grants and Scholarships – **www.arrl.org/arrl-foundation**
Advertising – **www.arrl.org/ads**

Interested in Becoming a New Ham?

www.arrl.org/newham
e-mail **newham@arrl.org**
Tel 1-800-326-3942 (US)

Contact Us

ARRL, the national association for Amateur Radio®
225 Main Street, Newington, CT 06111-1494 USA
Tel 1-860-594-0200, Mon-Fri 8 AM to 5 PM ET (except holidays)
FAX 1-860-594-0259, e-mail **hqinfo@arrl.org**, website – **www.arrl.org**

 Facebook
www.facebook.com/ARRL.org

 Follow us on Twitter
twitter.com/arrl · **twitter.com/w1aw**
twitter.com/arrl_youth · **twitter.com/arrl_emcomm**

 YouTube
www.youtube.com/ARRLHQ

The American Radio Relay League, Inc.

The American Radio Relay League, Inc. is a noncommercial association of radio amateurs, organized for the promotion of interest in Amateur Radio communication and experimentation, for the establishment of networks to provide communication in the event of disasters or other emergencies, for the advancement of the radio art and of the public welfare, for the representation of the radio amateur in legislative matters, and for the maintenance of fraternalism and a high standard of conduct.

ARRL is an incorporated association without capital stock chartered under the laws of the State of Connecticut, and is an exempt organization under Section 501(c)(3) of the Internal Revenue Code of 1986. Its affairs are governed by a Board of Directors, whose voting members are elected every three years by the general membership. The officers are elected or appointed by the directors. The League is noncommercial, and no one

with a pervasive and continuing conflict of interest is eligible for membership on its Board.

"Of, by, and for the radio amateur," the ARRL numbers within its ranks the vast majority of active amateurs in the nation and has a proud history of achievement as the standard-bearer in amateur affairs.

A *bona fide* interest in Amateur Radio is the only essential qualification of membership; an Amateur Radio license is not a prerequisite, although full voting membership is granted only to licensed amateurs in the US.

Membership inquiries and general correspondence should be addressed to the administrative headquarters: ARRL, 225 Main Street, Newington, Connecticut 06111-1494.

The Amateur's Code

The Radio Amateur is:

CONSIDERATE...never knowingly operates in such a way as to lessen the pleasure of others.

LOYAL...offers loyalty, encouragement and support to other amateurs, local clubs, and the American Radio Relay League, through which Amateur Radio in the United States is represented nationally and internationally.

PROGRESSIVE...with knowledge abreast of science, a well-built and efficient station and operation above reproach.

FRIENDLY...slow and patient operating when requested; friendly advice and counsel to the beginner; kindly assistance, cooperation and consideration for the interests of others. These are the hallmarks of the amateur spirit.

BALANCED...radio is an avocation, never interfering with duties owed to family, job, school or community.

PATRIOTIC...station and skill always ready for service to country and community.

—The original Amateur's Code was written by Paul M. Segal, W9EEA, in 1928.

Amateur Radio — All About Operating

Amateur Radio is all about operating — all the technology and procedures in the world are no substitute for hams getting on the air and making contacts. That's what this book is about — how hams send their signals and why. Hams have found dozens of ways to have fun and engage in useful activities on the air. You'll find many of those described here — both to provide guidance in participating and for your general interest in unfamiliar forms of Amateur Radio.

You may have taken an interest in ham radio because of a specific need or activity — public service, emergency communications, interest in electronics or even radio-controlled models! Right away, you'll find yourself immersed in Amateur Radio, learning the ropes of your preferred activity. As you operate and become more skilled, a curious thing will happen. You'll discover that there is considerable magic behind the front panel of your radio, out there between the antennas, and in the minds of your compatriot hams! Your Amateur Radio license is the gateway to exploring as much of that magic as you wish.

Amateur Radio provides opportunities to learn about and experiment with technology. It's also a way to learn electronic communication skills. It's a means to overcome the limitations of physical handicaps and enter an open arena of communications. It's fun and a great way to make friends. It's an opportunity to participate in public service activities. And it's an opportunity to serve your community and make your neighborhood a better place to live.

With all the communications technology available in the modern world, is there still a useful role for Amateur Radio? Certainly, there is! Part of the magic of everyday Amateur Radio arises from the "who's out there?"

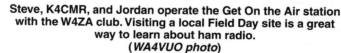

Steve, K4CMR, and Jordan operate the Get On the Air station with the W4ZA club. Visiting a local Field Day site is a great way to learn about ham radio.
(WA4VUO photo)

nature of all those hams sharing the bands. Whether you communicate with a regular circle of friends or spend your time tuning the bands in search of a new call sign, an unexpected surprise may be no farther away than your next CQ ("calling any station"). When disaster strikes and normal communications are knocked out for a time, hams step in and harness that magic for the public's benefit.

This *ARRL Operating Manual* covers the most popular activities in ham radio. No matter if you're completely new to Amateur Radio or an experienced ham looking for information on a new way to communicate, this book can help you decide what to operate, where to operate and how to operate. Think of your participation in Amateur Radio as a never-ending journey — there's always something new to explore, always something new to do!

Why Amateur Radio Exists

Amateur Radio owes its existence to international and national regulations. These regulations reflect the value of Amateur Radio as perceived by national and international leaders, giving it a place on the airwaves as a peer to commercial and military services. In the United States, the fundamental purpose of the Amateur Radio Service is expressed in the following principles outlined in Federal Communications Commission rule §97.1:

(a) Recognition and enhancement of the value of the amateur service to the public as a voluntary noncommercial communication service, particularly with respect to providing emergencycommunications.

(b) Continuation and extension of the amateur's proven ability to contribute to the advancement of the radio art.

Who Reads the *Operating Manual*?

The *Operating Manual* has something for just about every ham, no matter what their level of skill or how long they've been licensed. While it can't possibly cover all of the different activities heard on the ham bands, it can provide an introduction and guide to many of those activities.

In each section, we'll introduce you to the basic terminology and ideas behind that particular aspect of ham radio. You'll learn why hams operate that way and why it is of interest.

Following the introduction, we'll explain how to actually "do" that kind of ham radio. There might be specific equipment or technical know-how that is required. You might need to learn some new terms or concepts. Most types of operating have guidelines or conventions that you'll be expected to follow. When you finish reading a chapter, you'll have the basic ideas under your belt.

The goal of the *Operating Manual* is both to educate you on some of the many ways in which hams make use of our spectrum allocations and to provide you with the necessary information to get started yourself. Remember that no one is expected to know everything about ham radio! Treat this book as your personal launching pad to enjoying a broad range of what ham radio has to offer.

Beginning Hams

If you are just getting started in ham radio, you'll find the *Operating Manual* to be a feast of information about ham radio. You may have read about these activities and even engaged in a couple, but here is the mainstream of the service! Start by skimming the book from cover to cover. Then go back to the parts you found most interesting and read those chapters in detail. Try a few of the activities on the air, using the book as a confidence-boosting guide. If you enjoyed them, keep it up! If not, try something else — ham radio is supposed to be enjoyable and fun, not a job. Sooner or later, you'll find your "home" in ham radio. Keep the *Operating Manual* handy on your radio shack bookshelf as a reference and guide to on-the-air events and activities.

Intermediate Hams

Once you've been active for a while, you'll find yourself becoming comfortable with your favorite activities. You can use the *Operating Manual* to help you sharpen your skills as it describes the fine points of the service. By using the information here, you can avoid some of the common pitfalls and keep your enjoyment high as you learn.

You will probably find yourself branching out within ham radio, as well. For example, your main interest may be DXing, but you might be asked to provide some public service by working on a parade route communications team. Perhaps you've been working on earning awards, but have an opportunity to join a club multioperator contest team. It's time to grab your copy of the *Operating Manual* and do some reading about these unfamiliar activities! The information won't make you an instant expert, but it will help you get started as quickly as possible.

Experienced Hams

Once upon a time, reading *QST* every month was enough to keep a ham in touch with just about every significant type of operating in ham radio. No longer! Ham radio has grown to cover so many different activities that it's no longer possible for a single person to be an expert in every single one. New activities and types of operating are springing up all the time. New technology transforms old activities, as well. So even if you are the proverbial "jack of all trades," you'll find these chapters an introduction to something you haven't yet tried or a refresher on a familiar activity.

(c) Encouragement and improvement of the amateur service through rules which provide for advancing skills in both the communications and technical phases of the art.

(d) Expansion of the existing reservoir within the amateur radio service of trained operators, technicians, and electronics experts.

(e) Continuation and extension of the amateur's unique ability to enhance international goodwill.

These principles are quite broad, giving amateurs a lot of room to pursue their individual vision. As a result, Amateur Radio is continually changing and evolving — technologically and procedurally. At the same time, it carries these principles forward as traditions as old as radio itself. Amateur Radio, by definition, is the sum of the efforts of all amateurs.

Amateur Radio is a Service

If you have read the Public Service column and articles in *QST* and feature stories on the ARRL website (**www.arrl.org**) you've seen the exploits of hams from all walks of life who have selflessly donated their time by providing emergency communication. Many, many more hams provide this service than are given recognition by the media, but that's all part of being a ham — the intrinsic reward is the satisfaction of doing a job well. Just ask the hams who served in the aftermath of hurricanes, tornados, ice storms and other disasters large and small.

You may or may not be called at some time to provide this service to your community. But by being prepared, honing your on-the-air operating skills to their sharpest, maximizing your equipment to obtain the best from it, and being prepared to pitch in should the need arise, you will be ready. In so doing, you will derive untold hours of satisfaction from the exciting hobby we know as Amateur Radio.

The Diversity of Hams

With a desire to serve her community in disasters and other emergencies, a Washington woman signs up for classes in first aid and techniques to support the local fire department. After receiving some training in use of handheld radios, a newspaper notice of Amateur Radio classes catches her eye. After she passes her Technician exam she joins the local club and ARES® team. Soon, her enthusiasm convinces

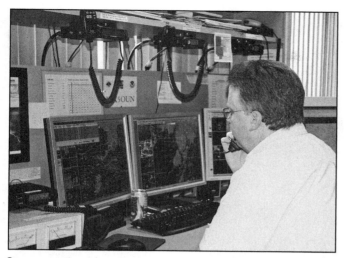

Severe weather often threatens lives and property in the Midwest. Hams like Rick, KI5GT, work with NOAA's SKYWARN program to report and track storms.

her husband to become licensed and join the fun. During a subsequent weather-related emergency, they provide valuable service to their fellow citizens.

A boy asks his father how radios and computers work. They talk a bit and then begin to experiment. The talks and experiments lead to further study and the topics broaden. The boy's interest in technology continues to grow. He studies for and passes his first Amateur Radio license examination, and shortly after that he upgrades. He enjoys communicating, but the technology is what really attracts his interest. What does his future hold? No doubt he'll have a career in some field of electronics.

The young woman, every inch a competitor, shouted with joy as she read the results of the recent on-the-air competition. Not only had she beaten everyone else in her entry

category in the contest, but she had also set a world record. She felt great! Elsewhere, a mechanic is working on a vehicle, but not to repair it for a customer. It's a special kind of mobile amateur station called a *rover*. The weekend of a major VHF+ contest is approaching quickly and he needs to have the new antenna mounts done in time to add to his team's score. They plan on operating from a plateau straddling a mountain pass. Will the vehicle be ready in time?

After work at his job in a large information technology department, the computer professional decides to work on his latest project — setting up a high-speed packet radio system for his club's digital Amateur Radio message-forwarding system. This is brand-new technology, so he's working with sketchy information, using his experience with networks and software to offer clues as to what he changes he should make. By mid-evening, he's able to connect his system with another high-speed node and pass several messages over the UHF radio link.

The middle-aged man turned in his chair when the computer beeped an alert. Yes! The station he had wanted to contact had been spotted on the air. That station was set up on an island in the Indian Ocean by a couple of hams, a husband-and-wife team who spend their vacations operating Amateur Radio from exotic locations. Yes, they have an antenna atop the apartment building where they live, but there's a big difference between operating from home and operating from an exotic location that great numbers of hams want to contact.

The young girl, having come home from school, went into her bedroom and turned on her radio. No music came from the radio. Instead, she picked up the microphone and called another Amateur Radio station. A familiar voice answered her call, "Hi, honey, how are you today? Over." She replied, "I'm fine, grandpa. Let me tell you what happened today..."

You might think you know these folks. It's possible, since they are real. But the descriptions fit many persons. All kinds of people enjoy communicating over the air. Kings and diplomats, homemakers and waiters, engineers and scientists, teachers and students, doctors and bookkeepers find fun, challenge and fulfillment in Amateur Radio. Day or night, hams are communicating with each other, helping others, doing technical experiments or just simply having fun by meeting new people.

The Wide Variety of Ham Activities

Hams are involved in all sorts of fun, challenging and fulfilling activities. That means not just from home, but on the move — in a car, or on a bike or hiking in the mountains. You might be on the sea or in the air — even in Earth orbit, where spacefaring hams have enjoyed using their radios from aboard the Space Shuttle and International Space Station.

The chapter titles of this book provide only partial insight into the scope of

On the air since before WWII, Bill, W4EHF, has been building equipment throughout his ham career and recently upgraded to Amateur Extra at the age of 93. (*K4MHM photo*)

Mother-daughter team KBØSQQ and KBØYHM operate 15 meter phone during the 2007 Field Day operation of the Boeing-Wichita club, KCØAHN. (*Charles Rasico photo*)

activities in which Amateur Radio operators are engaged. So what sorts of things do hams do?

Near, Far, Wherever You Are

Some enjoy communicating locally or training for disaster response or emergency communications using small, inexpensive, low-powered VHF/UHF radios that operate on fixed channels using FM voice. Repeaters extend their limited range by amplifying and retransmitting their signals. Depending on where the repeater is located, you can talk with other hams 50 or even 100 miles away. Distances up to 30 miles are common.

Others are enchanted with using the ionosphere to bounce HF signals to and from faraway places thousands of miles away. The object of their quest is distant stations (DX). They try to contact as many distinct political and geographic areas as they can. The quest is complete when the contact is confirmed with a *QSL* card — a colorful and interesting postcard confirming contact with another station — in the mail or via a contact confirmation service such as the ARRL's *Logbook of the World* (**www.arrl.org/logbook-of-the-world**).

Hybrids of the VHF/UHF repeaters and the Internet have been developed by hams to extend the range of communications of those low-power radios to HF distances. The Internet Radio Linking Project (IRLP, **www.irlp.net**), Echolink (**www.echolink.org**), Yaesu's WIRES-II (**www.yaesu.com**) and D-STAR (**www.icomamerica.com**) systems combine radio and digitized voice to connect portable and mobile hams around the world.

DX (ham shorthand for long distance) holds a special fascination for many hams. It can be correctly defined in different ways. To most amateurs, DX is the lure of seeing how far away you can establish a QSO — the greater the distance, the better. DX is a personal achievement, bettering some previous "best distance worked," involving a set of self-imposed rules.

DX can also be competitive on a large scale, as "DXers" try to break through the pileups of people calling a rare DX station. DXers often aim for one of the DX-oriented awards such as ARRL's DX Century Club® (DXCC®). DXing can be a full-time goal for some hams and a just-for-fun challenge for others. Regardless of whether you turn into a serious DXer or just have a little fun searching for entities you have yet to work, DXing is one of the most fascinating aspects of Amateur Radio.

Some enjoy the thrill and adventure of travel to and operating from the "other side of the pileup" from distant and exotic places. Hams often operate on a vacation trip to a warm island in the Caribbean to escape the freezing winter weather, or on a business trip to Europe or Asia. Others take special trips called *DXpeditions* to the ends of the Earth — Antarctica, desert islands and mountain kingdoms. There they make contacts at high rates for a few days as DXers around the world try to get their call signs "in the log."

Out of This World!

Hams are not limited to communication on the Earth. Many enjoy talking with astronauts and cosmonauts in orbit. Hams have been communicating with the Space Shuttle since

David, AJ5W, and Harry, KC5TRB, prepare a balloon for launch with an Automatic Packet Reporting System (APRS) tracker as part of the payload, a science experiment to measure ozone levels. (*KE5DTZ photo*)

Bruce, KØYW, traveled to the home of Alex, KH6YY, on Oahu to make earth-moon-earth (EME) or "moonbounce" contacts on the 23 cm microwave band.

You don't have to use big antennas to contact amateur satellites. This group from Boulder Hill Elementary in Montgomery, Illinois made contacts through amateur satellite AO-51 during the School Club Roundup using this handheld antenna and radio.

Owen Garriott, W5LFL, took his 2 meter handheld radio to orbit on mission STS-9 in 1983. W5LFL contacted 250 hams from space, even King Hussein of Jordan (call sign JY1)! Today, nearly all residents of the International Space Station (ISS) are hams and regularly make contact with hams on the ground. The ISS ham radio station even has its own call sign, NA1SS. In 2006, Bill McArthur contacted all 50 states and 100 countries, achieving the first WAS and DXCC from space.

Hams also communicate with each other through satellites that hams themselves have designed and built. On such amateur organization is AMSAT (**www.amsat.org**). It is fully funded by amateurs and builds professional-quality "birds." Some hams even bounce their signals to each other off the Moon. Others reflect their transmissions off of the active aurora or a short-lived meteor trail. Hams have been pioneers in many modes of communication, paving the way for many different commercial uses.

Competitions

The thrill of competition calls some hams to enter contests for a weekend of intense activity. It's a way to test station capability and operator skills. For the busy ham, it's a great way to cram a lot of contacts into a short period of time. For others, a contest involves operating away from home — perhaps with friends at a "super station" or on the road as a mobile or rover.

Contesting is to Amateur Radio what the Olympic Games are to worldwide amateur athletic competition: a showcase to display talent and learned skills, as well as a stimulus for further achievement through competition. Increased operating skills and greater station effectiveness may be the end result of Amateur Radio contesting, but the most common experience is *fun*.

The contest operator is also likely to have one of the better signals on the band — not necessarily by using the most elaborate or expensive station equipment, but by knowing how to get the most out of whatever resources are available. Competitive operation encourages continuous improvement in station and operator efficiency. Nearly every contest has competitors vying to see which one can work the most stations (depending on the rules of the particular contest) in a given time frame. In some contests, the top-scoring stations have consistently worked 100 or more stations per hour for the entire 48-hour contest period. Other contests are *sprints* — they run for just a few hours.

The ARRL contest program is so diverse that one contest or another appeals to almost every type of ham — the beginning contester and the old hand, the newest Technician and the most experienced Amateur Extra veteran, the "Topband" (160 meter) buff and the microwave enthusiast. Contest announcements appear in *QST* a few months before the contest, in *QST's* Contest Corral column, or

New licensee Dan, KC2RKB, exercises his skills, engaged in "search and pounce" while operating ARRL Field Day with his Dad Walter, WS2Z.

Scott, KP2/NE1RD, combined vacation with ham radio. He traveled to the US Virgin Islands during the 2006 ARRL DX Phone Contest and used a portable station to have a great time working stations in the contest.

on the ARRL website at **www.arrl.org/contests**. There is at least one contest for every interest. A summary of the contest results appear in *QST* while detailed scores and analysis are posted on the ARRL website.

Competition takes many forms. Hams who love to collect awards compete against themselves. Are they able to make contact with all the states? All the counties? All the prefectures of Japan or the provinces of Spain? The ARRL offers the awards listed in **Table 1.1**. Most other national amateur societies, private clubs and contest groups sponsor awards and certificates for various operating accomplishments. Many of the awards are very handsome paper certificates or intricately designed plaques very much in demand by awards chasers.

Some hams take to foot or vehicle with direction-finding equipment to see who's the best at finding a hidden transmitter. Their competitions may be local or international, such as the Amateur Radio Direction-Finding contests (**www.ardf-r2.org**).

Table 1.1
ARRL Operating Awards
(www.arrl.org/awards)

Award	Qualification
Worked All States (WAS)	QSLs from all 50 US state
Triple Play	LoTW confirmations from all 50 US states on voice, CW and digital modes
Worked All Continents (WAC)	QSLs from all six continents
DX Century Club (DXCC)	QSLs from at least 100 foreign entities
VHF/UHF Century Club (VUCC)	QSLs from many grid locators
A-1 Operator Club	Recommendation by two A-1 operators
Code Proficiency	One minute of perfect copy from W1AW qualifying run
ARRL Membership	ARRL membership for 25, 40, 50, 60 or 70 years

Working Cooperatively

Those involved in *public service*, including *emergency communications* ("emcomm"), and *traffic handling* have to work together cooperatively to get the job done. Over many years of training and practice, hams have developed on-the-air procedures and organizations to communicate efficiently and effectively. By studying them and practicing with your local groups, you will become a valued member of an important volunteer service. Public service communications make Amateur Radio a valuable public resource, one that has been recognized by Congress and a whole host of federal, state and local agencies that serve the public.

Traffic handling involves passing messages to others over the amateur bands. Messages can be informal or constructed according to the rules of the *radiogram*, the ham radio equivalent of the telegram. Hams handle *third-party traffic* (messages for nonhams) in both routine situations and in times of disaster.

Nets are regular gatherings of hams who share a mutual interest and who use the net (short for "network") to further that interest. Their most common purpose is to pass traffic or participate in one of the many other ham activities, from awards chasing and DXing to just plain old talking among longtime friends. In an emergency or following a disaster, however, the net transforms into a powerful on-the-air coordination and information-sharing machine!

County and state hunting nets are very popular since they provide a frequency to work that 49th and 50th state for the ARRL WAS (Worked All States) award or rare county. Service nets are used by mobile and marine stations to request assistance, pass messages, or let their status be known.

There are nets dedicated to beginner or slow-speed CW operation. These can help a newcomer sharpen operating skills. To find the frequencies and meeting times of nets in your area, use the online net search facility via the ARRL Net Directory page at **www.arrl.org/arrl-net-directory-search**.

Rag Chewing

"Chewing the rag" refers to getting on the air and spending minutes (or hours!) in interesting conversation on virtually any and every topic imaginable. Without a doubt, the most popular operating activity is rag chewing. The rag chew may be something as simple as a brief chat on a 2 meter or 440 MHz FM repeater as you drive across town. It also may be a group of friends who have been meeting on 15 meter SSB every Saturday afternoon for 20 years. The essential element is the same — hams talking to each other on any subject that interests them.

PSK31, Packet and Other Digital Modes

Many years ago, RTTY (Baudot radioteletype) was the only digital mode. As computers became popular, then almost essential in the ham shack, the number of digital modes available to hams has expanded quickly.

The first computer-based modes were the various flavors of AMTOR (Amateur Teleprinting Over Radio) and packet radio, or just "packet" for short. Packet requires either a full computer or a terminal (display and keyboard or terminal emulation software on a computer) at each end, in addition to a packet radio controller and the radios themselves. The Automatic Packet Reporting System (APRS), an offshoot of packet, is a popular application.

First conceived as a way for sailing hams to exchange messages while at sea, the Winlink 2000 amateur e-mail system (**www.winlink.org**) has become a staple of public service and message handling. The Winlink 2000 system operates on both HF (via the PACTOR family of protocols) and VHF/UHF frequencies (via packet radio), using Amateur Radio to collect and deliver e-mail.

PSK31 is a digital mode that has become very popular on the HF bands. It is a narrow-band, real-time digital mode that exploits the ubiquitous sound card. The software is even available free of charge over the web.

The development and improvement of digital modes is one of the most active areas of experimentation by amateurs.

Getting on the Air

Let's say you've done your homework. You've studied hard and you passed your license exam. Congratulations! Like many newcomers to Amateur Radio, you probably have a Technician license, giving you full privileges on the VHF and UHF amateur bands and limited privileges on some of the HF bands. (A colorful, free frequency privileges chart can be downloaded from **www.arrl.org/graphical-frequency-allocations**.) Getting on the air for you may be as simple as finding a new (or used) VHF hand-held radio, charging the batteries and then talking with your new ham friends through a local FM repeater.

This is exactly how many hams begin their amateur operation — reliable, fun communication with a small group of friends in their own and nearby communities. With your Technician license in hand, you also can talk or send Morse code (CW) through the amateur satellites or to space shuttle astronauts. Or, with some additional equipment and some easy-to-find software, you can explore the VHF digital modes such as APRS. In addition, you can use SSB voice or CW to contact other stations on the VHF and UHF bands. These modes require transceivers and antennas that are different from those used for FM.

Giorgio, IZ4AKS, enjoys working RTTY (radioteletype) and is shown here operating from 1A4A at the Knights of Malta enclave in the heart of Rome.

Getting Started in Ham Radio

Okay, so you're interested in Amateur Radio (you probably wouldn't be reading this book if you weren't!). We hope we've piqued your interest about some of the neat things hams do. So, how do you get the information you need about specific aspects of our fascinating hobby? How do you go about getting your first license? And how do you go about setting up a station so you can actually start communicating with other hams?

First, let us introduce you to an organization dedicated specifically to Amateur Radio. It is the ARRL — the national association for Amateur Radio — headquartered in Newington, Connecticut (**www. arrl.org**). The ARRL is the only not-for-profit organization set up to serve the more than 700,000 Amateur Radio operators (hams) in the United States, and it has been serving amateurs since 1914. You should become a member.

The ARRL produces a line of publications dedicated to the radio amateur, including the book you are now reading. These materials provide great ways to keep informed of news and technical developments. Moreover, through your ARRL membership you will be supporting ongoing efforts in the national and international arenas that will help ensure that ham frequencies remain ham frequencies in spite of pressures from commercial interests.

Just about anything you may need to know — whether it be from the technical or operating sides of the hobby — can be found in ARRL materials. The basic beginner's publication is *The ARRL Ham Radio License Manual*, which is used as a textbook by many instructors at local radio clubs.

The world-renowned ARRL journal, *QST*, published since 1915, is also an excellent source of technical, operating, regulatory and feature articles on all aspects of Amateur Radio. Since it is published each month, *QST* is a timely source of information all hams can use and a significant benefit of ARRL membership.

In addition to receiving *QST* by mail each month, ARRL members have access to the digital edition of *QST*. You can choose to read *QST* online or download the entire issue to your computer or laptop. Digital *QST* offers enhanced content, convenient access and a more interactive experience.

Contact the ARRL for membership information toll-free at 1-888-277-5289, or visit online at **www. arrl.org/join-arrl-renew-membership**.

ARRL on the Internet

The ARRL maintains an excellent website at **www.arrl.org**. The Internet-connected ham can find late-breaking Amateur Radio news, as well as columns, feature articles and information on virtually anything related to ham radio. A search engine helps visitors to zero in on specific pages, and a US call sign server is available to all. The Technology section has dozens of informative pages and articles open to all on topics of interest to hams.

ARRL members may register to access special website features and services. One of the most popular is the *QST* archives. Articles from 1915 through present day are available for download. Members can also search the indexes of *NCJ* (*National Contest Journal*), *QEX* (ARRL's technical experimenter's magazine) and *Ham Radio* magazine.

Members can search the online archive of *QST* "Product Review" columns from the past 30+ years. Product reviews provide no-nonsense technical and operating reviews of equipment to help guide your purchasing decisions.

In addition, ARRL members can sign up to receive free ARRL e-mail products. These include weekly editions of *The ARRL Letter* as well as W1AW/ARRL bulletins, ARRL Division and Section news, and newsletters full of contesting, emergency communications and club topics. You can also sign up to receive announcements of new ARRL products, ARRL membership expiration notification, and amateur license expiration notification.

On-the-Air Bulletins

W1AW is the Amateur Radio station maintained at ARRL HQ in Newington, Connecticut. Every week, W1AW is on the air at regularly scheduled times transmitting bulletins with news of interest to amateurs on CW (Morse code), phone (voice) and several digital (teletype) modes on various frequencies. In addition there are Morse code practice broadcasts. A schedule of W1AW transmissions appears regularly in *QST* and may also be obtained from **www. arrl.org/w1aw**.

Local Clubs

When you seek answers to your questions about ham radio, don't overlook another great source of information — the experience of your fellow hams. There is nothing hams like to do better than share the vast wealth of experience they have in the hobby. A question to a ham who has experience in a specific area is likely to bring you all kinds of data. A dedicated DXer will talk for hours on techniques for working a rare DX station. Similarly, an emergency communications volunteer will be only too happy to fill you in on local emergency communications procedures and training nets.

Amateur Radio clubs play an important role in putting hams in touch with each other. As a potential ham or a new ham, you might not know of an amateur in your immediate area. A good choice would be to try to find the time and meeting place for a nearby Amateur Radio club. What better source of information for the not-yet-licensed and the newly licensed than a whole club full of experienced hams? If you are not yet licensed, your local Amateur Radio club is also the place to find information, guidelines and courses that will prepare you for the FCC exams.

To find clubs in your area, check out the ARRL's online club search — **www.arrl.org/find-a-club**. There is also a toll-free telephone number for prospective hams: 800-32NEW HAM (800-326-3942), or you can send e-mail to **newham@arrl.org**.

Effective in February 2007, the FCC dropped all Morse code requirements for amateur licensing and awarded Technician licensees the same privileges on the HF bands as Novice licensees. That means you can use CW on portions of the 80, 40, and 15 meter bands. On 10 meters, you can try CW, SSB, RTTY and other digital modes! When the ARRL 10 Meter Contest rolls around in December, there's every reason for you to jump in and join the fun, too!

It's hard to resist the lure of the HF bands, where many of today's most experienced hams got their start in ham radio. You'll hear hams on the repeater or at your radio club talking enthusiastically about their adventures on those lower-frequency bands. Someone may regale you with tales of how she has made friends many thousands of miles away, across oceans and continents. She might talk about the magic of that time when a ham in Calcutta answered her CQ on 20 meters, recalling that the Indian ham was as interested as she is in jazz and programming computers.

To earn the right to transmit on *all* the HF bands, you'll need to pass the General license exam. At the summit is the Amateur Extra license, which allows access to every part of every ham band. The General license provides you with the opportunity to try every bit of ham radio there is — you'll never regret making the effort to upgrade!

In the Shack — Your Equipment

The first step in selecting your new station should be to make up a list to answer a few questions. Will you be operating HF or only VHF? How much room do you have — in other words, how big can your "shack" or operating position be? Do you have room outside for long antennas, such as HF dipoles, or high antennas such as HF verticals and VHF/UHF arrays? How much do you plan to spend, including rig, accessories, furniture, coax feed line and wire?

Some of these questions may not apply to your situation, and you may need to answer other questions not discussed here. The result of making your personal list, however, is to give you an idea of what you want, as well as your limitations.

The next step is to do some research. Take your time deciding what gear to get. Many sources of information on ham gear are available to you.

1) *Hands-on experience.* Try to use many different pieces of gear before you decide. This applies to VHF/UHF as well as HF gear. Ask a nearby ham friend or one or more of your fellow radio club members if you can use their station. Try your club's station. Note what you like and what features you don't care for in each of the stations you tried.

2) *Radio club members.* Ask members of your local radio club about their personal preferences in gear and antennas. Be prepared for a great volume of input. Every amateur has an opinion on the best equipment and antennas. Years of experimentation usually go into finding just the right station equipment to meet a particular amateur's needs. Listen and take note of each ham's choices and reasons for selecting a particular kind of gear. There's a lot of experience, time, effort and money behind each of those choices.

3) *Advertisements.* QST is chock-full of ads for all the newest up-to-date equipment, as well as some premium used gear. Read the ads, and don't be afraid to contact the manufacturers of the gear for further information. Their websites often have comparison charts and operating manuals you can download for free. Compare specifications and prices to get the best deal. If there is a dealer close to you, pay a visit and let them demonstrate some of the gear to you.

4) *Product Reviews.* QST also contains detailed Product Reviews, written by ARRL staff, that include reliable measurements made in the ARRL Laboratory. These definitive reviews pull no punches in describing the good and the less-desirable features of the equipment being evaluated.

5) *Websites and Internet interest groups.* A number of websites are devoted to equipment reviews and discussion. They range from general-interest sites that let members review all kinds of ham gear, to discussion groups or sites devoted to one manufacturer or even a specific model. Try using your favorite Internet search engine to look for information on models that interest you.

After you've made your choice (most hams will trade station equipment often during their ham careers, so don't worry about this being your final choice), consider the sources where you might find the right deal on a new or used transceiver. Remember to include shipping and handling in the cost, and inquire about warranty service. If you are inexperienced, try to enlist a seasoned amateur to help you before buying used equipment from any source. Several possible sources of equipment are:

1) *Local amateurs.* Many hams will have spare used gear and may be willing to part with this gear at a reasonable price. Be sure you know what a particular rig is going for on the open market before settling on a final price. If you are new to the hobby and you buy a rig from a local club member, you may be able to talk him or her into "Elmering" you (helping you) with the rig's installation and operation. Local clubs are the safest source of used equipment.

2) *Hamfests/flea markets.* Some radio clubs run small conventions called hamfests. Usually one of the big attractions of these events is a flea market where hams buy and sell used radios, antennas and accessories — often at reasonable prices. Local distributors and manufacturers of new ham gear and materials sometimes show up at these events, as well. Check the Convention and Hamfest calendar in *QST* or **www.arrl.org/hamfests-and-conventions-calendar** to search for an event in your area.

3) *Local ham radio or electronics dealers.* If you are lucky enough to live near a ham radio dealer or an electronics distributor that handles a line or two of ham gear, so much the better. The dealer can usually answer any questions you may have and will be pleased to assist you in purchasing your new gear or accessories.

4) *Internet.* The Internet is the most popular forum for buying and selling Amateur Radio equipment. In addition to websites run by manufacturers and dealers, you will find used equipment for sale in the "classified ad" sections of websites such as eHam (**www.eham.net**), QRZ (**www.qrz.com**) and QTH (**swap.qth.com**). You'll also find a wide variety of ham gear auctioned on eBay (**www.ebay.com**).

If you are experienced with tools and basic electronic construction, you may even consider building some simple gear from a kit or from an article in a magazine or book.

There's a lot of satisfaction to be had in telling the operator on the other end of your QSO, "The rig here is homebrew." *The ARRL Handbook* has extensive coverage of construction and basic-to-advanced electronics theory information.

How Much Power?

In the ham radio community, there are both *QRO* (power output up to the full legal limit of 1500 W) and *QRP* (5 W output — or less) enthusiasts. Most hams run 100 to 150 W, the power level of typical transceivers. There are times when it is necessary to run the full legal power limit to establish and maintain solid communications or to compete effectively in a DX contest on certain bands. Most often, the 100 W level is more than enough to provide excellent contacts.

Some hams find the low initial cost of low power (QRP) HF equipment very attractive, especially since some are available in kit form. Beginning operators who are still developing the skills of making contacts often find QRP frustrating, however. By all means, try QRP any time, but it's recommended that you first get some experience at the 100 W level so that you know what to expect on the HF bands.

On VHF the situation is slightly different. Unless you are trying to work several hundred miles in an opening or operate a weak-signal mode, a typical 5 W handheld or 50 W mobile radio is enough power when coupled with a good antenna for excellent local communications.

VHF/UHF Gear

If you're interested mainly in voice and maybe APRS or packet radio communication with local amateurs, all you need is a VHF/UHF FM transceiver. FM transceivers are available for hand-held and mobile use. A mobile rig can also

Jim Veatch, WA2EUJ, built this 6, 10 and 12 meter SSB/CW transceiver, named the DSP-610, for the ARRL Homebrew Challenge III.

be used at home if you have a 12 V battery or suitable power supply. More capable fixed-station "base" transceivers are intended for use at home.

Figure 1.1 illustrates the choices available for a VHF or UHF station and how portable, mobile and home (fixed) rigs and antennas can be used to create a station that suits your needs from wherever you operate.

1) *Hand-held transceivers.* Hand-held transceivers put out from under a watt to 5 W or more. If the hand-held you're considering is capable of high-power operation, you'll want to be able to switch to low power when possible to conserve the battery. Most hand-helds offer a HIGH/LOW power switch. Good used hand-held transceivers sell from under $100. New transceivers start at about $125. If you use your hand-held rig while inside the car, you'll probably be disappointed with the performance of the attached "rubber duck" antenna. A mobile antenna outside the metal shell of the car will work much better.

2) *Mobile transceivers* have power outputs ranging from 10 to 50 W and are used with *mag-mount* or permanently attached mobile antennas mounted on the vehicle. In populated areas with many repeaters, any more than 10 W is probably unnecessary. Mobile transceivers are available used from under $100. New transceivers start at about $150 for a 50 W unit.

3) *Fixed-station transceivers.* A mobile rig connected to a power supply or 12 V automotive battery makes a good fixed station radio. It also can be disconnected and moved into the car for mobile operation. Powering the rig from a battery has the added advantage of allowing emergency operation when the local power lines go down in a storm. A growing number of *all-band* fixed-station radios operate on the HF bands, as well as VHF and UHF. If you plan on operating HF from home, these would be a good choice. Home stations on VHF/UHF should always use external antennas if more than a few watts of power will be used.

4) *VHF packet radio.* Most VHF packet radio operation, including APRS, takes place on the 2 meter and 440 MHz bands. A mobile transceiver makes a good packet-radio station rig, too. You'll need a computer or terminal, plus a terminal node controller (TNC). Used TNCs are available, but new ones are only slightly more expensive. Newer units may offer "mailbox" features, where other hams can leave messages for you when you aren't home.

Remember that higher power levels can create an RF safety hazard. At the higher power levels of mobile and base transceivers, use external antennas and place mobile antennas away from the passenger compartment. For the higher-powered handheld transceivers, use a detachable speaker-mike and belt clip to keep the antenna away from your eyes and head. This important topic is discussed in the Safety chapter of *The ARRL Handbook*.

HF Equipment

It is a bit more challenging to put together an HF station than a VHF station. HF equipment generally covers more bands and modes and has greater requirements for frequency stability than an FM-only radio. Thus, HF gear is generally more expensive, and the antennas at HF are bigger than the

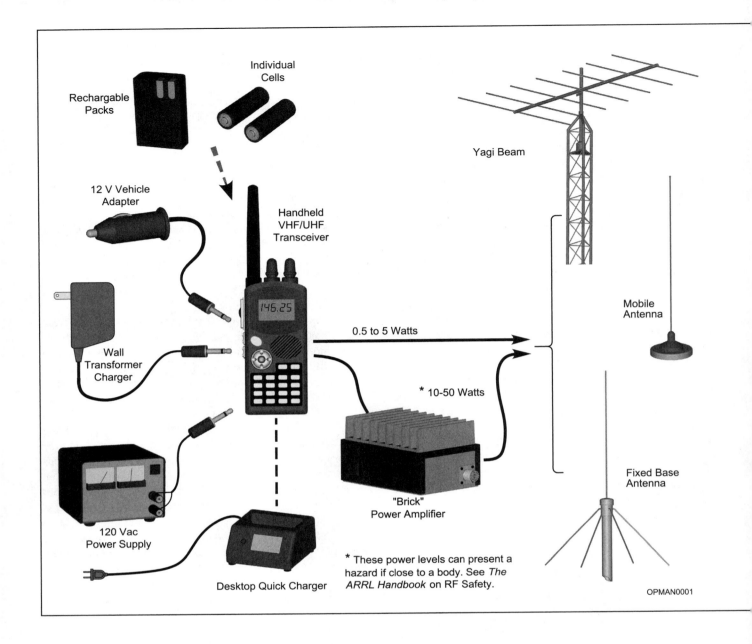

Rechargable Packs

Individual Cells

12 V Vehicle Adapter

Handheld VHF/UHF Transceiver

Yagi Beam

Wall Transformer Charger

146.25

0.5 to 5 Watts

Mobile Antenna

* 10-50 Watts

120 Vac Power Supply

"Brick" Power Amplifier

Fixed Base Antenna

Desktop Quick Charger

* These power levels can present a hazard if close to a body. See *The ARRL Handbook* on RF Safety.

OPMAN0001

flexible rubber antennas used on hand-held transceivers or the VHF ground-plane antenna mounted on the roof of your car or house.

There are so many different possible HF station configurations that it may be hard to choose the very best station to start out with. Most hams face other constraints — such as having a limited budget to spend for ham gear, or having restrictions on the size and location of antennas. Some hams have a difficult time installing any sort of antenna outdoors and they must resort to indoor or perhaps easily hidden "stealth" wire antennas.

1) *Transceivers.* HF transceivers (a transmitter plus a receiver) have been common since the late 1960s. Like all older gear, older transceivers are likely to have maintenance problems. Mobile use subjects a radio to a great deal of vibration and wide ranges of temperature. A rig showing signs of having been used for mobiling may not be a good choice for your first station.

Avoid antique vacuum-tube equipment for your first station. Years of aging and the higher temperatures can take their toll on electronic components. Tubes are expensive and those for old amateur gear can be hard to find. Unless you're very familiar with tube-type equipment or have a passion for vintage equipment, look for newer gear.

Transceivers manufactured in the 1970s were partly solid state. The transmitters usually had three tubes: two in the power amplifier and another serving as the driver stage. Some transceivers from this era had built-in ac power supplies. Mechanical parts, such as those used in the tuning assembly, may be impossible to obtain. Make sure everything works properly before you buy. Transceivers from this era probably won't operate on the 30, 17 and 12 meter bands, and some don't cover 160 meters either.

Transceivers manufactured after about 1980 featured fully solid-state designs. Tuning mechanisms had fewer mechanical parts to wear, and all-band operation became

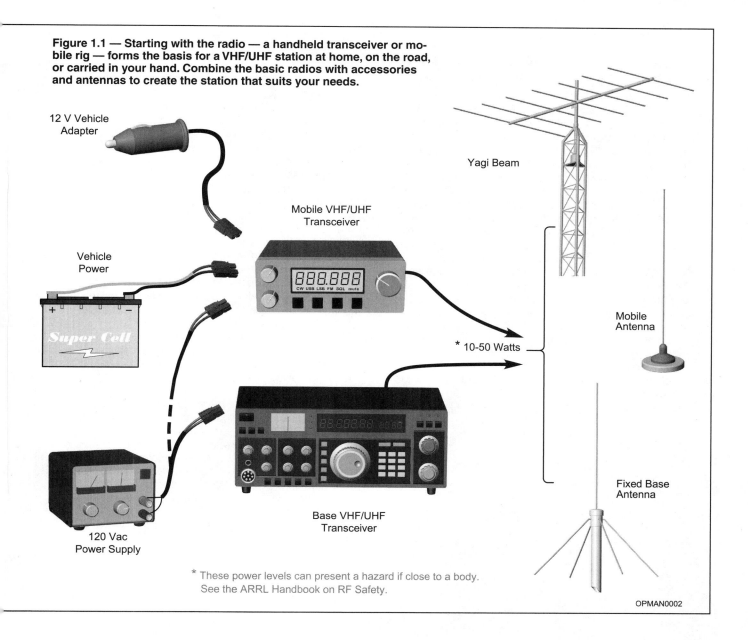

Figure 1.1 — Starting with the radio — a handheld transceiver or mobile rig — forms the basis for a VHF/UHF station at home, on the road, or carried in your hand. Combine the basic radios with accessories and antennas to create the station that suits your needs.

12 V Vehicle Adapter

Vehicle Power

Super Cell

120 Vac Power Supply

Mobile VHF/UHF Transceiver

888.888

CW USB LSB FM SQL mute

Base VHF/UHF Transceiver

88.888.88

* 10-50 Watts

Yagi Beam

Mobile Antenna

Fixed Base Antenna

* These power levels can present a hazard if close to a body. See the ARRL Handbook on RF Safety.

OPMAN0002

common. Many feature general-coverage receivers that tune continuously from below 100 kHz to 30 MHz. With the general-coverage receiver you can listen to time and frequency-standard stations such as WWV and WWVH and enjoy a variety of shortwave broadcasting.

Equipment manufactured in the past 10 years is the most desirable. These radios are fully solid state, microprocessor-controlled, and have data and control interfaces for digital modes and station accessories. Later models also incorporate *digital signal processing* (DSP) features that provide advanced filtering and noise reduction. The improved performance and reliability are well worth the relatively small premium in price over older equipment now approaching collectible status.

2) *Homemade equipment.* Although most hams will not want to design or build their first stations, if you have a background in electronics, you might want to "home-brew" some of the accessory items, such as tuners, meters, audio processing equipment and interfaces. Kits are available

from a variety of sources, and many proven circuits appear in *The ARRL Handbook*.

Accessories

A few accessories found in almost all stations either help set up and test equipment or help operate it.

SWR Indicator

This device is handy for testing an antenna and feed line when the antenna is first erected, and later to make sure the antenna is still in good shape. If an antenna tuner is used with a multiband antenna system, such as a 135-foot dipole or a G5RV antenna, an SWR (standing wave ratio) indicator is essential for ensuring the tuner is adjusted for a reasonable SWR. All modern HF transceivers include an SWR indicator. External SWR meters can cost as little as $30. If you plan to operate both VHF and HF you will probably have to buy one for HF and a second for VHF/UHF.

Real Radios Glow In the Dark

In many hobbies and avocations there are groups that specialize in traditional techniques and technology — wooden boats, steam power, bow and arrow hunting. While the majority of practitioners no longer utilize them, these venerable methods still perform their functions well and with unique qualities appreciated by their users. Amateur Radio's steam power is the vacuum tube and AM voice.

The vacuum tube, once king in electronics, is relegated to a few niche applications still not overrun by semiconductors. High-power amplifiers is where you'll find tubes still holding sway. There is also a certain romance to the tube rig. Unlike the quietly efficient chip-laden, microprocessor-controlled modern radio, a "steam radio" takes time to warm up, it has a characteristic aroma, and, with the lights low in the shack, the glow of filaments creates silhouettes of ventilation screens. When turned off, there is a delay as the pilot lamps and tubes cool, filaments (heaters to some) dropping from white-orange through cherry red to tungsten gray.

Audiophiles swear by the warm sound of their tube amplifiers with transformer-coupled outputs, and so do aficionados of antique radios. You'll find them tuning the bands like everyone else, answering CQs and holding nets. You might notice a different quality to their signals and, if you ask, they'll be glad to tell you about their old friends on the operating desk. As you browse the tables at the next hamfest, ask a few questions about that antique radio and see if the seller's face doesn't light up like a brand-new 811 final tube!

Hams have always taken pride in the quality and fidelity of their modulation. For some, the sound of an AM signal (the full, double-sideband-and-carrier AM) just can't be equaled by a SSB radio's steep filter skirts and sideband suppression. Because an AM transmitter does not remove frequencies below 300 Hz in order to eliminate the unwanted sideband and carrier remnants, the modulation can reproduce the warm basses of the voice.

A properly adjusted AM transmitter can sound very good indeed, including the high-frequency sibilants and fricatives that make speech crisp and understandable. Accordingly, there is a group of hams that enjoy using AM, even though it is not as efficient in its use of spectrum as are its modern cousins. You can often find AM-ers around 3885 or 14,286 kc (the old abbreviation for kHz), sometimes using antique rigs for a doubly interesting contact.

If you'd like to know more about ancient rigs, affectionately known as "boatanchors," and AM signals browse the ARRL AM pages at **www.arrl.org/am-phone-operating-and-activities**. More references may be found on AC6V's "Antique Ham Radios" and "AM'ers" Web pages (**www.ac6v.com**). If you'd like to listen to some vintage AM equipment or just give the AM button on your newer rig a try, watch for on-the-air events such as the Classic Exchange (**www.classicexchange.org**) or the Bruce Kelley Memorial 1929 QSO Party sponsored by AWA, the Antique Wireless Association (**www.antiquewireless.org**).

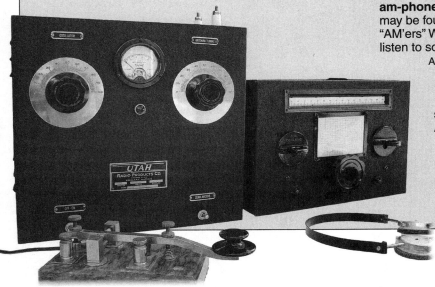

This Utah Junior transmitter and National FBXA receiver owned by W9AC date from the late 1930s and still make an appearance on the air from time to time.

Antenna Tuner

Although many transceivers include an internal antenna tuner, there are a number of reasons to have a separate tuner. They generally tune a wider range of impedances, are available with higher power handling ability, can be dedicated to specific antennas, and so forth. There are many antenna tuners available on the market, costing between $75 and $1500. (The more expensive models handle higher power and/or use microprocessor circuits for automatic adjustment.) The basic circuits are pretty simple, though, and many first-time homebrew projects are antenna tuners. (*The ARRL Handbook* and *ARRL Antenna Book* contain plans for build-ing them.) By carefully shopping at hamfest flea markets you can often assemble your own for less than $50 in parts.

Keys, Keyers and Paddles

If you're interested in CW, you will need some means of sending code. You should start with a straight key until you feel you have the proper rhythm. The next step is to buy an electronic keyer and paddles, or use your computer to send code. Most modern transceivers have keyers built in, so all you need is a paddle. Paddles may be standard or *iambic* — able to send alternating dots and dashes. The iambic type requires less hand motion but takes a bit longer to master. Keyers cost from

$20 to $250, and good paddles can cost $50 and up. Code-transmitting programs are available for most computers.

Computers

Computers have become a very valuable part of the ham shack. It is common to use a computer to send and receive Morse code, fax, slow-scan TV or digital modes. The same computer can be used for logging and record keeping, as well as connecting to the Internet. Many radios and accessories have computer control interfaces.

Most ham computer software is *Windows*-compatible, although the *Linux* and Macintosh communities are well represented. If you plan on using your computer to control amateur equipment, be sure it has at least one COM (serial) port or purchase USB-to-serial converters.

When considering a computer for the shack, remember that a computer uses various oscillators inside that can generate annoying spurious signals in your receiver. These signals may interfere with on-air signals you are trying to hear. Some computers can be very sensitive to the presence of radio-frequency energy (RF), such as that generated by your nearby transceiver. For help with this topic see *The ARRL RFI Book*, which contains an entire chapter on solving computer problems in the shack.

Test Meter

An inexpensive digital multimeter capable of measuring voltage, current and resistance is very helpful around the shack. High accuracy is not needed for most projects. A $15 to $30 unit will pay for itself the first time you need to check the integrity of a coax connector you've just installed.

Station Setup at Home

How you set up a home station is determined by how much space you have, and how much equipment you have to squeeze into it. The table should be about 30 inches high and 30 inches deep. An old desk makes a good operating table. Stacking radios on top of one another prevents ventilation and may cause them to overheat. Build shelves for your equipment — office supply and home improvement stores often have inexpensive desktop shelves that work well for radios. It's also easier to change cables and move equipment around when you use shelves. Make sure you can get behind the gear to plug or unplug cables.

Assuming you use a computer, its monitor should be centered in front of your keyboard at a comfortable viewing height. Avoid neck and eye strain — don't place the monitor too far above or to the sides of the keyboard. Place the radios to one side of the keyboard. Check that you can see the frequency display and reach the operating controls of your radios easily. Continuously reaching across a computer keyboard to tune or operate a radio will cause strain on your back, shoulder and arms.

To prevent fatigue when operating on CW, place your key or paddle far enough from the edge of the table so your entire arm is supported. If you're not using a headset with a boom microphone, the microphone can be mounted on a stand placed on the table or on an extension that reaches in from the back or side.

The best way to test the arrangement of your station is to sit in the operating chair and operate. Don't be afraid to rearrange your equipment if the layout turns out to be uncomfortable. This is also a good reason not to make your first layout too permanent! Adjust the height and angle of all equipment until it's easy to see and use. If some knobs are too low, try placing spacers or blocks under the front feet of the rig. Too high? Try placing the spacers under the rear legs.

AC and RF Grounding

Be sure to have an ac safety ground at your station and connected to all equipment. It's a good idea to not even plug in equipment until its case is grounded. Electrical codes require all recent construction to have grounded (3-wire) ac outlets.

Place a grounding strap or *bus* at the back of the equipment and ground all equipment to it with short leads. Then connect the ground bus to the earth ground as directly as possible using copper strap, heavy wire, or metal braid such as shield from coaxial cable or strips of flashing copper. Connect the ground bus to your ac safety ground.

An earth ground for RF, such as an outside ground rod, is highly desirable to avoid RF feedback and interference to your station equipment. A cold-water pipe may also be used if it is metallic and extends into the ground around your home. The path from the ground bus to the earth should be as short and direct as possible.

If you live on a higher floor and a direct connection to an earth ground is not available, use a ground bus and be sure all equipment is connected to it. This keeps all equipment at the same RF potential, giving RF current no reason to flow between the various pieces and cause problems.

Safety should be a prime consideration. Use a master switch and make sure other people in the house know where it is and how to use it. Consider running your shack through a *GFI* (ground fault interrupt) outlet. Unfortunately not all ham gear, especially older units, will operate with these devices.

Antenna Safety

Whatever antennas you select, install them safely. Don't endanger your life or someone else's for your hobby!
- Keep the antenna and its support well clear of any power lines, including the ac power service to your home.
- Make sure if the antenna or its support falls, it can't contact power lines.
- Install the antenna where it can't be easily contacted by people.

There are thorough discussions of antenna safety in *The ARRL Handbook* and *The ARRL Antenna Book*.

By detecting unbalanced line currents and shutting off the voltage when unbalance occurs, however, they could save your life!

Antennas

Antennas are important. The best (and biggest) transmitter in the world will not do any good if the signal is not radiated into the air. A good rule of thumb to follow is "always erect as much antenna as possible." The better your antennas, the better your radiated signal will be and the better you'll hear other stations. A good antenna system will make up for inadequacies or shortcomings in station equipment.

If you are thinking of a tower, talk to a few local hams before starting construction (or applying for a building permit). Local rules and ordinances may have a large impact on your plans. Many homes are also subject to *restrictive covenants* or other restrictions on external antennas. Be sure you know what you're allowed to do before digging a hole for a tower base, and get whatever building permits are required!

First VHF/UHF Antennas

One of the nice things about VHF and UHF operation is that the simplest antennas, if mounted high enough and clear of surrounding objects, will often do an excellent job. Ground planes, J-poles and simple beams can either be purchased at a reasonable cost or constructed in a home workshop. For example, if you want to test a two-element quad for 144 MHz, just take the design from the *ARRL Antenna Book*, build it from scrap wood and heavy gauge copper or aluminum wire, and run a few tests. The unit you built may not stay up for a long time in bad weather, but it will be fine for determining if this is the sort of antenna you want to put up permanently.

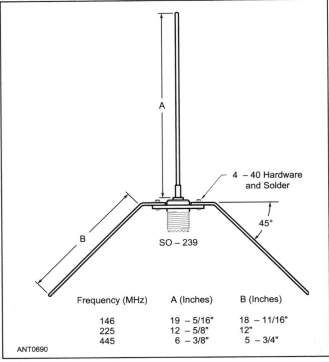

Frequency (MHz)	A (Inches)	B (Inches)
146	19 – 5/16"	18 – 11/16"
225	12 – 5/8"	12"
445	6 – 3/8"	5 – 3/4"

ANT0690

Figure 1.2 — A simple ground-plane antenna for VHF. The elements are made from ³⁄₃₂-or ¹⁄₁₆-inch brass welding rod or #10 or #12 bare copper wire.

A simple ground-plane antenna is shown in **Figure 1.2**. It can be mounted by taping the feed line and bottom connector to a pole so that the antenna extends above the top of the pole. It can also be suspended by a length of fishing line or synthetic twine by lengthening the vertical element and bending the extra length into a loop. One end of the line is fastened to the loop and the other end is supported by a tree branch or rafter.

A Simple HF Antenna

The most popular — and a very effective — first HF antenna is the half-wavelength dipole. It consists of a half wavelength of wire divided in the center by an insulator. The insulator is where a feed line from your station is connected to each half of the wire. This construction is illustrated in **Figure 1.3**.

The dipole is very easy to erect and has a low SWR (standing wave ratio). SWR is the measure of how well an antenna is tuned to the desired frequency and of the match between its feed point impedance and the feed line's characteristic impedance.

A dipole can be fed with 50 Ω coaxial cable and used on one band. A single-band dipole fed with low-loss feed line, such as window or open-wire line, can also be used on other bands. In fact with an antenna tuner, a balun, and a random-length center-fed dipole you can actually operate on any HF band.

Where to Put the Dipole?

The antenna should be as high and as far away from surrounding trees and structures as possible. Never put an antenna near power lines!

A dipole requires one support at each of its ends (perhaps trees, poles or even house or garage eaves), so survey your potential antenna site with this in mind. If you find space is so limited that you can't put up a straight-line dipole, don't give up! The dipole can also be held up by a single support in the middle with the ends secured closer to the ground — this is called an *inverted V*.

You can also slope or bend the dipole and it will still make plenty of contacts. You can put up an antenna under almost any circumstances, but you may need to use your imagination. Antennas want to work!

Dipole Antenna Parts

If this is the first time you have tried to put up a dipole by yourself, the following parts list will give you some guidance.

1) *Antenna wire*. #12 or #14 hard-drawn Copperweld (copper-clad steel) is preferred, so the antenna won't stretch. Stranded or solid copper wire will also work but if used for a long antenna, the wire will probably have to be trimmed once it's been under tension for a while. Wire of this gauge is strong enough to support itself as well as the weight of the feed line connected at its center. Always buy plenty of wire. It never goes to waste!

2) *Insulators*. You need one center and two end antenna insulators for a simple dipole.

3) *Clamp*. Large enough to fit over two diameters of your coaxial cable to provide mechanical support.

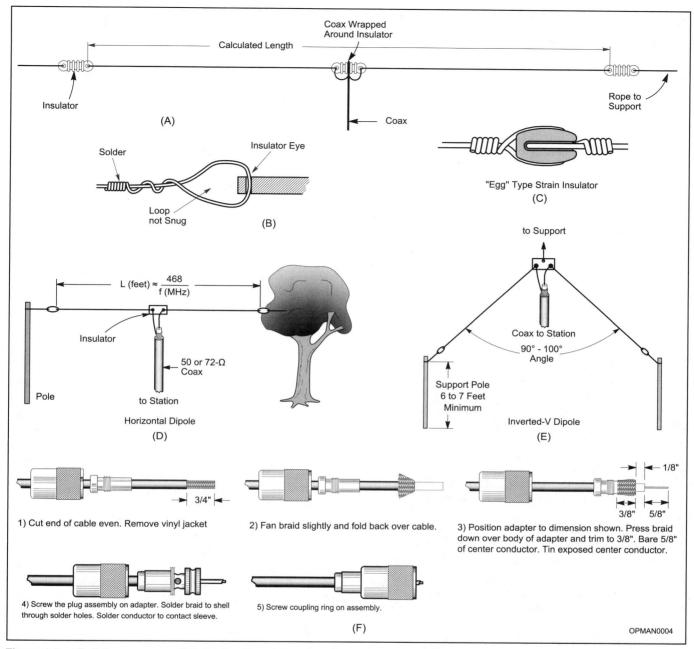

Figure 1.3 — Building your own HF dipole antenna is a popular project.

Labels within figure:

(A) — Calculated Length; Coax Wrapped Around Insulator; Insulator; Coax; Rope to Support

(B) — Solder; Insulator Eye; Loop not Snug

(C) — "Egg" Type Strain Insulator

(D) — Horizontal Dipole; $L \text{ (feet)} \approx \dfrac{468}{f \text{ (MHz)}}$; Insulator; Pole; 50 or 72-Ω Coax; to Station

(E) — Inverted-V Dipole; to Support; Coax to Station; 90° - 100° Angle; Support Pole 6 to 7 Feet Minimum

(F) —
1) Cut end of cable even. Remove vinyl jacket — 3/4"
2) Fan braid slightly and fold back over cable.
3) Position adapter to dimension shown. Press braid down over body of adapter and trim to 3/8". Bare 5/8" of center conductor. Tin exposed center conductor. — 1/8", 3/8", 5/8"
4) Screw the plug assembly on adapter. Solder braid to shell through solder holes. Solder conductor to contact sleeve.
5) Screw coupling ring on assembly.

OPMAN0004

4) *Coaxial Cable or "Coax."* Feed line made of a center conductor surrounded by an insulating dielectric. This in turn is surrounded by a braid called the shield and an outer insulating jacket. Use RG-58, RG-8X, RG-8, RG-213 or an equivalent. Look for coax with a heavy braid shield. Stick with brands sold by reputable ham radio dealers and avoid surplus or used cable for this first antenna.

A good alternative to coax is balanced open-wire or window line. Open-wire line is constructed using two parallel pieces of wire connected and spaced with plastic rods. Window line has a plastic jacket similar to TV 300-Ω wire with pieces of the center plastic removed to form "windows," lightening the line and reducing its losses. If you are sure you want to build a single-band dipole, stay with coax feed line, otherwise consider the tuner, balun and open-wire configuration.

5) *Connector.* Connects coaxial feed line to your rig. The standard connector on HF equipment is the SO-239 or "UHF" connector. You'll need a matching PL-259 connector for the coax. If your radio needs a different type of connector, check your radio's instruction manual for installation information. You also need connectors for the coax lines between your antenna tuner, SWR meter and your rig. If you are using an external antenna tuner or SWR meter, to connect them together you will need to make short coax *jumpers* that have a PL-259 on each end.

6) *Electrical tape and coax sealant.* This is needed to waterproof the connection between the coax feed line and the

Table 1.2

Antenna Lengths in Feet

	½ wavelength	¼ wavelength
80 m	126' 6"	63' 3"
40 m	65' 8"	32' 10"
15 m	22' 2"	11' 1"
10 m	16' 6"	8' 3"

Remember to add about 1 foot to each end of the dipole for tuning adjustment.

antenna. Otherwise water can get into the coax, eventually ruining the feed line.

7) *Supporting rope or cord.* You need enough to tie the ends of the antenna to a supporting structure and also reach the ground when the antenna is lowered. That's about twice the height of the support plus the distance from the support to the end of the antenna. Use UV-resistant cord or rope to avoid degradation from exposure.

8) *SWR meter or antenna analyzer.* If your radio doesn't have an SWR meter built-in, you'll need to purchase a separate unit. The SWR meter is required for antenna adjustment and then for antenna tuner adjustment when operating. SWR meters are readily available and inexpensive, making them easier to buy than to build. An antenna analyzer is a self-contained device that connects to the antenna feed line and transmits a very low power signal to display the antenna SWR over a range of frequencies.

Gather all the parts you'll need for your chosen antenna. Almost everything is available from your local electronics store or from suppliers advertising in *QST*. When this is done, the fun of actually putting together your antenna can begin.

Putting It Together

Assembly is quite simple. Your dipole consists of two lengths of wire, each approximately ¼ wavelength long at your chosen (or lowest) operating frequency. These two wires are connected in the center, at an insulator, to the feed line. In our antenna the feed line, which brings the signals to and from your radio, is coaxial cable. Calculate the length of the half-wave dipole by using this simple formula:

antenna length in feet = 468/frequency in MHz

(The information in **Table 1.2** has approximate lengths already calculated.) Now measure the antenna wire, keeping it as straight as possible. To the length in the table, add an additional 8 inches on each end of the wire (that's 16 inches per antenna half) to allow for the mechanical loop through the insulator.

Carefully assemble your antenna, paying special attention to waterproofing the coax connections at the center insulator. Don't solder the antenna ends until later, when tuning is completed. Just twist them for now. Route the coax to your station, leaving a drip loop wherever the cable goes through a wall or window. Cut the coax to a length that will leave some excess for strain relief so your rig won't be pulled around during strong winds! Install the connectors according to the diagrams in Figure 1.3. If you use an external SWR meter, connect it between the end of the antenna feed line and the transmitter.

One trick used by old-timers is the addition of a 10,000-Ω resistor, soldered directly across the center insulator of the dipole. An ohmmeter in the shack, when connected from one side of the feed line to the other, should measure this value of 10,000 Ω. If it measures an open circuit, it means the feed line is disconnected or broken. A short circuit means the feed line or the connector is shorted. The high-value resistor has no effect on the antenna or SWR. Left in place, it acts as a handy check on the antenna and feed line.

Raise the antenna into place and test it! Turn on your radio and reduce power to 10 W output or less. Follow the instructions in the radio's operating manual to measure SWR at several frequencies across the band for which the dipole was designed. Be sure to listen first and find a clear frequency so you don't unintentionally interfere with other hams using the band.

If the minimum SWR occurs at or near the desired operating frequency and the SWR is lower than 2:1 or so, your antenna is correctly tuned. Lower it, solder the ends of the antenna that are twisted around the insulators and hoist it back into place. Go operate!

If the *resonant frequency* at the minimum SWR is too low, the antenna is too long and it will need to be shortened. Lower it and remove six inches from each side of the dipole, then test SWR again. Keep notes! Assuming the resonant frequency increased when the antenna was shortened, keep shortening and testing until the resonant frequency is approximately correct. If the resonant frequency was too high, you can splice the antenna and add some length on each end. As the last step, when you are sure the length of the dipole is correct, solder the wire wrapped around the end insulators. When you complete the antenna, take a final set of SWR readings and keep them in a notebook for future reference, should you need to troubleshoot the antenna or feed line.

If you plan on building a number of antennas, a better way to tune the antenna that does not involve transmitting an unmodulated signal is to use an *antenna analyzer*. These instruments use extremely low power signals to measure SWR and are much more portable than a transmitter and SWR meter.

When all systems are go, get on the air and operate. As you settle into that first QSO with your new antenna, enjoy those feelings of pride, accomplishment and fun that will naturally follow. After all, that's what Amateur Radio is all about!

Problems and Cures

Many hams act as though the world will end if they put up an antenna and measure an SWR greater than 1.5:1. For most purposes an SWR of up to 3:1 is perfectly acceptable at HF with good-quality feed lines 100 feet or less in length.

A high SWR that does not change when you change the antenna length by a foot or more (HF only) probably means something more serious is wrong with your simple, one-band dipole. Check to see if your coax is open or shorted. Make sure your antenna isn't touching anything and that all your connections are sound.

On bands such as 80 meters, the antenna likely won't have a low SWR over the whole band. In this case, tune the antenna for the highest frequency part of the band on which you wish to operate (the shortest antenna length). When you want to use the lower part of the band, lower the antenna and temporarily attach short lengths of wire at the end insulators, using heavy alligator clips or split-nut wire clamps.

Mobile Stations

Mobile operation — from cars, RVs, boats and even bicycles — has experienced a renaissance in the past few years. The reason? Excellent, compact equipment and antennas! Hams have operated VHF and UHF from their vehicles for a long time, but with the advent of "all-band" radios that operate on everything from 160 meters through 70 cm, the mobile station no longer has to take a back seat to home operating.

This section introduces the most common mobile installation — for VHF/UHF FM operation. Then we'll extend the conversation to HF operating. Both types of installations have many aspects in common. While the vehicle is assumed to be a car, much of the information applies directly to other types of conveyance. Hamming while in motion places some extra requirements on the operator, too. If mobile operation sounds attractive to you, follow up with some of the resources listed at the end of the section.

Mobile Safety

Modern vehicles feature dozens of electronic gadgets and features for their owners, more than ever. A lot of work goes into making sure they are safe to use in a vehicle, especially on the road. When installing your mobile station, be sure to make safety your top priority.

Electrical Safety

Let's start with electrical safety. A vehicle moves and vibrates continuously while in motion. Your radio will also experience wide swings in temperature nearly every day. Any connection that's not secure is going to work its way loose in short order. If it's a radio signal connection — such as a cable or antenna — you'll experience erratic signals and possibly damage the radio.

Loose power connections can be much more dangerous. A vehicle's electrical system (and that includes any vehicle with batteries of any size) packs a lot of energy. An accidental short circuit will rapidly heat wire to the point where connectors oxidize and insulation melts. A vehicle fire is an expensive proposition! Make sure that all wiring is secure, protected against chafing or pinching by metal surfaces, and properly fused.

A common source of electrical problems is using wire or circuits that aren't adequately rated for the power requirements of the radio. Your radio's manual will specify the correct gauge wire to use. Follow that recommendation! At the very least, your radio may not operate properly if the resistance in the power wiring causes voltage at the radio to drop below the specified minimum. Overloaded wiring and connectors will also get quite hot and could start a fire.

Expect the worst to happen and protect yourself against it with proper fusing as shown in **Figure 1.4**. Follow the

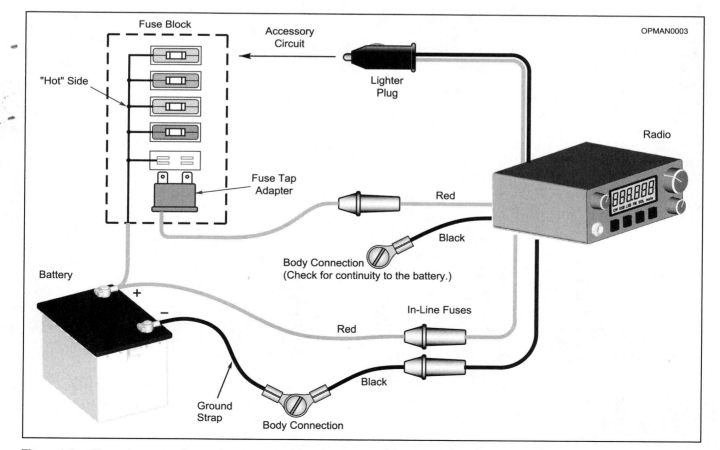

OPMAN0003

Figure 1.4 — There are several ways to power your mobile station. See text for discussion.

recommendations of the manufacturer of your vehicle for installing a radio or other device. *Never* connect power leads directly to the vehicle's power system without proper fusing!

To minimize noise and voltage drops in the power wiring, connect the fused power leads directly to the battery, if possible. It may be more convenient to connect the negative lead to the vehicle battery ground strap where it is attached to the body or engine block. Fuses in *both* the positive and negative power leads will protect your radio's power wiring in case a positive wire comes in contact with the radio body or positive lead.

Mechanical Safety

It's important to mount or constrain your radio so that it can not become a hazard to you or your passengers. Even in normal driving, a radio sliding around on a seat, underfoot, or on a dashboard can be a distraction at the minimum and an injury hazard at worst. Some states do not allow drivers to have any equipment mounted on the dashboard. Check your local regulations about requirements for mounting radios, then follow them. Your radio's user manual may also have some suggestions and recommendations.

In most cars, there is a place on the console where a radio might be installed. If so, and it will look acceptable to you, that's a good place to mount the radio. You'll be able to see the radio's front panel and the radio can look professionally installed. It will generally be secure, even in an accident.

If there's no convenient location for the whole rig, consider a radio with a detachable front panel and mount the radio under a seat or in the trunk. You'll probably need a *separation cable* or *separation kit* so that the microphone and *control head* (the panel with the operating controls and display) can be mounted up front and convenient where you are, while the body of the radio is elsewhere.

Figure 1.5 — When planning your mobile installation, the radio needs to be somewhere convenient. Transceivers with detachable control heads or faceplates are a great choice for modern cars. It's easier to find a home for a compact control head, and the main body of the radio can go under a seat or in the trunk.

Wherever you mount the radio, be sure it can't come loose in a crash and become an injury-causing projectile.

Cables can also get tangled in control wiring, springs, levers and all the other gadgetry in a car. Be very sure that the microphone, antenna, power and any other accessory cables are secure or that they can't wrap themselves around something or jam a pedal.

Driving Safety

You've heard about driving and talking on mobile phones and the hazards of inattention. Maybe you've observed it first hand because it's very common! Operating a mobile ham radio doesn't seem to be such a distraction because of the "push-to-talk" nature of ham communications. You're either talking or listening — never simultaneously, as in a telephone conversation.

Nevertheless, don't hesitate to terminate a contact whenever you think you might need extra concentration on the road. You'll often hear a ham say, "I have to drive here" or "Time for both hands on the wheel" and sign off. That's a good idea. Don't compromise your safety or that of other drivers for a contact. If the contact is that important, pull over and devote your full attention to it.

Another driving distraction is having the radio controls placed where you have to take your eyes off the road to use them. **Figure 1.5** shows one example of placing a radio's detachable front panel in a location convenient to the driver. Stuffing a radio between a seat and the console is a good example of how *not* to mount a radio. You'll have to turn your head and look down to turn knobs or press buttons if your microphone doesn't have duplicate controls. Be sure the radio or control head is mounted where you can pay attention to your number one job — driving!

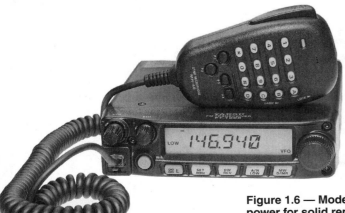

Figure 1.6 — Modern VHF/UHF FM radios are compact, yet they pack plenty of power for solid repeater and simplex contacts. Single-band radios like the Yaesu FT-1900 (left) are often the most economical, but dual-banders (2 meters/70 cm) like the Alinco DR-635 (right) offer more flexibility.

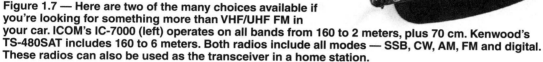

Figure 1.7 — Here are two of the many choices available if you're looking for something more than VHF/UHF FM in your car. ICOM's IC-7000 (left) operates on all bands from 160 to 2 meters, plus 70 cm. Kenwood's TS-480SAT includes 160 to 6 meters. Both radios include all modes — SSB, CW, AM, FM and digital. These radios can also be used as the transceiver in a home station.

VHF/UHF Mobile

The most common mobile installation for VHF and UHF mobile is a dual-band radio such as the one shown in **Figure 1.6**. They come with all the necessary mounting hardware, microphone, and power cabling for a proper installation. Many have a detachable front panel that can serve as a control head as described above. All have adequate power output. Choosing one is largely a question of picking the secondary features that you want — automatic CTCSS tone detection, number of memories, scanning, receiving outside the amateur bands and so forth.

The antenna for VHF and UHF mobile should be a vertically-oriented "whip" solidly mounted on a flat metal surface of the vehicle such as the roof or trunk. Removable antennas with a magnetic mount (*mag mounts*) are very popular and work well — if your vehicle has steel exterior surfaces, which not all vehicles do. If your vehicle has plastic or aluminum body surfaces, consult the vehicle dealer about mounting antennas on the vehicle. You may wish to use a mount-on-glass antenna that does not require a ground plane to function.

Running the antenna cable into the interior of the car can be a challenge. Mag mount antennas are usually temporary, so the cable may be run through a door seal. If so, make sure the cable is not pinched hard enough to be deformed. Another problem is water getting in around the cable, and you may have to experiment to find a spot where a cable will not give water a way in.

Trunk and hood mounts require a hole in the engine firewall or between the trunk and rear seat to run the cable. You may have to run the cable before installing the coax connector in order to fit through the existing holes. Engine firewalls often have spare holes plugged with a grommet or the cable can be squeezed in along side an existing wire bundle. In the trunk, look under the trunk liner and around the rear decking for ways into the passenger compartment. Regardless of which way you run the cable, be sure it won't be chafed or cut by the edges of brackets or other protruding metal.

HF Mobile

While you'll occasionally see a full-blown HF transceiver mounted in a larger car, truck or RV, the most common HF mobile rig is one of the "all-band" radios. Some of the available radios are shown in **Figure 1.7**. These rigs typically put out 100 W on all HF bands through 6 meters and sometimes include 2 meters and 70 cm. (222 MHz is not covered because this is not an amateur band in most places outside of the US.) With a single radio, you can cover all of the most-used amateur spectrum!

All-band radios are a little larger than most VHF/UHF FM mobile radios and also draw considerably more current at full power. This makes them a little more difficult to mount in the passenger compartment. Most can be operated with the front panel mounted as a control head. At least two antenna cables are required for these radios — one is dedicated to HF or HF and 6 meters. VHF and UHF may be combined into a single connection or they may be separate. All of the same cautions apply to installing HF radios as for VHF and UHF gear.

HF antennas bring their own special needs to the vehicle environment. A quarter-wave whip for 2 meters is less than 20 inches long, but the same antenna on 10 meters, the highest HF band, is approximately 8 feet long. On lower-frequency bands, the length of a full-size antenna rapidly becomes impractical for mobile operation. Most HF mobile antennas are coiled up, or *loaded*, to get the full electrical length crammed into a mobile-sized package. While this enables the antennas to be used while in motion, it also cuts their efficiency dramatically.

The ground connection to the vehicle is also critical on HF because the entire vehicle usually serves as the ground for the antenna. With the antenna efficiency already compromised, it becomes more important to avoid unnecessary ground losses. Many hams get good results using the "Hamstick" style mobile whips shown in **Figure 1.8**. You can see that multiple magnets are used, not only because the antennas are larger and require additional holding power, but because the extra surface area of the magnets makes a better electrical connection to the vehicle surface. Whip style antennas can also be used with bumper or trailer-hitch mounts with good results. The key is to keep the base of the antenna, where current is the highest, in the clear and as high on the vehicle as possible.

Another type of HF mobile antenna that has become increasing popular is the "screwdriver" antenna. So-named because the initial designs used an electric screwdriver motor to adjust the antenna length, the antenna is a fixed-length whip tuned by moving sliding contacts along a coil at its base. Fixed mobile antennas, such as the Hamsticks, are relatively narrow-banded and must be retuned or changed in order to operate on greatly different frequencies within one band — for example 40 meter phone and 40 meter CW. The screwdriver type of antenna is tuned by the motor and can be used over a wide frequency range.

Operating SSB or CW on HF, the VHF/UHF operator will be surprised at how noisy the bands sound compared to the higher bands and noise suppression of FM. At HF, there is a lot more atmospheric noise. Noise is also generated in abundance by nearby motors, electrical lines, and even the vehicle's own ignition and accessory systems. The noise blankers found in the mobile radios can take out the worst of noise, but the HF operator typically just develops an "ear" for copying through it. The resources listed at the end of this

Figure 1.9 — A separate communications speaker, such as the MFJ-383 shown here, can dramatically improve received audio quality and understandability in the mobile environment.

section list numerous techniques for identifying and reducing or eliminating "mobile noise."

Keeping any kind of log while in motion is awkward at best and unsafe at worst, unless you train yourself to take notes without looking away from the road. A better idea is to just pull over and write the information in the log. Some operators use a digital voice recorder if they want to keep moving but still log the stations they work. The information is transcribed later.

Mobile Accessories

As in the home shack, there are a number of useful accessories that can make radio easier on the road. One of the most useful is the communications speaker, shown in **Figure 1.9**. The speaker in mobile radios is not very effective if the radio is installed under a seat, in the trunk or in a console. The external speaker can be mounted where sound is directed at the driver. (Most states do not allow the use of headphones while driving; check your local motor vehicle laws before doing so.) The frequency response of these speakers is tailored to the mobile environment, as well.

Antenna tuners are another common addition to the mobile HF station, allowing a fixed antenna to be used over a wider range. Auto-tuners are particularly popular, especially among boaters who use a single length of wire as their antenna for all bands. Several manufacturers offer tuners intended for use with mobile stations.

Even CW can be used on the road! Most operators prefer using a paddle due to the inconvenience of trying to use a straight key in a car. Paddles can be mounted on leg clips that hold them steady. Shops that sell aviation accessories often have lapboards or kneeboards that are quite suitable for mobiling, since pilots share many of the same concerns with hams.

Mobiling Activities

What can you do on the air while you're also on the road? Quite a bit! For starters, you can ragchew on any band just

Figure 1.8 — Many HF mobile stations use the single-band "Hamstick" style whip antennas. A hefty, multiple-magnet mount is required both to hold the large antenna on the car at driving speeds and to provide enough coupling to the car's metal surfaces.

as well in motion as from home. In fact, the contacts tend to be longer because there are no interrupting phone calls or chores. Hilltopping on VHF and UHF is a popular practice, particularly during VHF+ contests.

If you like the idea of being the sought-after station, you may enjoy participating in the County Hunters program. Yes, people have actually made contact with all of the 3077 counties in the United States! A lot of those contacts are made with mobile stations, some of which have made a special trip to activity a lightly populated county or even two, transmitting from astride a county line. Your state QSO party probably encourages mobile operating, too, and out-of-state stations will be anxiously looking for you to increase their scores.

Mobile Resources

Browse the websites listed below for more information about mobile activities.

ARRL Mobile Information Page (**www.arrl.org/mobile-stations**); AC6V, Operating Modes (**www.ac6v.com/opmodes.htm**); KØBG, Website for Mobile Operators (**www.k0bg.com**); DX Zone's Mobile Page (**www.dxzone.com/catalog/Operating_Modes/Mobile**); Mobile Amateur Radio Awards Club, MARAC (**www.marac.org**); County Hunters (**www.countyhunter.com**); and ARRL Contest Corral (**www.arrl.org/contests**).

You can also find more technical information in *The ARRL Handbook* and *The ARRL Antenna Book*, as well as *Amateur Radio on the Move* and RSGB's *Amateur Radio Mobile Handbook*, all available from your favorite ham radio dealer or the ARRL Store.

Experience? Get on the Air!

Actual on-the-air operating experience is the best teacher. In this section, we will try to give you enough of the basics to

Your First Contact

Are your palms sweaty, hands shaking and is there a queasy herd of butterflies (wearing spikes, perhaps) performing maneuvers in your stomach? Chances are you're facing your first Amateur Radio QSO. If so, take heart! Although some may deny it, the vast majority of hams felt the same way before firing up the rig for their first contact.

Although nervousness is natural, there are some preparations that can make things go a little more smoothly. Practicing QSOs face-to-face with a friend, or perhaps with a member of the local Amateur Radio club, is a good way to ease the jitters.

Some find it useful to write down in advance information you will use during the QSO. You might even go so far as to write a script for what you expect. After a couple of contacts, however, you'll find that you need little prompting.

The ideal security blanket to have with you as you make your first few QSOs is your Elmer or another experienced ham. You'll find that after your initial nervousness wears off you will do just fine by yourself. And you will have honored a ham friend by allowing him or her the privilege of sharing your first on-the-air contacts.

be able to make (and enjoy!) your first QSO. Learn by doing and by listening to others. Don't be afraid to ask questions of someone who might be able to help. After all, we're in this hobby together, and assistance is only as far away as the closest ham.

How do you develop good operating habits? This *ARRL Operating Manual* is an excellent place to start. An entire chapter is devoted to each major Amateur Radio activity, from working DX to space communications. Each chapter has been written by a ham with considerable experience in that area. Experience, even through the words of others, is a powerful teacher. Take a look at the table of contents; you'll be amazed at the diversity and amount of good solid reference material you have at your fingertips.

Listen, Listen, Listen…!

The most efficient way to learn to do something is with a coach or *Elmer*. An Elmer is someone who helps a newcomer become an established, competent ham. Since there are established ways of doing things in the Amateur Radio Service because of rules or good practice, you'll learn most effectively by just plain, old-fashioned listening. All you need is a receiver and your ears.

Tune around the amateur frequency bands, and just listen, listen, listen. Listen to as many QSOs as you can. Learn how the operators conduct themselves, see what works for other operators and what doesn't, and incorporate those good operating practices into your own operating habits. You'll be surprised how much operator savvy you can pick up just by listening.

On-the-Air Experience for Newcomers

When you're ready, fire up the rig to make your first QSO. Go for it! Nothing can compare with actual on-the-air experience. Remember, everyone on the air today had to make their first QSO at some time or other. They had the same tentativeness you might have now, but they made it just fine. So will you.

It's the nature of the ham to be friendly, especially toward other members of this wonderful fraternity we all joined when we passed that examination. Trust the operator at the other end of your first QSO to understand your feelings and be as helpful as possible. After all, he or she was once in your situation!

The Bands

Operating on the VHF/UHF bands is relatively straightforward for most modes of operation commonly employed there. Operating on the HF bands is a quite a bit more variable, because the propagation depends on a number of factors that are quite literally in outer space. The main influence on the Earth's ionosphere is the Sun, but the magnetic field of the Earth gets into the act very much as well in determining how HF signals are propagated from one place to another.

The sidebar "Picking a Band" gives you a generalized idea of what to expect on both the HF and the VHF/UHF bands, and **Figure 1.10** shows the Amateur Radio frequency allocations in the US. Never forget, however, that part of the excitement and mystery of the HF bands lies in their

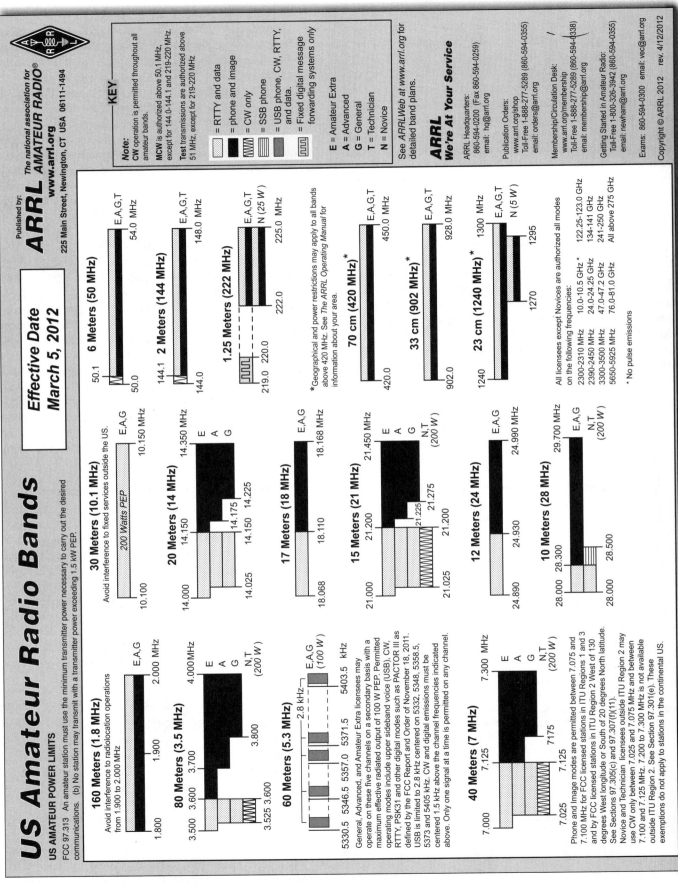

Figure 1.10 — Frequency Allocation Chart for US amateurs.

Table 1.3

The Considerate Operator's Frequency Guide

The following frequencies are generally recognized for certain modes or activities (all frequencies are in MHz) during normal conditions. These are not regulations and occasionally a high level of activity, such as during a period of emergency response, DXpedition or contest, may result in stations operating outside these frequency ranges.

Nothing in the rules recognizes a net's, group's or any individual's special privilege to any specific frequency. Section 97.101(b) of the Rules states that "Each station licensee and each control operator must cooperate in selecting transmitting channels and in making the most effective use of the amateur service frequencies. No frequency will be assigned for the exclusive use of any station." No one "owns" a frequency.

It's good practice — and plain old common sense — for any operator, regardless of mode, to check to see if the frequency is in use prior to engaging operation. If you are there first, other operators should make an effort to protect you from interference to the extent possible, given that 100% interference-free operation is an unrealistic expectation in today's congested bands.

Frequencies	Modes/Activities	Frequencies	Modes/Activities
1.800-2.000	CW	14.230	SSTV
1.800-1.810	Digital Modes	14.285	QRP SSB calling frequency
1.810	QRP CW calling frequency	14.286	AM calling frequency
1.843-2.000	SSB, SSTV and other wideband modes	18.100-18.105	RTTY/Data
1.910	SSB QRP	18.105-18.110	Automatically controlled data stations
1.995-2.000	Experimental	18.110	IBP/NCDXF beacons
1.999-2.000	Beacons		
		21.060	QRP CW calling frequency
3.500-3.510	CW DX window	21.070-21.110	RTTY/Data
3.560	QRP CW calling frequency	21.090-21.100	Automatically controlled data stations
3.570-3.600	RTTY/Data	21.150	IBP/NCDXF beacons
3.585-3.600	Automatically controlled data stations	21.340	SSTV
3.590	RTTY/Data DX	21.385	QRP SSB calling frequency
3.790-3.800	DX window		
3.845	SSTV	24.920-24.925	RTTY/Data
3.885	AM calling frequency	24.925-24.930	Automatically controlled data stations
3.985	QRP SSB calling frequency	24.930	IBP/NCDXF beacons
7.030	QRP CW calling frequency	28.060	QRP CW calling frequency
7.040	RTTY/Data DX	28.070-28.120	RTTY/Data
7.080-7.125	RTTY/Data	28.120-28.189	Automatically controlled data stations
7.100-7.105	Automatically controlled data stations	28.190-28.225	Beacons
7.171	SSTV	28.200	IBP/NCDXF beacons
7.285	QRP SSB calling frequency	28.385	QRP SSB calling frequency
7.290	AM calling frequency	28.680	SSTV
		29.000-29.200	AM
10.106	QRP CW calling frequency	29.300-29.510	Satellite downlinks
10.130-10.140	RTTY/Data	29.520-29.580	Repeater inputs
10.140-10.150	Automatically controlled data stations	29.600	FM simplex
		29.620-29.680	Repeater outputs
14.060	QRP CW calling frequency		
14.070-14.095	RTTY/Data		
14.095-14.0995	Automatically controlled data stations		
14.100	IBP/NCDXF beacons		
14.1005-14.112	Automatically controlled data stations		

ARRL band plans for frequencies above 28.300 MHz are shown in *The ARRL Repeater Directory* and on **www.arrl.org**.

Table 1.4

North American VHF/UHF/EHF Calling Frequencies

Band (MHz)	Calling Frequency	Band (MHz)	Calling Frequency
50	50.110 DX	432	432.010 EME
	50.125 SSB US, local		432.100 CW/SSB
	50.620 digital (packet)		446.000 National FM simplex frequency
	52.525 National FM simplex frequency	902	902.100
144	144.010 EME		903.100 East Coast
	144.100, 144.110 CW		906.500 National FM simplex frequency
	144.200 SSB		
	146.520 National FM simplex frequency	1296	1294.500 National FM simplex frequency
			1296.100 CW/SSB
222	222.100 CW/SSB	2304	2304.1 CW/SSB
	223.500 National FM simplex frequency	10000	10368.1 CW/SSB
			10280.0 WBFM

VHF/UHF Activity Nights

Some areas do not have enough VHF/UHF activity to support contacts at all times. This schedule is intended to help VHF/UHF operators make contact. This is only a starting point; check with others in your area to see if local hams have a different schedule.

Band (MHz)	Day	Local Time
50	Sunday	6 PM
144	Monday	7 PM
222	Tuesday	8 PM
432	Wednesday	9 PM
902	Friday	9 PM
1296	Thursday	10 PM

Picking a Band

By Jim Kearman, KR1S

160 and 80 Meters

Eighty meters, and its phone neighbor, 75 meters, are favorites for ragchewing. I frequently check out the upper frequencies of the CW subband. There I find both newcomers as well as old-timers trying to work the rust out of their fists. Around 3570 kHz you'll find the digital modes, including RTTY, PSK31 and packet. The QRP frequency is 3560 kHz. If you hear a weak signal calling CQ near 3560, crank down your power and give a call. Another favorite frequency is 3579.5 kHz. If you live in the eastern half of North America, listen for W1AW on 3581.5 (CW), 3597.5 (digital) or 3990 kHz (SSB). W1AW runs 1000 W to a modest antenna — an inverted V at 60 feet. If you can copy W1AW, you can probably work the East Coast, even with low power. AM operation is generally found between 3870 and 3890 kHz.

Even if you can't chase DX, you will find plenty to do on either band. Ionospheric absorption is greatest during the day, thus local contacts are common. At night, contacts over 200 miles away are more frequent, even with a poor antenna. Summer lightning storms make for noisy conditions in the summer, while winter is much quieter. You may also be troubled by electrical noise here. A horizontally polarized antenna, especially one as far from buildings as possible, will pick up less electrical noise.

Topband, as 160 meters is often called, is similar to 80 meters. QSOs here tend to be a bit more relaxed with less QRM. DX is frequent at the bottom of the band. Don't let the length of a half-wave dipole for 160 keep you off the band; a 25- or 50-foot "long wire" can give you surprisingly good results if a good ground system is available. One favorite trick is to connect together the center conductor and shield of the coax feed line of a 40- or 80-meter dipole and load the resulting antenna as a "T," working it against the station ground.

60 Meters

Unlike other HF amateur bands, 60 meters is *channelized*. This means that you have to operate on specific frequencies. Amateurs have secondary access to this band. They cannot cause interference to and must accept interference from the Primary Government users. Amateurs can transmit CW and PSK31 on the following channel-center frequencies: 5332.0, 5348.0, 5358.5, 5373.0 and 5405.0 kHz. Amateurs can also transmit upper sideband (USB) voice and PACTOR III on the following suppressed carrier frequencies (the frequencies typically shown on transceiver displays): 5330.5, 5346.5, 5357.0, 5371.5 and 5403.5 kHz.

Amateurs may transmit with an effective radiated power (ERP) of 100 W or less, relative to a half-wave dipole. If you're using a commercial directional antenna, FCC Rules require you to keep a copy of the manufacturer's gain specifications in your station records. If you built the directional antenna yourself, you must calculate the gain and keep the results in your station records.

When using a directional antenna, you must take your antenna gain into account when setting your RF output power. For example, if your antenna offers 3 dB gain, your maximum legal output power on 60 meters should be no more than 50 W (50 W plus 3 dB gain equals 100 W ERP).

Despite the limitations, it has intriguing potential. The propagation on 60 meters combines the best of 80 and 40 meters.

40 and 30 Meters

I must confess to being biased in favor of these bands, especially 40 meters. If I could have a receiver that covered only one band, it would be 40. Running 10 W from my East Coast apartment (indoor antenna) I can work European hams, ragchew up and down the coast, check into Saturday morning QRP nets, and listen to foreign broadcast stations besides. Yes, 40 is a little crowded. Look at the bright side: You won't be lonely. I think it's possible to work someone on 40 any time of the day or night.

In the US, Advanced and Extra licensees have voice privileges starting at 7125 kHz and the General band starts at 7175 kHz. Most other countries have SSB privileges down to 7050 kHz so don't be surprised if you hear voice stations below the US phone band. At night you may hear foreign broadcast stations above 7200 kHz. During the day, they won't bother you much. Forty is a good band for daytime mobile SSB operation, too. You'll find plenty of activity, and propagation conditions tend to be stable enough to allow you to ragchew as you roll along.

CW QRPers hang around and above 7030 kHz. Digital operators work around 7080 to 7125 kHz. Hams operating AM are typically around 7290 kHz.

The 30 meter band has propagation similar to 40 meters. Skip distances tend to be a little longer on 30 meters, and it's not so crowded. At present, stations in the US are limited to 200 W output on this band. DX stations seem to like the low end of the band, from 10100 to 10115 kHz. Ragchewers often congregate above 10115. We share 30 meters with other services, so be sure you don't interfere with them. SSB isn't allowed on 30, but you can use CW and the digital modes.

20 Meters

As much as I like 40 and 30 meters, I have many fond memories of 20 meters as well. When I upgraded my license to General in 1963, I made a beeline to 20 meters. To this day, I can't stay away for long. A 20 meter dipole is only 33 feet long, and that doesn't have to be in a straight line. Many US hams have worked their first European or Australian contacts with a dipole and 100 W.

Many hams consider 20 meters the workhorse DX band. At the bottom of a solar cycle, 20 meters may be usable in a particular direction for only a few hours a day. Even then, 20 is usually open to somewhere in the world throughout the day and night. For example, from New England, 20 is open to some part of South America for 24 hours a day, whatever the level of sunspots might be. On the other hand, 20 meters can be open to the Far East for as much as 13 hours of the day (with very weak signals) when sunspot activity is low, while it can be open all day during periods of high solar activity.

There's plenty of room on the band. CW ragchewers hang out from 14025 to 14070 kHz, where you start hearing digital stations. The international QRP frequency is 14060 kHz. The sideband part of the band is sometimes pretty busy and then it may be difficult to make a contact with low power or a modest antenna. Look above 14250 for ragchewers. Impromptu discussion groups that sometimes spring up on 20 SSB make for interesting listening, even if you don't participate. If you like photographs, look around 14230 kHz for slow-scan TV. You'll need some extra equipment (as discussed in the Image Communications chapter of this book) to see the pictures.

17, 15 and 12 Meters

Except during years of high solar activity, you'll do most of your operating during daylight hours. Propagation is usually better during the winter months. Seventeen and 12 meters aren't as crowded as 15 meters. Fifteen, though, is not nearly as crowded as 20. On 15, the QRP calling frequency is 21060 kHz. Don't forget that CW can be found all the way up to 21200 kHz. No special frequencies are used for QRP operation on 17 and 12. SSB operation is much easier on 17 and 12 because of lower activity. Low activity doesn't mean no activity — when those bands are open, you'll find plenty of stations to work. You only need one at a time, after all. Digital operation is found from 21070 to 21110 kHz, and around 18100 and 24920 kHz.

Practical indoor, outdoor, mobile or portable antennas for these bands are simple to build and install. It's even possible to make indoor beam antennas for the range of 18 to 25 MHz.

10 Meters

The 10 meter band stretches from 28000 to 29700 kHz. During years of high solar activity, 10 to 25 W transceivers will fetch plenty of contacts. When the sun is quiet, there are still occasional openings of thousands of miles. Ten meters also benefits from sporadic-E propagation. You'll find most sporadic-E openings in the summer, but they can happen anytime. Sporadic-E openings happen suddenly and end just as quickly. You may not be able to ragchew very long, but you'll be amazed at how many stations you can work.

SSB activity is heaviest in the Novice/Technician subband from 28300 to 28500 kHz. The lower end of the band (tune up from the bottom edge) is a good place to look for CW activity, as is the QRP calling frequency at 28060 kHz. You can operate 1200 baud packet radio on 10 meters, whereas we're limited to 300 baud on the lower bands. Digital operation takes place from 28070 to 28120 kHz.

Higher in the band, above 29000 kHz, you'll find amateur FM stations and repeaters, and the amateur satellite subband. AM operation is also popular between 29000 and 29200 kHz.

Operating on 50 MHz and Above

The VHF/UHF/microwave bands offer advantages to the low-power operator. The biggest plus is the relatively smaller antennas used. A good-sized 2 meter beam will easily fit in a closet when not in use. Portable and mobile operation on these bands is also easy and fun.

6 Meters

Six meters is perhaps the most interesting amateur band. When solar activity is high, worldwide QSOs are common. When solar activity is low, however, opportunities for long-distance communication decrease. Sporadic-E propagation, which I mentioned earlier, is the most reliable DX mode during periods of low solar activity.

With small antennas, like three-element beams, it's possible to work 1000 miles on sporadic E. Three-element 6 meter beams don't fit well inside houses or apartments, but you might be able to put one in an attic or crawl space. Even if you can only use a dipole, you'll be able to work locals, and snag some more distant stations when the band opens.

Just about any mode found on the HF bands is used on 6 meters. CW and SSB operation take place on the lower part of the band. Higher up you'll find FM simplex and repeater stations. Another mode you'll sometimes find on 6 meters is radio control (RC) of model planes, boats and cars.

2 Meters

Simply stated, 2 meters is the most popular ham band in North America. From just about any point in the US, you can probably work someone on 2 meters, 24 hours a day. Most hams know about 2 meter FM, APRS and packet radio operation, but CW and SSB are used here too. There's even an amateur satellite subband on 2 meters.

CW and SSB operation is done mostly with horizontally polarized antennas. FM and packet operators use vertical polarization, while satellites can be worked with either. A popular 2 meter antenna called a *halo* is perfect for indoor or mobile use on CW or SSB. The omnidirectional halo has no gain, but you'll be able to work locals, and up to 100 miles during band openings.

FM and packet usually require only a simple vertical antenna. The *ARRL Repeater Directory* will tell you what repeaters are available in your area. This book lists repeaters the bands from 29 MHz to 1.2 GHz and above.

The 222 and 430 MHz Bands

Every mode used on 2 meters is found on 222 except satellite communication. The 430 MHz or 70 cm band is second only to 2 meters in VHF/UHF activity. Multiband hand-held and mobile FM transceivers are available at prices only slightly higher than single-band rigs. If you think you'd like to try these bands in addition to 2 meters, look into a multiband rig.

One mode you'll find on 70 cm that isn't allowed on the lower frequencies is fast scan amateur television (ATV). Assuming you already have a broadcast TV set, all you need is a receive converter, transmitter, antenna and camera. Inexpensive cameras designed for home video use are fine for ATV. ATV repeaters may be found in larger metropolitan areas. They're listed in the *ARRL Repeater Directory*.

33 cm (902 MHz) and Up

As you go higher in frequency, the size of antennas gets smaller. This fact allows you to use very high-gain antennas that aren't very big. Commercial equipment is available for the bands through 10 GHz. You'll also find kits (the tuned circuits are etched onto the circuit boards).

Because antennas are so small, it's possible to have 20 to 30 dB gain antennas that fit in your car's trunk. In comparison, a big 20 meter beam might offer only 10 dB of gain. Operating from the field with battery-powered equipment is very popular, especially during VHF/UHF/ microwave contests. Thanks to high-gain antennas, contacts over several hundred miles are possible with equipment running 1 or 2 W.

unpredictability from day-to-day, or even from hour-to-hour. At the minimum of the solar cycle, the higher HF bands (15, 12 and 10 meters) are quiet most of the time. When sunspots start appearing once again, those bands fill with signals from around the world!

Table 1.3 shows the Considerate Operator's Frequency Guide, and **Table 1.4** shows the North American VHF/UHF/EHF Calling Frequencies. Try these frequencies first when looking for activity on a quiet band.

Propagation Beacons

By providing a steady signal on certain frequencies, HF beacons provide a valuable means of checking current propagation conditions — how well signals are traveling at the time you want to transmit.

The Northern California DX Foundation, in cooperation with the International Amateur Radio Union (IARU), has established a widespread, multiband beacon network. This network operates on 14.100, 18.110, 21.150, 24.930 and 28.200 MHz. These beacons transmit at a sequence of power levels from 100 W down to 0.1 W in a repeating sequence. A full description with the most up-to-date status is on the NCDXF web page: **www.ncdxf.org/pages/beacons.html**.

Operating — What, Where and How

You have read a little about the basics of ham radio and have some ideas about selecting a rig and station equipment and erecting a decent antenna system. Now it's time to learn a little more about how to go about playing the ham radio game.

To communicate effectively with other hams, we all need to use accepted operating procedures. The next part of this chapter briefly describes the major modes of ham radio communication and a few of the procedures and conventions that hams use on the air. Other chapters discuss the operating procedures for many specialized modes of communication in greater detail. But first we are going to look at operating HF voice and CW (Morse code).

Phone Operating Procedures

These phone or voice operating procedures apply to operation on the HF bands as well as SSB on VHF/UHF. Procedures used on repeaters are different since the operation there is channelized — that is, anyone listening to the repeater will hear you as soon as you begin to transmit. Therefore there is no need to call CQ. Each repeater may use a slightly different procedure. There is a complete discussion of repeater operations in the FM chapter of this book.

Learning procedures is straightforward: Listen to what others are doing, and incorporate their good habits into your

---

Table 1.5

The Phonetic Alphabet

When operating phone, a standard alphabet is often used to ensure understanding of call letters and other spelled-out information. Thus Larry, WR1B, would announce his call as Whiskey Romeo One Bravo if he felt the station on the other end could misunderstand his call. Phonetics are not routinely used when operating VHF-FM.

A — Alfa (**AL** FAH)
B — Bravo (**BRAH** VOH)
C — Charlie (**CHAR** LEE)
D — Delta (**DELL** TAH)
E — Echo (**ECK** OH)
F — Foxtrot (**FOX** TROT)
G — Golf (GOLF)
H — Hotel (HOH **TELL**)
I — India (**IN** DEE AH)
J — Juliet (**JEW** LEE ETT)
K — Kilo (**KEY** LOH)
L — Lima (**LEE** MA)
M — Mike (MIKE)
N — November (NO **VEM** BERR)
O — Oscar (**OSS** CAR)
P — Papa (PAH **PAH**)
Q — Quebec (KEY **BECK**)
R — Romeo (**ROW** ME OH)
S — Sierra (SEE **AIR** AH)
T — Tango (**TANG** OH)
U — Uniform (**YOU** NEE FORM)
V — Victor (**VIK** TORE)
W — Whiskey (**WISS** KEY)
X — X-Ray (**EX** RAY)
Y — Yankee (**YANG** KEY)
Z — Zulu (**ZOO** LOU)

Table 1.6

The RST System

Readability
1 — Unreadable
2 — Barely readable, occasional words distinguishable
3 — Readable with considerable difficulty
4 — Readable with practically no difficulty
5 — Perfectly readable

Signal Strength
1 — Faint signals, barely perceptible
2 — Very weak signals
3 — Weak signals
4 — Fair signals
5 — Fairly good signals
6 — Good signals
7 — Moderately strong signals
8 — Strong signals
9 — Extremely strong signals

Tone
1 — Sixty-cycle ac or less, very rough and broad
2 — Very rough ac, very harsh and broad
3 — Rough ac tone, rectified but not filtered
4 — Rough note, some trace of filtering
5 — Filtered rectified ac but strongly ripple-modulated
6 — Filtered tone, definite trace of ripple modulation
7 — Near pure tone, trace of ripple modulation
8 — Near perfect tone, slight trace of ripple modulation
9 — Perfect tone, no trace of ripple or modulation of any kind

If the signal has the characteristic steadiness of crystal control, add the letter X to the report. If there is a chirp, add the letter C. Similarly for a click, add K. (See FCC Regulations §97.307, Emissions Standards.) The above reporting system is used on both CW and voice; leave out the "tone" report on voice.

own operating style. Use common sense in your day-to-day phone QSOs, too:

(1) Listen before transmitting. Ask if the frequency is in use before making a call on any particular frequency.

(2) Give your call sign as needed, using the approved ITU (International Telecommunication Union) Phonetics. These phonetics are given in **Table 1.5**.

(3) Make sure your signal is clean and your audio undistorted. Do not turn your microphone gain up too high. If you have a speech processor, use it only when you are sure it is properly adjusted. Don't take the chance of transmitting spurious (out of band) signals.

(4) Only occupy the frequency as long as you need it. This gives as many operators as possible a chance to use the frequency spectrum.

(5) Give honest signal reports. **Table 1.6** lists what the various RST reports mean.

Whatever band, mode or type of operating you choose, there are three fundamental things to remember. The first is that courtesy costs very little and is often amply rewarded by bringing out the best in others. The second is that the aim of each radio contact should be 100% effective communication. The good operator is never satisfied with anything less. The third is that "private" conversations with another station are actually *public*. Keep in mind that many amateurs are uncomfortable discussing so-called controversial subjects such as sex, religion or politics over the air. Also, never unnecessarily give any information on the air that might be of assistance to the criminally inclined, such as when you are going to be out of town!

Using the proper procedure is very important. Voice operators say what they want to have understood, while CW operators have to spell it out or abbreviate. Since the speed of transmission on phone is generally between 150 and 200 words per minute, the matter of readability and understandability is critical to good communication. The good voice operator uses operating habits that are beyond reproach.

Correct phone operation is more challenging than it first may appear, even though it does not require the use of code or special abbreviations and prosigns. Most people have acquired imperfect habits of pronunciation, intonation and phraseology even before entering Amateur Radio! Remember that the other operator can't see you. Understanding you depends solely on your voice coming over the airwaves. It's easy to acquire bad habits of speech, so be prepared to put in a bit of effort to speak clearly and not too quickly. This is particularly important when talking to a DX station that speaks a different language.

Avoid using CW abbreviations (including "HI" which is CW for laughter) and Q signals on phone, although QRZ (for "who is calling?") has become accepted. Otherwise, plain language should be used. Keep jargon to a minimum. Some hams use "we" instead of "I," "handle" instead of "name" and "Roger" instead of "that's correct." These expressions are not necessary and do not contribute to better operating. No doubt you will hear many more.

Table 1.7

Q Signals

These Q signals are the ones used most often on the air. (Q abbreviations take the form of questions only when they are sent followed by a question mark.)

QRG	Will you tell me my exact frequency (or that of ___)? Your exact frequency (or that of ___) is ___ kHz.	QSL	Can you acknowledge receipt (of a message or transmission)? I am acknowledging receipt.
QRL	Are you busy? I am busy (or I am busy with ___). Please do not interfere.	QSN	Did you hear me (or) on ___ kHz? I did hear you (or ___) on ___ kHz.
QRM	Is my transmission being interfered with? Your transmission is being interfered with ___ (1. Nil; 2. Slightly; 3. Moderately; 4. Severely; 5. Extremely.)	QSO	Can you communicate with direct or by relay? I can communicate with ___ direct (or relay through).
QRN	Are you troubled by static? I am troubled by static ___. (1-5 as under QRM.)	QSP	Will you relay to ___? I will relay to.
QRO	Shall I increase power? Increase power. QRP Shall I decrease power? Decrease power. QRQ Shall I send faster? Send faster (___ WPM).	QST	General call preceding a message addressed to all amateurs and ARRL members. This is in effect "CQ ARRL."
QRS	Shall I send more slowly? Send more slowly (___ WPM).	QSX	Will you listen to ___ on ___ kHz? I am listening to ___ on ___ kHz.
QRT	Shall I stop sending? Stop sending.	QSY	Shall I change to transmission on another frequency? Change to transmission on another frequency (or on ___ kHz).
QRU	Have you anything for me? I have nothing for you.		
QRV	Are you ready? I am ready.		
QRX	When will you call me again? I will call you again at __ hours (on ___ kHz).	QTB	Do you agree with my counting of words? I do not agree with your counting of words. I will repeat the first letter or digit of each word or group.
QRZ	Who is calling me? You are being called by (on ___ kHz).	QTC	How many messages have you to send? I have ___ messages for you (or for ___).
QSB	Are my signals fading? Your signals are fading.	QTH	What is your location? My location is ___ .
QSK	Can you hear me between your signals and if so can I break in on your transmission? I can hear you between signals; break in on my transmission.	QTR	What is the correct time? The time is ___ .

Initiating a Contact

There are three ways to initiate a voice contact: call CQ (a general call to any station), answer a CQ, or call at the end of the other person's QSO. If activity on a band seems low and you have a reasonable signal, a CQ call may be worthwhile.

Before calling CQ, it is important to find a frequency that appears unoccupied by any other station. This may not be easy, particularly in crowded band conditions. Listen carefully — perhaps a weak DX station is on frequency.

Always listen before transmitting. Make sure the frequency isn't being used *before* you call. If, after a reasonable time, the frequency seems clear, ask if the frequency is in use, followed by your call: "Is the frequency in use? This is N1OJS." If as far as you can determine no one responds, you are ready to make your call.

CQ calls should be kept short. Long calls are unnecessary. If no one answers, you can always call again. Think of each CQ as an advertisement for your station. A caller tuning across your signal should hear a friendly voice, clean audio, and plenty of time between your CQs for them to respond.

If you do transmit a long call, a potential contact may become impatient and tune elsewhere. You may also interfere with stations that were already on the frequency but whom you didn't hear in the initial check. If two or three calls produce no answer, there may be interference on the frequency. It's also possible that the band isn't open.

An example of a short CQ call would be: "CQ CQ Calling CQ. This is N1OJS, November-One-Oscar-Juliet-Sierra, November-One-Oscar-Juliet-Sierra, calling CQ and standing by."

When replying to a CQ, give both call signs clearly — yours and the CQing station. Use the standard phonetics to make sure the other station gets your call correctly. Phonetics are necessary when calling in a DX pileup and initially in most HF contacts but not usually used when calling into an FM repeater.

When you are calling a specific station, it is good practice to keep calls short and to say the call sign of the station called only once followed by your call repeated twice. VOX (voice operated switch) operation is helpful. If properly adjusted, it enables you to listen between phrases so that you know what is happening on the frequency. "N1OJS N1OJS, this is W2GD, Whiskey-Two-Golf-Delta, Over."

Once contact has been established, it is no longer necessary to use the phonetic alphabet or sign the other station's call. According to FCC regulations, you need only sign your call every 10 minutes, or at the conclusion of the contact. (The exception is handling international third-party traffic; you must sign both calls in this instance.) A normal two-way conversation can thus be enjoyed, without the need for continual identification. The words "Over" or "Go Ahead" are used at the end of a transmission to show you are ready for a reply from the other station.

Signal reports on phone are two-digit numbers using the RS portion of the RST system (no tone report is required). The maximum signal report would be "59;" that is, readability 5, strength 9. On FM repeaters, RS reports are not appropriate. When a signal has fully captured the repeater, this is called "full quieting."

Many hams enjoy operating outdoors as part of a camping trip or other vacation. Tom, K7TPD, is shown here operating 40 meter CW on an outing with the Radio Society of Tucson K7RST.

CW Operating

Using Morse code is a common bond among many HF operators who take pride in their code proficiency. It takes practice to master the art of sending good code on a hand key, bug (semi-automatic key) or electronic keyer. It takes practice to get that smooth rhythm, practice to get that smooth spacing between words and characters, and practice to learn the sound of whole words and phrases, rather than just individual letters.

CW (standing for *continuous wave*) is an effective mode of communication. CW transceivers are simpler than their phone counterparts, and a CW signal can usually get through very heavy QRM (interference) much more effectively than a phone signal.

To reduce transmission time and increase efficiency when using Morse code, hams use shortcuts and abbreviations during a CW QSO. Many were developed within the ham fraternity, while some are borrowed from old-time telegraph operators. *Q signals* are among the most useful of these abbreviations. A list of the most popular Q signals is in **Table 1.7**. You don't have to memorize all the Q signals, just keep a copy handy to your operating table.

After using some of the Q signals and abbreviations a few times you will quickly learn the most common ones without needing any reference. With time, you'll find that as your CW proficiency rises, you will be able to communicate almost as quickly on CW as you can on the voice modes. A list of common CW abbreviations is in **Table 1.8**.

It may not seem that way to you now, but your CW sending and receiving speed will rise very quickly with on-the-air practice. For your first few QSOs, carefully choose to answer the calls from stations sending at a speed you can copy (perhaps another first-timer on the band?). Courtesy on the ham bands dictates that an operator will slow his or her code speed to accommodate another operator. Don't be afraid to call someone who is sending just a bit faster than you can copy comfortably. That operator will generally slow down to meet your CW speed. If necessary, ask the other operator to "PSE QRS" to slow down a little. Helping each other is the name of the game in ham radio.

Table 1.8
Some Abbreviations for CW Work

Although abbreviations help to cut down unnecessary transmission, make it a rule not to abbreviate unnecessarily when working an operator of unknown experience.

AA	All after	OC	Old chap
AB	All before	OM	Old man
ABT	About	OP-OPR	Operator
ADR	Address	OT	Old timer; old top
AGN	Again	PBL	Preamble
ANT	Antenna	PSE	Please
BCI	Broadcast interference	PWR	Power
BCL	Broadcast listener	PX	Press
BK	Break; break me; break in	R	Received as transmitted; are
BN	All between; been	RCD	Received
BUG	Semi-automatic key	RCVR (RX)	Receiver
B4	Before	REF	Refer to; referring to; reference
C	Yes (correct)	RFI	Radio frequency interference
CFM	Confirm; I confirm	RIG	Station equipment
CK	Check	RPT	Repeat; I repeat; report
CL	I am closing my station; call	RTTY	Radioteletype
CLD-CLG	Called; calling	RX	Receiver
CQ	Calling any station	SASE	Self-addressed, stamped envelope
CUD	Could	SED	Said
CUL	See you later	SIG	Signature; signal
CW	Continuous wave (i.e., radiotelegraph)	SINE	Operator's personal initials or nickname
DLD-DLVD	Delivered	SKED	Schedule
DR	Dear	SRI	Sorry
DX	Distance, foreign countries	SSB	Single sideband
ES	And, &	SVC	Service; prefix to service message
FB	Fine business, excellent	T	Zero (number)
FM	Frequency modulation	TFC	Traffic
GA	Go ahead (or resume sending)	TMW	Tomorrow
GB	Good-by	TNX-TKS	Thanks
GBA	Give better address	TT	That
GE	Good evening	TU	Thank you
GG	Going	TVI	Television interference
GM	Good morning	TX	Transmitter
GN	Good night	TXT	Text
GND	Ground	UR-URS	Your; you're; yours
GUD	Good	VFO	Variable-frequency oscillator
HI	The telegraphic laugh; high	VY	Very
HR	Here, hear	WA	Word after
HV	Have	WB	Word before
HW	How	WD-WDS	Word; words
LID	A poor operator	WKD-WKG	Worked; working
MA, MILS	Milliamperes	WL	Well; will
MSG	Message; prefix to radiogram	WUD	Would
N	No	WX	Weather
NCS	Net control station	XCVR	Transceiver
ND	Nothing doing	XMTR (TX)	Transmitter
NIL	Nothing; I have nothing for you	XTAL	Crystal
NM	No more	XYL (YF)	Wife
NR	Number	YL	Young lady
NW	Now; I resume transmission	73	Best regards
OB	Old boy	88	Love and kisses

To increase your speed, you may wish to continue to copy the code practice sessions from W1AW, the ARRL HQ station. (West Coast stations can tune in the West Coast runs as described in *QST* and on the ARRL website.) It might be a good idea to spend some time sending in step (on a code-practice oscillator — not on the air, of course) with a code training program; this approach will help develop your sending ability.

Correct CW Procedures

The best way to establish a contact, especially at first, is to listen until you hear someone calling CQ. CQ means, "I wish to contact any amateur station." Avoid the common operating pitfall of calling CQ endlessly; it clutters up the airwaves and keeps others from calling you. The typical CQ would sound like this: CQ CQ CQ DE K5RC K5RC K5RC repeated once or twice and followed by K. The letter K is a prosign inviting any station to go ahead. If there is no answer, pause for 10 seconds or so and repeat the call.

If you hear a CQ, wait until the ham finishes transmitting (by ending with the letter K), then call: K5RC DE W1HSR W1HSR AR. (AR is equivalent to *over*). In answer to your call, the called station will begin the reply by sending W1HSR DE K5RC R. That R (*roger*) means that he has received your call correctly. Suppose K5RC heard someone calling him, but didn't quite catch the call because of interference (QRM) or static (QRN). Then he might come back with QRZ? DE K5RC K (Who is calling me?).

The QSO

During the contact, it is necessary to identify your station only once every 10 minutes and at the end of the communication. Keep the contact on a friendly and cordial level, remembering that the conversation is not private and many others, including nonamateurs, may be listening. It may be helpful at the beginning to have a fully written-out script in front of you that is typical of the first couple of exchanges. A typical first transmission might sound like this: W1HSR DE K5RC R TNX CALL. UR 599 599 QTH NEVADA NAME TOM. HW? W1HSR DE K5RC KN. This is the basic exchange that begins most QSOs. Once these basics are exchanged the conversation can turn in almost any direction. Many people talk about their jobs, other hobbies, families, travel experiences, and so on.

Both on CW and phone, it is possible to be informal, friendly and conversational; this is what makes the Amateur Radio QSO enjoyable. During a CW contact, when you want the other station to take a turn, the recommended signal is KN (*go ahead, only*), meaning that you want *only* the contacted station to come back to you. If you don't mind someone else breaking in to join the contact, just K (*go ahead*) is sufficient.

Bill, EI/N7OU, says that there's nothing better than working CW with a battery powered rig on the beach during his recent walking tour of Ireland! (*Paula Moore photo*)

In Pursuit of...DX

"I'll never forget the thrill of my first DX contact. It was on 15 meters CW. I heard a G3 (a station in England) calling CQ, and no one answered right away so I decided to give it a try. Success! With a lump in my throat and sweat on my palms, I managed to complete my first DX QSO and become hopelessly hooked. DX is great!"

Many hams can tell a similar story. DX is Amateur Radio shorthand for *long distance*; furthermore, DX is universally understood by hams to be a station in a foreign country. Chasing DX is one of the most popular activities in our hobby. If you operate on the HF bands, you can get in on the fun!

You don't need a super kilowatt station and huge antennas. The beauty of DXing is that your operating skills can overcome deficiencies in your station equipment. Pick the right frequency band and the right time of day (or night) and the DX stations will be there — ready to talk to you.

Check the "How's DX?" column in *QST*. It contains tips on propagation and news of interest to DXers. And don't forget to subscribe or tune in to the weekly W1AW DX bulletin for the latest DX news. Good DX!

Ending the QSO

When you decide to end the contact or the other ham expresses the desire to end it, don't keep talking. Briefly express your thanks for the contact: TNX QSO or TNX CHAT — and then sign off: 73 SK KA1JPA DE WB1ENT. If you are leaving the air, add CL (*closing*) to the end, right after your call sign.

These ending signals, which indicate to the casual listener the status of the contact, establish Amateur Radio as a cordial and fraternal hobby. At the same time they foster orderliness and denote organization. These signals have no legal standing; FCC regulations say little about our internal procedures.

Conducting the Contact

Aside from signal strength, name, and location, it is customary to exchange power level and antenna. This information helps both stations assess conditions. Keep in mind that many hams will not know the characteristics of your *Loundenboomer 27A3* and your *Signal Squirter 4*. Therefore, you may be better off just saying that your rig runs 100 W output and the antenna is a trap dipole. Once these routine details are out of the way, you can proceed to discuss virtually anything appropriate and interesting.

DX Contacts

DX can be worked on any HF band as well as occasionally on 6 meters. When the 11-year solar sunspot cycle favors 10 meters, worldwide contacts on a daily basis are commonplace on this band. Ten

the other operator (once) for the pleasure of the contact and say good-bye:
"73, G4BUO this is W1BXY, Clear."

Output in Watts

UTC Recommended

RST is a report of signal quality and strength

This column may also be used for contest-exchange info received

	FIXED							VARIABLE			
DATE	FREQ.	MODE	POWER	TIME	STATION WORKED	REPORT SENT	REC'D	TIME OFF	COMMENTS / QTH / NAME / QSL VIA		QSL S	QSL R
16 Nov	3.537	CW	100	1800	KA1E8V	589	479	1835	Manomet, MA John	✓	✓
	10.140	RTTY	100	2031	WB3IMY	599	579	2102	Wallingford, CT Steve		
	50.145	SSB	10	2316	N1OJS	56	55		FN33 short opening!	✓	
17 Nov	28.025	CW	500	1605	KC4AAA	469	559	1607	South Pole - big pileup	✓	
	28.380	SSB	"	1622	DJ6QT	59	59	1626	Walter - Running QRP + dipole		
	24.950	"	100	1712	9Q1A	59	59		New one! F2YT	✓	✓
20 Nov	3.520	CW	1000	0316	ON4UN	549	569	0318	Belgium - John Excellent signal	✓	
	3.847	SSB	100	0336	KA0HJD	57	57	0357	Des Moines, IA Kristen		
	"	"	"	0336	W0SH	58	57	0357	Palm Bay, FL Gary collects old keys		
26 Nov	14.070	PSK	50	1316	KA1JPA	599	579	1328	CT Jodi New to PSK31	✓	
	18.148	SSB	100	1412	AB2E	55	55	1417	Darrell, looking for new states	✓	✓
	21.002	CW	1000	1516	EA8ZS	599	599	33	DX Contest		
	21.027			1518	S56A	599	599	15			

Figure 1.11 — The ARRL Log Book is adaptable to all types of operating.

This is all that is required. Unless the other amateur is a good friend, there is no need to start sending best wishes to everyone in the household including the family dog! Nor is this the time to start digging up extra comments on the contact that will require a "final final" from the other station (there may be other stations waiting to call in).

Also understand that during a band opening on 10 meters or on VHF, you should keep contacts brief so as many stations as possible can work the DX coming through during what may be a brief opportunity. Brevity is also expected when contacting a DXpedition operating from some exotic location for just a few days.

meters is an outstanding DX band when conditions are right and you don't need to run a lot of transmitter power to take advantage of it! A particular advantage of 10 for DX work is that effective beam-type antennas tend to be small and light, making for relatively easy installation. For these reasons, 10 meters is a favorite of many DXers.

Keep in mind that while many overseas amateurs have an exceptional command of English, they may not be familiar with many of our colloquialisms. Because of the language differences, some DX stations are more comfortable with the barebones type contact and you should be sensitive to their preferences. In unsettled propagation conditions, it may be necessary to keep the whole contact short. The good operator takes these factors into account when expanding on a basic contact.

When the time comes to end the contact, end it. Thank

Additional Recommendations

Listen with care. It is very natural to answer the loudest station that calls, but sometimes you will have to dig deep into the noise and interference to hear the other station. Not all amateurs can run a kilowatt or a large, high antenna. DX stations are also typically weaker than closer stations.

Use VOX or push-to-talk (PTT). If you use VOX, don't defeat its purpose by saying "aaah" to keep the relay closed. If you use PTT, let go of the mike button every so often to make sure you are not "doubling" with the other station. Don't filibuster.

Talk at a constant level. Don't ride the mike gain. Try to maintain the same distance between your mouth and the microphone. Keep the mike gain down to eliminate background noise. Follow the manufacturer's instructions for use of the microphone. Some require close talking, while some need to be turned at an angle to the speaker's mouth.

Guest Operator

An FCC rules interpretation allows the person in physical control of an Amateur Radio station to use his or her own call sign when guest operating at another station. Of course, the guest operator is bound by the frequency privileges of his or her own operator's license, no matter what class of license the station licensee may hold. For example, Joan, KB6MOZ, a Technician, is visiting Stan, N6MP, an Amateur Extra licensee. Joan may use her own call sign at N6MP's station, but she must stay within the Technician subbands. If Joan wishes to operate using Amateur Extra privileges, she can sign N6MP but only if Stan acts as the control operator.

When a ham is operating from a club station, the club call is usually used. Again, the operator may never exceed the privileges of his or her own operator's license. The club station trustee and/or the club members may decide to allow individual amateurs to use their own call signs at the club station, but it is optional. In cases where it is desirable to retain the identity of the club station (W1AW at ARRL HQ, for example), the club may require amateurs to use the club call sign at all times.

In the rare instance where the guest operator at a club station holds a higher class of license than the club station trustee, the guest operator must use the club call sign and his/her own call sign. For example, Dave NN1N, who holds an Amateur Extra license visits the Norfolk Technician Radio Club station, KA4CVX. Because he wants to operate the club station outside the Tech subbands, Dave would sign KA4CVX/NN1N on CW and "KA4CVX, NN1N controlling" on phone. (Of course, this situation would prevail only if the club requires that their club call sign be used at all times.)

UTC Explained

Ever hear of Greenwich Mean Time? How about Coordinated Universal Time? Do you know if it is light or dark at 0400 hours? This is important in Amateur Radio, so if you answered no to any of these questions, read on!

Keeping track of time can be pretty confusing when you are talking to other hams around the world. Europe, for example, is anywhere from 4 to 11 hours ahead of us here in North America. There are literally *dozens* of time zones around the world! Mass confusion would occur if everyone used their own local time without some single common reference time.

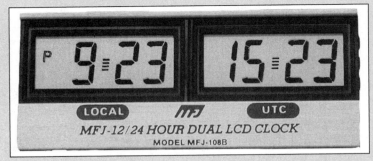

24-hour Universal Time is used both in station logs and on QSL cards.

To solve the issue of standardizing clocks, the time at Greenwich, England on the Prime Meridian of longitude has been universally recognized as the standard time in all international affairs, including ham radio. This is Coordinated Universal Time (abbreviated UTC). (For many years it was called Greenwich Mean Time or GMT.) Longitude on the surface of the Earth is measured in degrees east or west of the Prime Meridian (zero degrees), that runs approximately through Greenwich, England and is halfway around the world from the International Date Line. Using UTC when communicating with other hams means that wherever you are, you and the station you contact will be able to reference a common date and time.

Twenty-four-hour time also avoids the equally confusing question about AM and PM. If you hear someone say that a contact was made at 0400 hours UTC, you will know immediately that this was 4 hours past midnight, UTC, since the new day always starts just after midnight. Likewise, a contact made at 1500 hours UTC was 15 hours past midnight, or 3 PM (15 − 12 = 3) UTC.

Maybe you have begun to figure it out: Each day starts at midnight, 0000 hours. Noon is 1200 hours, and the afternoon hours merely go on from there. You can think of it as adding 12 hours to the normal PM time (2 PM is 1400 hours, 9:30 PM is 2130 hours, and so on). However you learn it, be sure to use the time everyone else does — UTC — as in the chart below.

The photo shows a specially made clock, with an hour hand that goes around only once every day, instead of twice a day like a normal clock. Clocks with a digital readout that show time in a 24-hour format are quite popular as a station accessory.

UTC	EDT/AST	CDT/EST	MDT/CST	PDT/MST	PST
0000*	2000	1900	1800	1700	1600
0100	2100	2000	1900	1800	1700
0200	2200	2100	2000	1900	1800
0300	2300	2200	2100	2000	1900
0400	0000*	2300	2200	2100	2000
0500	0100	0000*	2300	2200	2100
0600	0200	0100	0000*	2300	2200
0700	0300	0200	0100	0000*	2300
0800	0400	0300	0200	0100	0000*
0900	0500	0400	0300	0200	0100
1000	0600	0500	0400	0300	0200
1100	0700	0600	0500	0400	0300
1200	0800	0700	0600	0500	0400
1300	0900	0800	0700	0600	0500
1400	1000	0900	0800	0700	0600
1500	1100	1000	0900	0800	0700
1600	1200	1100	1000	0900	0800
1700	1300	1200	1100	1000	0900
1800	1400	1300	1200	1100	1000
1900	1500	1400	1300	1200	1100
2000	1600	1500	1400	1300	1200
2100	1700	1600	1500	1400	1300
2200	1800	1700	1600	1500	1400
2300	1900	1800	1700	1600	1500
2400	2000	1900	1800	1700	1600

Time changes one hour with each change of 15 degrees in longitude. The five time zones in the US proper and Canada roughly follow these lines.

*0000 and 2400 are interchangeable. 2400 is associated with the date of the day ending, 0000 with the day just starting.

Speech processing (often built into contemporary transceivers) is a mixed blessing. It can help you cut through the interference and static, but if too much is used, the audio quality suffers greatly. Tests should be made to determine the maximum level that can be used effectively, and this should be noted or marked on the control. Be ready to turn it down or off if it is not really required during a contact.

The speed of voice transmission (with perfect accuracy) depends almost entirely on the skill of the two operators concerned. Speak at a rate that allows easy understanding as well as permitting the receiving operator to record the information, if necessary.

Recordkeeping

Although the FCC does not require that amateur stations document their operations except for certain specialized occurrences, you can still benefit by keeping an accurate log. The FCC requires that you record the type of antenna and gain of any antenna other than a dipole that you use on the 60 meter band. This can be recorded in your log or kept on file separately. The FCC will also assume that you were the control operator for all contacts made from your station unless your log (or some other record) indicates otherwise.

Your Station Log

A well-kept log will help you preserve your fondest ham radio memories for years. It will also serve as a bookkeeping system should you embark upon a quest for ham radio awards, or decide to expand your collection of QSL cards.

Many amateurs have decided to computerize their log keeping because of its flexibility and additional features. There are many excellent computer programs for Amateur Radio logging, including specialized programs for contests and other types of operation. For a selection of programs, check the ads in *QST* or try AC6V's directory website at **www.ac6v.com/logging.htm**.

For the purposes of illustration, this section will refer to *The ARRL Logbook*, on sale at your local radio bookstore or directly from ARRL HQ. Many hams still keep a log on paper and a logbook (see **Figure 1.11**) provides a good method for maintaining contact data at your fingertips.

The log entry should include:

1) The call sign of the station worked.

2) The date and time of the QSO. Always use UTC (Universal Coordinated Time, sometimes also called GMT or Zulu time) when entering the date and time. Use UTC whenever you need a time or date in your ham activities. The use of UTC helps all hams avoid confusion through conversion to local time. See the sidebar "UTC Explained" for details.

3) The frequency or frequency band on which the QSO took place.

4) The emission mode used to communicate.

5) Signal reports sent and received.

6) Any miscellaneous data, such as the other operator's name or QTH that you care to record.

The FCC has devised a rather elaborate system of emission designators, but for logging simplicity most hams use the following common abbreviations:

Figure 1.12 — QSL cards are a longstanding ham radio tradition. They're often personalized with artwork and information about station equipment, antennas or other interests.

Abbreviation	Explanation
CW	telegraphy on pure continuous wave
MCW	tone-modulated telegraphy
SSB	single-sideband suppressed carrier
AM, DSB	double-sideband with full, reduced or suppressed carrier
FAX	facsimile
FM	frequency- or phase-modulated telephony
RTTY	radioteletype
PSK	PSK31 or similar mode
ATV or SSTV	fast-scan television or slow-scan television

QSLing

The QSL card is the final courtesy of a QSO. It confirms specific details about your two-way contact with another ham. Whether you want the other station's QSL as a memento of an enjoyable QSO or for an operating award, it's wise to have your own QSL cards and know how to fill them out. That way, when you send your card to the other station, it will result in the desired outcome (a confirming card sent back to you). And you'll be ready to respond if the other operator wants a QSL from you. Some examples are shown in **Figure 1.12**.

Your QSL

Your QSL card makes a statement about you. It may also hang in ham radio shacks all over the world. So you will want to choose carefully the style of QSL that represents you and your station. There are many QSL vendors listed in the Ham Ads section of *QST* each month, and others can be found online with your favorite search engine. A nominal fee will bring you samples from which to choose or you may design and/or print your own style. The choice is up to you. See the accompanying sidebar on the next page for more information on QSLs.

Electronic QSLing

Electronic QSLing — the paperless confirmation of contacts using computer systems — has caught on with many hams. As postage rates continue to rise, expect more QSLing to be done online. The ARRL's *Logbook of the World* system (**www.arrl.org/logbook-of-the-world**) stores hundreds of millions of contacts from more than 50,000 users (as of 2012)!

To use electronic QSLing systems, you'll need to store your log on your computer. The logging program then creates lists of your contacts and sends them to the QSLing system where they can be cross-referenced against other submitted contacts. The various QSLing systems all have their own security processes and not all of them are accepted by the many award sponsors, including the ARRL. Check to be sure your electronic contact confirmations will be accepted!

Other electronic systems accept QSO information from individual stations, then print and forward the paper QSLs at a price that is discounted from mailing separate cards.

Now Go Make Some Contacts

That finishes our quick tour of operating procedures. Your knowledge will grow quickly with on-the-air experience. Enjoy the learning process. Ham radio is such a diverse activity that the learning process never stops — talk to most long-time hams, and they'll tell you there is always something new to learn!

QSLing — The Final Courtesy

QSL cards are a tradition in ham radio. Exchanging QSLs is fun, and they can serve as needed confirmations for many operating awards. Even though electronic QSLing systems are replacing the old-style printed cards, hams will probably continue to exchange them after an initial contact.

You'll probably want your own QSL cards, so look in *QST* or online for companies that sell them, or you may even want to make your own. Modern color printers and computer software make that easy. Your QSL should be attractive, yet straightforward. All necessary QSO information on one side of the card will make answering a QSL a relatively simple matter.

A good QSL card should be the standard 3.5 × 5.5-inch size (standard post card size) and should contain the following information, written in permanent blue or black ink that won't fade with time or in light:

1) *Your call.* If you were portable or mobile during the contact, this should be indicated on the card along with the actual location from which the contact was made.

2) *The geographical location of your station.* Again, portables/mobiles should indicate where they were during the contact. If your location counts specially for an award such as Islands On the Air, include that information. Show your county (or parish or borough, etc) and your four-character or six-character Maidenhead grid locator.

3) *The call of the station you worked.* This isn't as simple as it sounds. Errors are very common here. Make sure it is clear if the call contains the numeral 1 (one), capital I ("eye") or lower case l ("el").

4) *Date and time of the contact.* Use UTC for both and be sure to convert the time properly from local time, if that's how you keep your log. It is best to write out the date in words to avoid ambiguity. Use May 10, 2012 or 10 May 2012, rather than 5/10/12. Most DX stations will use 8-2-12 to mean February 8, 2012. The day is written before the month in many parts of the world.

5) *Frequency.* The band in wavelength (meters) or approximate frequency in kHz or MHz is required.

6) *Mode of operation.* Use accepted abbreviations, but be specific. CW, SSB, RTTY, PSK31 and AM are clear and acceptable. FCC emission designations (J3E and so forth) are not always understood by DX stations.

7) *Signal report.* Use the RST system — 59, 569, and so on.

8) Leave no doubt the QSL is confirming a two-way contact by using language such as "confirming two-way QSO with" or "2 X" or "2-Way" before the other station's call.

Other items, such as your rig, antenna and so on, are optional but may hams like to include them.

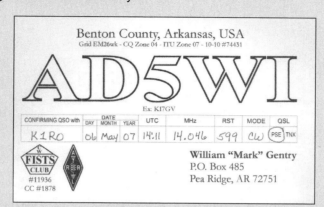

If you make any errors filling out the QSL, destroy the card and start over. Do not make corrections or mark-overs on the card, as such cards are not acceptable for awards purposes.

For QSLing within the United States, you can find the other station's address from many online call sign servers. Some websites just publish information directly from the FCC's database, while others such as QRZ (**www.qrz.com**) allow users to customize and update information in their records. If you really need the other station's QSL card, perhaps for an operating award, it's a good idea to include a self-addressed, stamped envelope (SASE).

Now comes the problem of how to get your QSLs to the DX station. You can send QSL cards directly to the DX station or the DX station's QSL manager, making sure to include a self-addressed envelope and return postage.

Sending them directly can be expensive, so many amateurs use the ARRL's QSL Service. This is an outgoing service for ARRL members to send DX QSL cards to foreign countries at a minimum of cost and effort.

To receive QSL cards from DX (overseas) stations, the ARRL sponsors incoming QSL Bureaus, provided free for all amateurs throughout the United States and Canada. Each call area has its own bureau staffed totally by volunteers. To expedite the handling of your QSL cards (both incoming and outgoing), be sure to follow the bureau's requirements at all times.

See the DXing chapter for much more information about exchanging QSL cards with DX stations, either directly or through the QSL bureau.

VHF/UHF— FM, Repeaters, Digital Voice and Data

For decades, FM has been a dominant mode of Amateur Radio operation. FM and repeaters fill the VHF and UHF bands, and most hams have at least one handheld or mobile FM radio. It wasn't always so, of course, and after decades of stability, change is creeping in again.

A BRIEF HISTORY

Until the late 1960s, the VHF and UHF Amateur Radio bands were mostly quiet, wide-open spaces. They were home to a relatively small number of highly skilled and dedicated operators who used high-power CW and SSB with large antennas on tall towers to defy the phrase "line-of-sight" that is generally applied to communication on these frequencies. But this operation used just a small fraction of the 4-MHz-wide bands at 6 and 2 meters, and an even smaller fraction of the 30-MHz-wide 70 cm (420-450 MHz) band. A somewhat larger number of hams enjoyed low power, local operation with AM transceivers on 6 and 2 meters. But still, our spectrum was greatly underutilized, while public safety and commercial VHF/UHF two-way operation, using FM and repeaters, was expanding rapidly.

Business and public safety band use grew so rapidly in the early '60s that the FCC had to create new channels by cutting the existing channels in half. Almost overnight, a generation of tube-type, crystal-controlled FM equipment became obsolete and had to be replaced with radios that met the new channel requirements. Radios that had seen service in everything from police cars and ambulances to taxicabs and cement trucks fell into the hands of hams for pennies on the original dollar. This equipment was designed to operate around 150 MHz and 450 MHz, just above the 2 meter and 70 cm ham bands. Putting these radios on the ham bands required new crystals, alignment, and sometimes some modification or new parts. A classic mobile installation from that era is shown in **Figure 2.1**. Hams who worked in the two-way radio industry led the way, retuning radios and building repeaters

that extended coverage. Other hams quickly followed, attracted by the noise-free clarity of FM audio, the inexpensive equipment, and the chance to do something different. They began filling the fallow ground of our VHF and UHF bands.

That initial era didn't last long. The surplus commercial equipment was cheap, but it was physically large. All-tube radios ran hot and consumed lots of power. And retuning the

Figure 2.1 — This classic mobile installation was shown in "Amateur FM and Repeaters" by Les Cobb, W6TEE, and Jay O'Brien, W6GDO, in October 1969 *QST*. The control head for the 2 meter FM transceiver is just to the right of the steering wheel, next to an HF mobile transceiver. In those days, the transceiver was usually a converted commercial tube-type monster mounted in the trunk.

Figure 2.2 — In the 1970s, solid-state amateur gear took over, with the entire radio fitting in the space needed for the old control heads. This Drake TR-22 from the early 1970s could be used in the car, at home or portable (it had rechargeable batteries!).

Figure 2.3 — We've come full circle, with today's detachable faceplates and extension cables for mounting our mobile radios under the seat or in the trunk. (*K0BG photo*)

radios required skills and test equipment that the average ham didn't have. By the early 1970s, American and Japanese manufacturers recognized an untapped market and began building solid-state equipment specifically for the Amateur Radio FM market such as the popular Drake TR-22 shown in **Figure 2.2**. The frequency synthesizer, perfected in the mid-1970s, eliminated the need for crystals. The stage was set for this little boom to become the explosion that changed the face of Amateur Radio. Few hams today don't operate at least some VHF/UHF FM, and for many hams, FM is Amateur Radio. Manufacturers have added plenty of new features to equipment over the years, but the basic FM operating mode remained the same. Radios have gotten a lot smaller, too (**Figures 2.3** and **2.4**).

Going Digital

In the 1980s, ham radio experimenters added a new twist to FM: digital data. The personal computer was just catching on. One aspect of that — computer-to-computer communication — was in early development using telephone lines. Why not radio? VHF/UHF FM proved to be ideal for this use. Hams began modulating their FM radios with tones and adapted the telephone X.25 protocol to radio, calling it AX.25. They called the whole system *packet radio* (the data is sent in short bursts called packets), and both telephone-based and radio-based systems grew in parallel. Bulletin boards (BBS) — central computers that allowed individuals to post and read files and text messages and send an early form of e-mail — were developed for both systems. The ham radio system was called PBBS for packet bulletin-board system, with a DX spotting and reporting version called the *DX PacketCluster*. It all peaked in popularity in the mid-1990s. After that, the Internet's broader reach and ease-of-use ended the telephone-based bulletin-board system.

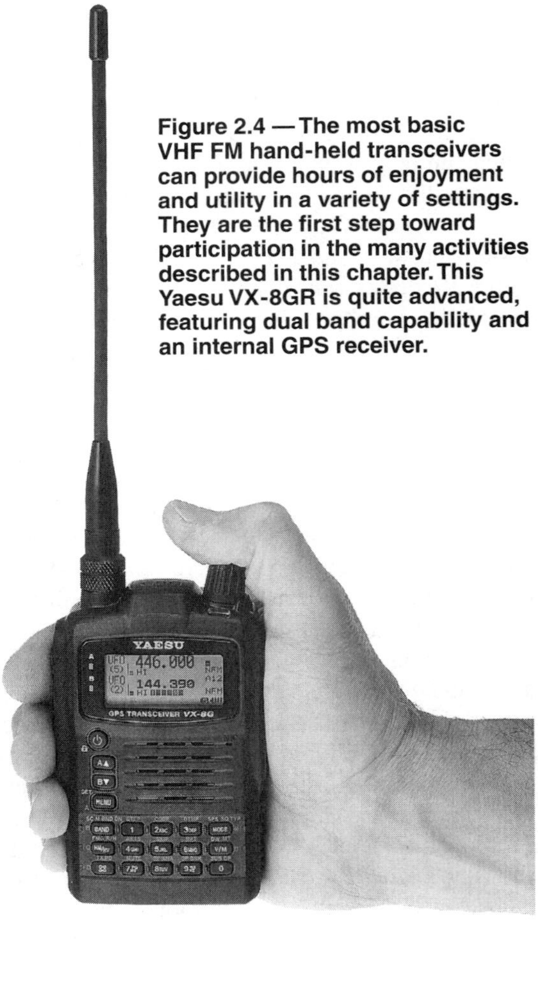

Figure 2.4 — The most basic VHF FM hand-held transceivers can provide hours of enjoyment and utility in a variety of settings. They are the first step toward participation in the many activities described in this chapter. This Yaesu VX-8GR is quite advanced, featuring dual band capability and an internal GPS receiver.

GLOSSARY

Access code — one or more numbers or symbols that are keyed into the repeater with a telephone tone pad to activate a repeater function, such as an *autopatch*.

Autopatch — a device that interfaces a repeater to the telephone system to permit repeater users to make telephone calls. Often just called the *patch*.

Channel — the pair of frequencies (input and output) used by a repeater (example — the 94 machine would use the frequency pair 146.340 and 146.940).

Channel step — the difference (in kHz) between FM channels. The common steps are 15 and 20 kHz for 2 meter repeaters, 20 kHz for 222 MHz repeaters, and 25 kHz for 440 MHz repeaters.

Closed repeater — a repeater whose access is limited to a select group (see *open repeater*).

Control operator — the Amateur Radio operator who is designated to control the operation of the repeater, as required by FCC regulations.

Courtesy tone — an audible indication that a repeater user may go ahead and transmit.

Coverage — the geographic area within which the repeater provides communications.

CTCSS — Continuous Tone Coded Squelch System. A system of subaudible tones that operate the squelch of a receiver when the corresponding subaudible tone is present on a transmitted signal.

Crossband — communications to another frequency band by means of a link interfaced with the repeater.

DCS — Digital Coded Squelch. A newer version of *CTCSS* that uses a subaudible digital code instead of an analog tone to selectively open a receiver's squelch.

DD — Digital Data. The 128 kbit/s data system on D-STAR's 1200 MHz radio.

Digipeater — digital repeater, a packet radio repeater.

Duplex — a mode of communication in which you transmit on one frequency and receive on another frequency.

Duplexer — a device that permits the use of one antenna for both transmitting and receiving with minimal degradation to either incoming or outgoing signals.

DV — Digital Voice, on the D-STAR system.

Frequency coordinator — an individual or group responsible for recommending channels for new repeaters with a minimum chance of interference to existing repeaters.

Full quieting — a received signal that contains no noise.

Handheld transceiver — a portable transceiver small enough to fit in the palm of your hand, clipped to your belt or even in a shirt pocket.

Hang time — the amount of time a basketball player remains airborne before dunking the ball. Or, the amount of time a repeater transmitter remains on the air after the user signal drops on the input. The courtesy tone beeps during the hang-time.

Input frequency — the frequency of the repeater's receiver (and your transceiver's transmitter).

Intermod — interference caused by spurious signals generated by intermodulation distortion in a receiver front end or transmitter power amplifier stage.

Key up — to turn on a repeater by transmitting on its input frequency.

Li-ion — Lithium-ion battery. Longer life, smaller and lighter than NiCd, Li-ion batteries are becoming more popular for use with handheld radios.

LiTZ — Long Tone Zero (the i is added for pronunciation). An alert system that uses a DTMF tone pad-sent zero (0) keyed for at least three seconds to request emergency or urgent assistance.

Machine — a repeater system (slang).

Magnetic mount, **mag-mount** — an antenna with a magnetic base that permits quick installation and removal from a motor vehicle or other metal surface.

NiCd — a nickel-cadmium battery that may be recharged many times; often used to power portable transceivers. Pronounced NYE-cad.

NiMH — nickel-metal-hydride battery; rechargeable, offers more capacity and lighter weight than an NiCd battery. Often used to power portable transceivers.

Offset — the spacing between a repeater's input and output frequencies.

Open repeater — a repeater that is available to all licensed amateurs.

Output frequency — the frequency of the repeater's transmitter (and your transceiver's receiver).

Polarization — the plane an antenna system operates in; most repeaters are vertically polarized.

Radio direction finding (RDF) — the art and science of locating a hidden transmitter.

Repeater Directory — an annual ARRL publication that lists repeaters in the US, Canada and other areas.

Separation, **split** — the difference (in kHz) between a repeater's transmitter and receiver frequencies. Also called *offset*. Repeaters that use unusual separations, such as 1 MHz on 2 meters, are sometimes said to have odd splits.

Simplex — a mode of communication in which you transmit and receive on the same frequency.

Squelch tail — the noise burst heard in a receiver that follows the end of an FM transmission, before the squelch system silences the speaker.

Time-out — to cause the repeater or a repeater function to turn off because you have transmitted for too long.

Timer — a device that measures the length of each transmission and causes the repeater or a repeater function to turn off after a transmission has exceeded a certain length.

Tone pad — an array of 12 or 16 numbered keys that generate the standard telephone dual-tone multi-frequency (DTMF) dialing signals; resembles a standard telephone keypad.

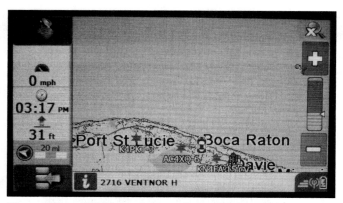

Figure 2.5 — APRS, the Automatic Packet Reporting System, is an extremely popular VHF activity. This AvMap GPS display has APRS specific features and plots the locations of received stations on a map.

Packet radio limped on. Today the ham radio PBBS system and the DX clusters are a shell of what they were in the '90s. But another specialty remains popular: *APRS*, the *Automatic Packet Reporting System*. APRS is best known for sending GPS location information over the air so a ham's position can be pinpointed on a map (**Figure 2.5**), but APRS is actually more than that — it can be a tactical information system for quickly distributing text and data to a group of hams. Using the Internet, APRS communication can be worldwide.

Going Even More Digital

At the start of the 21st century, anyone applying the term *digital* to Amateur Radio was almost certainly talking about text or files, not real-time audio. That is changing.

And anyone talking about worldwide ham radio communication was probably *not* talking about VHF/UHF FM. That is changing, too, and the changes are related.

Digitized audio has been common since audio compact discs (CDs) were introduced in the 1980s. In the '90s, technology advanced enough to reduce the bandwidth needed for digital audio, especially voice, to be carried over the Internet and narrowband radio circuits. The first digital-voice public safety radio systems appeared, generically called APCO-25, and a variety of Internet voice systems for conferencing and telephone-like use were developed under the general heading VoIP (Voice over Internet Protocol).

When the first generation of APCO-25 radios got old enough to be replaced, hams took some of the surplus radios and put them on the ham bands, echoing the dawn of Amateur Radio FM in the '60s. Hams also adapted VoIP for use linking repeaters over the Internet with networks labeled IRLP, EchoLink, WIRES and eQSO. And the Japan Amateur Radio League (JARL) developed a true ham radio digital voice (DV) and data standard called D-STAR, with a networked VHF/UHF repeater system that is making inroads around the world. A new commercial system, generically called DRM (Digital Mobile Radio), is creeping into ham radio, and at press time, one manufacturer is poised to offer a true Amateur Radio version of that mode to compete with D-STAR.

It will be decades, if ever, before DV supplants analog FM as the primary voice mode on VHF/UHF. But you will see it grow, and you will observe many similarities and a few differences in operation. VoIP is solidly entrenched in routine operation. Packet radio is hanging in there. Our VHF/UHF bands are busy places, indeed.

WHAT IS A REPEATER?

Let's take a few steps back and cover the basics. We'll start with FM voice repeaters, then move on to newer systems.

First, what exactly is a *repeater*? And why do we use one?

Without repeaters, the communication range between amateur VHF-FM mobile and handheld radios at ground level is limited — five to 15 miles between mobiles, and just a couple of miles between handhelds. The distance you can communicate is commonly referred to as *line-of-sight* — you can talk about as far as you can see. That's not technically true. VHF/UHF range is a little better than that, and there are some really significant exceptions, but the underlying principle that the higher the antenna, the greater the range, is valid. It's just hard to get a mobile or handheld antenna very high off the ground.

To extend our range, we use *repeaters*. See **Figure 2.6**. A repeater is a specially designed receiver/transmitter combination. Repeater antennas are located on tall towers, buildings, or mountains, giving repeaters much greater range than radios with antennas near the ground (**Figure 2.7**). When you're in range of a repeater, you can talk to everyone else in range of that repeater.

When you operate through a repeater, its receiver picks up your signal on the *input* frequency, and the transmitter retransmits — or repeats — you on the *output* frequency. Those two

frequencies are called a *repeater pair*, and the space between them is called the *offset*. Repeater pairs and offsets for each VHF/UHF band were standardized by the hams who developed repeaters in the 1970s, although there are some regional differences around the country.

Using a real-world example, one common 2 meter repeater pair is 146.34 and 146.94 MHz. In the shortcut language of FM, this would be called 34/94 (pronounced three-four, nine-four) or just simply 94 (nine-four). In this pair, 34 is the input frequency, and 94 is the output frequency. The offset for this and most 2 meter repeaters is 600 kHz, and nearly every radio manufactured for 2 meters since 1980 is pre-programmed for this offset. Given all the standards and the shortcut language, it's *almost* enough to say, "Meet me on the 94 repeater," without specifying the other details. Almost, but keep reading. Something called *tone* may get in the way. We'll explain shortly.

A repeater's range depends on a variety of factors, but primary are antenna height, terrain and output power. Those three factors apply not only to the repeater, but also to your station and the station you want to talk to. You have to factor all sides of this equation if you want to know how far you might be able to talk through a repeater. But it's not that complicated in practice.

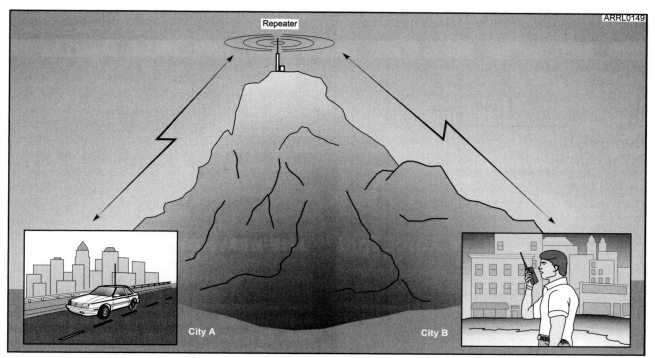

Figure 2.6 — A repeater extends the range of its users, allowing them to communicate over longer distances.

Here's another real-world example: level ground, a repeater antenna at 500 feet, and two mobiles running 50 W. Reliable coverage from such a system would extend about 30 miles from the repeater. "Fringe" coverage — distances where you can probably use the repeater but signals will be weak and may drop out — can extend another 20 miles or so. If one mobile is near the southern limit of the repeater's coverage area, and the other mobile is near the northern end, that could be almost 100 miles between them, *much* better than the five to 15 miles they could talk without a repeater.

Put that repeater on a mountaintop, and the coverage jumps to a radius of 100 miles or more — 200 miles between mobiles at opposite ends of the coverage area. Except that mountains usually come bunched together, and if you drive around the back side of the next mountain, it'll block your signal from the repeater.

When you ask about the coverage of a particular repeater, keep in mind that hams tend to think in terms of *maximum* range, not *reliable* range. If a ham heard someone hit a repeater from 120 miles out using a handheld once, they might tell you that repeater's range is 120 miles, when the realistic, everyday coverage is more like 40 miles. See the DX section later in this chapter.

Additional Features

Repeaters can have many features beyond just extending the range of mobile or handheld radios. Before cell phones became ubiquitous, the most popular feature was *autopatch* (*auto*matic telephone *patch*). A telephone line and special control equipment at the repeater allow you to make local phone calls from your radio. It's still a great backup, though today the most common call on an autopatch begins with, "Hi, honey, I forgot my phone."

Figure 2.7 — Amateur Radio repeaters often share tower space with commercial, public-safety and broadcast systems. The ham repeater antenna is the four-loop array mounted off the left side of the tower.

Autopatch is certainly not a replacement for a cell phone. You can't use Amateur Radio — including autopatch — for your business. You can't receive incoming calls, you can make only local calls, and your conversation is not at all private. Everybody else listening to the repeater hears your call.

Other common repeater features include voice announcements of the time, club meetings and activities; a talking S meter or voice recorder to let you know how well the repeater is hearing you; and a NOAA weather receiver to rebroadcast storm alerts. Now, the most commonly used feature is

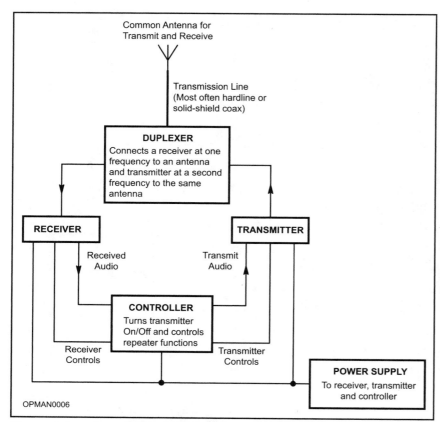

Figure 2.8 — Functional diagram of a repeater.

Figure 2.9 — Repeater systems aren't designed for cosmetic appeal. This photo shows the repeater, controller, and duplexer for a 2 meter repeater.

linking. The local repeater's coverage can be extended across the region, the state, even the world, via radio or the Internet, a topic we'll cover in more detail later.

Repeater Hardware

Check out **Figure 2.8**. Repeaters consist of the receiver and transmitter mentioned above, along with a couple more special devices. One is a *controller* that routes the audio between the receiver and transmitter, keys the transmitter, provides remote control for the repeater licensee or designated control operators, and all the special features listed above.

The second device is the *duplexer* that lets the repeater transmit and receive on the same antenna (**Figure 2.9**).

Think about it — a high power transmitter and a sensitive receiver, operating in close proximity within the same band, using the same antenna! You might think the transmitter would just blow away the receiver. But the duplexer keeps the transmit energy out of the receiver with a series of tuned circuits — very selective filters. Without a duplexer, the receiver and transmitter would need separate antennas, and those antennas would need to be 100 or more feet apart on a tower. Some repeaters do just that, but most use duplexers. A 2 meter duplexer is about the size of a two-drawer filing cabinet.

Receiver, transmitter, controller, and duplexer: the basic components of most repeaters.

HOW DO YOU USE REPEATERS?

There are literally thousands of repeaters across the US (and the world). Each one can have its own peculiarities and unique operating procedures, but there are some basics that apply to almost all of them. Any time you try to tell a ham how to operate a radio, you risk an argument. But then, that's what the *Operating Manual* is all about. So we'll take that risk, if you'll keep in mind that this is just a guide — ask about local practice!

Plain Old Talking

Mostly, you're here to get on the air and talk to people, right? So first you set your radio for the repeater you want to

use. Don't know how to find a local repeater frequency? The *ARRL Repeater Directory* is great for that. And in most areas, somebody has posted a listing of local repeaters on a website. They're great resources, but there's a problem you'll run into sooner or later: not all the repeaters listed are actually on the air. Some may be down for maintenance, but too many have been off the air for a long time, yet their owners keep reporting them as on the air. That's a problem just about everywhere. *Most* of the repeaters listed, though, will be available.

Once you've selected a repeater and dialed it up on your radio, the first thing you should do is...*listen* for a while. There are two reasons for just listening.

Join the Club

Repeaters and digital systems cost money for equipment, phone lines, power, rent and maintenance. If you use a repeater or digital system on a regular basis, or just rely on it being there when you need it, join the club or donate to the group that maintains it. Money and expertise, or sometimes just muscle, are equally appreciated. Then do feel free to use any other open system now and then, knowing you've done your part.

First, listen to observe operating procedure. Learn how the locals do it. But don't assume everyone you hear is doing it right. You'll hear good procedure and bad. Over time you'll sort it out.

Second — and this applies every time you flip on the radio — listen for a while because repeaters are party lines. Lots of people use them on and off throughout the day, and the one you've selected may be busy with another conversation right now. So listen first. (Does anyone remember what *party lines* are? Kids, ask your grandparents!)

If the repeater isn't busy, you can see if someone out there wants to talk. Key your transmitter and say something like "This is KN4AQ, listening." (Use your own call, not mine, please). You could, I suppose, call CQ, the traditional method for generating a contact on the HF bands. That never caught on with FM and repeaters, though, and someone will probably tell you not to do it. You certainly don't need a 30-second-long CQ designed to attract the attention of hams tuning across the band. On a repeater, your audience is already there, waiting with squelched receivers. So if you want to start a trend or become notorious, say, "CQ, this is KN4AQ."

When you release your transmit button, most repeaters will stay on the air for a few seconds (called *hang time*), and many will send some kind of beep (a *courtesy tone*). Then, the repeater transmitter drops off the air. The beep is there to remind everyone to leave a pause between transmissions in case someone wants to break in. Even if there's no beep, leave a pause. Somebody may have just come across a traffic accident and needs the repeater to report it. If nobody leaves a pause between transmissions, they can't break in.

If somebody answers you, then have a good time! You can talk about anything you want — there are not many rules about the content of Amateur Radio conversation. You can't use ham radio to conduct your business, but you can talk about where you work and what you do. Prime time TV language has been peppered with some mild profanity. Let's discourage that. You're not having a private conversation — you may have lots of listeners, some of them children. Keep that in mind as you choose language and subject matter.

How long do you talk? You share the repeater with other hams, from dozens to hundreds. Maybe somebody else wants to use the repeater when you're done. There's no firm rule. It depends on the time of day, and who else might want to use

the repeater. Rush hours are prime time for mobiles, evening is also a busy time, while 2 AM is pretty empty. Some repeaters are busy all day, and some are rarely used. Learn the local procedures and rules set down by the repeater's sponsor.

For a long time, the conventional wisdom has been that repeaters are for mobiles, and base stations should stay off of them during drive time. Ask the locals about that, too.

Three-Way Radio

Not all conversations are strictly two-way. Three, four or five or more hams can be part of a roundtable conversation (five or more will be pretty unwieldy). A freewheeling roundtable is a lot of fun...and it poses a problem: When the person transmitting now is done, who transmits next? Too often, the answer is *everybody* transmits next, and the result is a mess. The solution is simple. When you finish your transmission in the roundtable, specify who is to transmit next. "...Over to you, Rick. KN4AQ."

We Pause for Station Identification

The FCC rules say you must ID once every 10 minutes. Most repeater owners are big on clear identification when you use their repeaters, but you don't have to overdo it. Give your call sign when you first get on (this isn't required by the rules, but it's common practice), then about every 10 minutes, and again when you sign off. You don't have to give anyone else's call sign at any time, although sometimes it's a nice acknowledgment of the person you're talking to, like a handshake. (Actually, if you're handling third-party traffic through a foreign station, you do have to say that station's call sign when you sign off. Not a lot of that on repeaters.)

Breaking In

Since repeaters are shared among many hams, there are some times and reasons that a conversation in progress might be interrupted. You might break in to join the group and add your comments on the subject at hand. Someone might break in on you to reach someone else who is listening to the repeater. You might have to report an emergency. How to break in is an area of debate and disagreement. Here are some suggestions:

1) Pick a good time. If you have an emergency, a good time is *now*. That's why there's a pause between transmissions. Otherwise, listen a bit. Read the ebb and flow of the conversation. One of the fastest ways to establish a reputation as a jerk is to frequently butt your way onto the air without regard for the people already talking.

2) Give your call sign, and say what you want. When you've listened and decided it's okay to break in, transmit quickly when one station stops, before the beep, and say something like this: "KN4AQ, can I make a short call?" or "KN4AQ, can I add my 2 cents?"

3) What about saying "break?" Some hams will tell you that's the way to break in. The problem is that we don't all agree on exactly what "break" means. In some areas, "break" means "I just want to join in or make a call." "Break-break" means "I have very important traffic," and "break-break-break" means

"I have a dire emergency." Other areas don't use "break" at all. If your area uses some version of "break," go with the flow. But plain English works everywhere.

Maybe somebody's breaking in on you. What do you do? Easy — let them transmit, right now, unless you know absolutely and for sure that they do not have an emergency. Maybe somebody just says "break" or drops in their call, when what they really mean is "HELP!" So let them talk. Say "go ahead," and give your call sign. And if they're interrupting your perfectly good conversation for no reason but to hear themselves talk, well, bite your lip and be glad you know better.

The exception is when someone actually announces an emergency. Say something like "Go ahead, emergency." Then CLEAR THE DECKS! The station that declared the emergency then has the frequency, and unless they ask for your help, don't give it. Unless...always an unless...they obviously *don't* know how to handle the situation...and you *do*.

#$%~‡@&#+*!!

What was that I just heard? Foul language and nasty noises on the repeater? Jamming? Sounds like something straight out of CB! I'm *outraged*, and I'm gonna tell that sucker off! He can't get away with that on our repeater! Gimme that microphone!

Cool down. It doesn't happen often, but it does happen. It's a big world out there, and there are some bad people in it. Some of them find a ham radio now and then, and discover the delight of offending an audience.

The key word is *audience*. Deliberate interference and bad language are designed to make you react. The person doing it wants to *hear* you get mad. They love it. And if they don't get it, they go away, usually quickly. So when you hear the rare nasty stuff on the repeater, please ignore it completely. Don't mention it at all on the air. Don't mention that you're not mentioning it. Sometimes a repeater control operator will decide that the best way to handle the situation is to turn off the repeater for a while, but the rest of us should be silent.

Making an Autopatch Call

An autopatch allows you to make local phone calls from your Amateur Radio transceiver, through special control equipment and a telephone line connected to a repeater.

The autopatch may require an access code, much like a computer password, but sent in DTMF tones (Touch-Tones). Some repeaters have *open autopatch*, allowing anyone to use it. Their access code is often just a * (star), or maybe you just dial the number. Other repeaters have *closed autopatch*. The patch codes are disclosed to members only, although usually members are encouraged to place calls for hams traveling through town.

The procedure for using an autopatch depends on the policy of the repeater's sponsor, and on the design and programming of the control system. You really need to get some local information from the club or repeater owner before proceeding. This is a basic guide to prepare you for what to expect:

First, make sure the repeater isn't busy. If you've just turned on your radio and don't want to wait a minute to see if the channel is active, you might ask "Is the repeater in use? KN4AQ." If you have a clear channel, then here's what you do:

■ Identify yourself and your intentions: "KN4AQ autopatch." Then stop for a second, just in case the repeater wasn't really clear.

■ Key your transmitter again, then follow local procedure to dial the access code and the phone number. You may or may not hear the controller dial the call, but pretty soon you will hear the line ring.

■ The party you called says "hello," and you transmit and talk.

Most people on the telephone end get a little confused by autopatches until they've had some experience with them. When you are transmitting, they can't interrupt you, but they don't know that. You can reduce this problem by keeping your comments very short, and releasing your transmit button immediately after your last word.

Another common source of autopatch confusion is the Dead Phone Effect. When you transmit, some noise accompanies your voice on the phone line, even if you have a very good signal into the repeater. And when you stop transmitting, there's usually a little click or pop on the line, then it goes silent. The party on the line thinks the phone's gone dead. They will say "Hello? Hello? Are you still there?" or something like that. We enjoy it.

When you're done with the call, say good-bye, just like on a regular phone call, and let the party on the phone hang up. Then you hit the "kill code," which on many autopatches is the # button. And identify again, "KN4AQ, clear autopatch." Listen to make sure you successfully killed the patch (the repeater may talk to you, or beep, or just drop). Some repeater owners will ask for a bit more complex procedure, like identifying the person you were talking to.

Business calls on an Amateur Radio autopatch are a sensitive area. In 1993, the FCC relaxed the rules on some business-type communication. The FCC rules for Amateur Radio are available at **www.arrl.org**, and you should review all of them, but here we're specifically talking about §97.113, Prohibited Communications.

The FCC says you cannot use Amateur Radio for your business or employment, but you can use Amateur Radio for personal communications that involve dealing with a business. The often-cited example is "using an autopatch to order a pizza" — in the past, this would have been illegal. Now, this kind of call is legal, but some repeater owners still prohibit all types of "business" traffic.

DX!

Well, you probably won't be hearing Europe on 2 meter FM anytime soon (except via Internet linking), but VHF does have its own form of DX. Earlier we talked about a repeater that had about a 30-mile range. Usually. Sometimes, though, VHF/UHF "opens up," and stations can be heard for hundreds of miles. This weather-related phenomenon is a book-length subject (and ARRL has the book). Just know that VHF/UHF band openings are a double-edged sword.

It's exciting to talk to someone 200 miles away, and it's okay, too. But keep in mind that repeaters were designed to cover local territory, not half the country. So when the band opens up, there is the potential for lots of interference as well as lots of fun. Repeaters on the same frequency, 120 miles apart, will suddenly seem too close together. You could very easily be keying up two or more of them at once, even from a handheld! To be responsible, get to know where your signal is going (the *ARRL Repeater Directory* will help). Use a directional antenna, minimum power and keep your conversation short.

Almost every repeater is ringed by co-channel neighbors — repeaters using the same frequency — between 100 and 200 miles away. You'll want to be sensitive to those neighbors as you decide how much power and antenna to use when talking on your local machine.

How much power is too much? Within the local coverage area of most repeaters, 5 W into a mobile antenna is all you need. Some mobile radios can do 50 W, and that's excessive until you reach the fringe. At home, with an antenna up on the roof, 50 W is *really* excessive for talking through a local repeater. When the band is open, even a 5 W mobile signal can travel to the neighboring co-channel repeater. At those times, patience and courtesy will help a lot.

The 6 and 10 meter bands and repeaters are a special case. Those bands are subject to "skip" — signals refracting off the ionosphere from hundreds or thousands of miles away. Repeater owners and users generally welcome and enjoy this DX opportunity.

Simplex

You don't have to use a repeater to communicate on FM! You can use simplex, which means your radio talking to my radio directly. We do have that five-to-15-mile range — much more if we're using our home stations. So with that range, why not use simplex?

In the past, FM operators were advised to use simplex whenever they could, and reserve repeater use for those times when you were out of simplex range. Today there are plenty of repeaters, so that's not such an issue. Simplex offers its own challenges and rewards, so give it a try.

But don't just pick any old frequency your radio can generate to talk simplex! You may end up on the input of a repeater and interfere with people you can't hear. Use the Band Plan simplex channels shown in **Table 2.1**, beginning with 146.52 MHz, the national simplex channel. On the higher bands, 223.5 and 446.0 are the primary simplex channels.

Giving Directions

What's "giving directions" doing in a repeater operating guide? Just listen for a while, and you'll hear why. We give a lot of directions on repeaters, to locals in an unfamiliar part of town, and to traveling hams visiting the area. And, sad to say, too often we do it badly.

One person will give adequate directions, and someone

Table 2.1

Simplex Channels

Simplex channels in 15 kHz channel step areas*:

146.43
146.46
146.49
146.52 (National Simplex Channel)
145.55
146.58
147.42
147.45
147.48
147.51
147.54
147.57

Simplex channels in 20 kHz channel step areas:

146.42
146.44
146.46
146.48
146.50
146.52 (National Simplex Channel)
146.54
146.56
146.58
147.42
147.44
147.46
147.48
147.50
147.52
147.54
147.56
147.58

*This chart for the 15 kHz channel step areas leaves out the "15 kHz" channels (for example, 146.445 between 146.43 and 146.46) for a good reason. You need physical separation of many miles between stations using 15 kHz channel steps to avoid interference. With repeaters, this physical separation is part of the coordination process. But simplex channel use is not coordinated, so to reduce interference, avoid using the "15 kHz" channels.

else just has to break in to give his favorite shortcut. Or somebody gives a two-minute long string of street names and landmarks, non-stop. We fall all over each other trying to be too helpful!

If someone has given directions that will get the traveler to her destination, let it be. Make a correction only if the directions are dead wrong. If it's your turn to give the directions, keep them short and simple. And it might be helpful to find out where the mobile station is before telling him where to go!

Timers

Almost all repeaters have something called *timers*. A timer is a clock in the controller that starts counting down when you begin to transmit through the repeater. Typically this clock starts from about three minutes, though some can

Band Plans

The term *band plan* refers to an agreement among concerned VHF and UHF operators and users about how each Amateur Radio band should be arranged. The goal of a band plan is to reduce interference between all the modes sharing each band. Aside from FM repeater and simplex activity, CW, SSB, AM, satellite, amateur television (ATV) and radio control operations also use these bands. (For example, a powerful FM signal at 144.200 MHz could spoil someone else's long-distance SSB contact.) The VHF and UHF bands offer a wide variety of amateur activities, so hams have agreed to set aside space for each type.

When considering frequencies for use in conjunction with a proposed repeater, be certain both the input and output fall within subbands authorized for repeater use, and do not extend beyond the subband edges. FCC rules define frequencies available for repeater use.

Here is an example of the ARRL 2 meter band plan as modified for local use by SERA, the Southeastern Repeater Association, which is the recognized frequency coordinator in eight states. The band plan accommodates many different uses. Note that the band plan in your area may be different from this one. It's best to check with your local frequency coordinator if you have any questions.

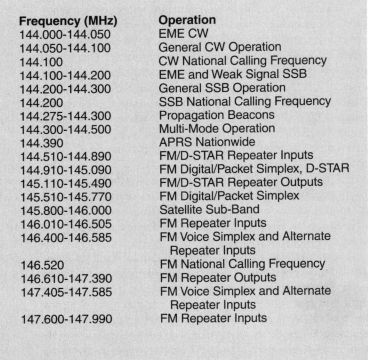

Frequency (MHz)	Operation
144.000-144.050	EME CW
144.050-144.100	General CW Operation
144.100	CW National Calling Frequency
144.100-144.200	EME and Weak Signal SSB
144.200-144.300	General SSB Operation
144.200	SSB National Calling Frequency
144.275-144.300	Propagation Beacons
144.300-144.500	Multi-Mode Operation
144.390	APRS Nationwide
144.510-144.890	FM/D-STAR Repeater Inputs
144.910-145.090	FM Digital/Packet Simplex, D-STAR
145.110-145.490	FM/D-STAR Repeater Outputs
145.510-145.770	FM Digital/Packet Simplex
145.800-146.000	Satellite Sub-Band
146.010-146.505	FM Repeater Inputs
146.400-146.585	FM Voice Simplex and Alternate Repeater Inputs
146.520	FM National Calling Frequency
146.610-147.390	FM Repeater Outputs
147.405-147.585	FM Voice Simplex and Alternate Repeater Inputs
147.600-147.990	FM Repeater Inputs

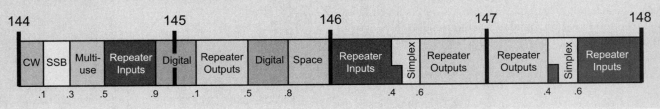

be shorter. If you transmit continuously through the repeater past its timer length, the repeater will go off the air (we call it "timing out"). Repeater timers usually reset when you, the user, stop transmitting. If the repeater has a courtesy beep, the timer may reset when you hear the beep. So to avoid being dumped by the repeater timer, you have to keep your transmissions under the timer length and always wait for the beep.

The three-minute timer is one way to comply with the FCC rules for stations being operated by remote control (most repeaters are remotely controlled). They are not designed as punitive measures for gabby hams...but come to think of it, given the party-line nature of repeaters, and the potential for that emergency traffic, it's a good idea to keep your brilliant monologues a bit shorter anyway. If you must ramble on, orator that you are, don't forget to let the timer reset, and check if somebody else needs the repeater, after a minute or two.

A common misconception is that timers keep repeater transmitters from overheating. Repeater transmitters are designed for continuous duty and don't need the rest.

WHAT BAND PLAN?

Yes, there is a plan organizing frequency use for the VHF and UHF bands (and, for that matter, every Amateur Radio band). For the most part, band plans are voluntary. The FCC regulates only a few modes and band segments. Band plans for HF are international, and you'll find them on the ARRL website. The ARRL also has band plans for VHF/UHF, though these are subject to modification by state and regional frequency coordination groups. There's a lot more going on than

FM and repeaters. The 2 meter and 70 cm bands have space for CW and SSB, beacons, packet, satellite operation and even EME (Earth-Moon-Earth) operation. The 70 cm band also includes fast-scan television. See the sidebar, "Band Plans" for a look at how one regional group has made sense of 2 meters.

The complete 2 meter band plan is even more detailed than that list shows. The repeater input and output segments are divided into more than 100 individual channels for repeaters and simplex operation. This channelized operation is also voluntary, but FM and repeaters wouldn't work if hams followed the HF practice of operating on any empty frequency they wanted to use.

The 2 meter band plan looks complex, perhaps even convoluted, doesn't it? That's because 2 meters grew in spurts, a little here, a little there. In the early 1960s, there was just a little AM and SSB activity clustered right above 145.0 MHz. FM and repeaters were barely getting started, around 146.94 MHz. The rest of the band was empty. FM began to grow, but it was constrained by FCC regulations that restricted Technician licensees to 145.0 – 147.0 MHz. Satellites were launched, packet was invented, and rule changes moved Techs, repeaters and the legacy SSB/CW activity around the band. Everyone needed a slice of the pie, and the result is the band plan you see in the inset. When teaching a class, I say that 2 meters is carved up like a Halloween pumpkin.

To make things even more confusing, within the FM and repeater segments of 2 meters there are two different channel steps: 15 kHz and 20 kHz. As shown in **Figure 2.10**, east of the Mississippi River, most states use 15 kHz steps for the repeater segment above 146 MHz and 20 kHz steps below 146 MHz, for reasons discussed later. Many western states, along with Michigan and Alabama, use 20 kHz

steps throughout the band. Look up your local plan in the *Repeater Directory*.

The 2 meter offset, though, is consistent nationwide at 600 kHz for almost every repeater. That offset is programmed in most radios sold today. Below 147.0 MHz, most repeater offsets are "negative" (the input frequency is the lower frequency), and above 147.0 MHz more offsets are "positive" (the input frequency is the higher frequency).

Channel Spacing

Why is channel spacing in some areas 15 kHz and 20 kHz in others? The FM parameters we use today were originally designed for 30 kHz channels, and that's what we used in the early 1970s. But as FM and repeater use exploded, we were quickly running out of channels for new repeaters in the major metro areas. The easy choice was to cut the channel steps in half, to 15 kHz. The 30 kHz spacing was wasteful, but 15 kHz pinched a little too hard. Our FM signals really occupy about 16 kHz of spectrum, and our receivers are designed to separate signals pretty well at about 20 kHz. To make 15 kHz work, adjacent channel repeaters need to be some distance apart so their signal is weak in the territory of their adjacent channel neighbor. Most areas use about 50-mile separation. You may find circumstances in which you want to hear a

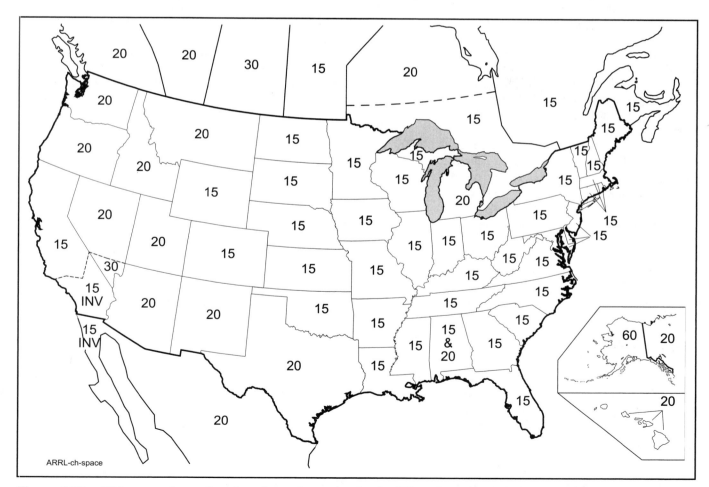

Figure 2.10 — This map shows 2 meter channel spacing in the US and southern Canada. Spacing is in kHz unless otherwise specified. Check with your regional frequency coordinator for more information.

repeater on one channel, but you get splatter from another repeater 15 kHz above or below it. You're probably about halfway between the two. Most of the time, though, the plan works well enough.

So what about 20 kHz? That came about with a rules change. Fearing that repeaters would overrun the entire 2 meter band, the FCC limited them to 146-148 MHz. The 15 kHz split took the pressure off for a little while, but soon all of those channels were used up, and the FCC opened the 144.5 – 145.5 MHz segment to repeaters (and gave the whole band to Technician licensees).

Repeater councils agreed that there were enough problems with the 15 kHz channel step arrangement that this new segment should use 20 kHz as the ideal channel spacing. After that, a group of states, beginning with Texas, saw logic in biting the bullet and going to 20 kHz across *both* repeater segments on 2 meters. They argued that even though that plan yielded fewer *total* channels, the flexibility gained by not having to separate adjacent-channel repeaters by 50 miles yielded more *usable* channels in metropolitan areas.

By this time most users were operating synthesized radios, so only the repeater owners had to buy crystals and retune duplexers. The plan was adopted in Texas and many other western states, and in Michigan and Alabama in the east. But the rest of the country decided not to follow. So we sit with two band plans to this day.

Narrowbanding

Remember that shift from 30 kHz to 15 kHz for commercial and public safety systems back in the 1960s that precipitated the Amateur Radio FM phenomenon? Well, it's happening to them again. The opening of the 800 MHz band took the pressure off of the 150 and 450 MHz spectrum for those users for a while, but the pressure is back on. And the result is an FCC mandate to put their equipment on another diet. They can choose 2.5 kHz deviation FM, or even more efficient digital, but they have to reduce to squeeze more channels into the existing spectrum.

This has confused some hams, who think we have to follow suit. We don't *have* to — the FCC doesn't limit our bandwidth the way they do the commercial folks. But we may *want* to, considering we're in the same boat about no room for new systems. Most of our radios manufactured in the last 10 years can operate narrowband FM. (That's the 2.5 kHz variety. We called 5 kHz deviation "narrowband" back in the day.) But it's not on the table for most frequency coordination groups yet. One reason: 10-year-old radios are not *old* in Amateur Radio. We're just figuring out how to use them! OK, just kidding. But our legacy stuff lasts a lot longer than our commercial cousins'. And we pay for our own equipment. So as good as the idea might seem on paper, it's going to be a long time before Amateur Radio FM goes all narrowband.

The Name Game

Now, before describing the band plans for the other VHF/UHF bands, this is as good a place as any for a review of the irregular way we refer to our bands. "6 meters" and "2 meters" are usually referred to that way, by their approximate wavelength, and rarely by their frequency (50 and 144 MHz, respectively). The next two bands, "222" and "440," are most commonly referred to by frequency and not by wavelength (1.25 meters and 70 centimeters, respectively). I'd wager that most hams don't even know that the 222 MHz band is also "one and a quarter meters." This inconsistent nomenclature is most likely just because it's easier to say "2 meters" and "440" — "70 centimeters" is a mouthful. Some hams call the 440 band just "UHF," though that ignores our other UHF bands at 900, 1200 and 2400 MHz. And one more note: You'll hear most old-timers call the 222 MHz band just "220," the band's original lower limit before we lost that bottom 2 MHz. Old habits die hard.

Now back to the band planning discussion.

The 440 MHz band is more regular, with all channel steps being 25 kHz (though some areas are in the process of dividing those in half — to 12.5 kHz — to make room for more repeaters). Everyone uses a 5 MHz offset, but in the early days, hams disagreed about which way to set the input and output frequencies, with some regions putting the repeater transmitter on the higher frequency (much of the northeast, most of the west, and southern California), and some regions putting it on the lower frequency (the southeast, Midwest, Texas, the Pacific northwest and northern California). That difference persists today.

The band is huge, running from 420 to 450 MHz. FM and repeaters fill the top 10 MHz (that's why it's called "440"). CW and SSB take a small sliver at 432 MHz, and a satellite band takes a bit more. The bulk of the band is reserved for ATV (amateur television) that requires 6 MHz per channel.

Six meter FM also has regular channel steps — 20 kHz — but regional differences in offset, with some areas using 1 MHz and some using 500 kHz. Check your local listing. The 6 meter FM calling frequency is another aberration. At 52.525 MHz, it does not conform to the 20 kHz channel step plan.

The 222 MHz band is the most regular of all. That band was the last to be occupied by FM and repeaters, and it was planned after the other bands were hashed out or left in an "agree to disagree" state. It uses 20 kHz channel steps and a 1.6 MHz offset throughout the band and throughout the country. The only areas of dispute are at the bottom of the band. When we lost the bottom 2 MHz in 1988, the band plan changed to accommodate CW and SSB operators on what had been repeater input channels. Not all of the repeaters that had been using that part of the band were willing or able to move to new frequencies.

Now, check out the frequency coverage of your shiny new 2 meter FM handheld. It covers the whole band, doesn't it? But if you use it any-old-where, you might interfere with someone — maybe an SSB operator, or a satellite station or a repeater input. Please stick to the band plan channels. If we all do that, we'll all get maximum use and enjoyment out of our bands.

HF Repeaters — Your DX Connection!

Imagine having a QSO with a station in Ecuador while you're on your way to work. Instead of a large HF rig under your dashboard, there is only a small transceiver that might easily be mistaken for a 2 meter FM unit at first glance. You're only running 10 or 20 W, yet the Ecuadorian station is giving you a 59 report. How is this possible?

Well, all the FM repeater action isn't confined to the VHF and UHF bands. There are a large handful of repeaters on 10 meters around the US and the world. "Wideband" FM is permitted only above 29.0 MHz, and there are four band-plan repeater channels (outputs are 29.62, 29.64, 29.66 and 29.68 MHz), plus the simplex channel 29.60 MHz. Repeaters on 10 meters use a 100 kHz offset, so the corresponding inputs are 29.52, 29.54, 29.56 and 29.58 MHz.

Repeater operation on 10 meters is a mixed blessing. Band openings have the potential for fun — you can key up a repeater thousands of miles away. That enjoyment is dampened by the interference generated when multiple repeaters are keyed up at the same time. The ARRL has a CTCSS plan to help reduce the problem, but not many repeater owners follow the plan, and too many leave their machines on "carrier access." Mostly what you'll hear on 10 meter FM are short, sometimes frustrating contacts, ended by interference from other stations or repeaters. But there are enough "golden nugget" contacts to make the mode popular with a lot of hams.

Frequency Coordination

The last step in band planning is frequency coordination. You've got all those repeaters, and all those channels, but who decides what repeater operates on what channel? That's the job of frequency coordinators. They range in size from individuals covering part of one state to large organizations covering multiple states. Someone wishing to put up a new repeater contacts their local frequency coordinator (listed in the *ARRL Repeater Directory*) to find out what frequency they can use that won't interfere with existing repeaters. That is, if there is an available frequency. In much of the country, all of the available 2 meter channels are occupied, and in a few larger cities, all of the 440 band channels are occupied.

It is an ongoing struggle to find available channels for new repeaters, but it is being done. Use of tone squelch, described later, allows repeaters to be placed a little closer together. Old repeaters are sometimes taken off the air when the owner loses interest, and a new one can occupy the channel. And too many repeaters exist only "on paper" — in the *Repeater Directory* and in the coordinator's database, but not actually on the air. When these repeaters are identified, they can be replaced by new systems.

Coordinators consider several parameters when they receive a request to coordinate a new repeater: distance to co-channel and adjacent-channel neighbors, antenna height, terrain and power. Repeaters can typically be located 75 to 125 miles apart on the same frequency, but particularly wide-coverage repeaters on mountaintops or tall towers need a little more separation. In areas that use 15 kHz channel steps, adjacent channel repeaters need about 50 miles between them.

Repeaters on 20 kHz channel steps need less separation, and some areas require no geographic separation between repeaters on 20 kHz adjacent channels.

The new DV (digital voice) modes are creating a challenge for frequency coordinators. D-STAR in particular is growing quickly enough that coordinators are receiving requests for new repeater channels that they don't have. D-STAR provides an advantage in spectrum use. Its signal is narrower than analog FM, so more D-STAR repeaters would fit in a given amount of spectrum. That may help over time when channels can be realigned to place DV repeaters on adjacent channels. For now, some DV repeaters are just occupying conventional channels, and some analog repeater owners have converted to DV on their existing channels. Some DV repeaters are being squeezed in between analog repeaters, with some distance helping to prevent interference. APCO-25 digital repeaters now in use take up almost as much spectrum as analog FM. A new generation of P-25 radios will use about the same spectrum as D-STAR. The new DMR systems use a little less spectrum than analog, but have the advantage of allowing *two simultaneous conversations* on the same channel, using time division multiplexing.

Frequency coordination is not *required* by the FCC, but the rules do says that if there is interference between repeaters, and one is not coordinated, the uncoordinated repeater "has primary responsibility to resolve the interference." FCC enforcement over the past 15 years has put some teeth into frequency coordination, and some uncoordinated repeaters have been taken off the air. The vast majority of repeaters are coordinated.

EMERGENCIES

Repeaters are excellent tools for emergency communication. That's why we leave a pause between transmissions — you never know when someone (you) will need the repeater in an emergency. Beyond local incidents, repeaters are in regular use by our Amateur Radio emergency organizations (ARES, RACES, SKYWARN and others) for training and during disasters.

ARRL Amateur Radio Emergency Service (ARES)

ARES® is the Amateur Radio Emergency Service, sponsored by the ARRL. During any kind of emergency, ARES operators will be using repeaters for local coordination and passing traffic. During these operations, the active repeater will probably be closed to regular conversations. But unless a major disaster has hit the area, there will be other repeaters available for regular activity. Ask the net control station for the status of the repeater.

Radio Amateur Civil Emergency Service (RACES)

RACES is a parallel program under the control of federal, state and local emergency managers. In many areas, hams have dual membership in RACES and ARES programs, and they are integrated and share the same leadership.

SKYWARN

We use repeaters to help the National Weather Service (NWS) in an operation called SKYWARN. Most areas of the country are covered by repeaters dedicated to SKYWARN during bad weather. When severe weather threatens your area, listen to your local SKYWARN repeater, and follow instructions from the net control station. Weather spotter reports fill in what the NWS calls "ground truth" — the actual conditions on the ground that Doppler radar can't detect directly. Many NWS offices have Amateur Radio stations that are activated for direct reports during severe weather. SKYWARN is a program of the NWS, but in many areas the Amateur Radio component is run by the local ARES leadership.

Public Service Events

Hams across the country regularly help civic and charitable organizations with communications during events such as bike-a-thons, marathons, triathlons and walks. This activity can keep a repeater very busy, so it isn't compatible with other hams chatting on the same channel. During the event a repeater will again be closed to routine operation. If you need to make a call, ask the net control station and most likely you can use the repeater for a minute with no problem. Participation in these events is good training for emergency communications. They carry a lot of traffic and give you practice communicating on busy channels, and all the traffic means something.

Nets

Repeaters are great places for nets, and there are lots of nets. A net, short for "network of stations," is an organized on-the-air activity. We've mentioned a few already, including SKYWARN and ARES, but there can be many other types: traffic nets, rag-chew nets, specialty topic nets, club information nets and more. Most nets meet on a specific frequency or repeater, on a regular schedule — some daily, and some weekly. When a net is active on a repeater, the repeater is closed to other activity. The net control station (NCS) is in charge of the frequency, and all communication should be directed to that station first.

You might be a little nervous the first time you check into a net. Listen carefully to see how it works, and when the net control station calls for check-ins, tell them it's your first net. They'll take some extra time with you to help figure it out. Many new hams find that checking into a net is the easiest way to make their first contact. You can find many local nets online at **www.arrl.org/arrl-net-directory-search**.

See the Emergency Communications chapter elsewhere in this book for much more information on training for and operating during emergencies.

INTERFERENCE

Interference is an overused word in FM and repeaters. Hams call any sound they don't expect to hear "interference," but I'm referring particularly to the sound of hams talking on your repeater's co-channel neighbor 100 miles away during a band opening. Unless that's preventing you from communicating, and you were using the frequency first, that's not interference.

But given that the hallmark of FM is silence when a desired signal is not present, any extraneous noise is at least unpleasant. There are several sources, and a few solutions.

One source is the neighboring repeater. You may hear that repeater, or its users may key up your repeater, especially during a band opening.

Another common source of noise is "intermod," short for intermodulation. That happens when two or more signals that are off your listening frequency mix and create a new signal (a mixing product) that is on the channel you've tuned to. Mixing is a fundamental principle of radio, but in this case it's working against you, not for you. The source of the signals could be strong nearby transmitters, in or out of the ham band (pager transmitters are often involved, because they run high power, are on the air a lot, and are modulated with annoying *beeeep booop braaaap* tones).

The culprit doing the mixing is likely your receiver. Some receivers are better at rejecting mixing products than others, and *QST* product reviews give specs on that.

Finally, the explosion of computer and other consumer electronics has filled the spectrum with weak signals. They don't carry far, but they're all around you — in your house, your neighbor's house and nearby businesses.

Solutions? For intermod, an external filter in your antenna line will help by keeping the offending signal from reaching your receiver. There are two types, *band pass* and *notch*. A band pass filter lets in only the ham band, and keeps the pagers and police dispatchers out. Most ham FM radios are designed to let you listen to the business and public safety bands (including the NOAA weather transmitters at 162 MHz). A band pass filter will take all that out. A notch filter will eliminate just a small slice of spectrum, usually the pager frequencies since they're a prime source. If that does the job, then you can listen to your repeater and still hear the cops chase the robbers, without the noise of intermod.

Radio Direction Finding

Radio direction finding (RDF), also known as foxhunting, rabbit hunting and hidden-transmitter hunting, is a very popular type of VHF/UHF FM radiosport.

Here's how the scene plays out. You and the ham club folks are sitting around the local diner on a seasonable Sunday evening. After coffee, someone suggests a rabbit hunt might be fun. Excitement begins to grow, all the old hands dash off for their special DF antennas and black boxes as someone is elected to be the rabbit. The rabbit then hides a transmitter in the woods, a park or other inconspicuous place. For this purpose the transmitter can simply be a small self-contained unit set to transmit a signal at appropriate intervals, or it might be you in your car with the PTT button in your hot little hand.

After an appropriate time interval, the others in the hunt (equipped with their direction-finding equipment), go out to try to be the first to find the hidden transmitter. It can take minutes, or it can last until the rabbit is asked

Specialized radio direction finding equipment makes it easier to hunt down hidden transmitters or sources of interference.

to identify the awesome place he or she located to hide! Foxhunting is great entertainment (and just as often keenly challenging team competition) at hamfests and club outings.

RDF also has a serious side. The FCC uses highly sophisticated DF equipment to track illegal signals to their source. Repeater operators can, and do, make use of the skilled DF and foxhunting folks on occasion to track down repeater jammers and unlicensed intruders. DF skills can also be handy for tracking down stolen transceivers that suddenly pop up on the air, obviously being operated by people who are not familiar with normal Amateur Radio operating procedures.

Locating a hidden transmitter is an art form and, like any other art, takes a great deal of practice to perfect. Homebrew DF antennas and equipment are both inexpensive and relatively easy to construct. So, next time you have the opportunity to participate in a foxhunt, take advantage of it to hone your direction-finding skills for the real thing.

Consumer electronics must be filtered at the source, and you'll need to consult a specialized reference such as *The ARRL RFI Book* for the details. Some of it can't be eliminated, and the section on coded squelch, next, might provide a workable solution.

So we're back to that neighboring repeater. Frequency coordination pushed it as far away as practical. Some repeater owners feel they're entitled to a clear frequency — after all, they're coordinated. That's not possible any more, given the number of repeaters on the air. Ham repeaters, like their business and public safety band neighbors, are increasingly turning to coded squelch to let everyone live together in peace.

Coded Squelch

Squelch is the circuit in FM radios that turns off the loud rush of noise that you would hear when there is no signal on the channel you're listening to. Most of the time, hams use *noise squelch*, also called *carrier squelch*, a squelch circuit that lets any signal at all come through. But there are ways to be more selective about what signal gets to your speaker or keys up your repeater. That's generically known as *coded squelch*, and more than half of the repeaters on the air require you to send coded squelch to be able to use the repeater. See **Figure 2.11**.

CTCSS

The most common form of coded squelch has the generic name *CTCSS* (continuous tone coded squelch system), but

(A)

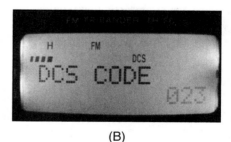

(B)

Figure 2.11 — Setting squelch codes in a Kenwood TH-F6 Handheld. (A) shows the menu for setting a CTCSS code, while (B) shows setting a DCS code. With most radios, selecting DCS sets the radio in encode and decode mode, while CTCSS allows an encode-only mode, or encode-decode.

is better know by Motorola's trade name PL (Private Line), or just the nickname "tone." It adds a "subaudible" tone to your transmitted audio, one of 50 very specific frequencies between 67 and 254 Hz (see **Table 2.2**). Yes, humans can hear these frequencies quite well, so they're *sub*audible only because your receiver's audio circuit is supposed to filter them out. A receiver with CTCSS will remain silent to all traffic on a channel unless the transmitting station is sending the correct tone. Then the receiver sends the transmitted audio to its speaker.

In commercial radio service, this allows Jane's Taxi Company and Bob's Towing Service to use the same channel without having to listen to each other's traffic. In Amateur Radio, some repeaters require users to send the correct CTCSS tone to use the repeater. This may mean the repeater is *closed*, for use only by members, but more likely it is simply being used to avoid being keyed up by users of their co-channel neighbor 100 miles away. Most radios built since the early 1980s have a CTCSS *encoder* built in, and most radios built since the early '90s also have a CTCSS *decoder* built in.

If your local repeater sends a CTCSS tone, you can use your decoder to monitor just that repeater, and avoid hearing the co-channel neighbor, intermod or the annoying fizzes of nearby consumer electronics.

DCS

A newer form of coded squelch is called DCS (digital-coded squelch). DCS appeared in commercial service because CTCSS didn't provide enough tones to keep everyone out of each other's hair, so DCS adds another hundred or so code options. DCS started showing up in ham radios around 2000. It's safe to say that few open repeaters (repeaters open to any and all users) use DCS, since older radios don't have it. It will be years, if ever, before DCS is in routine ham radio use, but there will certainly be specialized uses.

Don't confuse DCS with the new DV digital voice modes. DCS is added to ordinary analog FM voice — it doesn't make the voice signal digital in any way.

DTMF

DTMF (dual tone multi frequency) can also be used as a form of squelch, to turn a receiver on, though it's more often used to control various functions such as autopatch and talking S meters. Some repeaters that require CTCSS have a DTMF "override" that puts the repeater into carrier-squelch mode for a few minutes if you send the proper digits.

Tone Trouble

Coded squelch is useful in reducing the problems with unwanted signals, but it introduces some new problems. One is education. You have to teach your user community about the tone. Most hams get it pretty quickly these days, but there are a few who need a lot of hand-holding, or are just resistant to change. Repeater tone requirements are listed in the *ARRL Repeater Directory*, so they're not hard to find.

Travelers, though, have a big problem with tone. Say you're on the road away from home, scanning the band for activity. The radio stops on an active repeater, but you can't

Table 2.2
CTCSS Tone Frequencies

The purpose of CTCSS is to reduce cochannel interference during band openings. CTCSS-equipped repeaters and receivers respond only to signals transmitted with the required CTCSS tone. These receivers do not respond to signals on their inputs that lack the correct tone. The standard ANSI/EIA frequencies (in Hz) are as follows:

67.0	103.5	159.8	199.5
69.3	107.2	162.2	203.5
71.9	110.9	165.5	206.5
74.4	114.8	167.9	210.7
77.0	118.8	171.3	218.1
79.7	123.0	173.8	225.7
82.5	127.3	177.3	229.1
85.4	131.8	179.9	233.6
88.5	136.5	183.5	241.8
91.5	141.3	186.2	250.3
94.8	146.2	189.9	254.1
97.4	151.4	192.8	
100.0	156.7	196.6	

key it up because it requires CTCSS, and you don't know the tone frequency. You can look it up in the *Repeater Directory* — but that's not a good idea for a solo driver.

Newer radios have a "tone scan" feature that will hunt for the tone, *if* the repeater is sending tone. Most repeaters that require tone also transmit their tone, but they don't have to. Some radios make it easy to scan for tone, and some bury the function several layers deep in menus — again, not a safe activity for a solo driver. Some helpful repeaters announce their tone along with their voice ID. In some areas of the country, most of the repeaters use the same tone, so if you know one, you know them all.

It would be nice (and safer for drivers) if manufacturers responded to this significant problem with a way for radios to recognize and implement tone without operator intervention — tune in a repeater that's sending tone, and the radio automatically sets that tone for your transmission. No radios on the market today do this.

The best idea is to plan your trip in advance, and look up the repeater frequencies and tones you'll encounter along the way. Then program them into your radio's memories. The ARRL's *TravelPlus* CD-ROM repeater database makes this easier. And most newer radios can be programmed by computer with special software and an interface cable. It still takes some time, but these tools make radio operation on the road a lot easier and more fun.

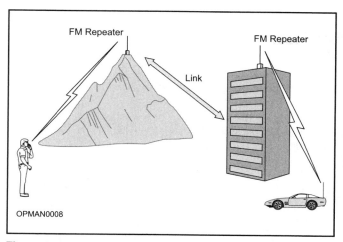

Figure 2.12 — Two FM repeaters linked via VoIP.

Figure 2.13 — A Yaesu FT-8900 being prepared for crossband repeat. On the right side (the "local" side) of the display, note that the frequency is part of the area's band plan for crossband repeat. The UHF frequency is protected by encode and decode CTCSS, and the power level is set to low.

LINKING AND CROSSBAND REPEATERS

Linked Repeaters

Most repeaters are stand-alone devices, providing their individual pool of coverage and that's it. But a significant number of repeaters are linked — connected to one or more other repeaters. Those other repeaters can be on other bands at the same location, or they can be in other locations, or both. This lets users communicate between different bands and across wider geographic areas than they can on a single repeater.

There are many ways to link repeaters. Sometimes 2 meter and 440 repeaters are on the same tower and can just be wired together, or they may even share the same controller. Repeaters within a hundred miles or so of each other can use a radio link — separate link transmitters and receivers at each repeater, with antennas pointed at each other. Repeaters farther apart can "daisy-chain" their links to cover even wider territory. There are a few linked repeater systems in the country that cover multiple states with dozens of repeaters, but most radio-linked repeater systems have more modest ambitions, covering just part of one or two states.

VoIP and the Internet, introduced earlier, have taken repeater linking to a new level, creating the ability to tie repeaters together around the world and in nearly unlimited number. **Figure 2.12** shows one example. We'll talk more about Internet linking shortly.

There are several ways linked repeaters can be operated, coming under the categories of *full-time* and *on demand*. Full-time linked repeaters operate just as the name implies — all the repeaters in a linked network are connected all the time. If you key up one of them, you're heard on all of them, and you can talk to anyone on any of the other repeaters on the network at any time. You don't have to do anything special to activate the network, since it's always there.

In an on-demand system, the linked repeaters remain isolated unless you take some action, usually by sending a code by DTMF digits, to connect them. Your DTMF sequence may activate all the repeaters on the network, or the system may let you address just one specific repeater, somewhat like dialing a telephone. When you're finished, another DTMF code drops the link, or a timer may handle that chore when the repeaters are no longer in use.

Crossband Repeat

Dual-band mobile radios — radios that cover two ham bands, usually 2 meters and 70 cm — are often designed to be mini-repeaters. Yes, you can run a little repeater right out of your car! This can be helpful if you want to operate a handheld radio but need the oomph of a mobile radio to reach a distant repeater. For example, you're on the lower level of the mall with your handheld. You can't reach the local repeater from down there, but you can reach your car in the parking lot. With a crossband repeater in your car, you can relay your signal from the mall to the main repeater.

Crossband repeat operation in most mobile radios is simple. See **Figure 2.13** for a typical example. When the crossband function is turned on, anything the radio hears on one band is retransmitted on the other. When the signal stops, the radio goes into receive on both bands and waits for the next signal, on either band, to repeat. So down in the mall, you transmit on UHF. Your mobile hears you on its UHF receiver, and repeats you to the main repeater on 2 meters using its VHF transmitter. When you stop, it begins hearing the main repeater on VHF, flips itself around and repeats the main repeater back to you using its UHF transmitter. Simple as that is, it can take a while to wrap your mind around the concept.

Is It Legal?

By ARRL Chief Technology Officer Brennan Price, N4QX, and ARRL General Counsel Chris Imlay, W3KD

What Part 97 regulations govern VoIP-assisted Amateur Radio?

All of them or none of them, depending on whether you're asking about the "VoIP-assisted" or the "Amateur Radio" part of VoIP-assisted Amateur Radio.

Many callers to the ARRL's Regulatory Information Branch over the last few years have focused on the novelty of the Internet when asking questions about the legal uses of certain systems. Such focus is misdirected. Part 97 does not regulate systems; it regulates stations. The Commission doesn't care what a ham has feeding his or her station; it cares that the station — not the Internet, but the station — is properly operated. And all the rules that apply to any Amateur Radio station apply to one that retransmits audio fed to it by VoIP.

Fine, so the Commission doesn't care about the VoIP part. Are there any particular rules of which a ham considering such an operation should be aware?

The obvious answer is all of them, but we'll focus on a few that are easy to overlook, particularly for stand alone, single channel operations. The main points to remember:

■ All stations must be controlled.

■ Only certain types of stations may be automatically controlled.

■ Simplex voice operations do not qualify for automatic control.

■ Any station that is remotely controlled via radio must utilize an auxiliary station to execute said control, and auxiliary stations are restricted in frequency.

It's not as hard as it sounds. All you have to do is think about the type of station you're operating and how it's controlled. Let's look at a few examples.

Two automatically controlled repeaters are linked via VoIP. Is this legal?

Forget the VoIP linking, because that's the Internet. We're talking about two repeaters. Are repeaters legal? Yes. May repeaters be automatically controlled? Yes. There is no difference between this setup and two repeaters linked by another wired mechanism or by auxiliary stations. Assuming the two linked stations are repeaters, it is difficult to conceive of a situation where a VoIP link would not pass regulatory muster. The only caveat is that the VoIP software must prevent nonhams from accessing the repeaters from the Internet. The key here is to avoid any configuration that would

(1) permit a non-ham to key an amateur transmitter without the presence of a control operator, and

(2) prevent the initiation by a non-ham of a message via an Amateur Station without the presence of a control operator.

Is it permitted to enable *automatically controlled* simplex nodes?

No. Only certain types of Amateur Radio stations may be operated unattended, under automatic control. This means that there is no human control either at the station location or at a distance. These types of stations are space stations, repeaters, beacons, auxiliary stations and certain types of stations transmitting RTTY or data emissions.

Simplex VoIP nodes are neither repeaters, beacons nor auxiliary stations. Presumably, most are within 50 kilometers of the Earth's surface and are therefore not space stations. The VoIP technology implies a voice transmission, not RTTY or data. Therefore, none of the stations that qualify for automatic control describe a simplex VoIP node, and such a station must be locally or remotely controlled (as any Amateur Radio station is allowed to be).

Locally or remotely controlled — what does that mean?

A simplex VoIP node may be locally controlled by an operator who is present at the node. Such a node may also be *remotely controlled* at some other point, with the operator issuing commands via a wireline or radio control link. If a radio control link is used, it must utilize an auxiliary station. Auxiliary stations may operate only on frequencies in the 2 meter band or higher, with the exception of these specific segments: 144.0 –144.5, 145.8–146.0, 219–220, 222.00–222.15, 431–433 and 435–438 MHz. It's this remotely controlled aspect that allows VoIP simplex nodes to operate legally — as long as they are on the right bands.

Let's consider some scenarios:

■ A control operator is stationed and active at the VoIP node on any frequency. This is a locally controlled station, not at all unlike a typical operation on FM simplex. This is legal.

■ A control operator communicates with and controls a simplex VoIP node with a handheld, transmitting and listening to the node on 223.52 MHz. This is wireless remote control. Such control must be executed by an auxiliary station and 223.52 MHz is an allowed frequency for such a station. This is legal.

■ A control operator operates a simplex VoIP node at 147.42 MHz and is stationed at the node's transmitter. User stations access the node on the same frequency. This is legal. The VoIP node is being locally controlled, and any station may be locally controlled.

■ A control operator operates a simplex VoIP node at 147.42 MHz. The control operator continually monitors the node's transmissions and can call a dedicated telephone line or use a dedicated Internet connection to turn the node on and off. User stations access the node on the same frequency. This is legal. The VoIP node is being remotely controlled via a wireline connection, and any station may be controlled in this manner.

■ A control operator communicates with and controls a simplex VoIP node with a multiband handheld, transmitting to and continuously monitoring the node on 147.42 MHz. He or she sends power on/off commands with the same handheld, also on 147.42 MHz. This is wireless remote control. Such control must be executed by an auxiliary station, and 147.42 MHz is an allowed frequency for such a station. This is legal. The VoIP node is being remotely controlled via an auxiliary station of appropriate frequency, and any station may be controlled in this manner.

■ Same configuration as either of the above two situations, except the control operator does not continuously monitor the VoIP node's transmissions. This operation is not legal. When a simplex VoIP node is enabled, it must be continually attended, either locally or remotely. A simplex VoIP node is no different than other FM simplex operations, and such operations may not be automatically controlled.

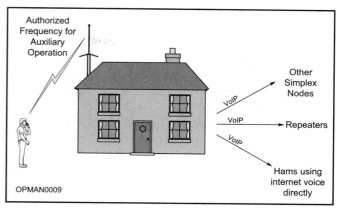

Figure 2.14 — A diagram of a VoIP simplex node. If a control operator is not physically present at the station location and the node is functioning with wireless remote control, the control link must follow the rules for *auxiliary* operation. See the sidebar, "Is It Legal?"

There are some problems that limit the utility of crossband repeat. The biggest problem is *hang-time* on the main repeater — the time after somebody stops talking, but the repeater stays on the air, beeps, and then finally drops. On many repeaters that's several seconds, and when two hams are in conversation, the repeater *never* drops until they're done. Your crossband repeater can't tell the difference between a ham's transmission through the repeater and the hang time afterward. It's all just one long signal being received. So if you, down in the mall, are listening to two hams talk, you can't break in until they're done. As long as they're talking, your mobile never stops sending a signal to you, and never listens for you. (Something else to keep in mind here is that your mobile is now transmitting a lot, and it is not designed for continuous transmission. Keep it in low power.)

A repeater can be made "crossband repeat friendly" by having a very short hang-time, or by a specially designed CTCSS system. If the repeater sends tone only when a signal is on the input, and turns it off during the hang-time, your crossband repeater can use the tone to know when to transmit and when to shut off, allowing you to access the repeater between transmissions normally. Or, if you can hear the main repeater directly on your handheld but just can't

get back to it, you can do one-way crossband repeat, from your handheld through the crossband mobile, but not from the repeater back to your handheld.

A few notes of caution: First, be very careful in configuring your crossband repeater. Choose frequencies wisely — your coordination group may have identified band segments for crossband repeat operation, so don't just plunk down anywhere you want. Do some research. And guard the "local" side of your crossband mobile with CTCSS or DCS. If you don't, and the squelch opens on your mobile, it will spew noise out to the main repeater. Crossband operation is particularly useful for emergency and public service event work, but a noise-spewing, out-of-control crossband mobile can render a vital repeater useless.

Second, maintain control. The FCC rules require you to be in control of the transmitter, but are not specific about how you do that. If you can reach the car in a few minutes from inside the mall, that's probably good enough. But don't stop paying attention to it or leave the area.

Finally, you are required to ID *both* of your mobile's transmitters with your call sign. How do you ID the transmitter that's sending the main repeater signal back to you? None of the crossband repeaters on the market has an ID system built in. So it isn't easy.

INTERNET LINKING

The Internet has expanded repeater linking exponentially, making worldwide communication through a local repeater commonplace. There are four Internet linking systems in common use. Two of them, IRLP and EchoLink, have reached critical mass in the US and are available almost everywhere.

Internet Radio Linking Project (IRLP)

IRLP is the most "radio" based linking system. User access is only via radio, using either simplex stations or repeaters, while linking is done using VoIP on the Internet. An IRLP system operator establishes a *node* by interfacing his radio equipment to a *Linux* based computer with an Internet connection, and then running IRLP software. Once that's set up, repeater users send DTMF tones to make connections, either directly to other individual repeater or simplex nodes (**Figure 2.14**), or to *reflectors* — servers that tie multiple nodes together as one big party line.

The direct connections work like on-demand linked repeaters. You dial in the node number you want to connect to (some systems have you add an access code first), and you are connected to the distant repeater (or simplex node, but repeaters greatly outnumber simplex nodes). Once connected, everyone on both ends can communicate. When you're finished, you usually take the link down with another DTMF sequence. Someone from a distant repeater can make a connection to you as well. Most nodes have a voice announcement that confirms the connection, and sometimes boasts a bit about the local system.

Reflectors work like a hybrid between on-demand and full-time linked repeaters. You can connect your local repeater to a reflector and leave it there all day, or you can connect for a special purpose (such as a net), and drop it when the event is over. Some reflectors are popular, busy places to connect and hear the world. Some are used for special events such as weather nets, and some just wait quietly for a connection.

If you have an underutilized repeater in your area, connecting it to a busy IRLP reflector will bring it to life during much of the day.

There are a couple thousand IRLP nodes online and working worldwide. There are about 30 reflectors operating, each of which has 10 independent "channels," so essentially 300 reflector paths are available. You can find more information at **www.irlp.net**.

EchoLink

EchoLink is the 800-pound gorilla of Internet linking, with thousands of users worldwide actively connected at any time, and tens of thousands more who could connect but are offline at the moment. EchoLink allows repeater connections as does IRLP, and has Conference Servers, similar to IRLP reflectors that permit multiple connections. The big difference, and the reason EchoLink is so much bigger, is that it allows individuals to connect to the network from their computers. You can download EchoLink client software from **www.echolink.org** (for *Windows*, and see the FAQ for Mac OS and *Linux*), register yourself, and then connect to any repeater, individual or conference. Many of your connections won't go over the air at all, but proof of a ham license is required to register, so you'll be talking only to other hams.

The EchoLink conference servers all have more or less specific functions. Some are just regional gathering places (Tennessee, Tokyo, Eastern Utah), while some are topic or activity based (SKYWARN and National Hurricane Center Nets, Jamboree on the Air, Boring Technical Talk).

To use EchoLink with a computer, you need a sound card, a headset (or a microphone and speaker), and an Internet connection. EchoLink will work with a good dial-up connection, but broadband is better. The software presents you with a list of every "station" on the system (a bit overwhelming), and each Conference. You double-click on a station to connect, and push your spacebar to talk. Your initial setup will include getting audio levels set correctly, and, if you use a router with a firewall, you may need to open some ports to allow the outbound EchoLink connection to pass through. Software and instructions are provided on the **www.echolink.org** website.

You can connect your EchoLink-enabled computer to your base station radio fairly easily through a sound card and create an on-air node. If you do, pick your frequencies carefully. Don't pipe EchoLink to a local repeater without permission from the repeater owner. Watch your power output level — your base station isn't meant for continuous duty, but a busy EchoLink connection could have it transmitting a lot. And if you decide to create a full-time link from a computer to a repeater, consider using a dedicated UHF link frequency rather than just a base station on the repeater input. Same goes for IRLP connections.

Other Systems

The two other Internet linking systems, WIRES-II and eQSO have not reached many US repeaters. WIRES-II sponsored by Yaesu, has a few US nodes, but many more in Japan. As with IRLP, it is an "all radio" system. eQSO is more popular in Europe and Asia, but in my brief survey, most of the nodes listed were off. As with EchoLink, it permits individual computer connections. It is the only system with provisions for non-hams ("SWL mode"). You can investigate them at **www.yaesu.com** and **www.eqso.org**.

Internet linking on both IRLP and EchoLink have become popular for emergency communications, with repeaters tied together for ARES and SKYWARN activity. The National Hurricane Center has been using both systems to take reports from hams as hurricanes approach landfall, and hams have been enthusiastic about participation. Of course, the Internet is infrastructure-dependent, and both power and Internet access tend to disappear when storms reach their peak. Not surprisingly, stations along the coast also tend to disappear from the nets as Internet connections are lost. But in many cases Internet linking does provide another valuable tool in the emergency communications toolbox.

In the early days of Internet linking, some hams questioned whether or not it was really "ham radio." While some curmudgeons may still doubt it, the answer has come back a resounding "yes."

DIGITAL VOICE (DV) — THE NEW HORIZON

APCO-25 and D-STAR are digital voice systems making inroads into VHF/UHF Amateur Radio repeater operation. "DMR" is a new player that's about to take off. While all are digital, they are incompatible systems. Each has its own advantages and disadvantages.

APCO-25

Sometimes called just P-25, APCO 25 is a commercial system that's been in use in public safety (police, fire, EMS) for well over 10 years. That means equipment is being "aged out" of commercial service and the old radios, often in very good condition, are cheap. Hams in some areas of the country have put P-25 repeaters on the air on the VHF and UHF ham bands. P-25 equipment was first marketed by Motorola under the brand Astro, and that's the brand you'll find most often on Internet auction sites. But now P-25 is available from most commercial two-way radio manufacturers, including ICOM, Kenwood and Vertex Standard (formerly the maker of Yaesu equipment for Amateur Radio). None of them, though, make P-25 equipment specifically for Amateur Radio or put P-25 capability into their ham radio lines.

Commercial P-25 equipment is not hard to modify for Amateur Radio. The right models can be reprogrammed for ham operation with software — no retuning required. And most models (and most repeaters) are dual-mode, analog and digital. So a repeater owner can convert an analog repeater to digital without leaving the analog users out in the cold. (Analog users will want to use CTCSS decode to avoid hearing the growl that P-25 makes in an analog receiver).

There are positives and negatives to operating a radio designed for commercial service. It'll probably be quite rugged, a plus if you're prone to dropping your handheld. And it may be more immune to intermod and other RF junk. To program it, though, you'll need to visit your local radio shop or a local ham who's purchased the software and cables needed. You could buy them yourself, but they're expensive, and for some radios, they're available only to licensed service shops. You won't have the flexibility of adding and changing frequencies and memories on the fly that you do with true ham equipment. And there are no dual-band radios available. To those hams who prefer commercial equipment, this is a worthwhile tradeoff.

On the air, APCO-25 radios work much like conventional analog FM radios. The audio is a bit "metallic" or "robotic," but there is no noise or mobile flutter. The signal stays full-quieting until it drops off at the weak-signal threshold. P-25 radios send a bit of data at the beginning of a transmission that you can program to include your call sign. That will show up on the display of the receiving station. They can also send this data at the beginning of an analog transmission.

In public safety systems, P-25 radios are often part of linked systems. The linking is done by external equipment that has not found its way into Amateur Radio systems. Most P-25 repeaters are stand-alone, or part of limited networks like their analog cousins. There's no reason they can't be linked to analog repeaters, or use IRLP or EchoLink.

D-STAR

The all-amateur digital voice mode for VHF-UHF is called D-STAR. It was developed by the Japan Amateur Radio League (JARL), and it was designed from the ground up to be a networked system. The repeaters have an Ethernet port for connection to the Internet through a Gateway computer located at the repeater site, though the repeaters can be operated stand alone with no Internet connection.

ICOM brought D-STAR to the US more than 10 years ago as a 1200 MHz system. In 2006 they introduced a broader line of VHF, UHF and dual band mobiles, handhelds and

repeaters. D-STAR handheld and mobile transceivers are all dual-mode, analog and digital, but the current ICOM repeaters are only digital. See **Figure 2.15**.

D-STAR shares P-25's slightly robotic sound and its clarity and freedom from noise and picket-fencing. Both systems have a bit of "garble" as signals hover at the weak-signal threshold, but most of the time a signal is either perfectly clear, or it's gone. Some D-STAR repeater operators report slightly better range with D-STAR than with analog FM, though they'll admit that at the threshold when a D-STAR signal disappears, you might be able to pick some audio out of a very noisy analog signal.

The basic D-STAR operating experience is similar to analog — push to talk, release to listen. But the ICOM repeater controllers have a minimal design. There's no hang-time, no courtesy tone. When you stop transmitting, usually you hear nothing. It's a little hard to tell if you've been heard until the station you're talking to returns and acknowledges your transmission. The repeater will send a short burst of data (its ID) after you let go. It's not audible, but you can see it on your S meter. Some of the "extras" of other repeater controllers such as voice ID, announcements and self-recording and replay (EchoTest), have been developed to run on the Gateway computer using an auxiliary program called *DPLUS*.

There's more to *see* with D-STAR. Your radio displays the call sign of the station you're listening to, and sometimes the call sign of the repeater you're talking through. Users can program a short text message that is sent with each transmission and scrolls through listener's displays. In addition, D-STAR's voice signal always carries with it a 1200 bit/s

Figure 2.15 — ICOM launched D-STAR with a single radio for 1200 MHz, but quickly followed with a line of VHF/UHF mobiles, handhelds and repeaters. Here is a complete ICOM D-STAR repeater and controller, along with the ID-800 mobile and IC-91AD handheld. This equipment is getting ready for operation on the KR4RAL repeater system in Raleigh, North Carolina.

data signal that can be used for text, small files — anything that fits in that low-speed connection. To use that data signal, you connect a computer with a special data cable. It can't be accessed from the radio directly. One program has taken the lead in using this data — *D-RATS* (**www.d-rats.com**). Originally a messaging program, *D-RATS* has expanded to include sending files, pictures, mapping, forms and its own networking.

D-STAR is designed to network using the Internet. An expensive 10 GHz system was developed for short-haul RF networking, but it never took off in the US. And so far, no one has engineered any other RF networking, so the Internet is it.

Repeaters can be linked to each other or to reflectors, similar to IRLP and EchoLink. And since most D-STAR repeaters have a limited number of local users, the reflectors help keep the repeaters busy and the local users entertained. This capability is actually an add-on, part of the *DPLUS* utilities package.

"Call sign routing," *the original* (and still available) D-STAR linking method was more unique, if less popular. D-STAR allows individual users to direct their signals to distant repeaters, or even to specific users, by putting call signs in a special address field of the radio. Since D-STAR radios transmit the user's call sign (also programmed into the radio, and embedded in the data stream with each transmission), the D-STAR network knows where each user is…or at least it knows the last repeater each user keyed up. So by entering a call sign of a user or a repeater, the D-STAR network can route your transmission to a specific repeater. But as interesting and potentially useful as this is, it's rarely used, while the DPLUS system that lets everyone talk to everyone on linked repeaters has become widely accepted.

All this capability is controlled by four call sign *fields*: YOUR, MY, RPT1 and RPT2. We can't explain them in detail here, but there are plenty of articles and tutorials on the web and in *QST*. (A good resource is "Repeaters from A to D — Analog to Digital," by Gary Pearce, KN4AQ, available for free download from **www.ARVN.tv/otherstuff**.) Once you have the basics, though, these fields are easy to program and use. They are filled by plain old ham radio call signs, and a very small number of additional control letters.

Note that anyone can talk through a single D-STAR repeater or through *DPLUS* linked repeaters, but to use the individual routing features and to control Gateway functions you must be registered with one Gateway somewhere on the network. That takes getting in touch with the local system operator, usually on their website, and filling out a form.

There are a few more cute things D-STAR radios can do. One is *call sign squelch*. Since call signs of both the calling and receiving party are part of the data stream, you can set your radio to respond only to a signal addressed to you, by call sign. This flows through the network transparently. There are break-in modes designed to allow a third party to break into a conversation between hams who are using call sign squelch, and there's an emergency mode that will override the volume control setting on some radios to get everyone's attention.

Finally, although ICOM is still the only manufacturer that has chosen to build D-STAR radios (even though anyone can), there are some additional devices on the market that help extend D-STAR's reach and usability.

The two most popular are the DV Dongle and the DV Access Point Dongle (DVAP), USB connected devices from Internet Labs. Both are small slabs of plastic that allow the user to connect to D-STAR repeaters via the Internet, running a software app on a computer (PC, Mac, *Linux*). The DV Dongle uses the computer audio system (mic/speakers or headset), and does the D-STAR encoding and decoding. The software lets the user pick a repeater or reflector to connect to and converse with anyone else on the repeater or reflector. The DVAP also uses the computer's Internet connection, but instead of doing its own vocoding, it has a little 10-mW 2 meter transceiver that lets a ham use a handheld D-STAR radio to talk through the network, even if there is no D-STAR repeater in the vicinity.

The DV Dongle and DVAP are very much plug-and-play devices. Another device, somewhat generically known as a Hot Spot, lets a D-STAR enthusiast connect a higher power FM radio to the D-STAR network. The Hot Spot (available in kits, and requiring a bit more investigation by the user) plugs into the 9600 bit/s packet port of the radio, which is then connected to a base station antenna. This lets you talk through the D-STAR network using your mobile D-STAR radio for whatever distance your base station can provide — usually a few miles.

Note that neither the Hot Spot nor the DVAP convert analog FM to D-STAR! They both require the user to be operating a D-STAR radio. There is a device that will turn an FM radio into a D-STAR radio. It's another not quite off-the-shelf kit called the DV Adapter. It does all the special call sign programming that D-STAR requires, in addition to doing the digital vocoding. Its outboard box makes mobile use iffy, but it does allow D-STAR on any band the radio can operate.

DMR

As this edition of the *Operating Manual* goes to press, a third digital voice system for VHF/UHF repeaters is gaining a foothold: DMR (Digital Mobile Radio). DMR is the generic name for a system developed for business/commercial use as a less expensive alternative to P-25. The most familiar brand name is Motorola's MotoTrbo, but there are many manufacturers making DMR compatible radios.

Not surprisingly, hams have adapted DMR to the ham bands. It's new enough that there isn't a big surplus equipment market, but some of the new DMR equipment is affordable enough for hams. As with P-25 equipment (and, for that matter, any commercial FM equipment adapted for ham radio use), the DMR radios brought in from the commercial arena are not user- or field-programmable. You need software and cables to set them up.

In commercial service, DMR permits repeater networking and has the capability to devote some of its data to text/files, as does D-STAR. Hams have extended the commercial networking capability already, and we can expect more innovation to adapt the system to Amateur Radio's unique needs and capabilities. The commercial radios do *not* permit the individual user to control networking functions the way D-STAR systems do.

In 2012, Yaesu introduced the first radio (a handheld) in a new line of DMR equipment built specifically for hams. They say the line will include handheld and mobile radios, and repeaters. This is intended to be direct competition to D-STAR. Details were vague, but the radio isn't compatible with P-25 or MotoTrbo.

So the stage is set for competition in VHF/UHF digital voice, if not a showdown. On one hand, the pool of hams willing to step into the digital voice arena has been limited, and multiple incompatible systems may make some hesitant to enter until they can determine a "winner." On the other hand, a second major manufacturer of ham radios may make digital voice more "legitimate" in the minds of hams who have been waiting.

Will D-STAR, P-25, DMR or any other digital voice mode make significant inroads into our existing analog repeater infrastructure? Will your analog radio become obsolete anytime soon?

Only time will tell. There's no question that with an analog-only radio you will be missing out on the leading edge of new technology, at least when it arrives in your area. But nobody expects analog repeaters to disappear anytime soon.

VHF/UHF DIGITAL DATA MODES

Let's move on to the VHF/UHF data modes, and keep in mind that with the advent of digital voice, our language must now change. We can no longer assume that "digital" means just text or files in Amateur Radio. ICOM splits their D-STAR nomenclature into DV (digital voice) and DD (for 128 kbit/s digital data). We'll ignore for now the question of whether digitized voice is actually "data," but that question does bedevil our attempts to fit digital voice into the framework of Part 97.

We'll also note only in passing that RTTY was the first digital mode in use on VHF/UHF, as it was on HF. The pre-computer era saw a number of teletype repeaters around the country, with a handful of operators using big, mechanically complex teletype machines. Few if any are still in operation. It's a curiosity that personal computers gave new life to RTTY on HF, while also making packet radio possible, which killed off RTTY on VHF.

Over the years, packet radio in the VHF/UHF spectrum has been its own roller-coaster ride. In the 1980s, interest in personal computers, and an international network of packet radio bulletin boards (PBBS), made packet *the* new mode, though even at its peak, only a fraction of the ham population had packet stations. Many who did operate packet, though, were wildly enthusiastic. The PBBS network with its automatic mail forwarding capability permitted hams to originate e-mail at their local 2 meter PBBS and have it delivered anywhere in the world where there was a PBBS. It could take a day for delivery cross-country, but remember, this was long before the Internet was widely available, and the general public had nothing like it. Our 1200 bit/s speed was state-of-the-art, or better. Some telephone modems were running just 300 bit/s in those days.

By the early 1990s, the PBBS network was so popular that it became overloaded with the amount of e-mail and bulletins it had to handle. In some areas, the spectrum became overloaded, too. But just as hams were beginning to experiment with higher speed packet (9600 bit/s and even 56 kbit/s), the Internet and its seemingly inexhaustible e-mail capabilities arrived and we all but abandoned the PBBS network.

But packet didn't die. Many PBBSs are still around, and packet radio is being used for other applications.

Closing the '90s and continuing into the new century, local DX PacketClusters continue to operate in conjunction with Internet DX spotting. APRS (the Automatic Packet Reporting System), though, inherits most of the packet radio legacy of equipment, tower sites and interest. And Winlink 2000 on VHF/UHF is giving new life to packet for ARES and emergency applications. Given that, it's worth spending some time reviewing what packet is and how to put together and operate a packet station. The data side of D-STAR and DMR are truly "infant" technologies, but we'll take a look at their possibilities too, before we close this chapter.

What is Packet?

It's hard to tell the short story, but I'll try. Packet is error free digital communications (or at least it can be) from one computer to another. It can be live "keyboard to keyboard," like the various forms of instant message chat sessions on the Internet (and like RTTY, PSK31 some of the other "real-time" HF digital modes). But more often it is more like e-mail, with messages and small files passed through bulletin boards and mailboxes to be read later. Or it can be short bits of information such as the weather at a home station, or the location of a mobile station.

To move these messages around, the output of a computer — text or files — is assembled into bundles or "packets" of data (usually about 100 or so characters). Each packet is transmitted as a rapidly shifting pair of audio tones that modulate an FM transmitter using AFSK (audio frequency shift keying, similar to RTTY on FM). The audio tones represent the zeros and ones of a serial binary data stream. The tones on the FM signal travel through the air, are received and demodulated, the packets are checked for integrity, then disassembled and the information is fed to a computer. If the information sent is text, it goes to a display for you to read. If the information is a file, it goes to your hard drive. Or it might place an icon on a map.

To be error free, two packet stations (and no more than two) operate in a *connected* mode — that is, they examine each other's packets, and send an "acknowledgement" packet each time a good packet is received. If a packet is reported as bad, or isn't acknowledged at all, it's sent again. If the signal path fades, the computers keep trying for a while. Eventually they'll connect again and continue, or give up.

Packet stations can also operate *unconnected*. This mode is required if multiple stations are involved, as it would be overwhelming for several stations, perhaps dozens of stations, to try to acknowledge everyone else's packets. But operating unconnected means that the system will not be error free.

The Packet System

The other end of packet communication can be a direct connection to another ham, just like voice simplex, but it's more likely to be a "node," also called a "digipeater." Examples of nodes are the PBBSs, DX PacketClusters or APRS nodes, but there can also be simple stand-alone nodes whose only function is to relay signals. There aren't many full-fledged repeaters dedicated to packet, partly because by the time packet got popular there wasn't much spectrum available for more repeaters, and partly because with digipeaters, we don't really need them.

Digipeaters are simplex devices that receive a packet, then re-send it more or less immediately after it's been received, all on one channel. A central PBBS might be ringed by digipeaters that help outlying users who can't reach the PBBS directly. Those digipeaters don't have to be on the same frequency as the PBBS. They can use a link radio, preferably on another band, to forward packets between you and the PBBS. It takes more hardware, but it eases congestion on a busy packet channel.

What Frequency?

PBBS activity on 2 meters started on 145.01 MHz, and much of it remains there. So if you're looking for local activity, that's a good place to start. Other popular packet channels are 145.03, .05, .07 and .09. In some areas, packet systems can be found on channels between 144.91 and 144.99 MHz, between 145.51 and 145.77 MHz, and on some FM voice simplex channels (which doesn't make voice operators happy). If you listen on those channels, you may hear the "braaap" of 1200 bit/s packet, or the "psssssh" of 9600 bit/s packet.

DX PacketClusters will almost certainly *not* be on 145.01, so check with local DXers and packet operators. APRS is almost exclusively on 144.39 MHz, having moved from 145.79 MHz due to interference with satellite and space station activity. But speaking of space, the ISS and some satellites have packet capability.

There is no packet equivalent of the *ARRL Repeater Directory*. You'll have to search local resources to see what's on the air in your area. Information on the web is surprisingly sparse in many areas, with lots of old, outdated sites still hanging around to mislead you.

Assembling a VHF Packet Station

Most packet stations need a computer and a radio. Then they need a way to create and control the data packets and the audio tones that carry them. There are several ways to do this:

1) *A terminal node controller* (*TNC*) — a separate box

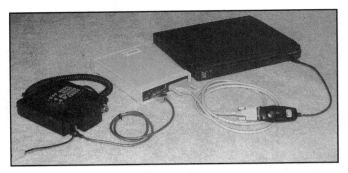

Figure 2.16 — Here is one way to put together a packet station. A TNC, in this case a Kantronics KamPlus, is connected between the radio (an ICOM IC-207H) and a laptop computer. The radio connection is made through the dedicated data port, which leaves the microphone and speaker connections free for voice communication. The connection to the computer goes though a 25-pin to 9-pin modem cable, and a serial-to-USB adapter before plugging into the laptop's USB connection.

containing the hardware and firmware that does most of the work, as shown in **Figure 2.16**. The TNC includes a modem, and the computer mostly acts as a "dumb terminal" — just a keyboard and display.

2) *A stand-alone modem*, and TNC emulation software in the computer.

3) *A sound card* and computer control software, which puts all the work on the computer.

4) *A "built-in,"* with the TNC integrated into the radio. Alinco, Kenwood and Yaesu offer radios that have TNCs built in, and integrated into the radio operation to some degree.

There are advantages and disadvantages to doing it each way.

TNC

The hardware device that handles the signal between the computer and the radio is called the TNC. For transmitting, a TNC assembles the computer's data into packets and encodes the tones that are fed to the radio's input. When receiving, the TNC gets the tones from the radio, decodes them, pulls the data out of the packets and sends it along to the computer for display.

Half of the TNC is the modem (*mod*ulator/*dem*odulator), the circuit that creates and decodes the tones that are transmitted over the air. The other half is the "intelligence" — the firmware that puts the packets together and takes them apart, and contains all the user commands. Some TNCs also include a mini-PBBS, usually called a mailbox, that lets you receive messages from other packet operators when your computer is off and your radio is unattended. Convenience, and that unattended mailbox operation, are the big advantages of a TNC. But it's the most expensive solution.

Modem

Packet modems are available that just create and decode the tones and let you use your computer for the "intelligence." Packet modems are usually bundled with TNC-emulation software. Modems are cheaper than TNCs, but you have to have your computer up and running to use them.

Sound Card

Software is available that lets your computer do everything, and uses the sound card to create and decode the audio tones. The only external connections are the audio cables from the sound card to and from your radio, and a connection from the PC serial port to the radio's PTT. That's the cheapest solution — your cost is a few wires and connectors. But "sharing" your sound card with other programs means you'll pay a price in convenience unless you've dedicated a computer to digital radio operation. Since many of us have an extra, older computer lying around collecting dust, that's not the extravagance it might seem to be.

Most of the software is written for the *Windows* operating system, but there are programs for Mac OS and *Linux* as well. Some programs are freeware, and some are shareware. A web search for "Amateur Radio packet software" will yield a wealth of resources. Be careful, though. Packet radio's roots go well back into the DOS era, so not all of it will work with modern computers.

AGWPE (AGW Packet Engine) is one of those free *Windows* programs that's popular today. The *AGWPE* software is available for download in the "HAM" section at **www.sv2agw.com**.

By the way, sound card software is also having a large impact on some other forms of VHF and HF digital communication. In fact, once you have your computer set up for a program such as *AGWPE*, you're ready to try other intriguing digital modes that use sound-card-based software, including some digital *voice* modes such as *WinDRM*. You've already installed the necessary cables and interface hardware, so all you need to do is start a new program!

Built-in TNC

Alinco, Kenwood and Yaesu all have radios with built-in TNCs.

Alinco has monoband mobiles, and with the addition of a GPS, they will function as stand-alone APRS "trackers." That is, they can be set to beacon the location of the vehicle without operator intervention, once they've been set up using a computer. Leave the computer connected, and you can use two-way APRS and more conventional packet features. Alinco's TNC has a "limited function set," though. An aftermarket TNC is available that expands the packet capability, especially for APRS. But neither TNC offers a built-in PBBS or mailbox. Their aim is clearly at APRS.

Kenwood and Yaesu have both mobile and handheld dual-band radios with built-in TNCs. Again, with an external computer, more complete packet operation is possible, but these systems, too, are aimed more at APRS. Each radio lets you control some APRS functions from the radio's display and panel buttons, and each displays some APRS information. With a GPS connected, you can see things such as distance and bearing to other APRS stations, and read messages, bulletins and weather information. You can originate messages,

though without a keyboard, it's a little tedious. And the radios will show lists of stations received.

All the radios will operate in conventional FM voice mode. When Alinco's mobiles are switched to data mode, that's all it will do. The Kenwood and Yaesu models can operate APRS on one "side" of the radio, and voice on the other. Of course, they can't be transmitting and receiving in the same band at the same time, so if you're operating 2 meter voice and packet, they stop receiving packets during voice transmissions, and when they send a packet beacon, the voice channel receiver drops out for a moment. On the other hand, if you're talking on UHF and using packet on VHF, it's like having independent radios.

Radio Equipment

There is a lot of detail to consider in making the data side of packet radio software work, and we'll review some of that shortly. That detail seems to make some packet operators overlook the "radio" side of the equation. How much radio do you need? How much power? How much antenna? And do you want to operate 1200 bit/s, or move up to 9600 bit/s or faster?

If you're going to make your voice radio double as your packet system, those questions may be moot. If that system is able to hit all the area voice repeaters, it'll probably hit the packet systems as well. Most radios today are "9600-ready," and if yours is, you're set for that, too.

But using your voice radio for packet is a compromise, since packet operation can go on in the background while you are operating or monitoring voice repeaters. Even with the Kenwood and Yaesu dual-band built-ins, you have to dedicate half the radio to packet. If you've got the means for a second radio and antenna, you can have a more effective station. But you shouldn't compromise on the radio or antenna. It has to work as well as, or better than, your voice radio. That's because a bunch of transmitters — nodes, digipeaters and other users — will be sharing the channel with you. TNCs are designed to wait until a channel is clear before transmitting, but if other stations can't hear you, they won't wait for you, so they might begin transmitting while you're on the air, clobbering you at the receiver you're trying to reach. If you can't hear them, your TNC might initiate a transmission while they're on the air. The more stations that can hear each other in a geographic area, the better the system works. A signal in your geographic area that you can't hear is called a *hidden transmitter*. A puny signal that just barely reaches the desired node will be a hidden transmitter to a lot of other stations, and it will have trouble on a busy packet channel.

So get that packet antenna up in the air, and use a radio with 25 to 50 W. That may seem like violating the spirit (and rules) about running minimum power, but in this case you're doing everyone a favor.

Most radios made since the mid '80s will work fine for 1200 bit/s packet. Most modern radios will have dedicated packet connections so you don't have to plug into the mic connector and come out of the speaker jack. Many radios made since the late '90s have 9600 bit/s capability as well.

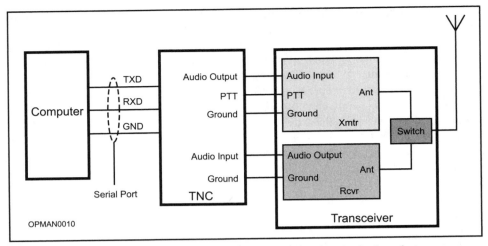

Figure 2.17 — The components and their interconnection in a typical packet radio station.

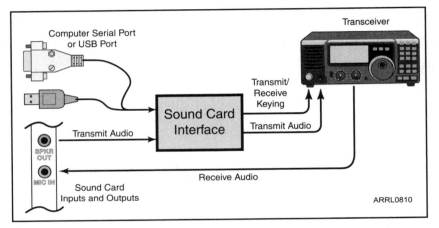

Figure 2.18 — A diagram of a typical setup for VHF digital communication using sound card software. The sound card interface handles the tasks of matching audio levels between the radio and the computer, and keying the radio. Commercial interfaces from a number of vendors can be found in the advertisements in *QST*.

That's a big improvement in speed, if there's a 9600 bit/s system in your area. Packet's popularity has waned, so 9600 systems are rare.

Hardware Connections

TNC Connection

The TNC has at least two connectors: a computer port and a radio port (**Figure 2.17**). TNCs that can do 9600 bit/s may have a separate radio port for the higher speed connection.

The computer port connects to your computer's serial port. Here again you may see packet's 1980s roots — older TNCs use a 25-pin RS-232 connector, while most computers have a 9-pin connecter, *if* they have a serial port at all! You can use a 25-pin to 9-pin adapter or cable, and if you don't have a serial port, you can use a USB-to-serial adapter. Newer TNCs come ready for USB.

The TNC's radio port requires four connections to the radio equipment: audio input, audio output, push-to-talk

(PTT) and ground. Some radios have dedicated connectors for data, often an 6-pin mini-DIN. If your radio doesn't, you can use the microphone and speaker/headphone connections, but the data connector is better because the radio's volume control won't affect the level of the audio going to the TNC. You can turn the volume up to check on the received signal, then turn it down for operation (packet signals aren't very pleasant to listen to). And you won't have to unplug the TNC and plug in the mic to switch to voice operation.

The TNC will have level controls for output to the radio, and possibly for the input from the radio. Adjust those according to the TNC's manual.

Sound Card Connections and Levels

If you are using your sound card rather than a hardware TNC, we need to spend some time discussing the connections to your sound card. Look at **Figure 2.18** for an illustration of a typical configuration. (This discussion focuses on *Windows* based computers, but similar connections and controls are available for Mac OS and *Linux* based computers.)

Connect the audio from your receiver to either the MIC INPUT or LINE INPUT on the computer. If you have a choice, use the LINE INPUT — it will match the signal level from your radio better. Laptops don't have a LINE INPUT, but the MIC INPUT software should have an adjustment to compensate.

For your transmit audio connection, you're looking for LINE OUTPUT, though laptops may just have a HEADPHONE OUTPUT. If you have hum, a line-coupling transformer of 1:1 ratio and 600 Ω impedance should help.

Don't use the digital input or output of your sound card. Even though you're operating a digital mode, you're making an analog audio connection between the computer and the radio.

Setting Sound Card Levels

Previous editions of the *ARRL Operating Manual* gave detailed instructions on how to set sound card levels for transmit and receive. The addition of new generations of operating systems and the wide variety of computers available make this impossible. But I'll tell you that you need to figure out how it works in your computer.

Find the controls for playback or "volume." This will set the *output* level that you'll send to your radio. And turn off or mute all of the other "system" sounds that the computer can make — the bings and bleeps, and "you've got mail" announcements. All those things will head on out to the radio, too, and you really don't want them!

The controls for "recording" or "input" will adjust the level you receive from the radio. Note that you'll sometimes have two or more places to adjust levels in both the transmit and receive audio path. Without measuring equipment to insert at each stage, it can be difficult to know where to set each. You don't want one way *up*, and the other way *down* to compensate. That can add noise, distortion, or both to your signal. Start with a mid-range adjustment, and listen to your transmitted or received signal for level and distortion.

TNC Command(s) and Control

If you buy a full, commercial TNC, you'll need a way to talk it — a program that lets you do actual packet operation. It will probably come with an operating program, which may be good enough, but there are several more advanced programs out there. The one I've used the most, *KaWin* for Kantronics TNCs, was last updated in 1997! Most of the programs out there are of that vintage, except the APRS programs, which are still being updated, and Winlink 2000, which is current.

Actually, TNCs can be operated by a simple terminal program (the program in *Windows XP* is called *HyperTerminal*), or, for that matter, a dumb terminal. TNCs have a long list of "command-line" type instructions for both set-up and operation. The details are in the instruction manuals. The control programs are just more elegant front ends that feed the commands to the TNC.

You can leave most of the TNC's settings at their default, but whether you use an operating program or just *HyperTerminal*, you'll need to fill in some blanks and adjust some parameters. One blank is your call sign, called MYCALL in the TNC's firmware. The TNC will be sending your call sign for identification and to make connections, so it has to know who you are (or is it who "it" is). A packet station's call sign often includes a *secondary station identification* (SSID) that further identifies the station. The SSID is a dash, followed by a number from 1 to 15, for example KN4AQ-3. You need this because a single packet station may be available for live keyboarding using one SSID, a mailbox using another SSID, and as a digipeater using yet another SSID. Each is a separate setting in the TNC.

An important setting is TXDELAY. That sets how long the TNC waits between "pushing" the PTT and sending data. We're talking about tenths of a second here. Some transmitters take two or three tenths of a second to get up to power, stabilize on frequency and send audio. Some can do it in well under a tenth of a second. In the world of packet, three-tenths of a second is a long time. About 200 to 300 milliseconds is typical for most 2 meter radios and 1200 bit/s. Shorter is a little better, so trim the time until things stop working, then add some back.

A TNC will keep a list of all the stations it has heard, noting whether it heard them directly or through a digipeater, and when they were heard (if you set the DAYTIME parameter). That's another reason to have a dedicated packet station. To see that list, you ask for the MHEARD list. You can watch all the packet traffic on a channel scroll by your screen if the MONITOR command is turned ON, or just see packets sent to you with it OFF.

There are several old books that go into detail explaining TNC functions and setup. Some are out of print, but you can probably find them at hamfests. A good free, online resource is by Larry Kenny, WB9LOZ, at **www.choisser.com/packet**. It's telling that the website says "The author is no longer active in packet radio; however he has left this material on the Internet for access by those who might find it helpful." This page was #2 in a recent Google search, after the ubiquitous Wikipedia listing.

On the Air

Once you've gotten your TNC connected and configured, it's time to make it play! If there's still a PBBS in your area, there's a pretty good chance it, or a node connected to it, is on 145.01 MHz. That was the original packet frequency on 2 meters. But you'll need to talk to local packet operators to see what frequencies are in use in your area.

To communicate with another station, a node or a PBBS, you *connect* to it. That puts you in the error-free mode mentioned earlier. Using your software, you enter the call sign (and SSID) of the station you want to connect to, and probably press the ENTER key. The TNC keys your radio and sends a connect request. If that station hears you, it responds quickly. Your TNC acknowledges the response, and the TNC's CONNECTED light comes on.

Now you're ready to communicate. If you've connected to an individual station, and the operator is present, you can have a real-time, keyboard-to-keyboard chat very much like the various instant message programs on the Internet. If the operator is not present, you can enter his or her personal mailbox and leave a message (and retrieve a message left for you). TNCs respond to a limited number of commands from remote stations. You can tell it to send you its MHEARD list — the list of all the stations it's heard recently.

If you've connected to a PBBS there won't be a live operator, but you've got a wider list of options to select from. You can list and read bulletins, and send and receive mail and bulletins. Some will have Internet connections so you can pass e-mail through the radio to the Internet. Talk to the sysop for more complete instructions.

At 1200 bit/s, packet operation will seem very slow compared to the Internet on a broadband connection. If signals are poor or the channel is busy, it can be excruciatingly slow, especially if you're trying to read a long message. Short messages can transfer quickly, though.

DX PacketCluster

DXers discovered the power of packet early in the game, and it's changed DXing for better or worse. In the good old days, DXers tuned the bands, hoping to come across a station in a needed country, or "entity" as they call them today. They knew about DXpeditions and rare country activations from bulletins in magazines, but that information was weeks or months old. Some areas had VHF voice repeaters dedicated to DX, so after someone worked a station, they announced it on the repeater.

Then they chased away stations who came on to rag-chew.

Packet supercharged DX reporting, or spotting as it's called. Before the Internet, DXers built PacketCluster systems — PBBS type packet nodes with specialized software — around the country, and linked them to cover wider regions (that's the "cluster" part). The PacketCluster is an easy way to report the call sign, country, frequency, time, strength and other useful parameters of the DX signal, and the location of the receiving station. That information quickly pops up on the display screen of all the other DXers in the region. You can configure the cluster to filter the spots you receive by band, country, mode and other ways so you only see spots of the stations you really need for an award or contest. PacketClusters also support quick, instant-message type notes between stations, and bulletins and e-mail like PBBSs.

PacketClusters operate in the connected mode — the cluster itself makes an individual connection to each station logged on — and you use your routine packet software. Spots are sent individually to you and everyone else logged in. That's quite a burst of traffic when a spot arrives. The Cluster does the filtering based on parameters you set, so it doesn't waste time sending you spots you don't want. There is specialized software available for picking off spot information while unconnected.

The downside of DX PacketClusters, according to some hams anyway, is that it makes DXing more like shooting fish in a barrel. It also makes things harder because "packet pile-ups" appear instantly. But the system is entrenched and it's not going away.

Although the Internet has largely usurped the DX PacketCluster function, RF systems remain on the air in many areas. You can search for a local system at **www.dxcluster.info**.

DX PacketClusters have their own unique set of commands for entering and retrieving spots. And many of them request or require specific TNC settings for users. Find your local sysop for that information.

Automatic Packet Reporting System (APRS)

Just as packet systems in general were succumbing to competition from the Internet, APRS appeared, leading to a resurgence of interest (and TNC sales). Some handheld and mobile radios include APRS capabilities or built-in TNC options.

When operating APRS, you, or a device at your station (GPS, weather monitor), send a bit of information to your TNC, which sends it to your radio for transmission on 144.39 MHz. An APRS digipeater relays your packets to all local stations, and to all surrounding digipeaters, which in turn relay your packet to all *their* local stations. That puts your data in the hands of stations for a hundred or so miles around. One of those stations also puts your information on the Internet, where it can be seen worldwide.

What information do you send? Many hams think of APRS first as a position reporting system, based on sending GPS location, speed and altitude data via packet to be displayed on a map. That concept is so infused with APRS that hams often think the acronym means "automatic *position* reporting system" (and for a brief time, it used to). But as APRS developer Bob Bruninga, WB4APR, describes it on his own website, **www.aprs.org**, "The Automatic Packet Reporting System was designed to support rapid, reliable exchange of information for local, tactical real-time information, events or nets." All kinds of information can be exchanged across a region quickly using APRS. Bob lists text messages, weather info, traffic reports, repeater, event, EchoLink and IRLP node location and info and more, in addition to location data for fixed and mobile stations. "Think of APRS as a signaling channel to reveal *all* Amateur Radio resources and live activities that are in range of the operator at any instant in time," he writes. And he's not done adding features and attempting to make APRS *the* Amateur Radio messaging system. His recent talks before the ARRL/TAPR Digital Communications Conference are available on video at my website at **www.arvn.tv**.

On the receive end of things, you generally see some kind of map on your display, something like the one in **Figure 2.19**, showing the location of all the area APRS stations. For moving stations, the display can show the direction, speed and altitude as well. Other windows or boxes display the text notes, weather information and other data being sent. Maybe it's that map that makes people think P is for Position.

APRS Software and Hardware

To use APRS, you'll need some specialized software. Standard packet communication software won't do. A wide variety of software is available — more than we can fairly list here. Some of it includes maps (usually with limited detail), and some is designed to overlay APRS data on commercial mapping software, which gives it street-level detail. Like PBBS and DX PacketClusters, APRS has a list of special commands for telling your packets what to do. Your software handles most of those. For example, if you want to send a text message, you type the call sign of the recipient in a box, type the message in another box, and click SEND.

Unlike PBBS and DX PacketCluster systems, APRS uses only unconnected packets. That means that APRS data is not error-free. If you miss a packet due to interference or a signal fade, it's gone. Nobody's going to ask your TNC for an acknowledgement. But most APRS data is repeated routinely, so you'll get it next time. Text messages do have their own system for sending back an acknowledgement, but it's not guaranteed.

At home, the hardware you need is standard packet-system

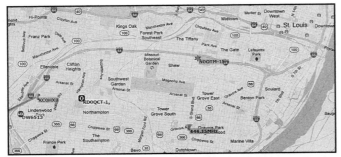

Figure 2.19 — This is a screen capture from www.aprs.fi of APRS activity around St. Louis, Missouri. It shows many stations, and the tracks of several GPS-equipped mobiles. The site is highly customizable, and it has a history function that goes back years.

stuff — computer, TNC, radio, antenna. If you have an old TNC, or buy a used one, check to see if its firmware supports GPS data. You may need a firmware upgrade. In the US and Canada, all routine APRS traffic is on 144.39 MHz at 1200 bit/s. Special event traffic can be handled on other frequencies.

Mobile APRS is another story. You can run a full APRS station with a laptop computer and APRS software, or a radio with a built in TNC (**Figure 2.20**), or you can have a transmit-only system that beacons your location, called a "tracker." Either way, you add a GPS to the mix.

For a full mobile station, you need a computer with two ports — one for the TNC and one for the GPS — or a TNC that accepts GPS information directly. Newer GPS receivers have USB connections, but some TNCs are built to connect to serial ports. If you have a newer laptop without a serial port, you can use a USB-to-serial adapter. The software will forward the GPS information to the TNC. The program will beacon your location as you move. How often it beacons is one of several parameters you'll need to set. Some programs get very detailed, allowing you to send a beacon when you've turned a corner, and send more beacons when you're moving at high speed, fewer when going slowly or stopped.

With a tracker, you have the GPS, the TNC and the radio, but no computer except to initially set things up. The GPS plugs into the TNC directly. There are some special, small TNCs on the market designed just to be trackers, and some TNC/radio combinations. The only receiving they do is to make sure they don't transmit when a channel is busy. With a tracker, you drive down the road, letting the world (including family and friends) know where you are. They don't need APRS to find you—there are several websites that will display your location. More on that in a minute.

"Path" Setting

As I mentioned earlier, digipeaters relay your packets to all the local stations, and also to all the surrounding digipeaters. Those digipeaters relay your packets again. So stations 100 or so miles away can see your location and information directly via RF. But your packets, and everyone else's, have to stop being relayed sometime, or 144.39 will be hopelessly overloaded, a problem that began to occur in the early 2000s.

To limit your relays, you load a parameter that sets how many relays your packet can have, and each digipeater reduces that number by 1 until it hits zero. Usually you want your information relayed only once or twice. The actual terminology you'll see in your software is "via WIDEn-N." This uses a parameter in the TNC called the "unproto path," which is a way to have *unconnected* packets relayed by digipeaters that otherwise would only be talking to stations that have connected to them. The "N" is the number of APRS digipeaters that should relay the packet, and the recommended number is 2 for fixed stations in metropolitan areas, and 3 for stations in very rural areas. That would look like "via WIDE2-2" for most stations.

To see a very elaborate explanation of this, and a recommendation for something called "proportional pathing" for

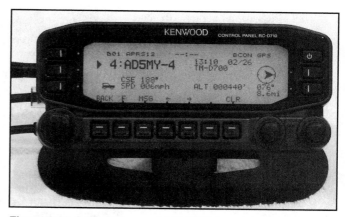

Figure 2.20 — The Kenwood RC-D710 is a control head that works with several Kenwood transceivers to add a TNC and APRS capability without an external computer. Yaesu offers a radio with similar functions.

trackers, do a web search for the phrase "fix14439" (as in fix 144.39 MHz because it was broken).

APRS on the Internet

If you zoom out on an APRS map being fed by a radio that's been monitoring for a while (an hour or so), you may see stations all across the region, not just within the range of two or three digipeaters. How did *they* get on the map?

The APRS network uses the Internet extensively for passing location information, messages and lots of other data. Somewhere near your local digipeater is one or more IGate stations that pick the signals off of local digipeaters and feed it to the APRS Internet System (APRS-IS). The *IGate* stations also send data back to the digipeater, and that's where those more distant station locations came from.

As the APRS network has become busier, IGates are sending less distant information to be relayed by RF. Instead, you can use the Internet to view APRS operation worldwide. One of the most popular is **aprs.fi** (Figure 2.19). This is an easy-to-use site that uses Google Maps to display all the APRS activity worldwide (which is too much to absorb). It lets you zoom into any area you want, and filter a variety of parameters until you see what you're looking for. It includes years of historical data, letting you look into the past for a specific station's APRS activity.

The original site for APRS on the web was **www.findu.com** and it's still in operation. It's not as easy to use as **aprs.fi**, but it has its own wealth of information.

This Internet connectivity allows you to send text messages from any APRS station to any APRS station, anywhere in the world covered by a digipeater and an IGate. And you can send a message to any e-mail address by addressing an APRS message to EMAIL, then putting the e-mail address as the first "word" of the message, and then the short text message. It would look like this:

EMAIL
then
kn4aq@arrl.net Hello, Gary. Are you going to the hamfest this weekend?

The APRS e-mail server will send you an acknowledgement, which you'll probably receive, but no guarantees.

Propagation Network (PropNET)

"If the band is open and nobody is transmitting, can anybody hear it?"

That's the question at the top of the **www.propnet.org** website. Participating PropNET stations beacon signals using packet and PSK31 (with location information) on some HF and VHF bands, including 160, 30, 10, 6 and 2 meters. Receiving stations automatically forward the data to a PropNET server, and the results are available instantly on a series of maps on the PropNET website. See **Figure 2.21**. PropNET needs all the receiving stations it can get. Perhaps you'd like to help. In any case, it's interesting to see band-opening information in real time.

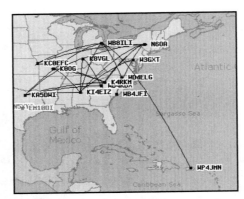

Figure 2.21 — This screen-shot from the www.propnet.org website shows a real-time view of a band opening on 10 meters.

Winlink and VHF/UHF Packet

Winlink 2000 is often thought of as a PACTOR based HF e-mail system for sailboats and RVers. But the developers of Winlink 2000, and its client programs *RMS Express*, *Airmail* and *Paclink MP* (which bridges e-mail with Winlink 2000), are eager for you to know that it is growing on VHF and UHF as well, primarily as a vehicle for ARES® and served agency related emergency communications. On VHF/UHF, the Winlink 2000 system uses packet, D-STAR, or IEEE 802.11 Wi-Fi, but not PACTOR.

A VHF/UHF Winlink 2000 system can restore e-mail operation to an EOC that has lost its Internet connection or e-mail server, if there's a TELPAC Gateway within range. (VHF/UHF stations equipped to transfer *Paclink MP* messages to the Internet are called TELPAC [TELnet-to-PACket] Gateways.) If there is no VHF/UHF system in range, or if a widespread disaster has knocked the local TELPAC out, a Winlink HF system can handle the traffic. It won't be a 5 Mbit/s connection, to be sure, but it will get e-mail moving, with limited size attachments.

In practice, a Winlink 2000 equipped EOC, Red Cross office or any other emergency venue that has lost its Internet connection from a disaster or broken e-mail server, and that is equipped with a laptop computer with *Paclink*, a TNC, and a VHF radio and antenna, may continue their emergency e-mail operation using the Winlink 2000 radio e-mail domain. *Paclink MP*, running on the agency local area network (LAN), acts like any other e-mail server. However, on the outbound side, *Paclink MP* sends the data through an automatic hierarchical routing scheme — including Telnet, IEEE 802.11 links, D-STAR, packet, or HF PACTOR — via a TNC and radio, depending on the priority set for each of the five output levels available. For the level of priority set to packet, the TNC and radio will communicate to the Winlink 2000 network through the TELPAC Gateway, which forwards it for processing to one

of the Winlink 2000 PMBOs. If the agency has an 802.11 based wireless network, a ham can provide the link from a mobile station parked outside.

As useful as this is, not enough hams know about it, and it's sometimes been hard to "sell" it to emergency management officials. But ARES groups around the country are beginning to experiment with or implement the system, as documented in articles published in *QST*. For more information, see the main Winlink 2000 website at **www.winlink.org**.

D-STAR Data

While D-STAR's digital voice capability is getting most of the attention, system operators say that the real power of D-STAR is in its data capability.

D-STAR has two very different data modes. The DV (voice) signal is part of a 4800 bit/s data stream. Of that, 2400 bit/s are used for the actual digitized voice, 1200 bit/s are used for "overhead" including forward error correction, and 1200 bit/s are going along for the ride as a data stream, called "low speed data," available to the user. D-STAR repeaters and Gateways pass the entire 4800 bit/s stream, so the data goes wherever the voice signal goes. You can send data while talking, just talk, or just send data — it's all the same signal.

To take advantage of this data stream, you need a computer and an optional interface cable, and some software. The low-speed data mode is not accessible from the radio front panel. As I mentioned earlier, the D-RATS multi-function program has become the go-to software for D-STAR data operation.

For more data power, think higher. Higher frequency, and higher speed. ICOM's 1200 MHz radio, the ID-1, supports 4800 bit/s DV with low-speed data like all the D-STAR radios, but it can also operate 128 kbit/s data through an Ethernet port on the back of the radio. ICOM calls this mode "DD." The 1200 MHz repeater rack uses a repeater for 4800 bit/s voice+data, and a separate data radio for 128 kbit/s data. The data radio shares its Internet connection with the radios in the field, and all you need to do is connect your computer to the ID-1's Ethernet port and fire up a browser. The radio appears as a network connection.

Of course 128 kbit/s is not considered "high speed" anymore. It's about double a good dial-up connection, but way below even the slowest DSL or cable connection. It is good enough for browsing sites that are not graphics-laden, but remember that all stations using the repeater are sharing that 128 kbit/s, so if several hams are pulling down data, they'll all experience a slowdown.

Emergency response agencies that are excited about having e-mail restored through ham radio will be ecstatic about having Internet browsing available. Much of the information they send and receive uses a browser interface. That capability has been used at the Marine Corps Marathon in Washington, DC, for several years, and worked well. For years, hams staffing first-aid stations along the Marathon route have been using packet to send information on patients to a command center, where the data was transferred into a database. Using D-STAR, operators in the field could tap the database directly using a browser, entering and retrieving information.

They learned a few important lessons. First, the 1200 MHz data signal is fairly wideband compared to D-STAR or FM voice (about 150 kHz wide), so it needs a stronger signal to work over a given distance. Second, you need to turn off all automatic software updates on a computer using D-STAR to reach the Internet. Myriad programs will unexpectedly launch their updates — anti-virus programs, media players, and *Windows* itself can bring the network to its knees trying to pull many huge upgrade files through the narrow pipe.

Despite the challenges, the system worked quite well and has become a permanent part of the event.

In 2012, a new company, NW Digital Radio (**www. nwdigitalradio.com**) announced a radio that can do D-STAR digital data and other packet/digital modes. It operates on 70 cm, at up to 56 kbps (half of ICOM's 1200 MHz DD rate), but it opens a new DD "world." With an add-on board, it will also do D-STAR voice, so it becomes the first non-ICOM D-STAR radio.

Are you digital yet? Right now, there's a pretty good chance that you are an "all-analog" ham. And analog isn't going away anytime soon. But more digital is on the way.

VHF/UHF — Beyond Repeaters

The radio spectrum between 30 and 3000 MHz is one of the greatest resources available to the radio amateur. The VHF and UHF amateur bands are a haven for rag chewers and experimenters alike; new modes of emission, new antennas and state-of-the-art equipment are all developed in this territory. Commercial transceivers or transverters are available for the bands through 10 GHz, and building your own gear is very popular as well. Propagation conditions may change rapidly and seemingly unpredictably, but the keen observer can take advantage of subtle clues to make the most of the bands. Most North American hams are already well acquainted with 2 meter (144 MHz) or 70 cm (440 MHz) FM. For many, channelized repeater operation is their first exposure to VHF or UHF. However, FM is only part of the VHF/UHF story! A great variety of SSB, CW and digital activity congregates on the low ends of the bands from 6 meters all the way to the end of the radio spectrum — and even to light beyond.

Steve, N2CEI, and Sandra, K4SME, used this rover station to operate from 12 grids during the 2011 ARRL June VHF Contest. They made QSOs on all bands from 6 meters through 10 GHz.

OVERVIEW

How are the Bands Organized?

One of the keys to using this immense resource properly is knowing how the bands are organized. Each of the VHF and UHF bands is many megahertz wide, huge in comparison to any HF band. Different activities take place in separate parts of each. Even in the low ends of each VHF and UHF band, where SSB, CW and digital activities congregate, there is a lot of space. Thus established and widely known *calling frequencies* help stations find each other.

By knowing the best frequencies and times to be on the air, you will have little trouble making plenty of contacts, working DX, and otherwise enjoying the world above 50 MHz. **Figure 3.1** shows suggested plans for using CW and SSB on the VHF and UHF bands.

By far the two most popular bands are 6 and 2 meters, followed by 70 cm. The 1.25 meter (222 MHz) and 33 cm (902 MHz) bands are not available worldwide. For that reason, commercial equipment is more difficult to find for these bands, and thus they are less popular.

The next two higher UHF bands at 23 cm (1296 MHz) and 13 cm (2304 MHz) are attractive, in part due to more commercial equipment being offered to meet the demands of amateur satellite operators.

There is plenty of space on the VHF and higher bands for rag chewing, experimenting, working DX and many other activities unknown to the HF world. This means that whatever you like to do — chat with your friends across town, test amateur television or bounce signals off the moon — there is

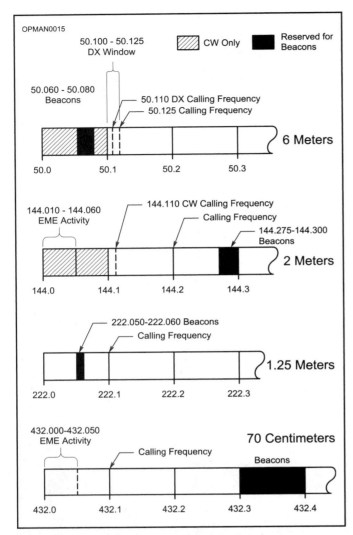

Figure 3.1 — Suggested CW and SSB usage on the most popular VHF and UHF bands. Activity on 144 MHz and higher centers around the calling frequencies.

Table 3.1
North American Calling Frequencies

Band (MHz)	Calling Frequency
50	50.090 general CW 50.110 DX only 50.125, general SSB 50.260 Digital/WSJT
144	144.110 CW 144.140 Digital/WSJT 144.200 SSB
222	222.100 CW, SSB
432	432.100 CW, SSB
902	902.100 CW, SSB 903.100 CW, SSB (East Coast)
1296	1296.100 CW, SSB
2304	2304.1 CW, SSB
10,000	10,368.1 CW, SSB

frequencies is that they are not for rag chewing. After all, if a dozen other stations want to have a place to monitor for calls, it's really impolite to carry on a long-winded conversation on that frequency.

In most areas of the country, everyone uses the calling frequency to establish a contact, and then the two stations move up or down a few tens of kHz to chat. This way, everyone can share the calling frequency without having to listen to each other's QSOs. You can easily tell if the band is open by monitoring the call signs of the stations making contact on the calling frequency — you sure don't need to hear their whole QSO!

On 6 meters, a *DX window* has been established in order to reduce interference to DX stations. This window, which extends from 50.100 to 50.125 MHz, is intended for DX QSOs only. The DX calling frequency is 50.110 MHz. If you make a DX contact and expect to rag chew, you should move up a few kHz to clear the DX calling frequency. US and Canadian 6 meter operators should use the domestic calling frequency of 50.125 MHz for non-DX work. Because of increased crowding in the low end of the band in recent years, 50.200 MHz is becoming more popular as an alternative calling frequency. Once again, when contact is established, you should move off the calling frequency as quickly as possible.

Activity Nights

Although it is possible to scare up a QSO on 50 or 144 MHz almost any evening (especially during the summer), in some areas of the country there is not always enough activity to make it easy to make a contact. Therefore, informal *activity nights* have been established so you will know when to expect some activity. Each band has its own night.

Table 3.2
Common Activity Nights

Band (MHz)	Day	Local Time
50	Sunday	6:00 PM
144	Monday	7:00 PM
222	Tuesday	8:00 PM
432	Wednesday	9:00 PM
902	Friday	9:00 PM
1296	Thursday	10:00 PM

plenty of spectrum available. VHF/UHF is a great resource!

The key to enjoyable use of this resource is to know how everyone else is using it and to follow their lead. Basically, this means to listen first. Pay attention to the segments of the band already in use, and follow the operating practices that experienced operators are using. This way, you won't interfere with ongoing use of the band by others, and you'll fit in right away.

All of the bands between 50 and 1296 MHz have widely accepted calling frequencies (see **Table 3.1**). When there is little happening on the band, these are the frequencies operators will use to call CQ. For that reason, these are also the frequencies they are likely to monitor most of the time. Many VHF operators have gotten into a habit of tuning to one or more calling frequencies while doing something else around the shack. If someone wants a contact, you will already be on the right frequency to hear the call and make a contact.

The most important thing to remember about the calling

Table 3.2 shows the most common activity nights, but there is some variation in activity nights from place to place. Check with someone in your area to find out about local activity nights.

Activity nights are particularly important for 222 MHz and above, where there are relatively few active stations on the air on a regular basis. If you have just finished a new transverter or antenna for one of these bands, you will have a much better chance to try them out during the band's weekly activity night. That doesn't mean there is no activity on other nights, especially if the band is open. It may just take longer to get someone's attention during other times.

Local VHF/UHF nets often meet during activity nights. Nets provide a regular meeting time for hams on 6 and 2 meters primarily, although there are regional nets at least as high as 1296 MHz. Several regional VHF clubs sponsor nets in various parts of the country, especially in urban areas. For those whose location is far away from the net control's location, the nets may provide a means of determining if your station is operating up to snuff, or if propagation is enhanced. Furthermore, you can sometimes catch a rare state or grid locator checking into the net. For information on the meeting times and frequencies of the nets, inquire locally.

Where Am I?

One of the first things you are bound to notice on the low end of any VHF band is that most QSOs include an exchange of grid locators. For example, instead of trying to tell a distant station, "I'm in Canton, New York," I say instead "My grid is FN24." It may sound strange, but FN24 is easier to locate on a grid locator map than my small town.

So what are these grid locators? They are 1° latitude by 2° longitude sections of the Earth. A grid locator in the center of the US is about 68 by 104 miles, but grids change size and shape slightly, depending on their latitude.

Each locator has a unique two-letter/two-number identifier. The two letters identify one of 324 worldwide fields, which cover 10° latitude by 20° longitude each. There are 100 locators in each field, and these are identified by the two numbers. Exactly 32,400 grid locators cover the entire Earth. Two additional letters can be added for a more exact location, as in FN24kp. The extra two letters uniquely identifies a locale within a few miles.

There are several ways to find out your own grid square identifier. You can start by consulting **Table 3.3** and **Table 3.4**. By following the instructions shown in the tables, you will be able to locate your own grid. The hardest part is finding your location on a good map that has latitude and longitude on it; the rest is easy. Most high-quality road maps have this on the margins. Or, you could go a step further and download the topographic map of your immediate area from the US Geological Survey (**nationalmap.gov**). Once you have your latitude and longitude, the rest is a snap!

The ARRL publishes a colorful, 27 × 39-inch Amateur Radio Map of North America (see **Figure 3.2**) that shows grid squares for the continental United States and most populated areas of Canada. This map is available from ARRL online at **www.arrl.org/shop**. If you are keeping track of grids for VUCC (the VHF/UHF Century Club award — see the **Operating Awards** chapter), you can mark each grid as you work it. The ARRL also publishes a *World Grid Locator Atlas*, available from the web catalog as well.

For more grid locator information and resources, point your browser to **www.arrl.org/grid-squares**.

Table 3.3
How to Determine Your Grid Locator

1st and 2nd characters:
Read directly from the map.

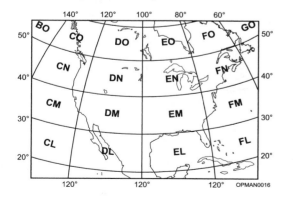

3rd character: Take the number of whole degrees west longitude, and consult the following chart.

Degrees West Longitude	Third Character	Degrees West Longitude	Third Character	Degrees West Longitude	Third Character
60-61	9	88-89	5	114-115	2
62-63	8	90-91	4	116-117	1
64-65	7	92-93	3	118-119	0
66-67	6	94-95	2	120-121	9
68-69	5	96-97	1	122-123	8
70-71	4	98-99	0	124-125	7
72-73	3	100-101	9	126-127	6
74-75	2	102-103	8	128-129	5
76-77	1	104-105	7	130-131	4
78-79	0	106-107	6	132-133	3
80-81	9	108-109	5	134-135	2
82-83	8	110-111	4	136-137	1
84-85	7	112-113	3	138-139	0
86-87	6				

4th character: This number is the same as the 2nd single digit of your latitude. For example, if your latitude is 41° N, the 4th character is 1; for 29° N, it's 9, etc.

This four-character (2-letter, 2-number) designator indicates your 2° by 1° grid locator for VUCC award purposes.

Table 3.4

More Precise Locator

To indicate location more precisely, the addition of 5th and 6th characters will define the *sub-grid*, measuring about 4 × 3 miles in the central US. Longitude-latitude coordinates on maps, such as US Department of the Interior Surveys, can be extrapolated to the nearest tenth of a minute, necessary for this level of locator precision. *This is not necessary in the VUCC awards program.*

5th character: If your number of degrees longitude is an *odd* number, see Figure A. If your number of degrees longitude is an *even* number, see Figure B.

6th character: Take the number of minutes of latitude (following the number of degrees) and consult the following chart.

Odd Longitude* (Figure A)

Minutes W. Longitude	5th Character
0-5	L
5-10	K
10-15	J
15-20	I
20-25	H
25-30	G
30-35	F
35-40	E
40-45	D
45-50	C
50-55	B
55-60	A

Even Longitude* (Figure B)

Minutes W. Longitude	5th Character
0-5	X
5-10	W
10-15	V
15-20	U
20-25	T
25-30	S
30-35	R
35-40	Q
40-45	P
45-50	O
50-55	N
55-60	M

Minutes N. Latitude	6th Character	Minutes N. Latitude	6th Character
0-2.5	A	30.0-32.5	M
2.5-5.0	B	32.5-35.0	N
5.0-7.5	C	35.0-37.5	O
7.5-10.0	D	37.5-40.0	P
10.0-12.5	E	40.0-42.5	Q
12.5-15.0	F	42.5-45.0	R
15.0-17.5	G	45.0-47.5	S
17.5-20.0	H	47.5-50.0	T
20.0-22.5	I	50.0-52.5	U
22.5-25.0	J	52.5-55.0	V
25.0-27.5	K	55.0-57.5	W
27.5-30.0	L	57.5-60.0	X

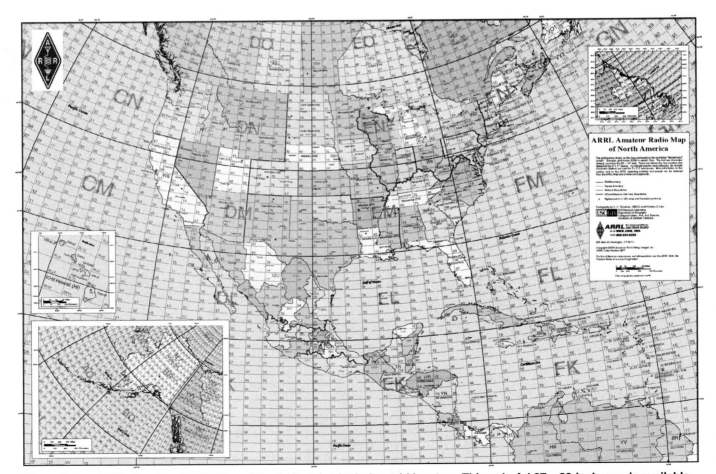

Figure 3.2 — ARRL Amateur Radio Map of North America includes grid locators. This colorful 27 × 39-inch map is available from the ARRL at www.arrl.org/shop.

PROPAGATION

Normal Conditions

What sort of range is considered normal in the world above 50 MHz? To a large extent, range on VHF is determined by location and the quality of the stations involved. After all, you can't expect the same performance from a 10 W rig and a small antenna on the roof as you might from a kilowatt and stacked beams at 100 feet.

On 2 meter SSB, a typical station probably consists of a low-powered multimode rig (SSB/CW/FM), followed by a 100 W amplifier, or one of the HF/VHF/UHF transceivers that includes SSB/CW at 50 to 100 W on this band. The antenna might be a single long Yagi at around 50 feet, fed with low-loss coax.

How far could this station cover on an average night using SSB? Location plays a big role, but it's probably safe to estimate that you could talk to a similarly equipped station about 200 miles away almost 100% of the time. Naturally, higher-power stations with tall antennas and low-noise receive preamps will have a greater range than this, up to a practical maximum of about 350-400 miles in the Midwest, less in the hilly West and East. It is almost always possible to extend your range significantly by switching from SSB to CW or a digital mode.

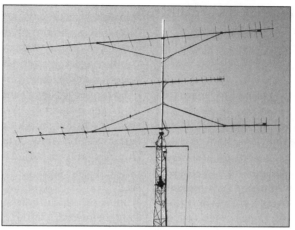
These Yagis for 144 and 432 MHz belong to Gedas, W8BYA, in grid EN70 (Indiana).

On 222 MHz, a similar station might expect to cover nearly the same distance, and perhaps 100 miles less on 432 MHz. This assumes normal propagation conditions and a reasonably unobstructed horizon. This range is a lot greater than you would get for noise-free communication on FM, and it represents the sort of capability the typical station should seek. Increase the height of the antenna to 80 feet and the range might increase to 250 miles, probably more, depending on your location. That's not bad for reliable communication!

Band Openings and DX

The main thrill of the VHF and UHF bands for most of us is the occasional band opening, when signals from far away are received as if they are next door. DX of well over 1000 miles on 6 meters is commonplace during the summer, and the same distance at least once or twice a year on 144, 222 and 432 MHz in all but mountainous areas.

DX propagation on the VHF/UHF bands is strongly influenced by the seasons. Summer and fall are definitely the most active times in the spectrum above 50 MHz, although band openings occur at other times as well.

There are many different ways VHF and UHF signals can be propagated over long distances. These can be divided between conditions that exist in the *troposphere* (the weather-producing lowest 10 miles of the atmosphere) and the *ionosphere* (between 50 and 400 miles high). The two atmospheric regions are quite distinct and have little effect on each other.

Tropospheric Ducting — or Simply "Ducting"

Ducts are responsible for the most common form of DX-producing propagation on the bands above 144 MHz. Ducts are like natural waveguides that trap signals close to the Earth for hundreds of miles with little loss of signal strength. They come in several forms, depending on local and regional weather patterns. This is because ducts are caused by the weather. Ducts may cover only a few hundred miles, or they may include huge areas of the country at once.

Radiation Inversion (mostly summer). This common type of weak duct is caused by the Earth cooling off in the evening. The air just above the Earth's surface also cools, while the air a few hundred meters above remains warm. This creates an inversion that refracts VHF/UHF radio signals. If there is little or no wind, there may be a gradual improvement in the strength of signals out to a range of 100-200 miles (less in hilly areas) as evening passes into night.

Owen, K3CB, is an active VHF/UHF operator from Maryland. The racks at the left house high power amplifiers that are helpful for contacts over marginal paths. (*K1RA* photo)

Rich, K1HTV (foreground), and Chuck, W4XP, operate a VHF contest with the K8GP team. (*K1RA photo*)

Radiation ducts mostly affect the bands above 144 MHz, and are seldom noticeable at 50 MHz.

Broad, regional ducts (late summer and early fall). These are the DXer's dream! In one of these openings, stations as far away as 1200 miles (and maybe more) are brought into range on VHF/UHF. The broad, regional type of ducting opening is caused by stagnation of a large, slow-moving high-pressure system. The stations that benefit the most are often on the south or western sides (the so-called back side) of the system. This sort of sluggish weather system may often be forecast just by looking at a weather map.

Wave-cyclone tropo (spring). These openings don't usually last long. They are brought about by an advancing cold front that interacts with the warm sector ahead of it. The resulting contrast in air temperatures may cause thunderstorms along the front. If conditions are just right, a band opening may result. These openings usually involve stations in the warm sector ahead of the cold front. You may feel that there's a pipeline between you and a DX station 1000 miles or more away. You may not be able to contact anybody else!

There are several other types of tropo openings, but space doesn't allow more than a brief discussion here. Coastal breezes sometimes cause long, narrow tropo openings along the East and Gulf Coasts. Rarely, cold fronts may cause brief openings as they slide under warmer air. US West Coast VHFers are always on the alert for the California-to-Hawaii duct that permits 2500-mile DX. For a very complete discussion of all the major forms of weather-related VHF propagation, see "The Weather That Brings VHF DX," by Emil Pocock, W3EP, in May 1983 *QST*.

The Scatter Modes

Long-distance communication on the VHF and lower UHF bands is possible using the ionosphere. Some modes are within the reach of modest stations, especially with advanced digital modes. Others require very large antennas and high power. They all have one thing in common: They take advantage of the scattering of radio waves whenever there are irregularities in the atmosphere. Very briefly, the main types are:

Tropospheric scatter. Scattering in the troposphere is actually the most common form of propagation. You use it all the time without even knowing it. Tropo scatter is what creates ordinary beyond-line-of-sight contacts every day. It is the result of scattering from blobs of air of wavelength size that have slightly different temperature or humidity characteristics than surrounding air. Maximum tropo-scatter distance is the same as your normal working distance. There is a maximum theoretical tropo-scatter distance at VHF/UHF using amateur techniques of about 500 miles, regardless of frequency.

Ionospheric forward scatter. Scattering from the D and lower reaches of the E layers propagate VHF signals from 500 to a maximum of about 1000 miles. Signals at 50 MHz are apt to be very weak and fade in and out of the noise, even for the best equipped pairs of stations. Forward scatter contacts are much rarer at 144 MHz. SSB usually is not effective. The best times are at mid-day.

Meteor scatter. When meteors enter the Earth's atmosphere, they ionize a small trail through the E layer. This ionization typically lasts only a few seconds at 50 MHz, and for even shorter periods at higher frequencies. Before it dissipates, the ionization can scatter, or sometimes reflect, VHF radio waves. Meteor scatter signals may not last long, but they can be surprisingly strong, popping suddenly out of the noise and then slowly fading away. It is quite common on 6 meters, less so on 2 meters, and rare indeed on 222 and 432 MHz. No successful QSOs have been completed at higher frequencies. Operating techniques for this mode are discussed later.

Sporadic E (E$_s$ or E-skip)

This type of propagation is the most spectacular DX-producer on the 50 MHz band, where it may occur almost every day from late May to early August. A less intense E$_s$ season also occurs during December and January. Sporadic E is most common in mid-morning and again around sunset during the summer months, but it can occur any time, any date. E$_s$ occurs on 2 meters several times a summer somewhere across the US.

E$_s$ is the result of the formation of thin but unusually dense clouds of ionization in the E layer. These clouds appear to move about, intensify, and disappear rapidly and without warning. The causes of sporadic E are not fully understood.

Reflections from sporadic-E clouds make single-hop contacts of 500 to 1400 miles possible on 50 MHz and much more rarely on 144 MHz. Sporadic E contacts are possible but very rare on 222 MHz. Multi-hop E$_s$ contacts commonly provide several coast-to-coast openings on 6 meters each summer and even opportunities to work Europe and Japan! The longest sporadic-E contacts are in excess of 6000 miles, but these are rare.

Sporadic-E signals are usually quite strong, allowing even the most modest station to make long-distance contacts. Openings may last only 15 minutes or go on all day. So far,

Testing the Limits of 6 Meter Sporadic E

The longest sporadic E contacts are in excess of 13,000 km. Some propagation experts such as Han, JE1BMJ, suspect the signal loss from that many E_s hops is too high for the distance. In 2006, Han proposed a theory called Short-Path Summer Solstice propagation where long distance 50 MHz propagation takes place via chordal type hops. This would reduce path loss as the signals would not touch the Earth. You may read his original paper online at **equina.web.fc2.com/sssp0.pdf**.

Since Han proposed his theory, it has been revised and critiqued. Some long distance E_s openings that have been studied such as Hawaii to North America in 2000 and 2009 were shown to be multi-hop E_s or nE_s (n = the number of E_s hops). Others appear to have chordal type ducting present. Gene Zimmerman, W3ZZ (SK),presented an excellent discussion of the current thoughts on extreme long distance E-Layer propagation by Jim Kennedy, KH6/K6MIO, in the "World Above 50 MHz" column in April 2011 *QST*.

The distinction between chordal ducting and nE_s long distance openings can be important. With chordal ducting, you may have no warning the band is open for extreme DX until you actually hear the DX station. An example would be JE1BMJ and JL8GFB appearing out of the blue on a dead 6 meter band during a hot summer afternoon in the Midwest. With nE_s openings, you will often hear single and double hop E_s stations before the longer distances come in. The time of day is important — the vast majority of summer openings between North America and Japan have centered around 2300 UTC. — *Jon Jones, NØJK*

---

there has been no satisfactory way to predict when these elusive openings will make their appearance, but they are exciting when they do happen.

Aurora (Au)

The aurora borealis, or northern lights, is a beautiful spectacle that is seen occasionally by those who live in Canada, the northern part of the USA and northern Europe. Similar southern lights are sometimes visible in the southernmost parts of South America, Africa and Australia. The aurora is caused by the Earth intercepting a massive number of charged particles thrown from the Sun during a solar storm. These particles are funneled into the polar regions of the Earth by its magnetic field. As the charged particles interact with the upper atmosphere, the air glows, which we see as the aurora. These particles also create an irregular, moving curtain of ionization which can propagate signals for many hundreds of miles.

Like sporadic E, aurora is more evident on 6 meters than on 2 meters. Nevertheless, 2 meter aurora is far more common than 2 meter sporadic E, at least above 40° N latitude. Auroral propagation is also possible on 222 and 432 MHz, and many tremendous DX contacts have been made on these bands. Current record distances are over 1000 miles on 144, 222 and 432 MHz.

Aurora can be predicted to some extent from current reports of solar and geomagnetic activity, which can be found on most DX clusters, on websites sponsored by the National Oceanic and Atmospheric Administration, and on WWV broadcasts. At 18 minutes past each hour, WWV transmits a summary of the condition of the Earth's geomagnetic field. If the K index is 4 or above, you should watch for Au. Many VHFers have learned that a high K index is no guarantee of an aurora. Similarly, K indices of only 3 have occasionally produced spectacular radio auroras at middle latitudes. When in doubt, point the antenna north and listen!

Several websites provide information for early warning of auroral propagation. Space Weather (**www.spaceweather. com**) and Aurora Sentry (**www.aurorasentry.com**) are two good resources for this.

Auroral DX signals are highly distorted. CW is the most practical mode, although SSB is sometimes used. Stations point their antennas generally northward and listen for the telltale hissing note that is characteristic of auroral signals. More about operating Au is presented later.

Auroral E (AuE)

Signals propagated by auroral-induced sporadic E sound very much like ordinary E-skip, but its causes and timing are quite different. Auroral E is induced by the same conditions that give rise to auroras, and like aurora, AuE is more common at northerly latitudes. Auroral E may accompany unusually strong auroras, but is more usually observed after midnight across the northern tier of states and Canada. Distances covered are similar to sporadic E.

Transequatorial Field-Aligned Irregularities (TE)

This unusual propagation mode creates paths of 2500 to 5000 miles on 50 MHz, and less commonly on 144 and 222 MHz. It involves some strict requirements. TE works only for stations equally distant from the geomagnetic equator. Common TE paths are from the Mediterranean to southern Africa, southern Japan to Australia, and the Caribbean and Venezuela to Argentina. The geomagnetic equator is displaced considerably to the south of the geographic equator in the Americas, so that only US stations from south Florida to southern California can normally make TE contacts into Argentina and Uruguay. TE-to E_s hook-ups on 50 MHz sometimes extend the possible coverage much further north.

TE appears almost exclusively in late afternoon and is more common around the March and September equinoxes, especially in years of high solar activity or when there is a geomagnetic storm. Signals have an unmistakable fluttery quality. TE is caused by two unusually dense regions of F-layer ionization that appear just north and south of the geomagnetic equator. Neither region is capable of propagating VHF signals over such long distances separately, but when linked together at the proper angles, some long north-south paths can result.

Earth-Moon-Earth (EME or Moonbounce)

This is the ultimate VHF/UHF DX medium! EME operators use the Moon as a passive reflector for their signals, and QSO distance is limited only by the diameter of the Earth. Any two stations who can simultaneously see the Moon may be able to work each other via EME. QSOs between the USA and Europe or Japan are commonplace on VHF and UHF by using this mode. That's DX!

In 2010, this group of hams activated the 1000 foot diameter antenna of the Arecibo Observatory on 432 MHz EME. (left to right) WA3FET, K1JT, WP4G in front of WP3R and NP4A. AA6EG was behind the camera.

Marc, N2UO, in North Carolina uses this homebrew 20 foot dish for 1296 MHz EME. (*N2UO photo*)

Previously the territory of only the biggest and most serious VHFers, moonbounce has now become more widely popular. Thanks to the efforts of pioneer moonbouncers such as Bob Sutherland, W6PO, and Al Katz, K2UYH, hundreds of stations are active, mainly on 144 and 432 MHz. This huge increase in activity especially by a handful of stations with gigantic antenna arrays, has encouraged many others to try making contacts via the Moon.

Improvements in technology — low-noise preamplifiers, better antenna designs and DSP-based digital modes — have made it easier to get started. Also, several individuals have assembled gigantic antenna arrays, which make up for the inadequacy of smaller antennas. The result is that even modestly equipped VHF stations (150 W and one or two Yagis) are capable of making moonbounce contacts on CW with the large stations. Activity is constantly increasing. There is even an EME contest in which moonbouncers compete on an international scale.

Moonbounce using CW requires larger antennas than most terrestrial VHF/UHF work. In addition, you must have a high-power transmitting amplifier and a low-noise receiving preamplifier to work more than the biggest guns. A modest CW EME station on 144 MHz consists of four long boom Yagi antennas on an azimuth-elevation mount (for pointing at the Moon), a kilowatt amplifier and a low-noise preamplifier mounted at the antenna. On 432 MHz, the average antenna for EME stations is eight long Yagis. You can make contacts with a smaller antenna, but they will be with only larger stations on the

The lure of DX inspires VHF operators to travel, just as it does on HF. Eltje, PA3CEE, and Rene, PE1L, brought these 2 meter antennas to Mauritius, an island in the Indian Ocean. Operating as 3B8EME, they worked 340 stations via the Moon using the JT65 digital mode.

other end. Some UHFers have also built large parabolic dish antennas.

With the introduction of DSP-based digital modes, the hardware requirements for EME are much simpler. The JT65 mode in the *WSJT* software package allows decoding of signals 10 dB or more weaker than the humans can detect. That opens the world of EME to stations with 50 to 100 W and a single antenna. (More on *WSJT* is presented later in this chapter.)

HOW DO I OPERATE ON VHF/UHF?

Normal Conditions

The most important rule to follow on VHF/UHF, like all other amateur bands, is to listen first. Even on the relatively uncrowded VHF bands, interference is common near the calling frequencies. The first thing to do when you switch on the radio is to tune around, listening for activity. Of course, the calling frequencies are the best place to start listening. If you listen for a few minutes, you'll probably hear someone make a call, even if the band isn't open. If you don't hear anyone, then it's time to make some noise yourself!

Stirring up activity on the lower VHF bands is usually just a matter of pointing the antenna and calling CQ. Because most VHF beams are rather narrow, you might have to call CQ in several directions before you find someone. Several short CQs are always more productive than one long-winded CQ. But don't make CQs too short; you have to give the other station time to turn the antenna toward you.

Give your rotator lots of exercise; don't point the antenna at the same place all the time. You never know if a new station or some DX might be available at some odd beam heading. VHFers in out-of-the-way locations, far from major cities, monitor the bands in the hope of hearing you.

Band Openings

How about DX? What is the best way to work DX when the band is open? There's no simple answer. Each main type of band opening or propagation mode requires its own techniques. This is natural, because the strength and duration of openings vary considerably. For example, you wouldn't expect to operate the same way during a 10-second meteor burst QSO as during a three-day tropo opening.

The following is a review of the different main types of propagation and descriptions of the ways that most VHFers take advantage of them.

Tropospheric Ducting

Tropospheric ducts, whatever their causes, affect the entire VHF through microwave range, although true ducting is rarely observed at 50 MHz. Ducts often persist for hours at a time, sometimes for several days, so there is usually no panic about making contacts. There is time to listen carefully and determine the extent of the opening and its likely evolution.

Ducts are most common in the Mississippi Valley during late summer and early fall, and they may expand over much of the country from the Rocky Mountains eastward. Sprawling high-pressure systems that slowly drift southeastward often create strong ducts. The best conditions usually appear in the southwestern quadrant of massive highs.

Along the East Coast, ducting is more common along coastal paths of up to 1000 miles and sometimes longer. Stations in New England have worked as far as Cuba on 2 meters this way. The mountainous west rarely experiences long-distance ducting.

This void is partially made up by one of the most famous of all ducting paths, which creates paths from the West Coast

Dave, K1RZ, is a perennial top scorer in the VHF contests. (*K1RA photo*)

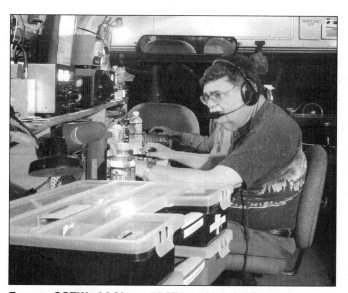

Former *QST* World Above 50 MHz columnist Gene Zimmerman, W3ZZ (SK) working the night shift at the K8GP contest station. Gene didn't just chronicle the events on the bands above 50 MHz; he was very active presence on the VHF+ bands as well. (*K1RA photo*)

Jon, WØZQ, is a regular in the ARRL 10 GHz and Up Contest each summer. (*W9FZ photo*)

to Hawaii. The famous trans-Pacific duct opens up several times a year in summer, supporting often incredibly strong signals over 2500 miles on 144 MHz through at least 5.6 GHz. Several world distance records have been made over this path. Other common over-water ducts appear across the Gulf of Mexico, mostly in early spring.

Ducts can be anticipated by studying weather maps and forecasts. Many VHFers also check television stations, especially in the UHF range, for early warnings of enhanced conditions. Check beacons on 144 MHz and higher, especially those you cannot ordinarily hear. Keep in mind that most forms of ducting intensify after sunset and peak just after sunrise. All of these techniques can enhance your chances of catching a ducting opening.

The APRS reporting network can show in real time the presence of and extent of tropospheric openings on 144 MHz (**aprs.mountainlake.k12.mn.us/**). There is an early warning system for the California-to-Hawaii duct at **dx.qsl.net/propagation/tropo.php**.

Ionospheric Forward Scatter

This mode is not used to its full potential, probably because forward scatter signals are often weak and easily overlooked. The best chances are for cooperating stations using CW in a quiet portion of the 50 or 144 MHz bands. Schedules may enhance the chances of success, but in any case, patience and a willingness to deal with weak fluttery signals is required. Contacts are sometimes completed via meteor scatter enhancement that by chance occurs at the same time.

Meteor Scatter

Meteor scatter is very widely used on 50 and 144 MHz, and it has been used on 222 and 432 as well. Operation with this exciting mode of DX comes under two main headings: prearranged schedules and random contacts. Either SSB or CW may be used, although SSB is more popular in North America. European-style high-speed CW meteor scatter

techniques, which use a computer to send and help receive Morse code sent at several hundred to several thousand characters per minute, has caught on in the US. The popular digital modes used for meteor scatter, based on *WSJT* software, are discussed in the next section.

Most SSB and CW meteor scatter work is done during major meteor showers, and stations often arrange schedules with stations in needed states or grid locators. In a sked, 15-second transmit-receive sequences are the norm for North America (Europeans use longer sequences). One station, almost always the westernmost, will take the first and third 15 second periods of each minute and the other station takes second and fourth. This is a very simple procedure that ensures that only one station is transmitting when a meteor falls. See accompanying sidebar.

A specific frequency, far removed from local activity centers, is chosen when the sked is set up. It is important that both stations have accurate frequency readout and synchronized clocks, but with today's technology this is not the big problem that it once was. Schedules normally run for ½ hour or 1 hour, especially on 222 and 432 MHz where meteor scatter QSOs are well earned!

The best way to get the feel for the meteor scatter QSO format is to listen to a couple of skeds between experienced operators. Then, ask around for the call sign of veteran meteor scatter operators in the 800-1000 mile range from you (this is the easiest distance for meteor scatter). Contact them and arrange a sked. After you cut your teeth on easy skeds, you'll be ready for more difficult DX.

A lot of stations make plenty of meteor scatter QSOs without the help of skeds. Especially during major meteor showers, VHFers congregate near the calling frequency of each band. There they wait for meteor bursts like hunters waiting for ducks. Energetic operators make repeated and brief CQs, hoping to catch an elusive meteor. When meteors blast in, the band comes alive with dozens of quick QSOs. For a brief time, normally five seconds to perhaps 30 seconds, 2 meters may sound like 20 meters! Then the band is quiet again...until the next meteor burst!

The quality of shower-related meteor scatter DX depends on three factors. These three factors are well known or can be predicted. The most important is the *radiant effect*. The radiant is the spot in the sky from which the meteors appear to fall. If the radiant is below the horizon, or too high in the sky, you will hear very few meteors. The most productive spot for the radiant is at an elevation of about 45° and an azimuth of 90° from the path you're trying to work. The second important factor is the velocity of the meteors. Slow meteors cannot ionize sufficiently to propagate 144 or 222 MHz signals, no matter how many meteors there are. For 144 MHz, meteors slower than 50 km/s are usually inadequate (see accompanying sidebar detailing major meteor showers). Third, the shower will have a peak in the number of meteors that the Earth intercepts. However, because the peak of many meteor showers is more than a day in length, the exact time of the peak is not as important as most people think. Two interesting references are "Improving Meteor Scatter Communications," by Joe Reisert, W1JR, in June 1984 *Ham Radio*, and "VHF Meteor Scatter: an Astronomical Perspective," by M. R. Owen, W9IP, in June 1986 *QST*.

It takes a lot of persistence and a good station to be successful with random meteor scatter. This is mainly because you must overcome tremendous interference in addition to the fluctuations of meteor propagation. At least 100 W is necessary for much success in meteor scatter, and a full kilowatt will help a lot. One or two Yagis, stacked vertically, is a good antenna system. Antennas with too much gain have narrow beamwidths, and so often cannot pick up many usable meteor scatter bursts.

In populated areas, it can be difficult to hear incoming meteor scatter DX if many local stations are calling CQ. Therefore, many areas observe 15 second sequencing for random meteor scatter QSOs, just as for skeds. Those who want to call CQ do so at the same time so everyone can listen for responses between transmissions. Sometimes a bit of peer pressure is necessary to keep everyone together, but it pays off in more QSOs for all. The same QSO format is used for scheduled and random meteor scatter QSOs.

Meteor Scatter with *WSJT*

It may come as a surprise to learn that meteors are plunging into Earth's atmosphere around the clock, not just during annual meteor showers. Dust-grain meteors leave so-called *underdense meteor trails* that will reflect VHF radio signals, albeit briefly (seconds or fractions of seconds). Even in this narrow window of time, it is possible to communicate with bursts of digital data over distances of more than 1000 miles.

Joe Taylor, K1JT, set out to design a digital encoding scheme and software package to enable amateur QSOs using the brief *pings* (signal reflections) from underdense meteor trails. The result led to a computer program called *WSJT* (for "Weak Signal Communication, by K1JT") that implements a signal protocol called FSK441. The mode works so well that it has been rapidly embraced by the VHF fraternities in Europe and North America, and is now making inroads in Africa and the South Pacific as well.

If your station is capable of weak signal SSB work on the 6 meter or 2 meter bands — say, if you have 100 W or more to a modest Yagi up at least 40 feet — then with the help of *WSJT* you should be able to work similarly equipped stations in the 500-1100 mile range at nearly any time of the day or year. (On the minimum end of the scale, *WSJT* QSOs have been made with as little as 10 W.) With a higher antenna and more power, QSOs out to 1300 or 1400 miles become possible. QSOs have already been made with *WSJT* on 222 MHz as well, and contacts on 432 MHz might be possible near the peak of a major meteor shower.

What Do You Need?

WSJT requires an SSB transceiver, a computer running the *Windows* operating system, and a soundcard interfaced to the radio's "microphone in" and "speaker out" ports. *Linux* versions are also available. You will, of course, need a station capable of weak signal work on one or more VHF bands. The

SSB/CW Meteor Scatter Procedure

This sidebar covers SSB/CW meteor scatter procedures. See the text for information on digital mode meteor scatter operation with WSJT.

In a meteor scatter QSO, neither station can hear the other except when a meteor trail exists to scatter or reflect their signals. The two stations take turns transmitting so that they can be sure of hearing the other if a meteor happens to fall. They agree beforehand on the sequence of transmission. One station agrees to transmit the 1st and 3rd 15 seconds of each minute, and the other station takes the 2nd and 4th. It is standard procedure for the westernmost station to transmit during the 1st and 3rd.

It's important to have a format for transmissions so you know what the other station has heard. This format is used by most US stations for CW and SSB :

Transmitting	*Means you have copied*
Call signs	nothing, or only partial calls
Call plus signal report (or grid or state)	full calls-both sets
ROGER plus signal report(or grid or state)	full calls, plus signal report (or grid or state)
ROGER	ROGER from other station

Remember, for a valid QSO to take place, you must exchange full call signs, some piece of information, and acknowledgment. Too many meteor QSOs have not been completed for lack of ROGERs. Don't quit too soon; be sure the other station has received your acknowledgment. Often, stations will add 73 when they want to indicate that they have heard the other station's ROGER.

Until a few years ago, it was universal practice to give a signal report which indicated the length of the meteor burst. S1 meant that you were just hearing pings, S2 meant 1-5 second bursts, and so on. Unfortunately, virtually everyone was sending S2, so there was no mystery at all, and no significant information was being exchanged.

Grid locators have become popular as the piece of information in meteor scatter QSOs. More and more stations are sending their grid instead of S2. This is especially true on random meteor scatter QSOs, where you might not know in advance where the station is located. Other stations prefer to give their state instead.

WSJT program is available for download free of charge at the website **physics.princeton.edu/pulsar/K1JT**.

You will need a sound card interface such as the ones discussed in the **HF Digital Communications** chapter. The DTR or RTS line of one of the computer's serial communication (COM) ports is used to key your transmitter's push-to-talk (PTT) line. Connections are also required between the transceiver audio output and computer sound card input, and

Meteor Showers

Every day, the Earth is bombarded by billions of tiny grains of interplanetary debris, called meteors. They create short-lived trails of E-layer ionization which can be used as reflectors for VHF radio waves. On a normal morning, careful listeners can hear about 3-5 meteor pings (short bursts of meteor reflected signal) per hour on 2 meters.

At several times during the year, the Earth passes through huge clouds of concentrated meteoric debris, and VHFers enjoy a meteor shower. During meteor showers, 2 meter operators may hear 50 or more pings and bursts per hour. Here are some data on the major meteor showers of the year. Other showers also occur, but they are very minor.

Major Meteor Showers

Shower	Date range	Peak date	Time above quarter max	Approximate visual rate	Speed km/s	Best Paths and Times (local)
Quadrantids	Jan 1-6	Jan 3/4	14 hours	40-150	41	NE-SW (1300-1500), SE-NW (0500-0700)
Eta Aquarids	Apr 21-May 12	May 4/5	3 days	10-40	65	NE-SW (0500-0700), E-W (0600-0900), SE-NW (0900-1100)
Arietids	May 29-Jun 19	Jun 7	?	60	37	N-S (0600-0700 and 1300-1400)
Perseids	Jul 23-Aug 20	Aug 12	4.6 days	50-100	59	NE-SW (0900-1100), SE-NW (0100-0300)
Orionids	Oct 2-Nov 7	Oct 22	2 days	10-70	66	NE-SW (0100-0300), N-S (0100-0200 & 0700-0900), NW-SE (0700-0800)
Geminids	Dec 4-16	Dec 13/14	2.6 days	50-80	34	N-S (2200-2400 and 0500-0700)

vice versa. If your computer is already set up for packet radio, APRS or one of the sound-card-based HF digital modes, you already have everything you need to operate *WSJT*.

Timing is critical when it comes to *WSJT* meteor scatter because stations typically transmit for 30 seconds and then listen for 30 seconds. You will need a method of synchronizing your computer clock with UTC to an accuracy around one second or better. If you have an Internet connection and you are using *Windows XP*, look under Date and Time in the Control Panel. There you will find a function that will synchronize your PC. Otherwise, try a synchronizing utility program called *Dimension 4* that you can download from the web at **www.thinkman.com/dimension4/**.

How Does It Work?

The encoding scheme used in *WSJT* was designed to make the best use of signals just a few decibels above the receiver noise, exhibiting rapid fading and Doppler shifts up to 100 Hz, and typically lasting from 20 to a few hundred milliseconds. One *WSJT* protocol uses a four-tone frequency shift keying at a rate of 441 baud. The adopted scheme has been given the technical name FSK441, although most people seem to be calling it simply "the *WSJT* mode."

An FSK441 transmission contains no dead spaces between tones or between characters; the typical short messages exchanged in meteor scatter QSOs are sent repeatedly and continuously, usually for 30 seconds at a time.

Figure 3.3 shows a screen-capture image of *WSJT* in operation. At the top of the form are two graphical areas. The larger one displays a "waterfall" spectrogram in which time runs left to right and audio frequency increases upward. The smaller graphical window at the right displays two spectral

plots, also on a dB scale. The purple line graphs the spectrum of audio-frequency noise, averaged over the full 30 seconds; in the absence of any strong signal, it effectively illustrates the receiver's passband shape. The red line displays the spectrum of the strongest detected ping. Yellow tick marks at the top of this plot area (and also at the left, center, and right of the larger area) indicate the nominal frequencies of the four FSK441 tones.

The large text box in the middle of the *WSJT* screen dis-

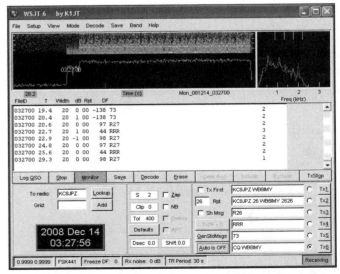

Figure 3.3 — A powerful meteor scatter burst received with *WSJT* software during the Geminids meteor shower. (*courtesy WB8IMY*)

plays decoded text from any pings detected in the receiving interval. One line of text appears for each validated ping.

Meteor scatter is not a communication mode well suited to rag chewing. QSOs can be completed much more easily if you adhere to a set of standard procedures. A standard message format and message sequence helps the process considerably. *WSJT* generates standard messages automatically, as illustrated in the text boxes at the lower right of Figure 3.3. The formats of the messages are designed for efficient transfer of the most essential information: the exchange of both call signs, a signal report or other information, and acknowledgments of same. Timed message sequences are necessary, and *WSJT* defaults to 30 second transmitting and receiving periods. Although other intervals can be selected, it helps to minimize QRM from nearby stations if everyone adheres to one standard. According to the procedures used by common consent in North America, the westernmost station transmits first in each minute.

At the start of a QSO, you should send the other station's call and your own call alternately. Then, as the QSO proceeds…

1. If you have received less than both calls from the other station, send both calls.

2. If you have received both calls, send both calls and a signal report.

3. If you have received both calls and a report, send R plus signal report.

4. If you have received R plus signal report, send RRR.

5. If you have received RRR — that is, a definite acknowledgment of all of your information — your QSO is officially complete. However, the other station may not know this, so it is conventional to send 73 (or some other conversational information) to signify that you are done.

Signal reports are conventionally sent as two-digit numbers chosen from nonoverlapping ranges. The first digit characterizes the lengths of pings being received, on a 1-5 scale, and the second estimates their strength on a 6-9 scale. The most common signal reports are "26" for weak pings and "27" for stronger ones, but under good conditions reports such as "38" and higher are sometimes used. Whatever signal report you decide to send to your QSO partner, it is important that you do not change it, even if stronger pings should come along later in the contact. You never know when pings will successfully convey fragments of your message to the other end of your path, and you want your received information to be consistent.

The 6 and 2 meter calling frequencies in common use for *WSJT* in North America are 50.260 and 144.140 MHz. Typical practice for calling CQ is to send something like CQ U5 K1JT or CQ D9 K1JT, indicating that you will listen for replies up 5 kHz or down 9 kHz from your transmitting frequency, and will respond on that frequency. However, the easiest way to initiate a QSO is to post an online invitation on a web page known as Ping Jockey Central at **www. pingjockey.net/**. Someone at a suitable range from you will likely reply to such a posting, suggesting a specific frequency, and your QSO can begin. The ranges of frequencies now being used for *WSJT* in North America are 50.270-50.300 and 144.100-144.150 MHz.

More WSJT Modes

The latest version of *WSJT* also offers JT65 (**Figure 3.4**), a digital mode for moonbounce communication, and JT6M, a mode designed primarily for 6 meter ionospheric scatter work. For complete details and more in-depth operating instructions, go to **physics.princeton.edu/pulsar/K1JT**.

Sporadic E

Sporadic-E signals are generally so loud and openings last long enough that no special operating techniques are necessary to enjoy this mode. On 6 meters, 10 W stations with simple antennas can easily make contacts out to 1000 miles or so. The band may open for hours on any summer day, with signals constantly shifting, disappearing and reappearing. A sporadic-E opening on 2 meters is much less common and typically lasts for less than an hour. Signals out to 1000 miles or so can be unbelievably strong, yet there is reason to be more alert. E-skip openings on 2 meters are rare and do not usually last long.

The main question for those hoping for sporadic E is when the band will open. Aside from knowing sporadic E is more common in summer mornings and early evenings than any other times, there is no satisfactory way to predict E-skip. It can appear any time.

Sporadic E affects lower frequencies first, so you can get some warning by listening to 10 meters. When E-skip shortens to 500 miles or so, it is almost certain that there is propagation somewhere on 6 meters. Some avid E-skip fans monitor TV channel 2 or 3 (if there is no local station) for signs of sporadic E.

Aurora and Auroral E

Aurora favors stations at high latitudes. It is a wonderful blessing for those who must suffer through long, cold winters

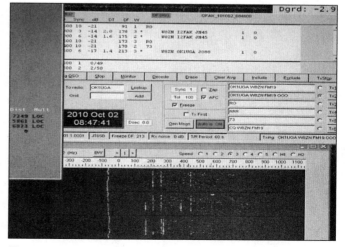

Figure 3.4 — JT65 in use at W8ZN during an EME contest. (*K1RA* photo)

This stack of Yagis is responsible for the potent 6 meter signal from the station of Dave, K1WHS, in Maine. (*K1WHS photo*)

During the peak years of the solar cycle, worldwide DX on 6 meters is possible via F layer propagation. During the 2001 solar peak, Holly, NØQJM, and Arliss, W7XU, traveled to Easter Island (CEØY) and put a "New One" into the logs of 6 meter DXers worldwide. (*W7XU photo*)

because other forms of propagation are rare during the winter. Aurora can come at almost any time of the year. New England stations get Au on 2 meters about five to 10 times a year, whereas stations in Tennessee get it once a year if they're lucky. Central and Southern California rarely hear aurora.

The MUF of the aurora seems to rise quickly, so don't wait for the lower-frequency VHF bands to get exhausted before moving up in frequency. Check the higher bands right away.

You'll notice aurora by its characteristic hiss. Signals are distorted by reflection and scattering off the rapidly moving curtain of ionization. They sound like they are being transmitted by a leaking high-pressure steam vent rather than radio. SSB voice signals are so badly distorted that often you cannot understand them unless the speaker talks very slowly and clearly. The amount of distortion increases with frequency. Most 50 MHz Au contacts are made on SSB, where distortion is the least. On 144, 222 and 432 MHz, CW is the only really useful means of communicating via Au.

If you suspect Au, tune to the CW calling frequency (144.110) or the SSB calling frequency (144.200) and listen with the antenna to the north. Maybe you'll hear some signals. Try swinging the antenna as much as 45° either side of due north to peak signals. In general, the longest-distance DX stations peak the farthest away from due north. Also, it is possible to work stations far south of you by using the aurora; in that case your antenna is often pointed north.

High power isn't necessary for aurora, but it helps. Ten-watt stations have made Au QSOs but it takes a lot of perseverance. Increasing your power to 100 W will greatly improve your chances of making Au QSOs. As with most short-lived DX openings, it pays to keep transmissions brief.

Aurora openings may last only a few minutes or they may last many hours, and the opening may return the next night, too. If WWV indicates a geomagnetic storm, begin listening on 2 meters in the late afternoon. Many spectacular Au openings begin before sunset and continue all evening. If you get the feeling that the Au has faded away, don't give up too soon. Aurora has a habit of dying and then returning several times, often around midnight. If you experience a terrific Au opening, look for an encore performance about 27 to 28 days later, because of the rotation of the Sun.

Auroral-E propagation is nearly a nightly occurrence in the auroral zone, but it may accompany auroras at lower latitudes. Do not be surprised to hear rough-sounding auroral signals on 6 meters slowly turn clear and strong! Auroral E is probably more common after local midnight after any evening when there has been an aurora. Auroral E propagation can last until nearly dawn. Six meter contacts up to 2500 miles across northern latitudes (such as Maine to Yukon Territory) are not uncommon. Two meter auroral E may also be commonplace in the arctic, but it is very rarely observed south of Canada.

PROPAGATION INDICATORS

The Internet is a great resource for keeping abreast of VHF/UHF band openings. In addition to the DX Cluster spotting network, there are several VHF-specific websites such as the ON4KST chat rooms (**www.on4kst.com**) and DX Sherlock (**www.vhfdx.info**).

Active VHFers keep a careful eye on various propagation indicators to tell if the VHF bands will be open. The kind of indicator you monitor is related to the expected propagation. For example, during the summer it pays to watch closely for sporadic E because openings may be very brief. If your area only gets one or two per year on 2 meters, you sure don't want to miss them!

Many forms of VHF/UHF propagation develop first at low frequency and then move upward to include the higher bands. Aurora is a good example. Usually it is heard first on 10 meters, then 6 meters, then 2 meters. Depending on your location and the intensity of the aurora, the time delay between hearing it on 6 meters and its appearance on 2 meters may be only a few minutes, to as much as an hour, later. Still, it shows up first at low frequency. The same is true of sporadic E; it will be noticed first on 10 meters, then 6, then 2.

Tropospheric propagation, particularly tropo ducting, acts in just the reverse manner. Inversions and ducts form at higher frequencies first. As the inversion layer grows in thickness, it refracts lower and lower frequencies. Even the most avid VHF operator may not notice this sequence because of lower activity levels on the higher bands. It may be true that ducting affects the higher bands before the lower ones, but it is more likely to be noticed first on 2 meters, where many more stations are normally on the air. Six meter tropo openings are very rare because few inversion layers ever develop sufficient thickness to enhance such long-wavelength signals.

How can you monitor for band openings? The best way is to take advantage of commercial TV and FM broadcast stations, which serve admirably as propagation beacons. Television Channels 2 through 6 (54-88 MHz) are great for catching sporadic E. As the E opening develops, you will see one or more stations appear on each channel. First, you may see Channel 2 get cluttered with stations 1000 miles or more away, then the higher channels may follow. If you see strong DX stations on Channel 6, better get the 2 meter rig warmed up. Channel 7 is at 175 MHz, so you rarely see any sporadic E there or on any higher channels. If you do, however, it means that a major 2 meter opening is in progress!

The gap between TV Channel 6 and 7 is occupied partly by the FM broadcast band (88-108 MHz). Monitoring that spectrum will give you a similar feel for propagation conditions.

Several amateurs have built converters to monitor TV video carrier frequencies. A system like this can be used to keep track of meteor showers. It's a way of checking to tell if meteors are plentiful or not, even if there appears to be little activity on the amateur VHF bands. It also can alert you to aurora and sporadic E.

The Internet provides VHF+ DXers with access to real-time propagation prediction tools only dreamt of in the past. This DX Sherlock map shows a 50 MHz opening in July 2011. (*Courtesy DX Sherlock/EA6VQ*)

EME: EARTH-MOON-EARTH

EME, or moonbounce, is available any time the Moon is in a favorable position. Fortunately, the Moon's position may be easily calculated in advance, so you always know when this form of DX will be ready. It's not actually that simple, of course, because the Earth's geomagnetic field can play havoc with EME signals as they leave the Earth's atmosphere and as they return. Not only can absorption (path loss) vary, but the polarization of the radio waves can rotate, causing abnormally high path losses at some times. Still, most EME activity is predictable.

The most popular band for EME is 144 MHz, followed by 432 MHz. Other bands with regular EME activity are 1296 and 2304/2320 MHz. You will find many more signals off the Moon during times when the Moon is nearest the Earth (perigee), when it is overhead at relatively high northern latitudes (positive declination), and when the Moon is nearly at full phase. The one weekend per month which has the best combination of these three factors is informally designated the activity or skeds weekend, and most EMEers will be on the air then. This is particularly true for 432 EME; 144 MHz EME is active during the week and on non-skeds weekends as well.

CW EME Procedures

The majority of CW EME QSOs are made without any prearranged schedules and usually without rigid transmitting time-slot sequencing. Just as in CW QSOs on HF, you transmit when the other station turns it over to you. This is particularly true during EME contests, where time-slot transmissions slow down the exchange of information. Why take 10-15 minutes when two or three will do?

Moonbounce procedure for scheduled CW QSOs is different on 144 and 432 MHz. On 144 MHz, schedule transmissions are 2 minutes long, whereas on 432 they are 2½ minutes long. In addition, the meaning of signal reports is different on the two bands (see **Table 3.5**). Note that M reports aren't good enough for a valid QSO on 2 meters but they are good enough on 432. On both bands, if signals are really good, then normal RST reports are exchanged.

On 144 MHz, each station transmits for 2 minutes, then listens as the other station transmits. Which 2-minute sequence you transmit in is agreed to in advance. During the schedule, at the point when you've copied portions of both calls, the last 30 seconds of your 2-minute sequence is reserved for signal reports; otherwise, call sets are transmitted for the full 2 minutes.

On 432 MHz, sequences are longer. Each transmitting slot is 2½ minutes. You either transmit first or second. Naturally, first means that you transmit for the first 2½ minutes of each 5 minutes.

On 222 MHz, some stations use the 144 MHz procedure and some use the 432 MHz procedure. Which one is used is determined in advance. On 1296 and above, the 432 procedure is always used.

EME operation generally takes place in the lowest parts of the VHF bands: 144.000-144.070; 222.000-222.025; 432.000-432.070; 1296.000-1296.050. Terrestrial QSOs are strongly discouraged in these portions

Table 3.5
CW EME Signal Report and Meaning

Report	144 MHz	432 MHz
T	Signal just detectable	Portions of calls copyable
M	Portions of calls copyable	Complete calls copied
O	Both calls fully copied	Good signal, easily copied
R	Both calls and O signal report copied	Calls and report copied

Bob, KD3UY, used this simple antenna and the JT65 digital mode to make contacts on 2 meter EME. He wrote about his experience in "Moonbounce on a Budget" in January 2011 *QST*. (*KD3UY photo*)

Ty, K3MM (foreground), and Terry, W8ZN, working EME on 2 meters using JT65. (*K1RA photo*)

of the bands. Activity on 10 GHz EME, which requires only a few watts when used with dish antennas 10 feet or more in diameter, is becoming increasingly popular.

Digital Modes for EME

As with meteor scatter, digital modes have appeared for EME as well. The *WSJT* software suite includes a mode known as JT65. This software has made moonbounce contacts possible using sound-card-equipped PCs, single Yagi antennas and 150 W or less — a feat that seemed impossible just a few years earlier. It is possible that JT65, and digital modes that will likely appear in the future, will finally put EME communication within the grasp of amateurs with limited antenna space and equally limited bank accounts. For more information, see **physics.princeton.edu/pulsar/k1jt**, **www. dxmaps.com/jt65bintro.html** and **www.bigskyspaces. com/w7gj/6memetips.htm**.

HILLTOPPING AND PORTABLE OPERATION

One of the nice things about the VHF/UHF bands is that antennas are relatively small, and station equipment can be packed up and easily transported. Portable operation, commonly called hilltopping or mountaintopping, is a favorite activity for many amateurs. This is especially true during VHF and UHF contests, where a station can be very popular by being located in a rare grid. If you are on a hilltop or mountaintop as well, you will have a very competitive signal. See accompanying sidebar for further information.

Hilltopping is fun and exciting because hills elevate your antenna far above surrounding terrain and therefore your VHF/UHF range is greatly extended. If you live in a low-lying area such as a valley, a drive up to the top of a nearby hill or mountain will have the same effect as buying a new tower and antenna, a high-power amplifier and a preamplifier, all in one!

The popularity of hilltopping has grown as equipment has become more portable. There are many high power, good performing HF + 6 meter radios on the market such as the ICOM IC-7410, Yaesu FT-950, Kenwood TS-590S, Elecraft K3 and Ten-Tec 599 Eagle to name a few. These transceivers operate from a 13.8 V dc supply, have about 100 W output on 6 meters and are small enough for portable use. Other models offer 25 W up to 75 or 100 W on 144 and 432 MHz, and a couple even cover 1296 MHz with optional modules. You need no other power source than a car battery, and even with

Bruce, W9FZ, is a frequent "rover" in VHF contests. (*W9FZ photo*)

Matt, KC3WD, at the controls of his rover station. He once called roving "an exercise in sleep deprivation." (*K1RA photo*)

VHF Hilltopping

Operating from high locations in the clear is as old as VHF operating itself. In 1934, Ross Hull erected a directive antenna at Seldon Hill in West Hartford, Connecticut, home to several members of the League headquarters staff. He immediately made contact with Boston area hams, some 100 miles distant. Over the next few weeks, it became obvious to Hull and others that routine contacts on the 5 meter band were possible far beyond the line of sight. Hull wrote of his experiments in *QST*, describing how his "hilltopping" extended his range.

Many present-day amateurs are not able to put up antennas that can "command a frequency" from home. However, as Ross Hull learned so many years ago, taking a station to a high mountain or even just a clear hilltop can often produce a booming signal. High above home stations, with clear views of the horizon and no local noise, a 100 W transceiver and small Yagi antenna can perform as well as — or sometimes better than — a kilowatt feeding a large antenna down in the city. With modern compact solid-state amplifiers, it's easier than ever to bring 500 W or more to a portable location.

I can recall starting in VHF with tube-type radios from Gonset and Swan. Portable operation with these heavy radios and the required large ac generators meant lugging hundreds of pounds of gear up steep hillsides. Nowadays, 100 W solid state radios weigh but a few pounds, operate from a car battery, and allow easy portable operation on 50 MHz through 432 MHz. Add solid-state transverters and the band choices extend up through the microwaves.

Location, Location, Location

This is important. If you are planning to make portable operation your primary mode of getting on the air, you need to find a site within a reasonable drive, say an hour or two. To explore potential sites, look at topographic maps or Google maps within that range of home. You need to check for access roads, the condition of the access roads (four-wheel drive required?) and potential hazards.

Next you need to figure out whom to contact for access. Be sure you have secured permission from the landowner or government agency in charge. This may be simple verbal permission (which I received for the "Cattle Pens" in the Flint Hills) or written permission from the state or national agency (such as a park service) in charge of the facility. Written permission is preferred. Permission to use sites near telecommunications equipment or military bases may be more difficult to secure.

You need to check out the site first before operating from it. Take a weekend to drive up after performing your preliminary research first. One way to test a site is to bring a 2 meter handheld and key up repeaters in the area. This can give an idea of how well the site plays. Listen for interference. Some good sites may already have commercial services or cell towers. Are there trees around? Foliage absorbs signals on 432 MHz and up. "Bald knobs" such as those found in Arkansas are better than hills covered with trees, although trees aren't as much of a problem on 6 meters.

Your Station

The first consideration is power. Some park sites may already have 120 V outlets in the area. That makes it easy. Other sites may require you to carry batteries to run the radios. Two sites I use are accessible by car, and I run the radios from the car battery. For contests or other prolonged operating periods, a small gasoline-powered generator along with batteries is a great power source. *QST* has reviewed several inverter generators that are small and light enough for hilltopping.

Some 20 years ago, typical portable stations used a 10 W or 25 W multimode transceiver and a "brick" (solid state 100 W amplifier). Some models worked on a single band, while others covered three or four bands. These older radios and brick amplifiers may be found at hamfests or on Internet swap sites and can provide an introduction to VHF/UHF operation.

There are many modern radios that work great portable, and you may already have one in your station. I have used the ICOM IC-706MkII (50 and 144 MHz) and the Yaesu FT-897 (50, 144 and 432 MHz) which work great in this setting. The Yaesu FT-817 and FT-857, Kenwood TS-590S, Ten-Tec Eagle and Elecraft K3 radios are good choices as well. The ICOM IC-9100 and Kenwood TS-2000 cover 6, 2 and 432 MHz and can work with on 1296 MHz with optional modules. The modern radios are usually 100 W on 6 meters, 50 to 100 watts on 2 meters and 25 to 75 W on 70 cm.

You often don't need an amplifier, but if you opt for higher power there are several solid-state models available, including 500 to 1500 W 6-meter solid-state amplifiers from M² and Tokyo Hy-Power.

Antennas

As for antennas, suitable models are available from M², Directive Systems, Cushcraft and other vendors. Although horizontally polarized omnidirectional antennas are available (usually loops of some sort) loop, I would recommend starting with a 3 element Yagi on 6 meters. For the higher bands, Yagis with boom lengths of 10 feet or less work well and are easier to manage. If you want to build an antenna yourself, the Quagi is a good portable antenna. See **commfaculty.fullerton.edu/woverbeck/quagi.htm**. Kent Britain, WA5VJB, has some great designs for a variety of bands (see **www.wa5vjb.com/yagi-pdf/cheapyagi.pdf**).

You may put the antennas up on 5 or 10 foot sections of TV mast and guy them as shown in Figure 3.5. The key is to come up with something that is easy to carry and erect. I use the 5 foot sections because they will fit inside of a car. A 2 foot cross piece of aluminum tubing mounted with U-bolts can help turn the antenna. I have also used fence posts to support the mast. Lash it firmly in several places or the wind will turn it.

In a tropo opening or contest, you may wish to move stations from band to band. Thus it's a

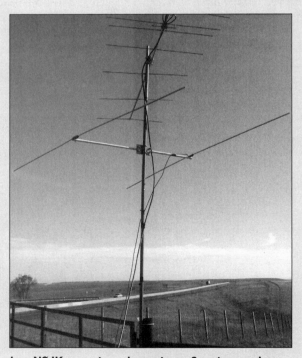

Jon, NØJK, uses two elements on 6 meters and seven elements on 2 meters hilltopping. Small antennas are easy to erect and rotate from most portable locations. (*NØJK photo*)

The "portable extreme" 6 and 2 meter antennas used by Mike, K7ULS, take hilltopping to a higher level. (*K7ULS photo*)

good idea to put antennas for 222, 432 and higher bands on the same mast as the 2 meter Yagi. A station is often worked on 2 meters first, so the antenna can be "peaked up" before moving to a higher frequency band such as 432 MHz where the antenna beamwidth is narrower. A 6 meter antenna can be on its own mast.

Of course, some operators bring larger antennas on their portable adventures. For example, Mike, K7ULS, even works EME portable while mountaintopping in Utah.

Creature Comforts

Most of my hilltopping is done for a few hours at a time. You will want to bring along water, soda, coffee, snacks or whatever food and drink you prefer. If you are staying overnight, a van or RV is helpful. Some operators also set up tents or tarps, though these can come down in high winds. If you like being outdoors, the camping aspects can be as appealing as operating the radio. Cooking burgers on the fire under the canopy of stars and seeing meteor trails is some of the fun.

Even though you might be operating portable in June or July, don't expect the same T-shirt weather on the hilltop that you have at home. Be sure to bring heavier clothing — jacket, long pants, long sleeve shirt and so on — particularly if you are operating after dark. Also, don't forget bug spray, sunscreen and a hat, and to watch for ticks. Be very aware of the weather forecast and any local thunderstorm activity. The high location may put you at increased risk for lightning strikes. If you see lightning or hear thunder, it's time to stop operating and seek shelter until the storm passes. Your car can protect you.

What's Next?

By now you may be thinking, "I can do this. It sounds like fun — let's give it a try!" As with most new activities, start out slowly. Consider setting up on an easily accessible area during the afternoon of a VHF contest on either 6 or 2 meters and using one of the 13.8 V transceivers mentioned above. I'd recommend 6 meters in the ARRL June VHF Contest or the CQ Worldwide VHF Contest in July. Two meters is busy in the ARRL September VHF Contest.

Bring a single small Yagi and perhaps 15 or 20 feet of mast. Practice setting up the antenna in your backyard to be sure you have all the needed hardware and can manage the installation on your own.

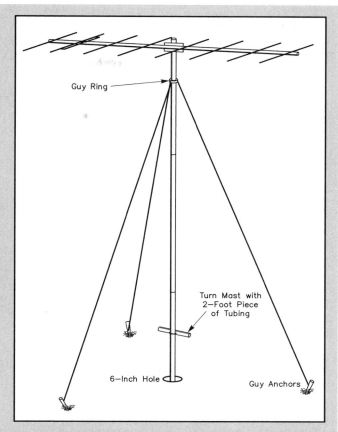

Figure 3.5 — A portable mast, assembled from interlocking sections of aluminum tubing or commercial mast, can raise one or two small Yagis to a height of 25 feet. The mast is rotated by hand.

Once you are set up, you may be able to make many contacts hundreds of miles away. I have worked DX stations on 6 meters while operating portable, most recently JW7QIA in June 2012 from my portable site west of Lawrence, Kansas. It is great to be working DX and enjoying the outdoors.

There are some disadvantages to depending on portable operation rather than a home station. On the DX cluster you may see some good DX spotted in your area, but it will take some time to drive to the portable site and set up. Some VHF/UHF openings are short-lived, and it can be frustrating to go to all the effort to set up and then find that the DX is gone.

Sometimes you can anticipate an opening. For example, you might see that stations east of you are working Europe on sporadic E. You can set up your portable station and the opening may have reached your area by the time you are ready. Tropo and aurora propagation is also predictable to a degree using modern Internet sites such as the tropo maps at **www.dxinfocentre.com** or solar data at **www.spaceweather.com**. With the latest generation of smart phones and tablets, it's easier than ever to access DX cluster spots and VHF/UHF chat sites in the field. Although these tools are a big help in finding DX, operating portable is like fishing: sometimes you will go out and not catch anything. Other times, you fill your log.

Be sure to take time to enjoy being outdoors while you are there. I find being out in the Flint Hills is peaceful and relaxing. Even if I do not work anything good on the radio, the time is well spent. — *Jon Jones, NØJK* a simple antenna your signals will be outstanding.

Many VHF/UHFers drive to the top of hills or mountains and set up their station. A hilltop park, rest area or farmer's field are equally good sites, so long as they are clear of trees and obstructions. You should watch out for high-power FM or TV broadcasters who may also be taking advantage of the hill's good location; their powerful signals may cause inter-modulation problems in your receiver.

Antennas, on a couple of 10-foot mast sections, may be turned by hand as the operator sits in the passenger seat of the car. A few hours of operating like this can be wonder-fully enjoyable and can net you a lot of good VHF/UHF DX. In fact, some VHF enthusiasts have very modest home stations but rather elaborate hilltopping stations. When they notice that band conditions are improving, they hop in the car and head for the hills. There, they have a really

excellent site and can make many more QSOs.

In some places, there are no roads to the tops of hills or mountains where you might wish to operate. In this case, it is a simple (but sometimes strenuous) affair to hike to the top, carrying the car battery, rig and antenna. Many hilltoppers have had great fun by setting up on the top of a fire tower on a hilltop, relying on a battery for power.

Some VHF/UHFers, especially contesters, like to take the entire station, high power amplifiers and all, to hilltops for extended operation. They may stay there for several days, camping out and DXing. Probably the most outstanding ex-ample of this kind of operation is seen during VHF contests, from stations operating in the multioperator category. Dozens of operators and helpers bring equipment for 6 meters through microwaves to the highest mountaintops and contact every-one within range.

CONTESTS

The greatest amount of activity on the VHF/UHF bands occurs during contests. VHF/UHF contests are scheduled for some of the best propagation dates during the year. Not only are propagation conditions generally good, but activity is always very high. Many stations come out of the woodwork just for the contest, and many individuals and groups go hill-topping to rare states or grids.

A VHF/UHF contest is a challenging but friendly battle between you, your station, other contesters, propagation and Murphy's Law. Your score is determined by a combination of skill and luck. It is not always the biggest or loudest station that scores well. The ability to listen, switch bands quickly and to take advantage of rapidly changing propagation condi-tions is more important than brute strength.

There are quite a few contests for the world above 50 MHz. Some are for all the VHF and UHF bands, while others are for one band only. Some run for entire weekends and others for only a few hours. Despite their differences, all contests share a basic similarity. In most North American con-tests, your score is determined by the number of contacts (or more precisely, the number of QSO points) you make, times some multiplier, which is most often grid locators. In most of the current major contests, you keep track of QSOs and multipliers by band. In other words, you can work the same station on each band for separate QSO and multiplier credit.

Listed below are the major VHF through microwave con-tests in North America. Other contests are popular in Europe and Asia, but these are not listed here because information about them is not usually available to most of us. All the listed contests are open to all licensed amateurs, regardless of their affiliation with any club or organization. Contests are announced in *QST*, *CQ* and online contest calendars. See the contest sponsor's website for detailed rules. For more informa-tion about contesting, see the **Contesting** chapter of this book.

1) *ARRL January VHF Contest*: This contest is a long-time favorite of clubs because it permits club members to

Dave, KM3T, is active in VHF contests as well as HF events. Here he's operating with the K8GP team from Spruce Knob in West Virginia. (*K1RA photo*)

pool their individual scores for the club's total. In addition, individuals and multioperator groups compete. Scores are determined by total QSO points per band multiplied by the number of grid squares worked per band. Activity is quite high during this midwinter contest, even though propagation conditions are often poor.

2) *ARRL June VHF Contest*: This contest is the highlight of the contest season for most VHFers. Scheduled for the second full weekend of June, the June VHF Contest is often the most exciting of the major contests. Conditions on all the VHF bands are usually good, with 6 meters leading the way. This contest covers all the VHF and UHF bands, and QSOs and multipliers are accumulated for each band. Score is determined by multiplying QSO points per band by grid locators per band. Single band and multiband awards are

Portable operation is always popular in the VHF/UHF contests. Stu, WØSTU, braved the elements to put this modest station for 50, 144 and 432 MHz on the air from grid DM79 in Colorado during the January VHF Contest. (*NØOLD photo*)

The June VHF Contest often brings some excitement in the form of sporadic E openings and good DX. If the band is open, listen for Zalo, XE3N, from grid EL60 in Mexico. (*XE3N photo*)

given to high-scoring individuals in each ARRL section. In addition, multioperator groups compete against each other, and the competition can be fierce!

3) *CQ Worldwide VHF Contest*: This contest is international in scope and is usually held over a July weekend on 6 and 2 meters. Score is the number of different grid locators worked per band, times the number of QSO points per band. A multitude of awards are available.

4) *ARRL UHF Contest*: As its name suggests, this contest is restricted to the UHF bands (plus 222 MHz). It takes place over a full weekend in August. All UHF bands are permitted, and grids are the multiplier. Less equipment is involved for this contest than for contests which cover all VHF/UHF bands, so many groups go hilltopping for the UHF Contest.

5) *ARRL September VHF Contest*: The rules for this contest are identical to those for the ARRL June VHF Contest. By the second weekend of September, most 6 meter sporadic E has disappeared, but tropo conditions are often extremely good. Therefore, the bands at 144 MHz and above are more active during the September contest. Some of the best tropo openings of recent decades have taken place during this contest, and they are made even better by the high level of activity.

6) *ARRL 10-GHz and Up Cumulative Contest*: Yes, there is a contest for those hardy souls who inhabit the microwave world of 10 GHz and higher. It takes place over two late summer weekends. Operators who change their locations during the contest may work the same stations over again. Scoring is the cumulative total of QSO points and distance of each contact in kilometers, for each band used. This is great fun, as nearly all participants head for their favorite hilltops and mountaintops for maximum range.

7) *ARRL EME Contest*: This contest is devoted to moonbounce. It takes place over several weekends, usually in the fall, with one weekend reserved for 2304 MHz and up and two weekends for 50-1296 MHz. The date of the contest is different each year because of the variable phase of the Moon. The dates are usually chosen by active moonbouncers to coincide with the best combination of high lunar declination, perigee and the full phase of the Moon. This contest is international in scope. Score is the number of QSO points made via EME per band, multiplied by the number of US call districts and ARRL countries per band. You can enter using analog modes, digital modes, or a combination of both. Hundreds of EMEers participate in this challenging test of moonbounce capability.

Contests are lots of fun, whether you're actively competing or not. You don't have to be a full-time competitor to participate or to enjoy yourself! Most participants are not really competing in the contest, but they get on the air to pass out points, to have fun for awhile, and to listen for rare DX. Others try their hardest for the entire contest, keep track of their score and send their logs in for awards. Either way, the contest is a fun challenge.

If you don't plan on being a serious competitor, then you just need to know the exchange. The exchange is the minimum information that must be passed between each station to validly count the QSO in the contest. In all of the terrestrial VHF contests sponsored by the ARRL you need only send and receive calls and grids, with acknowledgments each way. Other contests require some different information, such as serial numbers or signal reports, so it pays to check the rules to make sure.

A serious contest effort requires dedication and effort, as well as a station that can withstand a real workout. Contests are a challenge to operators and equipment alike. A good contest score is the result of hard work, a good station and favorable propagation. A good score is something to be proud of, especially if there is lots of stiff competition. And with the popularity of VHF and UHF contests these days, competition is always stiff!

Serious contesting requires using a computer logging program. Several are available through vendors who advertise in *QST*, *NCJ* and other journals. Laptop computers are favored because they tend to produce less interference to the VHF bands and they are easier to take on portable operations. You can submit your log electronically via e-mail or on a disk. Check the current contest rules for exact requirements.

Many operators don't feel that their stations are competitive on all the VHF and UHF bands. This is no problem. You can contest on one, two, or as many bands as you like. Indeed, some contesters specialize. Most contest results recognize achievements on each band separately. This has the advantage of concentrating your efforts where your station is the strongest, allowing you to devote full time to just one band. You don't need to be high powered to compete as a single-band entry. Location makes a lot of difference, and hilltopping single-banders have had tremendous success, particularly if they go to a rare grid square.

Other operators like to try for all-band competition. In this case, it's a real advantage to be able to hop from one band to another. You can quickly check 6 meters for activity while also tuning 2 meters. Or, if you work a rare grid on one band, you can take advantage of the opportunity by asking the other station to switch bands right then. Some contesters work one station on all possible bands within two minutes by band hopping! This is a speedy way to increase your grids and QSOs.

There are several other entry classes for the major VHF contests and variations on these classes in other events. (Check the rules for each contest, as entry classes vary somewhat.) Multioperator entries involve more than one operator. Many large multioperator efforts have operating positions for a dozen or more separate bands. Now that is an effort to put together! If your group is not ready for the big time, limited multioperator entries submit scores for four bands only.

In either case, successful multiop stations have learned to work cooperatively. The ability to operate simultaneously on several bands without mutual interference is important. Multiop efforts also have a foolproof system for passing messages from one operating position to another, especially referrals of a station from one band to another. If the operator of the 2 meter station in a multioperator entry works WØVD, for example, that operator may suggest immediately moving to 222 MHz and then 432 MHz. A message has to be sent to the operators at the 222 and 432 MHz positions to expect a call from WØVD at a particular frequency and time. Handwritten notes are simple and convenient if the operating positions are close together. Several logging programs have sophisticated features to pass messages among several computers that are networked together.

The rover class allows a station with one or two operators to move among two or more grid locators during the contest. Rovers may contact the same stations all over again from a different grid. Most rovers operate from a car, van or truck specially equipped for convenience and efficiency. Hilltops in rare grids are favored rover sites. Rovers must move the entire station, antennas and power supply to qualify. Special scoring rules apply to rovers.

Other popular entry classes appeal to single operators who contest with modest stations. The limited single operator does not limit the number of bands you may operate, but does place maximum power limits on each band. The single-operator QRP class limits power output on all bands to a maximum of 10 W. Stations must run on a portable power source and may not be located at fixed or home locations.

Jim, KK6MC, used this simple rover setup to visit many rare grids in the Southwest. (*KK6MC photo*)

SOURCES OF INFORMATION

Many VHF/UHF operators like to keep abreast of the latest happenings on the bands such as new DX records, band openings or new designs for equipment. There are many excellent sources for current information about VHF/UHF. In addition, they provide a way to share ideas and ask questions, and for newcomers to become familiar with operation above 50 MHz. Information sources include nets, newsletters, published columns, websites and e-mail lists (also known as e-mail "reflectors"). You can find links to a number of VHF/UHF resources at **www.arrl.org/the-world-above-50-mhz**.

Nets

Several nets meet regularly on the HF and VHF bands so that VHF/UHFers can chat with each other. These are listed below. It's a good idea to listen first, before checking in the first time, so you'll know the format of the net. Some nets like to get urgent news, scheduling information and other hot topics out of the way early, and save questions and discussion until later. Others are more free-form. You can learn quite a bit just by tuning in to these nets for a few weeks. Regular participants in the nets are often very knowledgeable and experienced. The technical discussions which sometimes take place can be very informative.

1) *Nets on 75 meters*. The Central States VHF Society (**www.csvhfs.org**) sponsors a net on 3.818 MHz each Sunday evening (0230 UTC). It is open to all those interested in VHF and higher. The net provides a terrific source of technical information and is a good place to arrange for schedules and experimental tests.

A similar informal VHF net meets on Monday evenings (0200 UTC Tuesday, 0100 UTC during the summers) on 3.843 MHz. Both frequencies are also used for spontaneous nets, especially during contests, meteor showers and other unusual VHF propagation events.

2) *VHF Nets*. There are dozens of weekly nets that operate on 144 MHz around the country. Many 2 meter nets are sponsored by the Sidewinders on Two (SWOT) Amateur Radio Club. For current information on these nets, check the SWOT website at **www.swotrc.net**.

Other nets on 50 through 1296 MHz are sponsored by regional clubs, including the Northeast Weak Signal Society (New England), Mt Airy VHF Society (eastern Pennsylvania) and Western States Weak Signal Society (California). Other nets are run by local groups. Check locally for dates, times and frequencies.

3) *EME Nets*. International EME operators meet on 14.345 MHz each Sunday to arrange EME schedules and pass information. At 1600 UTC, the 432 MHz and higher EME crowd occupies the frequency. Starting at 1700 UTC, the more numerous 144 MHz EME operators gather. The 2 meter EME net often goes for more than an hour.

4) *International 6 meter Liaison*. Avid 6 meter DX operators around the world monitor 28.885 MHz whenever there is a chance for intercontinental DX. There is no formal net, but it is a place to exchange information (especially on current propagation conditions), arrange schedules, and pass other information related to 6 meter operating.

AWARDS

Several awards sponsored by ARRL help stir activity on the VHF and higher bands. (See the **Operating Awards** chapter.) Many of those originally designed for HF operators, including Worked All States (WAS), Worked All Continents (WAC) and DX Century Club (DXCC) are also coveted by operators on 6 meters and higher. The VHF/UHF Century Club (VUCC) is designed only for the world above 50 MHz.

WAS requires contacts with all 50 United States. Like other ARRL awards, QSL cards are required. The quest for this award has probably been responsible for much of the technical advancement of VHF/UHF operation during the past three decades. Moonbounce activity has benefited most directly because WAS on any band above 144 MHz requires EME capability. Even so, more than a dozen stations in the central part of the US have worked 48 states without resorting to moonbounce.

During the peak of the most recent sunspot cycle, F_2 openings made transcontinental 6 meter contacts common for many months. Amateurs in the continental US worked Alaska, Hawaii and tons of DX during that time. In quiet years, multi-hop E_s openings occur each summer to provide the slim chance of WAS on 6 meters.

Using portable moonbounce stations, several enterprising groups have mounted EME-DXpeditions to rare states.

This has allowed quite a few hard working VHF/UHFers to complete WAS, even when there was no resident EME activity in some states. Hams have earned WAS on 2 meters, 222 MHz, 432 MHz and even 1296 MHz!

Many 6 meter operators have also worked all continents with the assistance of F_2 propagation. WAC is not impossible on the higher bands, as many 144 and 432 EME stations have accomplished this feat. WAC on the higher bands depends on EME activity from under-represented continents.

Several top-scoring stations in the annual EME contests have made QSOs on all continents during a single weekend. The rarest continent is probably South America, where only a small handful of EMEers are active. WAC is not possible on 222 or 902 MHz because these bands are not authorized for amateur use outside of ITU Region 2 (North and South America).

DXCC is also within the capability of the VHF crowd. Hundreds of DXCC awards have already been earned by 6 meter operators from around the world — unthinkable just 20 years ago. Even more astonishing are the 2 meter EME operators with DXCC certificates hanging on their walls! There is no technical reason why DXCC cannot be claimed on higher bands. It simply requires more EME activity from other countries.

PROBLEMS

With the ever-increasing sharing of the VHF and UHF spectrum by commercial, industrial and private radio services, a certain amount of interference with amateur operation is almost inevitable. Amateurs are well acquainted with interference, and so we normally solve interference problems by ourselves.

Cable television interference (CATVI) results from some cable systems distributing their signals, inside shielded cables, on frequencies which are allocated to amateurs. As long as the cable remains a closed system, in which all of their signal stays inside the cable and our signals stay out, then everything is usually okay. Despite the design intentions, cable systems are deteriorating because of age and have begun to leak. When a cable system leaks, your perfectly clean and proper VHF signal can get into the cable and cause enormous amounts of mischief. By the same token, the cable company's signals can leak out and interfere with legitimate amateur reception.

Other forms of radio frequency interference (RFI) are a common complaint of owners of unshielded or poorly designed electronic entertainment equipment. Amateur transmissions, especially high power, may be picked up and rectified, causing very annoying problems. RFI may include stereos, video-cassette recorders and telephones. The symptoms of RFI usually include muffled noises that coincide with keying or SSB voice peaks.

A few general principles may help in beginning your search for a solution to TVI/RFI problems:

1) Be sure your transmitter is clean, all coax connectors are tightened, and a good dc and RF ground is provided in your shack — before you look elsewhere for the cause of the problem.

2) With CATVI, remember that it is the cable company's responsibility to keep its system closed and in compliance with FCC rules. Unfortunately, the FCC's limits are loose enough that in some cases there will be interference-causing leakage from the system which is still within FCC limits. In that case, there is no easy solution to the problem. You may be pleasantly surprised by the cooperative attitude of some cable TV operators. (Cable company technicians often have worked overtime trying to solve CATVI complaints, but not everyone is so fortunate.)

3) In dealing with RFI, the main goal is to keep your RF out of the entertainment system. This is often solved rather simply by bypassing the speaker, microphone and power leads with disc ceramic capacitors. In other cases, particularly some telephones, you must also employ RF chokes. For further information on RFI and CATVI, consult *The ARRL RFI Book*, published by ARRL.

Several other types of interference plague VHF/UHF amateurs. These are the receive-only kinds of interference, which just affect your receiving capability. One form has already been mentioned: CATV leakage. For example, cable channel E is distributed on a frequency in the middle of the amateur 2 meter band. If the cable system leaks, you may experience very disruptive interference. Reducing leakage or perhaps eliminating the use of channel E may be satisfactory. This problem has vexed stalwart VHFers already, and no end is in sight.

Scanner birdies may be a problem in your area. All scanners are superheterodyne-type receivers, which generate local oscillator signals, just as your receiving system does. Unfortunately, many scanners have inadequate shielding between the local oscillator and the scanner's antenna. The result is radiation of the oscillator's signal each time its channel is scanned — a very annoying chirp, swoosh or buzz sound every second or so. If the scanner's local oscillator frequency happens to fall near a frequency you're listening to, you'll hear the scanner instead. Amateurs can easily pick up 10-15 scanner birdies within 5 kHz of the 2 meter calling frequency. Very little can be done about this problem aside from installing tuned traps in everyone's scanners — an unattractive prospect to most scanner owners.

Many amateurs who operate 432 MHz have lived with radar interference for years. Radar interference is identified by a very rapid burst of noise which sounds vaguely like ignition noise, repeated on a regular basis. Although some radars are being phased out, many remain. Amateurs are secondary users of the 420-450 MHz band, so we must accept this interference. The only solution may be directional antennas which may null out the interference, not a very satisfying alternative in some cases. 432 MHz EMEers sometimes hear radar interference off the Moon!

Disaster, Public Service and Emergency Communications

Providing disaster response, public service or emergency communications is a major function of Amateur Radio and a major justification of our access to the limited, valuable frequency spectrum. Hams are engaged in these activities for many reasons, including public service, excitement and adventure. They work side-by-side with disaster relief agency officials from the Red Cross, Salvation Army, government emergency management and other entities, supplementing their communications of

David Johnston, KD8BQN, of Fort Collins, Colorado, provides communications support during the High Park fire. (*WØFT photo*)

potentially life and property saving messages. It is a historic function, dating back to the beginnings of radio and Amateur Radio. Hams develop a sense of deep camaraderie and team

spirit that results from working with their peers in what sometimes are desperate circumstances.

The ARRL's Amateur Radio Emergency Service (ARES®) program is the primary platform on which Amateur Radio disaster response and emergency communications is conducted in this country, and it has been the forebearer of public service since 1935. In this chapter, you will learn the basics of emergency communications operating, plans and procedures, as well as the landscape of emergency management in the post-9/11 era, under the premier program in the United States — ARES.

EMERGENCY MANAGEMENT: A RAPIDLY CHANGING ENVIRONMENT

The emergency management and public safety slate is changing rapidly in numerous ways in response to a number of drivers. In a recent report, the Federal Emergency Management Agency (FEMA) painted a dramatic picture of what future challenges will be like for the emergency management community, Amateur Radio's primary served entity. It cites globalization, technological development, demographic shifts, technology, environmental changes and economic uncertainty as drivers of new approaches, tools and capabilities that will be required of emergency managers. The paper, entitled "Crisis Response and Disaster Resilience 2030: Forging Strategic Action in an Age of Uncertainty,"

was released in January 2012. It is available for download from **www.fema.gov/library**.

The main challenge seen by FEMA is "increasing complexity and decreasing predictability in [emergency management's] operating environment. Complexity will take the form of more incidents, new and unfamiliar threats, more information to analyze (possibly with less time to process it), new players and participants, sophisticated technologies, and exceedingly high public expectations."

FEMA sees limited future funding for emergency management: These constraints will push emergency managers to find creative ways to deal with shortfalls. They will need to

Hurricane Katrina

During our nation's unprecedented Hurricane Katrina relief effort, Amateur Radio and the ARRL stepped up and delivered a vital public service. For 37 days, more than 200 Amateur Radio operators from 35 states and Canada deployed to the field through the American Red Cross processing center in Montgomery, Alabama.

The storm surge damaged roads, buildings, vehicles and equipment, left people homeless, and knocked out power, sealing off almost all communications. But as Katrina subsided, another massive surge immediately took its place. I'm talking about the immense and sustained surge of recovery activity on the part of Amateur Radio to help assist the impacted people and relief agencies in the region.

Amateurs of all genders, ages, types and backgrounds voluntarily deployed to counties, communities and towns to set up stations at kitchens, shelters and emergency operations centers. Amateur Radio operators provided critical communications and passed hundreds of messages in and around the devastated region. Amateurs in the field selflessly served in many capacities, working long hours, living in terrible conditions, contending with heat, bugs, ants and in many cases much worse.

While deployed the Amateur Radio operators supported many served agencies and hundreds of people in need. The Montgomery operation supplied amateurs to The Salvation Army, American Red Cross, church or religious organizations, emergency management agencies and emergency operations centers.

During this event, my experiences affirmed that Amateur Radio operators are much more than hobbyists.

Red Cross and SATERN volunteer Ben Joplin, WB5VST, in Oklahoma City, is interviewed by local news media after getting word through to Louisiana officials that 15 people were stranded on a roof there. (*N7XYO photo*)

After Hurricane Katrina struck, Amateur Radio became a primary means of communication for those in Bay St. Louis, Mississippi.

I saw amateurs sacrifice, contribute and succeed in providing many weeks of critical communications and additional services to meet dynamic and unique needs. Amateurs created interoperable emergency communications systems where there were none and saved lives as a result. Moreover, they brought the love of a hobby, a variety of communications, contesting, training, and public service skills; and most of all applied the amateur "can-do spirit" to help people in need.

It was a pleasure getting to meet hundreds of amateurs who worked to do the right thing for this relief effort. My appreciation and admiration extends to all Amateur Radio operators, at home or in the field, who served in this massive relief effort! — *Greg Sarratt, W4OZK, ARRL Southeastern Division Director*

find new ways "to ensure interoperability of personnel, equipment, systems, and functions." Thus, the private sectors will likely play an increasingly active role in meeting emergency management needs, said FEMA.

FEMA feels that climate change is the major environmental force confronting the emergency management community in the United States: "Climate change impacts are expected to increase the severity, frequency, or scale of extreme weather events, droughts, floods, sea-level rise, precipitation patterns, and the spread of life-threatening diseases.

The most visible impacts will likely result from an increase in the magnitude and frequency of natural disasters."

Compounding these drivers is the evolving terrorist threat. All of these factors will have a significant impact on emergency management.

Implications for Amateur Radio

For us as radio amateurs active in disaster response communications, the primary implication is clear: more opportunity for serving. But, along with that opportunity, comes the need for more "professionalism," which translates to more training and qualifications to enhance our utility to the public safety community. Our goals are to:

1) establish good relationships with local and county emergency managers, sheriff's offices and other officials;

2) train, get certified and register for their volunteer rosters; and

3) learn new languages and the cultural needs of new communities as demographics shift in the nation.

Social media has transformed how Americans communicate with one another, and we as radio amateurs and disaster response and emergency communications operators need to set up social media accounts for alerting and for information sharing and management. We will see a new emphasis on supporting neighborhood Community Emergency Response Teams (CERT) with ARES communications. Remember, our great asset to emergency management professionals is that we are decentralized. We are already in neighborhoods and don't need to deploy and travel in potentially dangerous circumstances to perform our communications mission.

Since the events of 9/11 and Hurricane Katrina, the mantra in the public safety field has been *interoperability* — the ability for all jurisdictions and disciplines to communicate with each other as seamlessly as possible. Offering an interoperability communications solution across emergency support functions (ESFs) and departments is what hams have been known for, and for a long time.

"Professionalization" of Volunteers

FEMA noted that "volunteers serve in both operational and support emergency management roles," and that "databases contain pre-approved rosters of volunteer emergency management personnel with skills/qualifications." FEMA said that there is a de facto "professionalization" of volunteer corps going on currently with opportunities for advanced training, certification, and granting of appropriate authorities.

In the Amateur Radio emergency communications world, we are undergoing the "professionalization" of our ARES personnel through FEMA Incident Command System (ICS) and National Incident Management System (NIMS) training. (ICS and NIMS are discussed in detail later in this chapter.) We are also being pre-approved, qualified and registered on emergency operations center (EOC) databases of volunteers at the local level. That trend will continue at an ever-increasing rate.

As an example of what roles Amateur Radio can play in areas where it may have been shut out before, FCC staffer Curt Bartholomew recently reported that Amateur Radio was involved in the government's annual continuity (devolution) exercise for the first time ever, with the scenario of a catastrophic event (nuclear attack) crippling Federal agencies' headquarters and personnel. In this exercise, with electronic communications down, agencies must relocate (devolve) far away from the capitol district and re-staff with out-of-state personnel and resume functioning. Past exercise scenarios have included cyber attacks, geomagnetic storms, natural disasters, chemical attacks, and biological attacks.

In the nuclear attack scenario, wireless communications resources would be limited, and the only systems that might be usable include limited satellite communications (SATCOM), limited TV/radio broadcasting, Family Radio Service (FRS), General Mobile Radio Service (GMRS), Citizens Band (CB), Multi-Use Radio Service (MURS), HF Automatic Link Establishment (HF-ALE) and Amateur Radio, according to Bartholomew. Under a real devolution scenario, Amateur Radio operators may get called to assist Federal agencies with disaster communications. Bartholomew cited a September 2011 *QST* article, "Optimizing Amateur Radio Resources for Major Disasters," by Victor Cid, W3CID, and Andrew Mitz, WA3LTJ, as an example of what radio amateurs can bring to the table.

NEW ERA: EMPHASIS ON TRAINING

"For many years, Amateur Radio has longed to be taken seriously by governmental authorities as a professional-quality resource in disaster response. Although there are areas of the country where achieving and maintaining emergency management agencies' respect is still a struggle, Amateur Radio's service during 9/11 and the major hurricane disasters of the 21st century has brought us a new level of respect and new opportunities at the national level.

"Being taken seriously as a resource comes with a price, however. It is a price that must be paid by individual volunteers, not in dollars but in precious personal time. When the federal government instituted the National Incident Management System (NIMS), it imposed a set of requirements on state and local emergency management agencies and their personnel. Affected personnel included not only paid employees of emergency management and related agencies but also volunteers such as those in volunteer fire companies, ARES,

and RACES. If the emergency management agencies are to continue receiving federal funds, personnel must complete a number of FEMA training courses having to do with the Incident Command System (ICS) and NIMS. Individuals who do not complete the training will not be allowed to participate, even as volunteers.

"These FEMA courses are free of charge, available online or sometimes in person at emergency management offices, and not particularly difficult. The courses are useful in familiarizing volunteers with the specialized vocabulary and principles of the Incident Command System and showing where communications fits into the ICS structure. This is valuable knowledge, because if radio amateurs — particularly those in leadership positions — cannot 'talk the talk,' then authorities may well assume that we cannot 'walk the walk.'

"These formal requirements are here to stay and more

Public service events provide a great training opportunity. At the Oklahoma City Memorial Marathon, hams helped co-ordinate "Snatch and Grab" vehicles dispatched to pick up runners who had withdrawn from the Marathon. Volunteers included Brian Teters, AE5MT (foreground), Andrew Wolfe, KE5YBC (center) and Richard Sharp, KE5NCR (back-ground). (*KE5KQL photo*)

Emergency Management Institute

FEMA

This Certificate of Achievement is to acknowledge that

RICHARD PALM

has reaffirmed a dedication to serve in times of crisis through continued professional development and completion of the independent study course:

IS-00100.b
Introduction to Incident Command System
ICS-100

Issued this 9th Day of August, 2012

Tony Russell
Superintendent
Emergency Management Institute

0.3 IACET CEU

FEMA courses are an excellent resource for emergency communications volunteers.

may follow. At the national level, Amateur Radio has earned the respect we always wanted, bringing us closer to the emergency management establishment. The challenge now is persuading both casual ARES volunteers and experienced volunteers to meet the requirements that follow from being part of the system. The national-level ARRL must be aware of that and develop ways to help local and Section ARES officials bring their volunteers, both old-timers and newcomers, into the new era." — *ARRL President Kay Craigie, N3KN*

Current Trends

There has been a steady rise in interest in the ARRL and FEMA courses by emergency preparedness operators, both serious and casual. In a recent survey by the ARRL Emergency Communications Advisory Committee (ECAC) of the ARRL Field Organization on ARES topics, 55% of the ARRL Sections require certain minimum training for active members. Of those sections requiring training and certifications, 38% require the ARRL *Introduction to Emergency Communi-cations* course; 75% require the FEMA IS-100 course on the ICS; 71% require the IS-200 course on *ICS for Single Resources and Initial Action Incidents*; 67% require IS-700, *Introduction to the National Incident Management System (NIMS)*; and 51% require IS-800, on the *National Response Framework (NRF)*.

Of served agencies, it was reported that 78% require specific training of their volunteers: 12% require the ARRL emergency communications course; 77% require IS-100; 65% require IS-200; 75% require IS-700; and 52% require IS-800. Other courses are required, too. Some 90% of respondents answered yes to the question "Is ICS widely taught and actively used by agencies in your area?" About 75% reported that most ARES members are ICS-trained, and 68% said that the current ARES organizational structure interfaces well with the ICS.

Recommended Courses

With the above as a backdrop, it is easy to see why attempting to draft a set of recommended courses and certifications for ARES volunteers and other emergency preparedness operators is like trying to hit a moving target, but here are some basic recommendations.

■ The ARRL *Introduction to Emergency Communication* — This online course is designed to provide basic knowledge and tools for any disaster communications volunteer. Prerequisites include IS-100 *Introduction to the Incident Command System*; and IS-700 on the *National Incident Management System*. The ARRL also recommends IS-250 on *Emergency Support Function 15*; and IS-288 on *The Role of Voluntary Agencies in Emergency Management*.

The ARRL course covers The Framework: How You Fit In; The Networks for Messages; Message Handling; What Happens When Called; Operations and Logistics; Safety and Survival; and What to Expect in Large Disasters. It includes required student activities, along with a 35-question final assessment.

■American Red Cross or American Heart Association *CPR* (cardiopulmonary resuscitation) and *AED* (automated external defibrillator) — These courses are widely held on hospital and college campuses, and at Red Cross offices and centers. Providing communications functions in an actual emergency or disaster is physically demanding, and stressful on body systems. The likelihood of an ARES volunteer having to assist, or possibly save the life of someone with CPR is increased many times over the lay public. Just do it.

■ FEMA IS-100 *Introduction to Incident Command System* — This course is a must-have certification not only because it is a requirement of most local, county and state agencies, but also because it imparts an understanding of the contemporary emergency management structure in which we all work. How can you function as a viable communicator when you do not have a basic idea of what is going on around you on a disaster scene? You can't, of course. Government agencies manage emergencies and disasters using the ICS, which gives multiple jurisdictions and disciplines the same play book with which to work together efficiently. You need to know how it works.

■ FEMA IS-700 *National Incident Management System* — This course introduces and overviews the National Incident Management System (NIMS), which serves as a "consistent nationwide template to enable all government, private-sector, and nongovernmental organizations to work together during domestic incidents." The NIMS course is the other shoe for the government's emergency response framework, and as such, should be near the top of any ARES volunteer's list of courses to take.

■ FEMA IS-200 *ICS for Single Resources and Initial Action Incidents* — According to FEMA, this course is "designed to enable personnel to operate efficiently during an incident or event within the Incident Command System (ICS). IS-200 provides training on and resources for personnel who are likely to assume a supervisory position within the ICS." This is probably the first course to consider taking after the courses discussed above are completed.

■ FEMA IS-230 *Fundamentals of Emergency Management* — Garth Kennedy, W9KJ, the emergency manager for the Naperville, Illinois Emergency Management Agency (EMA), recommends this course. He says, "I manage a large emergency management agency. Most of our volunteers do not understand what constitutes 'Emergency Management.' As a result, we require IS-230 for any certification level in all of our specialties. I recommend adding this course to your list so ARES operators will more fully understand the environment in which they work."

ARRL recommends the following as core courses.

■ For the rank-and-file ARES field operator: ARRL EC-001 as discussed above, a basic SKYWARN class, FEMA IS-100 and IS-200 as previously discussed, and CPR/First Aid/AED. Additional FEMA courses: Browse them. Take them.

■ For ARES leaders including Emergency Coordinators (ECs), District ECs (DECs) and Section Emergency Coordinators (SECs), ARRL HQ recommends ARRL EC-016, entitled *Public Service and Emergency Communications Management for Radio Amateurs,* designed to train licensed Amateur Radio operators who will be in leadership and managerial roles organizing other volunteers to support public service activities and communications emergencies. HQ also recommends an Advanced SKYWARN class; and FEMA IS-700 on NIMS, IS-800 on the *National Response Framework*, and IS-802 on *Emergency Support Function #2 — Communications*. And finally, Red Cross Disaster Services training is recommended, even if you do not work directly with Red Cross in your area. You should be aware of how the Red Cross conducts field operations, an issue that was raised during the Hurricane Katrina mega-response.

THE EMERGENCY COORDINATOR: LEADERSHIP AND UNDERSTANDING OUR ROLE

Your first step on your path to becoming an emergency communications operator is to contact your local Emergency Coordinator (EC). Leading every good disaster response or emergency communications operator is a good EC. What makes a good EC? Answer: the character of the individual and his or her true understanding of what motivates people and how they can be led by example and good people skills. And most importantly, the EC must have a firm grasp of our role in the Emergency Operations Center (EOC), or indeed with any served agency: We serve the agencies. They do not serve us. That's why we call them served agencies. We are there to be an asset to them, not a liability. We are there to make their jobs of providing professional emergency and disaster management to the public easier if we can. We are there to try to provide a seamless, almost transparent communications service. We do not force ourselves on them. Agency officials must know our limitations and capabilities, and we most know our own limitations and their expectations. The EC has a realistic self-appraisal.

A good EC is intelligent, well educated, experienced and has a professional, friendly demeanor. The EC presents himself or herself in a professional manner — for example,

Jeff Brady, N9WSV, provides a damage assessment in the aftermath of tornados in Clark County, Indiana. (*N9WSV photo*)

wearing a pair of khaki pants and wrinkle-free polo shirt. The EC should be physically fit. He or she is cool, calm and collected under fire, and never a hothead or whiner, neither argumentative nor demanding. He or she leads by example and consequently earns the respect of all parties. The EC is where the rubber meets the road in the ARES program, and you should contact him or her first.

Planning

More than any other facet of Amateur Radio, disaster response or emergency communication requires a plan — an orderly arrangement of time, personnel and activities that ensures that performance is smooth and objectives are met. Basically, a plan is a method of achieving a goal. Lack of a plan could hamper urgent operations, defer crucial decisions or delay critical supplies. Be sure to analyze what emergencies are likely to occur in your area, develop guidelines for providing communications after a disaster, know the proper contact people and inform local authorities of your group's capabilities.

Start with a small plan, such as developing a community awareness program for severe-weather emergencies. Next,

test the plan a piece at a time, but redefine the plan if it is unsatisfactory. Testing and drills using simulated disaster scenarios teaches communicators what to do in a real emergency, without a great deal of risk. Finally, prepare a few contingency plans just in case the original plan fails.

One of the best ways to learn how to plan for emergencies is to join your local ARES group (see the sidebar, "How to Get Started"), where members train and prepare constantly in an organized way. Before an emergency occurs, register with your Emergency Coordinator. The EC will explain to civic and relief agencies in your community what the Amateur Service can offer in time of disaster.

Communications for city or rural emergencies each require a particular response and careful planning. Large cities usually have capable relief efforts handled by paid professionals, and there always seems to be some equipment and facilities that remain operable. Even though damage may be more concentrated outside a city, it can be remote from firefighting or public works equipment and law enforcement authorities. The rural public then, with few volunteers spread over a wide area, may be isolated, unable to call for help or incapable of reporting all of the damage.

It's futile to look back regretfully at past disasters and wish you had been better prepared. Prepare yourself now for emergency communications by maintaining a dependable transceiver and antenna setup and an emergency power source. Have a plan ready and learn proper procedures.

Procedures

Aside from having plans, it is also necessary to have procedures — the best methods or ways to do a job. Procedures become habits, independent of a plan, when everyone knows what happens next and can tell others what to do. Actually, the size of a disaster affects the size of the response, but not the procedures.

Procedures that should be widely known before disasters occur include how to coordinate or deploy people, equipment and supplies. There are procedures to use a repeater and an

Principles of Disaster Response Communications

It is impossible to state exact rules that will cover every situation that arises. The good amateur faced with a disaster situation may, however, benefit greatly from certain rules of thumb. These rules are, or should be, part of his/her training in his/her ARES group. They are presented here and should be reviewed by all amateurs, even those not active in disaster communications preparation.

1. **Keep the QRM level down**. In a disaster, many of the most crucial stations will be weak in signal strength. It is most essential that all other stations remain silent unless they are called upon. If you're not sure you should transmit — don't. Our amateur bands are very congested. If you want to help, study the situation by listening. Don't transmit unless you are sure you can help by doing so. Don't ever break into a disaster net just to inform the control station you are there if needed.

2. **Monitor established disaster frequencies**. Many localities and some geographical areas have established disaster frequencies where someone is always (or nearly always) monitoring for possible calls. When you are not otherwise engaged, it is helpful simply to sit and listen on such frequencies, some of which are used for general conversation as well as disaster preparedness drilling. On CW, SOS is universally recognized, but has some legal aspects that should be considered where the need is not truly crucial. On voice, one can use "Mayday" (universal, the phone equivalent of SOS) or, to break into a net or conversation with the word "emergency."

3. **Avoid spreading rumors**. During and after a disaster situation, especially on the phone bands, you may hear almost anything. Unfortunately, much misinformation is transmitted. Rumors are started by expansion, deletion, amplification or modification of words, exaggeration or interpretation. All addressed transmissions should be officially authenticated as to their source. These transmissions should be repeated word for word, if at all, and only when specifically authorized. In a disaster emergency situation, with everyone's nerves on edge, it is little short of criminal to make a statement on the air without foundation in authenticated fact.

4. **Authenticate all messages**. Every message which purports to be of an official nature should be written and signed. Whenever possible, amateurs should avoid initiating disaster or emergency traffic themselves. We do the communicating; the agency officials we serve supply the content of the communications.

5. **Strive for efficiency**. Whatever happens in an emergency, you will find hysteria and some amateurs who are activated by the thought that they must be "sleepless heroes." Instead of operating your own station full time at the expense of your health and efficiency, it is much better to serve a shift at one of the best-located and best-equipped stations. This station will be suitable for the work at hand, and manned by relief shifts of the best-qualified operators. This reduces interference and secures well-operated stations.

6. **Select the mode and band to suit the need**. It is a characteristic of all amateurs to believe that their favorite mode and band is superior to all others. For certain specific purposes and distances, this may be true. However, the merits of a particular band or mode in a communications emergency should be evaluated impartially with a view to the appropriate use of bands and modes. There is, of course, no alternative to using what happens to be available, but there are ways to optimize available communications.

Long experience has developed the following advantages:

CW Mode
1. Less interference in most amateur bands.
2. More secure communications — contents of communications are much less likely to be intercepted by the general public to start rumors or undue concern.
3. Simpler transmitting equipment.
4. Greater accuracy in record communications.
5. Longer range for a given amount of power.

Voice Mode
1. More practical for portable and mobile work.
2. More widespread availability of operators.
3. Faster communication for tactical or "command" purposes.
4. More readily appreciated and understood by the public.
5. Official-to-official and phone-patch communication.

Digital Modes
1. Less interference in most amateur bands.
2. More secure communications — contents of communications are much less likely to be intercepted by the general public to start rumors or undue concern.
3. More widespread availability of operators.
4. Greater speed in record communication than some of the other modes.
5. Error correction (in most but not all digital modes).
6. The potential for message store and forward capability, and for "digipeating" messages from point A to point Z via numerous automatically controlled middle points.

The well-balanced disaster organization will have CW, phone and digital mode capabilities available in order to utilize all of the advantages. Of course, one must make the best use of whatever is available, but a great deal of efficiency is lost when there is lack of coordination between the different types of operation in an emergency. Absolute impartiality and a willingness to let performance speak for itself are prime requisites if we are to realize the best possible results.

7. **Use all communications channels intelligently**. While the prime object of emergency communications is to save lives and property, Amateur Radio is a secondary communications means; normal channels are primary and should be used if available. Emergency channels other than amateur which are available in the absence of amateur channels should be utilized without fear of favoritism in the interest of getting the message through.

8. **Don't broadcast**. Some amateur stations in an emergency situation have a tendency to emulate broadcast techniques. While it is true that the general public may be listening, our transmissions are not and should not be made for that purpose. Broadcast stations are well equipped to perform any such service. Our job is to communicate for, not with, the general public.

9. **Communication support and NTS**. Within the disaster area itself, the ARES is primarily responsible for communications support. When disaster strikes, the first priority of those NTS operators who live in or near the disaster area is to make their expertise available to their Emergency Coordinator where and when they are needed. For timely and effective response, this means that NTS operators need to talk to their ECs before the time of need so that they will know how to best respond.

ARES Personal Checklist

The following represents recommendations of equipment and supplies that ARES members should consider having available for use during an emergency or public service activity. Use this list as a guideline and supplement it as appropriate for your needs.

Forms of Identification

✓ ARES Identification Card
✓ FCC Amateur Radio license
✓ driver's license

Radio Gear

✓ VHF transceiver
✓ microphone
✓ headphones
✓ power supply/extra batteries
✓ cigar lighter power cable
✓ spare fuses
✓ patch cords/adapters (coax and audio)
✓ antennas with mounts
✓ extra coax
✓ SWR/power meter
✓ laptop computer with digital mode software (if needed)

Writing Gear

✓ pen/pencil/eraser
✓ clipboard
✓ message forms
✓ logbook
✓ note paper

Personal Gear (short duration)

✓ snacks
✓ liquid refreshments
✓ throat lozenges
✓ personal medicine
✓ aspirin
✓ extra pair of prescription glasses
✓ sweater/jacket

Personal Gear (72-hour duration)

✓ foul-weather gear
✓ three-day supply of drinking water
✓ cooler with three-day supply of food
✓ mess kit with cleaning supplies
✓ first-aid kit
✓ personal medicine
✓ aspirin
✓ throat lozenges
✓ sleeping bag
✓ toilet articles
✓ mechanical or battery-powered alarm clock
✓ flashlight with batteries/lantern
✓ candles
✓ waterproof matches
✓ extra pair of prescription glasses

Tool Box (72-hour duration)

✓ screwdrivers
✓ pliers
✓ socket wrenches
✓ electrical tape
✓ battery-operated/120 V soldering iron
✓ solder
✓ volt-ohm meter

Other (72-hour duration)

✓ HF transceiver
✓ hatchet/ax
✓ saw
✓ pick
✓ shovel
✓ siphon
✓ jumper cables
✓ generator with spare spark plugs
✓ kerosene lights, camping lantern or candles
✓ ⅜-inch rope
✓ highway flares
✓ extra gasoline and oil

---

autopatch, to check into a net and to format or handle traffic. Because it takes time to learn activities that are not normally used every day, excessively detailed procedures will confuse people and should be avoided.

Specific Procedures

Your EC will have developed a procedure to activate the ARES group, but he or she will need your help to make it work. A telephone alerting "tree" call-up, even if based on a current list of phone numbers, might fail if there are gaps in the calling sequence, or members are not near a phone, or there is no phone service.

Consider alternative procedures. Use alerting tones and frequent announcements on a well monitored repeater to round up many operators at once. An unused 2 meter simplex frequency can function for alerting; instead of turning radios off, your group would monitor this frequency for alerts without the need of any equipment modifications. Since this channel is normally quiet, any activity on it would probably be an alert announcement.

During an emergency, report to the EC so that up-to-the-minute data on operators will be available. Don't rely on one leader; everyone should keep an emergency reference list of relief-agency officials, police, sheriff and fire departments, ambulance service and ARES and National Traffic System (NTS) nets. Be ready to help, but stay off the air unless there is a specific job to be done that you can handle efficiently. Always listen before you transmit. Work and cooperate with the local civic and relief agencies as the EC suggests. During a major emergency, copy special W1AW bulletins for the latest developments.

Afterward, let your EC know about your activities, so that a timely report can be submitted to ARRL HQ. Amateur

Radio has won glowing public tribute in emergencies. Help maintain this record.

"Experience is the worst teacher: it gives the test before presenting the lesson" (Vernon's Law). Train and drill now so you can be prepared for an emergency.

ON THE AIR TRAINING EXERCISES

Practical on-the-air activities, such as ARRL's Field Day and Simulated Emergency Test offer additional training opportunities on a nationwide basis for individuals and groups. Participation in such events reveals weak areas where discussion and more training are needed. Also, drills and tests can be designed specifically to check dependability of emergency equipment or to rate training in the local area.

ARRL Field Day

The ARRL Field Day (FD) gets more amateurs out of their cozy shacks and into tents on hilltops than any other event. You may not be operating from a tent after a disaster, but the training you will get from FD is invaluable.

In ARRL Field Day, a premium is placed on sharp operating skills, adapting equipment that can meet challenges of emergency preparedness and flexible logistics. Amateurs

assemble portable stations capable of long-range communications at almost any place and under varying conditions. Alternatives to commercial power in the form of generators, car batteries, solar power and other sources are used to power equipment to make as many contacts as possible. FD is held on the fourth full weekend of June, but enthusiasts get the most out of their training by keeping preparedness programs alive during the rest of the year. See **www.arrl.org/field-day** for more information on this popular event.

ARRL Simulated Emergency Test

The ARRL Simulated Emergency Test (SET) offers volunteers an opportunity to build disaster response and emergency communications skills. The purposes of SET are to:

■ Help amateurs gain experience in communicating, using standard procedures under simulated emergency conditions, and to experiment with some new concepts.

■ Determine strong points, capabilities and limitations in providing emergency communications to improve the response to a real emergency.

■ Provide a demonstration, to served agencies and the public through the news media, of the value of Amateur Radio, particularly in time of need.

The goals of SET are to:

■ Strengthen VHF-to-HF links at the local level, ensuring that ARES and NTS work in concert.

⋏Mike Powloka, KT1Q, maintains contact through the K1SV repeater as part of his group's annual Simulated Emergency Test exercises in Bennington, Vermont. (*N1WWW photo*)

➢Assistant Emergency Coordinator Tom Olley, KG4VUB, operates from a shelter location in the Cherokee County, Georgia, Simulated Emergency Test. (*WB4NWS photo*)

Oregon ARES SHAKE EX 2011: An Earthquake Disaster SET

Perhaps tomorrow or within our lifetime, a major earthquake will strike the Pacific Northwest. Within 30 minutes, a tsunami similar to that which devastated Japan in 2011, will occur along the Oregon Coast. Just one month after the Japanese disaster, Oregon ARES volunteers conducted a statewide Simulated Emergency Test (SET) to test their readiness to respond to just such a disaster. Although the SET was planned well before the events in Japan, the realization that similar events could happen in Oregon added to the authenticity of the exercise.

Geologists tell us that, historically, earthquakes in our region (the Cascadia Subduction Zone) occur with alarming regularity at intervals of about 300 years. Since the last major earthquake was in 1700, another Cascadia earthquake could occur at any time. Should Oregon be struck by an event like Japan's, there would likely be catastrophic, widespread damage within western Oregon and an immediate need for ARES disaster communications support.

The SHAKE EX 2011 SET was designed to test the ability of ARES units to exchange very high volumes of written messages between the county emergency managers and the Oregon Emergency Management (OEM) office in the state capitol, Salem. Much of the radio traffic exchange occurred over the Oregon ARES Digital Network (OADN), which uses Winlink HF and VHF radio systems funded by the State of Oregon following the major windstorms of 2007.

In addition to state-level, statewide communications activities, many counties held their own local drills in coordination with their local emergency managers, medical facilities and Community Emergency Response Teams (CERT). The local drills typically included establishment of HF radio systems at remote locations using portable Field Day-style antennas. Local drills included the transmission of photographs by radio to county and state EOCs and relaying simulated damage reports between stations.

In total, EOCs in 14 Oregon counties participated in SHAKE EX 2011. In addition, EOCs in six cities and eight medical facilities were activated for the drill. About 130 members of Oregon ARES participated throughout the state, sending and receiving about 2000 messages within the six-hour period of the exercise. Most of the traffic was sent by HF and VHF using the Winlink OADN system. During the height of the SET activity, OEM operators were receiving about one message per minute from ARES operators throughout Oregon.

The Oregon ARES Digital Network consists of HF radios equipped with PACTOR 3 modems as well as VHF/UHF radios equipped with TNCs for local Winlink RMS gateways. Both radio systems are used with laptop computers loaded with Winlink *Airmail 3* software. With a few exceptions, each county EOC has an identical set of equipment. Training of ARES units receiving the equipment was completed in 2009 during installation. Since then, quarterly connectivity exercises and the twice-yearly statewide SETs have helped ensure that the OADN system remains fully operational.

Lessons Learned

During a disaster of the scale anticipated during this SET, there will likely be an overwhelming volume of emergency written and tactical traffic exchanged among emergency managers. At such times, it is essential that the flow of messages from ARES radio operators to and from these officials be accurate, efficient and timely. Although the technology used by ARES units to get the message delivered worked quite well, it soon became apparent that the flood of messages being received at many EOCs simply overwhelmed anyone's ability to methodically log, manage and distribute them. Several options have been proposed to deal with this data management issue.

During SHAKE EX 2011, Curry County (Oregon) Emergency Services Coordinator Don Kendall, N6VKW (left) and Curry County EC Bob Wilkinson, W7VN, discuss transportation disruption resulting from the probable collapse of the Patterson Bridge over the Rouge River. (*W7RFC photo*)

The demonstrated ability of Oregon ARES volunteers to successfully support the large volume of written and tactical traffic demands of Oregon's emergency managers under the limited restrictions imposed during this SET were impressive, but tougher operating restraints to test emergency power and peer-to-peer connectivity have yet to put our operators and stations to the real test. — *Vincent Van Der Hyde, K7VV, Oregon Section Emergency Coordinator, and John Core, KX7YT, Oregon Section ARES SET Coordinator*

- Encourage greater use of digital modes for handling high-volume traffic and point-to-point welfare messages of the affected simulated-disaster area.
- Implement the Memoranda of Understanding between the ARRL, the users and cooperative agencies.
- Focus energy on ARES communications at the local level.
- Increase use and recognition of tactical communication on behalf of served agencies; using less amateur-to-amateur formal radiogram traffic.

Help promote the SET on nets and repeaters with announcements or bulletins, or at club meetings and publicize it in club newsletters. SET is conducted on the first full weekend of October. However, some groups have their SETs any time during the period of September 1 through November 30, especially if an alternate date coincides more favorably with a planned communications activity and provides greater publicity. Specific SET guidelines are announced in *QST*.

Drills and Tests

A drill or test that includes interest and practical value makes a group glad to participate because it seems worthy of its efforts. Formulate training around a simulated disaster such as a tornado or a vehicle accident. Elaborate on the situation to develop a realistic scenario or have the drill in conjunction with a local event. Many ARRL Section Emergency Coordinators (SECs) have developed training activities that are specifically designed for your state, section or local area. County Emergency Managers are often well practiced in setting up exercises that can help you sharpen your communications and general emergency reaction skills.

During a drill:

1) Announce the simulated emergency situation, activate the emergency net and dispatch mobiles and portables to served agencies.

2) Originate messages and requests for supplies on behalf of served agencies by using tactical communications. (Don't forget to label each message with a "this is a drill only" header, no matter what mode is used to transmit it.)

3) Use emergency-powered repeaters and employ digital modes. Use and test a simplex frequency.

4) As warranted by traffic loads, assign liaison stations to receive traffic on the local net and relay to your section net. Be sure there is a representative on each session of the section nets to receive traffic coming to your area.

After a drill:

1) Determine the results of the emergency communications.

2) Critique the drill.

3) Report your efforts, including any photos, clippings and other items of interest, to your SEC or ARRL HQ.

Public Event Communications

The local ARES group often finds itself providing radio communications support for town parades, bicycle tours, boat races, marathons and so forth. These events provide radio amateurs with excellent on-the air experience and training for when disasters come along. Take advantage of all of these opportunities to hone your skills, and those of your local ARES organization. See the *ARRL Special Events Communications Manual* for additional tips on operating public events.

Net Operator Training

Network discipline and message-handling procedures are fundamental emergency preparedness concepts. Training should involve as many different operators as possible in Net Control Station (NCS) and liaison functions; don't have the same operator performing the same functions repeatedly or you will lose valuable training experience for the other members of the group. There should be plenty of work for everyone. Good liaison and cooperation at all levels requires versatile operators who can operate different modes. Even though phone operators may not feel comfortable on digital modes, and vice versa, encourage net operators to gain familiarity on all modes by giving them proper training. They can learn by logging for a regular operator in that mode.

If no local emergency or traffic net exists, you or your

Public service events are excellent training for emergency communications. Amateurs in Michigan provided communications for an annual dog sled race using a variety of Amateur Radio modes and technologies. At left, an ATV station at the Start/Finish line was used to monitor teams' progress about 2 miles away. At right, Webster, W8QBX, collected and recorded times called in from various crossings, and Marv, KC8MLD, passed them to the Start/Finish line via digital modes. (*KC8JLH photos*)

club should consider initiating a net on an available 2 meter repeater, and coordinate these efforts with the trustee(s) of the repeater you'll use. Encourage club members to participate in traffic-handling activities, either from their home stations or as a group activity from a message center.

Ask your ARRL Section Emergency Coordinator, county Emergency Manager or Emergency Coordinator to conduct a seminar for your group on communicating with first responder personnel such as police, firefighters or emergency medical technicians. They use procedures that are different from those used in Amateur Radio. It is likely that your ARES and/or Radio Amateur Civil Emergency Service (RACES) group will need to communicate with them in real situations.

For more information on NTS and traffic handling, see the **Traffic Handling** chapter.

HANDLING MESSAGES

Message handling is the essence of emergency communications by radio amateurs. Following a disaster, the potential customers for Amateur Radio services include both official organizations communicating among themselves, and citizens who are without the conventional means to contact their friends and family. It is difficult for the service provider to place an exclusive priority on one or the other, particularly if the means exist to service both customers. Regardless of the method used, the customer being serviced, or who is providing the service, effective communications requires the successful completion of all three major communications phases of origination, transport, and delivery. Originating messages from within a disaster area requires a minimum of one Amateur Radio operator, is often the primary focus, and can usually be accomplished. Without the concurrent provision for the transport and delivery phases, however, originating messages is futile.

Traditional Amateur Radio networks consist of at least two Amateur Radio operators on a common mode and frequency, which satisfies all three communications phases. As the distance between the origination and destination locations increases, additional operators are required to relay the messages: the transport and delivery phases. Irrespective of the mode and frequency used, these are referred to as manual networks, and all function similarly.

Semiautomatic networks require an Amateur Radio operator to originate a message, but use automatic systems to execute the transport and delivery phases. These systems provide higher speed and accuracy, require specific and detailed addresses, and require additional equipment at the origination point. The best known of these systems is Winlink 2000, which treats all messages as having the same priority. Semiautomatic networks are ill-suited for high priority warning communications, and should never be used to the exclusion of near real-time networks, such as voice. *The greatest value to the customer is provided when all available communications networks are used.*

Emergency Operations Center (EOC)

Amateur Radio emergency communications and message handling are frequently parts of the Incident Command System (ICS), and emergency operations center (EOC) functioning. See **Figure 4.1**. The ICS is a way to control initial and subsequent activities in emergency and disaster situations, and is the standard management model used by

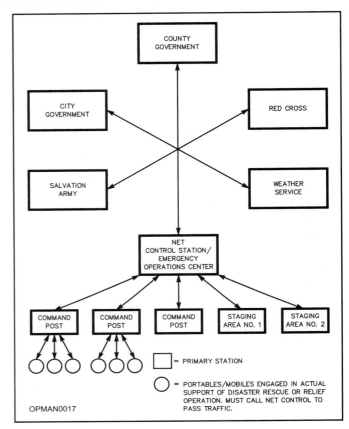

Figure 4.1 — The interaction between the EOC/NCS and the command post(s) in a local emergency.

all levels of government for disaster response.

Consider an automobile accident where a citizen or an amateur, first on the scene, becomes a temporary Incident Commander (IC) when he or she calls for or radios a message for help. A law enforcement officer is dispatched to the accident scene in a squad car and, upon arriving, takes over the IC tasks. Relief efforts, like those in this simple example of an automobile accident, begin when someone takes charge, makes a decision and directs the efforts of others.

The EOC responds to the IC through message communications and subsequent dispatching of equipment and helpers, anticipating needs to supply support and assistance. It may send more equipment to a staging area to be stored where it can be available almost instantly or send more people to react quickly to changing situations. All of this depends on message handling; in many instances, by radio amateurs.

If the status of an accident changes (a car hits a utility pole, which later causes a fire), the IC sends a message to the EOC with an updated report then keeps control even after the support agencies arrive and take over their specific responsibilities: Injuries — medical; fires — fire department; disabled vehicles — law enforcement or tow truck; and utility poles — utility company. By being outside the perimeter of dangerous activities, the EOC can use the proper type of radio communications, concentrate on gathering data from other agencies and then provide the right response.

Whether there is a minor vehicle accident or a major disaster operation, the effectiveness of the amateur effort in an emergency depends mainly on handling information.

THE INCIDENT COMMAND SYSTEM (ICS)

An incident is an occurrence, either caused by humans or natural phenomena, that requires response actions to prevent or minimize loss of life or damage to property and/or the environment. Examples of incidents include:

- Fire, both structural and wildland.
- Natural disasters, such as tornados, floods, ice storms or earthquakes.
- Human and animal disease outbreaks.
- Search and rescue missions.
- Hazardous materials incidents.
- Criminal acts and crime scene investigations.
- Terrorist incidents, including the use of weapons of mass destruction.
- National Special Security Events, such as Presidential visits or the Super Bowl.
- Other planned events, such as parades or demonstrations.

Given the magnitude of these types of events, it's not always possible for any one agency alone to handle the management and resource needs.

Partnerships are often required among local, state, tribal, and federal agencies. These partners must work together in a smooth, coordinated effort under the same management system.

The Incident Command System, or ICS, is a standardized, on-scene, all-hazard incident management concept. ICS allows its users to adopt an integrated organizational structure to match the complexities and demands of single or multiple incidents without being hindered by jurisdictional boundaries.

ICS has considerable internal flexibility. It can grow or shrink to meet different needs. This flexibility makes it a very cost-effective and efficient management approach for both small and large situations. (The previous description is from FEMA Independent Study Course IS-100.)

The Incident Command System uses *clear text and common terms*. The ability to communicate within the ICS is absolutely critical. An essential method for ensuring the ability to communicate is by using common terminology and clear text. All communications are to be in plain English. That is, use clear text. Do not use radio codes, agency-specific codes or jargon. ICS establishes common terminology allowing diverse incident management and support entities to work together.

The ICS command function may be carried out in two ways:

- As a *Single Command* in which the Incident Commander will have complete responsibility for incident management. A Single Command may be simple, involving an Incident Commander and single resources, or it may be a complex organizational structure with an Incident Management Team.
- As a *Unified Command* in which responding agencies and/or jurisdictions with responsibility for the incident share incident management.

Major ICS functions such as planning, logistics, operations, finance and working with the press are described in detail so the organization size can change to match the particular incident's requirements. The IC can consist of only a single individual for a small incident or it can expand to a Command Staff for a large incident.

ICS has a concise span of control. Since management works well with a small number of people, the ICS typically is designed so that throughout the system, no leader has more than about five people reporting to them.

In some areas the ICS evaluates and determines what resources will be needed to start recovery. Amateur communicators are typically within the Logistics Section, Service Branch and Communications Unit of an ICS (**Figure 4.2**).

National Incident Management System (NIMS)

On February 28, 2003, President Bush issued Homeland Security Presidential Directive-5. HSPD-5 directed the Secretary of Homeland Security to develop and administer a National Incident Management System (NIMS). NIMS provides a consistent nationwide template to enable all government, private-sector, and nongovernmental organizations to work together during domestic incidents. You can also find information about NIMS at **www.fema.gov/nims/**.

While most emergency situations are handled locally, when there's a major incident help may be needed from other jurisdictions, the state or the federal government. NIMS was developed so responders from different jurisdictions and disciplines can work together better to respond to natural disasters and emergencies, including acts of terrorism. NIMS benefits include a unified approach to incident management; standard command and management structures; and empha-

Amateur Radio in Context in the EOC

After the events of 9/11 and Hurricane Katrina, changes in the emergency management and public safety arenas were inevitable. Two leaders of the Flagler County, Florida, EOC team were questioned to see how these changes have affected them and their EOC operations. Troy Harper is emergency management chief, and Bob Pickering, KB4RSY, is the emergency management technician. Both are veterans in their positions, with vast experience in all aspects of the EOC and public safety. Pickering is a communications specialist and a former County Employee of the Year.

On the topic of telecommunications, two words were first off their lips: "interoperability" and "redundancy." Since Katrina, the mantra in the field has been "let's get to where we can talk to each other," which applies to inter-agency communications and also to intra-EOC functioning. Their goal has been to "patch" communications systems together so that the ability to talk across system, function and agency is seamless, regardless of the radio or Internet service employed. For example, in the EOC's Public Safety Answering Point (PSAP) dispatch center "E-911," Harper had their system join the *Florida Interoperability Network* of voice over Internet protocol (VoIP) for instantaneous communications and networking with other public safety agencies throughout the large state.

The EOC's primary workhorse and backbone for EOC operations remains their robust, hardened analog/digital 800 MHz trunking system, with many enhancements added in the post-Katrina years. They now have more physical antenna sites throughout the county, five in total, with another single site backup. The trunking system provides all communications between the EOC and those county government officials and workers involved with the various emergency support functions (ESFs). The system is also "hard-patched," or linked into the more old-fashioned, but tried and proven VHF FM system for redundancy and also communications with Fire/Rescue and the Department of Forestry, which operate primarily on this mode. The EOC's pagers are also on this VHF system that has a single repeater and a backup simplex functioning. Pickering picked up his beaten-up, heavy duty Maxon handheld and beamed as he demonstrated instant communications across the entire Flagler EOC grid of radio and Internet systems. He can communicate with other EOCs, agencies and functions on his radio. Their VHF and UHF systems operate just above the amateur 2 meter and 70 cm bands.

Flagler Emergency Management Chief Troy Harper (right) and Emergency Management Technician Bob Pickering, KB4RSY, at the Flagler County, Florida, Emergency Operations Center. (*K1CE photo*)

The EOC also has access to the Shared Resources HF Radio Program (SHARES), an HF system sponsored by the National Communications System, with which the ARRL has a formal Memorandum of Understanding. It promotes interoperability between HF radio systems used by the federal departments and agencies. "This role has taken on added importance with the widespread purchase and use of Automatic Link Establishment (ALE) technology throughout the HF radio community," according to the NCS website.

For communications with the mega Florida state EOC facility at Tallahassee, Harper and Pickering just pick up the phone (fancy name: the Public Switched Telephone Network, or PSTN). If the landline is out or overloaded, the EOC relies on *EMnet*, (Emergency Management Network), a satellite-based emergency messaging system serving state and municipal government emergency operation centers, police, firefighters, broadcasters, hospitals, and other organizations in the state. It's a voice/data over IP system that is monitored at the Flagler EOC 24/7. They test it daily.

Formerly, the Auxiliary Communications room at the EOC featured a full HF Amateur Radio station, fixed mobile VHF/UHF FM radios and a bay of docked dual-band

sis on preparedness, mutual aid and resource management.

Tactical Traffic

Whether traffic is tactical, by formal message, packet radio or amateur television, success depends on knowing which to use, and how to use it.

Tactical traffic is first-response communications in an emergency situation involving a few operators in a small area. It may be urgent instructions or inquiries such as "send an ambulance" or "who has the medical supplies?" Tactical traffic, even though unformatted and seldom written, is particularly important in localized communications when working with government and law-enforcement agencies. Note, however, that logs should be kept by hams passing tactical traffic. A log may be relevant later for law enforcement or other legal actions, and can even serve to protect the Amateur Radio operator in some situations.

The 146.52 MHz FM calling frequency — or VHF and UHF repeaters and net frequencies (see **Figure 4.3**) — are typically used for tactical communications. This is a natural mobile radios on desktops. Now, that equipment is sorted by type and kept and maintained in hard-sided cases ready for instant deployment to the field to be operated by registered and certified amateur teams. More on this program later.

The EOC also relies on the General Mobile Radio Service (GMRS) on UHF FM, CB REACT, and others for communications with volunteers in the field in a disaster scenario. The EOC actively maintains dual-band, multi-mode radios that are monitored constantly for situational awareness with GMRS, the airport, and the marine environment (Flagler county has 19 miles of Atlantic Ocean coastline).

Turning the corner into the main Operations Room, where each ESF has a desk, computer and communications systems, the specialists pick up the phone first. If phones are not working, they can pick up a deployable ground-based voice/data/Internet capable satellite phone (*TracStar*), similar to the old INMARSAT units, but with greater functionality and lower cost. They can also communicate with the state EOC through the *ESATCOM* satellite system, and it offers connectivity with land mobile systems, too.

New Systems Being Evaluated

Harper and Pickering are evaluating "new" communications options, modes that have been in traditional use by radio amateurs for a long time: SSTV, APRS, and burst messaging systems similar to packet radio. They are also looking to new cellular broadband networks, especially *LTE Advanced*, a new standard for wireless communication of high-speed data for mobile phones and data terminals that will allow more interoperability with handheld radios and cell phones for communications with other EOC operators in the field in the region.

Amateur Radio in the EOC

In 2010, Flagler County Emergency Services, the governmental agency responsible for the management of the large EOC, elected to change the way it coordinates with volunteers, including several citizen-based emergency communications groups. Instead of having volunteer communicators and operators serve the EOC via liaison with leaders of the volunteer groups as it has been done traditionally across the country, emergency management now recruits, selects, registers, and manages the volunteers directly by having each volunteer apply and be trained for specific duties under the direct supervision of EM officials.

The program is open to all residents of Flagler County. All volunteers in this organization are trained, issued uniform shirts and given an identification badge. Members will be under the direction of Flagler County Emergency Management for preparedness, response, recovery and mitigation efforts. The program boasted 85 members, even before a public roll-out.

There are several units within the volunteer auxiliary: E-Comm, Training, Marketing/Recruitment, Logistics and Landing Zone. The initial members of the E-Comm unit were all radio amateurs, GMRS licensees, and trained SKYWARN spotters. The E-Comm unit is responsible for providing auxiliary communications support in the event of a disaster, under the direction of the EOC and under the umbrella of NIMS/ICS protocols. The EOC also trains CERT teams throughout the county, which use mostly GMRS and Family Radio Service (FRS) radios for communications.

Requirements for membership include the FEMA ICS courses IS-100 and IS-700, on ICS and NIMS protocols. Volunteers are credentialed and "typed" or classified by their training certifications and experience, and placed in a database so that as a situation develops, the EOC can alert the appropriate type of volunteers needed.

Harper and Pickering on Amateur Radio

As far as the most important elements necessary to keep Amateur Radio useful and relevant in today's continually evolving EOC environment: "Stick to Amateur Radio's core values of simplicity and on-the-fly innovation, while not losing sight of new technologies like D-STAR," they said. Harper and Pickering also said that Amateur Radio is their "When All Else Fails" system, but with the interoperability, redundancy and hardening of their own systems, the likelihood of all else failing is remote. They expressed that radio amateurs can increase their value to emergency management by branching out and broadening their training and capabilities as volunteers into other areas besides just radio communications: "Gone are the days when a radio amateur just sits at a table with his handheld in front of him waiting for messages to be handed to him for relaying, and no other function," they said. The bottom line is, the EOC wants people cross-trained for the fastest, most effective response to save lives and property as possible. The more hams can contribute to this effort, the more valuable they will be," Harper and Pickering concluded.

ICS Communications Discipline

Important considerations related to Incident Command System communications include:
- Observing strict radio/telephone procedures.
- Using plain English in all communications. Codes should not be used in radio transmissions. Limit the use of discipline-specific jargon, especially on interdisciplinary incidents.
- Limiting radio and telephone traffic to essential information only. Plan what you are going to say.
- Following procedures for secure communications as required.

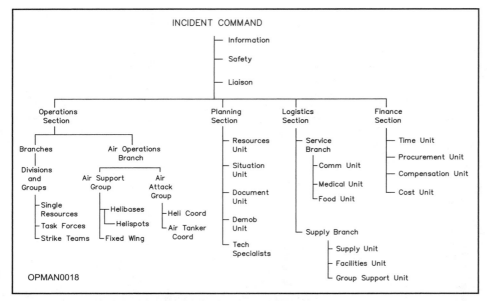

Figure 4.2 — The Incident Command System structure.

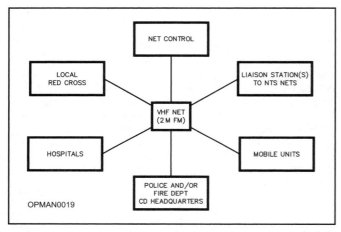

Figure 4.3 — Typical station deployment for local ARES net coverage in an emergency.

choice because FM mobile, portable and fixed-station equipment is so plentiful and popular. However, the 222 and 440 MHz bands provide the best communications from steel or concrete structures, have less interference and are more secure for sensitive transmissions.

One way to make tactical net operation clear is to use tactical call signs — words that describe a function, location or agency. Their use prevents confusing listeners or agencies who are monitoring. When operators change shifts or locations, the set of tactical calls remains the same; that is, the tactical call remains with the position even if the operators switch. Amateurs may use tactical call signs such as "Parade Headquarters," "Finish Line," "Red Cross," "Net Control" or "Weather Center" to promote efficiency and coordination in public service communication activities. However, amateurs must identify with their FCC-assigned call sign at the end of a transmission or series of transmissions and at intervals not

to exceed 10 minutes.

Another tip is to use the 12-hour local time system (for example, 1:15 PM) for time and dates when working with relief agencies, unless they understand the 24-hour or UTC systems.

Taking part in a tactical net as an ARES team member requires some discipline and following a few rules:

1) Report to the Net Control Station (NCS) as soon as you arrive at your assigned position.

2) Ask the NCS for permission before you use the frequency.

3) Use the frequency for traffic, not chit-chat.

4) Answer promptly when called by the NCS.

5) Use tactical call signs.

6) Follow the net protocol established by the NCS.

7) Always inform the NCS when you leave service, even for a short time.

In some relief activities, tactical nets become resource or command nets. A resource net is used for an event that goes beyond the boundaries of a single jurisdiction and when mutual aid is needed. A command net is used for communications between EOCs and ARES leaders. Yet with all the variety of nets, sometimes the act of simply putting the parties directly on the radio — instead of trying to interpret their words — is the best approach.

Formal Message Traffic

Formal message traffic is long-term communications that involve many people over a large area. It's generally cast in standard ARRL message format and handled on well-established National Traffic System (NTS) nets, primarily on 75 meter SSB, 80 meter CW or 2 meter FM (see **Figure 4.4**). Formal messages can be used for severe weather and disaster reports. These radiograms, already familiar to many agency officials and to the public, avoid message duplication while ensuring accuracy. Messages should be read to the originators before sending them, since the originators are responsible for their content. When accuracy is more important than speed, getting the message on paper before it is transmitted is an inherent advantage of formal traffic. Make sure to understand equivalent forms in ICS formats, as these will also be very familiar to Incident Commanders and other ICS personnel.

Packet Radio

Packet radio is a powerful tool for traffic handling, especially with detailed or lengthy text or messages that need to be more secure than those transmitted by voice. Prepare and edit messages offline as text files. These can then be sent error free in just seconds, an important timesaver for busy traffic channels. Public service agencies are impressed by fast

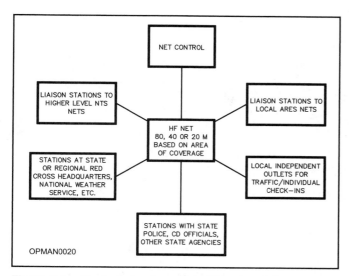

Figure 4.4 — Typical structure of an HF network for emergency communications.

and accurate printed messages. Packet radio stations can even be mobile or portable. Relaying might be supplemented by Winlink 2000 (**www.winlink.org**), a system equipped to handle messages among HF, the Internet and packet radio VHF stations.

Image Communications

Image communication offers live pictures of an area to allow, for example, damage assessment by authorities. Amateur television (ATV) in its public service role usually employs portable fast-scan television (FSTV), which displays full motion, has excellent detail, can be in color and has a simultaneous sound channel. Although a picture is worth a thousand words, an ATV system requires more equipment, operating skill and preparation than using a simple FM radio.

Video cameras and 420 – 430 or 1240 – 1294 MHz radios can transmit public service images from a helicopter to a ground base station equipped with video monitors and a video recorder. Image communication works well on the ground, too. Video coverage of severe weather adds another dimension to your ability to serve the public.

Slow scan TV (SSTV) is also popular for damage assessment. Portable SSTV operations can use a digital still image camera, laptop computer and handheld or mobile transceiver. Signals may be relayed through a repeater to increase their range. More information on these modes may be found in the **Image Communications** chapter.

Automatic Packet Reporting System (APRS)

APRS is an Amateur Radio technology that incorporates Global Positioning System (GPS) receiver tracking, weather instrumentation stations, digital cartography mapping, radio direction finding equipment and comprehensive messaging in one package. APRS has been adopted by some SKYWARN and ARES organizations as frontline technology for severe weather operations. Such a system provides accurate,

real-time weather telemetry that SKYWARN operators and National Weather Service meteorologists use to issue severe weather warnings and advisories.

A combination of APRS and Emergency Management Weather Information Network (EMWIN) can be used to transmit warnings to field spotters to help track a storm's movement as well as report tornados or hail. A mobile APRS with GPS capability can be an essential tool during and following a large scale disaster to pinpoint critical locations in an area void of landmarks, such as forest fires or search and rescue activities. New APRS-friendly radios put tactical messaging capability in the palm of your hand. See the **VHF/ UHF — FM, Repeaters and Digital Voice and Data** chapter for more information on these modes.

D-STAR

D-STAR (Digital Smart Technologies for Amateur Radio) is a digital voice and data protocol developed for Amateur Radio. While there are other digital on-air technologies such as APCO's P25 being used by amateurs that have come from other services, D-STAR is designed specifically for amateur service use. D-STAR offers voice communication and slow data transfer, using half-duplex, digitized voice transmissions, with digitized voice/audio signals and short data messages being supported. Voice and audio streams are transmitted synchronously to support communications quality reproduction. Data and voice/audio transmissions are interleaved, and routed via an international network of repeaters and reflectors connected via the Internet. D-STAR has been around for a while and is becoming well established in some regions of the US. In northeast Florida, for example, D-STAR has seen extensive use in disaster response and emergency communications.

Other Modes

Winlink 2000, IRLP, EchoLink and WIRES-II, APCO25, HF sound card modes and Automatic Link Establishment (ALE) are all additional modes and tools to help emergency communications operators answer questions such as: Can you transfer supply lists or personnel assignments between emergency operations sites? Can you get critical e-mails to the Internet if a connection goes down? Can you relay digital images of damage at specific locations? Can you track the locations of emergency personnel and display them on computer maps?

The above are critical questions that must be addressed in the contemporary ARES and emergency communications scene.

Internet

The Internet provides a fluent, high-speed conduit to communicate locally or over great distances. During non-emergency conditions, websites and e-mail are essential tools to help keep ECs in touch with many served agencies. Amateur Radio operators can contact their local organization or publicize emergency preparedness activities. Some Emergency Operation Centers have installed satellite-based Internet facilities with backup generator electricity.

Add Television to Your ARES Tool Kit

This is a TV success story for a local ARES group. The Boulder County, Colorado, ARES group (District 11) — known as BCARES — has experienced much success working with our county's emergency services organizations; in particular, fire and law enforcement. BCARES's tool kit includes all of the usual ham services, including HF/VHF/UHF voice communications, repeaters and various digital modes on HF plus packet on VHF/UHF with back-bone linked digipeaters. But, what Boulder County Public Safety lacked most was the specialty mode that we had to offer: television. Amateur television (ATV) is the one BCARES capability that really excites our served agencies.

We started offering TV services 20 years ago at the encouragement of Captain Bill McCaa, KØRZ, of the Boulder County Sheriff's Office. McCaa was in charge of all of the Sheriff's communications and computer operations and the county regional 911 center. Over the past few years BCARES has received many more requests for assistance using TV than for all other communication modes.

TV offers the agency information in ways never imagined by us or them. It provides them with situational awareness, a buzzword for what is happening on the ground. It helps remove the need for many voice communication exchanges for information that is already contained in the video imagery. Television allows the Incident Commander at the Incident Command Post (ICP) to actually see what is happening at the scene(s) of the incident, be it a fire, flood, hazmat issue, riot, or SWAT operation. With this information, the Incident Commander is better able to make appropriate command decisions. Via our 2 meter TV net controller, the Incident Commander is able to request BCARES cameras to provide him with specific images and information. We are able to routinely provide television and other communication services in a completely infrastructure-free manner.

Many times every year, BCARES is asked by our local law enforcement and fire departments to provide TV coverage of both real emergencies and also multi-agency training exercises. These have included large forest fires, flash floods, hazardous materials incidents, civil disturbances, large political demonstrations and protests, Halloween on the Pearl St. Mall, University of Colorado football games and SWAT operations. Boulder County ranks as the leading flash flood threat zone in the state of Colorado and BCARES is specifically written into county emergency planning.

BCARES' shining moment occurred in September 2010 when the Four Mile Canyon fire burned more than 6400 acres of forest and destroyed 166 homes. BCARES assisted firefighters by providing live TV coverage from mountaintops back to the 911 center for a week. At the end, BCARES was credited with saving several homes. See the related article in May 2011 *QST*.

When most hams think of ATV, they immediately assume it is slow scan television (SSTV). This is not what BCARES does. Our TV is commercial-grade, live video with full color and sound transmissions. On the 70 cm band, we run full 6 MHz bandwidth, vestigial upper sideband (VSB) TV transmissions. We use the same frequencies as used by cable TV. This allows our TV signals to be received directly on unmodified cable-ready TV receivers. For example, cable Channel 57 equals 421.25 MHz, and Channel 58 equals 427.25 MHz. We also use the amateur 23 cm and 13 cm bands for FM ATV. (See the **Image Communications** chapter for more information on these systems.)

A few Boulder County hams have their own home ham TV stations. With the exception of a Monday night TV net, there is little routine ham TV activity in the county. When we have a BCARES operation going, there may be

Actual BCARES Flagstaff mountain video camera footage of slurry bombing runs on the forest fire. (*KH6HTV photo*)

as many as four or five TV channels lighting up and becoming active simultaneously on the 70 cm and 23 cm bands. Out of the 80+ BCARES members, about half are TV trained and capable of operating our TV equipment.

When using TV for ARES operations, the same FCC rules and guidelines apply as for voice and data transmissions. We use common sense and decency along with the FCC rules to determine which pictures are appropriate to transmit. BCARES has turned down some requests for TV, typically for foot and bicycle races, when we determined they were for commercial, rather than valid public safety purposes.

BCARES forest fire spotter and video team member Jim Andrews, KH6HTV, on the summit of Flagstaff mountain. (*KB9TTI photo*)

BCARES uses commercial, off-the-shelf, consumer-grade, Sony video camcorders. Our latest cameras are high-definition, but we only transmit conventional standard definition pictures. Using 1080i high-definition cameras results in much better quality images, even when transmitted in analog 480i, standard definition. The Sony camcorders include an infrared night vision capability that has been useful for low-light operations. For example, images we provided to the fire chief of a 2002 forest fire on the outskirts of Boulder revealed nighttime hot smoke clouds that were not obvious to the naked human eye. Through a long telephoto lens, the chief was able to follow the progress of his fire crews advancing up the mountainside toward the fire line.

In our 911 center equipment cache, we have several complete, portable TV transmitters packaged in backpacks. They are complete ready-to-go kits with Sony HD-TV camera, tripod, transmitter, antenna and battery. A flexible 70 cm antenna is mounted high on the camera tripod, with a coax feed from the transmitter in the backpack. A 12 V, 7 amp-hour battery is sufficient for three hours or more of continuous TV transmission.

Television has proved to be very useful to the Boulder County public safety agencies and as a result has gotten a lot more hams active in public service. There is nothing worse than having a group of dedicated ARES volunteers that never get called upon to serve. After a while they lose interest. Then, when they are really needed, they are not available, or they are untrained. With TV, that has happened far less to BCARES. We get called upon a lot. We recommend that other ARES groups consider adding TV to their ARES tool kits. — *Jim Andrews, KH6HTV, Boulder, Colorado ARES; TV Repeater Trustee WØBCR*

AMATEUR RADIO GROUPS

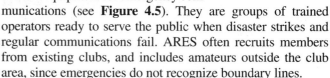

The Amateur Radio Emergency Service (ARES)

In 1935, the ARRL developed what is now called the Amateur Radio Emergency Service (ARES), an organization of radio amateurs who have voluntarily registered their capabilities and equipment for emergency communications (see **Figure 4.5**). They are groups of trained operators ready to serve the public when disaster strikes and regular communications fail. ARES often recruits members from existing clubs, and includes amateurs outside the club area, since emergencies do not recognize boundary lines.

Are you interested in public service activities or emergency preparedness? Join ARES in your area and exchange ideas, ask questions and help with message centers, sports events or weather spotting. Any licensed amateur with a sincere desire to serve is eligible for ARES membership. The possession of emergency-powered equipment is a plus, but it is not a requirement. An ARES group needs to refresh its training with meetings, scheduled nets, drills or real emergencies. An effective ARES group is to our benefit, as well as to the benefit of the entire community. Information about ARES may be obtained from your ARRL Section Manager (contact information is available from **www.arrl.org** or a recent issue of *QST*).

The Amateur Radio Emergency Service has responded countless times to communications emergencies. ARES also

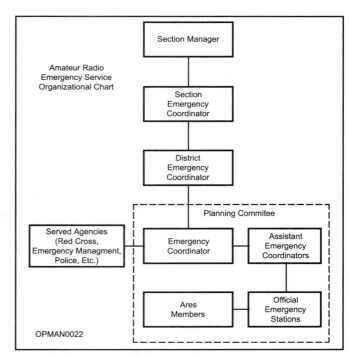

Figure 4.5 — Section structure for ARES.

introduces Amateur Radio to the ever-changing stream of agency officials. Experience has proven that radio amateurs react and work together more capably in time of emergency when practice has been conducted in an organized group. There is no substitute for experience gained — before the need arises.

Official Emergency Station (OES)

After you get some ARES training and practice, you might want to refine your skills in emergency communications. If you possess a full ARRL membership, there are several opportunities available. The first is the OES appointment, which requires regular participation in ARES including drills, emergency nets and, possibly, real disaster situations. An OES aims for high standards of activity, emergency preparedness and operating skills.

Emergency Coordinator (EC)

Next, when you feel qualified enough to become a team leader of your local ARES group, consider the EC appointment, if that position is vacant in your area. An EC, usually responsible for a county or similar geographic area, is the person who can plan, organize, maintain response-readiness and coordinate for emergency communications (see **Figure 4.6**).

Much of the work involves promoting a working relationship with local government and agencies. The busy EC can hold meetings, train members, keep records, encourage newcomers, determine equipment availability, lead others in drills or be first on the scene in an actual disaster. Some highly populated or emergency-prone areas may also need one or more Assistant Emergency Coordinators (AEC) to help the EC. The AEC is an appointment made by an EC. The AEC position can be held by a ham with any class of license; they need not be ARRL members.

District Emergency Coordinator (DEC)

If there are many ARES groups in an area, a DEC may be appointed. Usually responsible for several counties, the DEC coordinates emergency plans between local ARES

George Forsyth, AA7GS, operated the North Central Montana ARES communications van from this location along the banks of the Missouri River. ARES supported exercises at the Wild Land Fire Academy, which provides certification training for volunteer and contract wild land firefighters. (*AE7JJ photo*)

groups, encourages activity on ARES nets, directs the overall communication needs of a large area or can be a backup for an EC. As a model emergency communicator, the DEC trains clubs in tactical traffic, formal traffic, disaster communications and operating skills.

An Assistant DEC (ADEC) may assist the District Emergency Coordinator with general leadership matters as the DEC's alternate, or the ADEC may be assigned to handle a specific important function that does not fall within the scope of the duties of the DEC's other assistants.

Section Emergency Coordinator (SEC)

Finally, there is one rare individual who can qualify as the top leader of the emergency structure in each ARRL Section — the SEC. Only the Section Manager can appoint a candidate to become the SEC. The SEC does some fairly hefty work on a section-wide level: making policies and plans and establishing goals, selecting the DECs and ECs, promoting ARES membership and keeping tabs on emergency preparedness. During an actual emergency, the SEC follows activities from behind the scenes, making sure that plans work and section communications are effective.

An Assistant SEC (ASEC) may assist the Section Emergency Coordinator with general leadership matters as the SEC's alternate, or the ASEC may be assigned to handle a specific important function that does not fall within the scope of the duties of the SEC's other assistants.

ARRL Field Organization

The overall leader of the ARRL Field Organization in each section is the Section

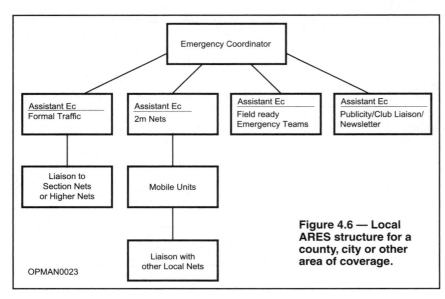

Figure 4.6 — Local ARES structure for a county, city or other area of coverage.

OPMAN0023

Manager, who is elected by the ARRL membership in that section. For further details on the Field Organization, visit these ARRL web pages for more information: **www.arrl.org/ field-organization** and **www.arrl.org/sections**.

Radio Amateur Civil Emergency Service (RACES)

The Radio Amateur Civil Emergency Service (RACES) was set up in 1952 as a special phase of the Amateur Radio Service conducted by volunteer licensed amateurs. It is currently designed to provide emergency communications to local or state governmental agencies during times when normal communications are down or overloaded.

RACES operation is authorized during periods of local, regional or national civil emergencies by the FCC upon request of a state or federal official. While RACES was originally based on potential use during wartime, it now encompasses all types of emergencies and natural disasters. RACES is usually administered by a state-level Office of Emergency Management.

Amateurs operating in a local RACES organization must be officially enrolled (registered). RACES operation is conducted by amateurs using their own primary station licenses, and by existing RACES stations. The FCC no longer issues new RACES (WC prefix) station call signs. Operator privileges in RACES are dependent upon, and identical to, those for the class of license held in the Amateur Radio Service. All of the authorized frequencies and emissions allocated to the Amateur Radio Service are also available to RACES on a shared basis.

When operating in a RACES capacity, RACES stations and amateurs registered in the local RACES organization may not communicate with amateurs not operating in a similar capacity. See FCC regulations for further information.

Although RACES and ARES are separate entities, the ARRL advocates dual membership and cooperative efforts between both groups whenever possible. The RACES regulations make it simple for an ARES group whose members are all enrolled in and certified by RACES to operate in an emergency with great flexibility. Using the same operators and the same frequencies, an ARES group also enrolled as RACES can "switch hats" from ARES to RACES or RACES to ARES to meet the requirements of the situation as it develops. For example, during a "non-declared emergency," ARES can operate under ARES, but when an emergency or disaster is officially declared by a state or federal authority, the operation can become RACES with no change in personnel or frequencies.

Where there currently is no RACES, it would be a simple matter for an ARES group to enroll in that capacity, after a presentation to the civil-preparedness authorities. For more information on RACES, contact your State Emergency Management, or FEMA.

The National Traffic System

In 1949 the ARRL created the National Traffic System to handle medium and long-haul formal message traffic through networks whose operations can be expedited to meet the needs of an emergency situation.

The main function of NTS in an emergency is to link various local activities and to allow traffic destined outside of a local area to be systematically relayed to the addressee. In a few rare cases, a message can be handled by taking it directly to a net in the state where the addressee lives for rapid delivery by an amateur there within toll-free calling distance. However, NTS is set up on the basis of being able to relay large amounts of traffic systematically, efficiently and according to an established flow pattern. This proven and dependable scheme is what makes NTS so vital to emergency communications. See the **Traffic Handling** chapter for more information on NTS.

Additional details on ARES and NTS can be found online in these ARRL resources: *Public Service Communications Manual*, (**www.arrl.org/public-service-communications-manual**); *NTS Manual* (**www.arrl.org/nts-manual**), and the *ARRL Net Search* (**www.arrl.org/net-directory-search**). Information on emergency and public service communications also appear regularly in *QST*.

This American Red Cross Emergency Communications Vehicle carries many different kinds of communications gear, including Amateur Radio. Increasingly, amateurs must be familiar with the various communications systems used by served agencies in addition to Amateur Radio. (*Elizabeth Leslie photos*)

GOVERNMENT AND NGO RELIEF AGENCIES

Government and non-governmental organizations (NGOs) as relief agencies provide effective emergency management to help communities in disasters. They often rely on normal communications channels, but even reliable communications systems may fail, be unavailable or become overloaded in an emergency. Furthermore, in disaster situations, agency-to-agency radio systems may be incompatible.

Fortunately, Amateur Radio communicators can serve and support in these situations. We can bridge communications gaps with mobile, portable and fixed stations. We also supply trained volunteers needed by the agencies for collection and exchange of critical emergency information.

As government and relief agencies become more dependent on volunteer programs, they quickly recognize the value of efforts of radio amateurs who serve the public interest. This public recognition is important support for the continued existence and justification of Amateur Radio.

By using Amateur Radio operators in the amateur frequency bands, the ARRL has been and continues to be in the forefront of supplying emergency communications, either directly to the general public or through various agencies. In fact, there are several organizations that have signed formal agreements with the ARRL: American Red Cross; National Weather Service; Department of Homeland Security — Citizen Corps, FEMA; Association of Public-Safety Communications Officials — International; National Communications System; National Association of Radio and Telecommunications Engineers; Salvation Army; Society of Broadcast Engineers; Quarter Century Wireless Association; and Radio Emergency Associated Communication Teams. Each of these agreements is available on the ARRL website at **www.arrl.org/served-agencies-and-partners**.

The American National Red Cross and the Salvation Army extend assistance to individuals and families in times of disaster. Red Cross chapters, for example, establish, coordinate and maintain continuity of communications during disaster-relief operations (both national and international). These agencies have long recognized that the Amateur Radio Service, because of its excellent geographical station coverage, can render valuable aid.

In June 2003, ARRL became an official affiliate program of Citizen Corps, an initiative within the Department of Homeland Security (DHS) to enhance public preparedness and safety. The new Statement of Affiliation (SoA) makes ARRL an affiliate under the four charter Citizen Corps programs — Neighborhood Watch, Volunteers in Police Service, Community Emergency Response Teams and Medical Reserve Corps. The League joins the National Safety Council, Points of Light Foundation, National Voluntary Organizations Active in Disaster, National Volunteer Fire Council, National Fire Protection Association, Save A Life Foundation and The Jaycees as Citizen Corps affiliate programs. Today, Citizen Corps groups are at the community and state levels to assist first responders.

The Statement of Affiliation calls on the Department of Homeland Security and ARRL to raise public awareness of Amateur Radio as a safety resource. DHS and ARRL will cooperate in providing training and accreditation for Amateur Radio emergency communications. They will work together to promote the formation of local Citizen Corps councils and assist them with education, training and volunteer service opportunities that support first responders, disaster relief organizations and community safety efforts.

ARRL has worked very closely with the Federal Emergency Management Agency (FEMA) beginning in 1984 when a Memorandum of Understanding was inked that helped ARRL volunteers coordinate their services with emergency management at all levels of government. FEMA's job was as a "last responder," as opposed to first responders (the local, county and state emergency management agencies).

The National Communication System (NCS) is a confederation of government agencies and departments established by a Presidential Memorandum to ensure that the critical telecommunication needs of the Federal Government can be met in an emergency. The ARRL Field Organization continues to participate in communications tests sponsored by NCS to study telecommunications readiness in any conceivable national emergency. Through this participation, radio amateurs have received recognition at the highest levels of government.

The Association of Public Safety Communications Officials — International (APCO) and amateurs share common bonds of communications in the public interest. APCO is made up of law enforcement, fire and public safety communications personnel. These officials have primary responsibility for the management, maintenance and operation of communications facilities in the public domain. They also establish international standards for public safety communications, professionalism and continuity of communications through education, standardization and the exchange of information.

The National Weather Service (NWS) consists of a national headquarters in Washington, DC, six regional offices and over 200 local offices throughout the US. The ARRL Field Organization cooperates with NWS in establishing SKYWARN networks for weather spotting and communications. SKYWARN is a plan sponsored by NWS to report and track destructive storms or other severe weather conditions.

An increased awareness of radio amateur capabilities has also been fostered by ARRL's active participation as a member of the National Volunteer Organizations Active in Disaster (NVOAD). NVOAD coordinates the volunteer efforts of its member-agencies (the Red Cross and Salvation Army are among its members).

ARRL and radio amateurs continue to accelerate their presence with these agencies. This enhanced image and recognition of Amateur Radio attracts more "customers" for amateurs and our communications skills.

WORKING WITH SERVED AGENCIES

Amateur Radio affords public safety agencies like those listed above and local police and fire officials, with an extremely valuable resource in times of emergency. Once initial acceptance by the authorities is achieved, an ongoing working relationship between amateurs and safety agencies is based on the efficiency of our performance. Officials tend to be very cautious and skeptical about those who are not members of the public safety professions. At times, officials may have trouble separating problem solvers from problem makers, but they often accept communications help if it is offered in the proper spirit.

Here are several image-building rules for working with served agencies:

- *Maintain group unity.* Work within ARES, RACES or local club groups. Position your EC as the direct link with the agencies.
- *Be honest.* If your group cannot handle a request, say so and explain why. Safety personnel often risk their lives based on a fellow disaster worker's promise to perform.
- *Equip conservatively.* Do not have more signs, decals and antennas than used by the average police or fire vehicle. Safety professionals are trained against overkill and use the minimum resources necessary to get the job done.
- *Look professional.* In the field, wear a simple jumpsuit or jacket with an ARES patch to give a professional image and to help officials identify radio operators.
- *Respect authority.* Only assume the level of authority and responsibility that has been given to you.
- *Publicize Amateur Radio.* If contacted by members of the press, restrict comments solely to the amateurs' role in the situation. Emergency status and names of victims should only come from a press information officer, or the government agency concerned.

Local ARES volunteers are the heart and soul of emergency communications. Williamson County (Tennessee) EC Bill Gerth, W4RK (left), operates at the Williamson Medical Center station with Allen Lovett, K4XXG, the Director of Medical Services for the county.

The public service lifeline provided by Amateur Radio must be understood by public safety agencies before the next disaster occurs. Have an amateur representative meet with public safety officials in advance of major emergencies so each group will know the capabilities of the other. The representative should appear professional with a calm, businesslike manner and wear conservative attire. It is up to you to invite the local agencies to observe or cooperatively participate with your group.

Shifting Needs of Served Agencies
Cross-Training in Agency Functions

More cross-training in served agency functions will add value to our contributions. Especially in the case of the American Red Cross, amateurs can increase their value to the agency by taking advantage of training courses offered for several disaster relief functions: damage assessment, shelter management, mass care and feeding, for examples.

Traditionally, amateurs have declined to perform functions unrelated to their primary radio communication interest and training. Indeed, ARRL literature has cautioned amateurs against providing unrelated services, encouraging them to concentrate on their role as radio communicators only. The caution was founded on a healthy concern that amateurs performing unrelated functions for which they were not trained would become liabilities rather than assets, and cause Amateur Radio to lose credibility. However, if we do not broaden our perspective on Amateur Radio's traditionally limited role, we minimize our utility and risk finding ourselves outside looking in when it comes to serving agencies engaged in future disaster relief. Proper training and certification in the various functions are the keys to a successful bid for greater utility and corresponding perpetuation of our public service tradition.

Integration with Other Systems

Integration of amateur systems with non-amateur systems will increase utility and value. APRS, an Amateur Radio developed technology, now incorporates computers, the Internet, weather stations and the GPS. As another example, Winlink 2000 developers have interfaced Internet e-mail and HF radio using PACTOR. Hybrid systems such as these may represent an opportunity to enhance our contributions to served agencies for the future. Emergency managers and NWS personnel all appreciate the value of APRS and similar systems in gathering information, and supporting communications from locations not serviced by their own.

Cross-Training with Other Radio Systems

More cross-training with other radio systems will make amateur operators more valuable in the EOC. A Collier County, Florida, emergency manager said at a Florida conference that he has a need for operators who are capable of operating *all* communication systems in the EOC. "When hams come in, they should be able to operate anything."

Thus, we may not only need to integrate amateur systems with other systems, but we may also want to promote programs to train our ARES volunteers to develop proficiency with new systems that do not directly integrate with Amateur Radio. Over the last few years, Florida has seen members of Amateur Radio response teams carrying cell phones and pagers. During Hurricane Andrew, municipal agencies often tasked amateurs with operating government radios. In 1992, most municipal communication employed conventional two-way radio. Today, it's 800 MHz trunking. Do amateurs today know what a trunked radio system is and how it operates? Could our volunteers operate a satellite telephone terminal to relay messages? And move it from one location to another and aim it correctly at the satellite?

The Telecommunications Committee of the Florida Emergency Planners Association (FEPA) has been asked to extend training to ARES and RACES operators in new technologies adopted by county and state emergency management agencies, rendering our amateurs more valuable in the emergency operations center. When the dust settles in a disaster, we will be remembered for how useful we were to the overall response, not whether we were using our own equipment or someone else's.

Interagency Communication

We should continue to emphasize our role in providing interagency communications during multi-agency responses. The provision of interagency communication has always been a solid, traditional role for Amateur Radio, and it appears that the need will be perpetuated for the future. Despite the institution of new telecommunication technologies in the public safety sector, there is a continuing inability of responding agencies to communicate with one another at a disaster site. As emergency responses become more sophisticated and the proliferation of new disaster response agencies continues, the need for interagency communications at a disaster site will become even more profound.

A Unified Front

Amateurs need to present a unified front to the agencies they serve. Infighting and turf wars, especially between ARES and RACES, are as old as the program itself. Toss in the mix of clubs who claim monopolies over served agencies and emergency responses in their communities, and the result is confusion and disorganization as seen by the agency officials who don't have the time to deal with it.

An educational campaign with our volunteers and clubs should be undertaken to ensure that Amateur Radio presents an orderly, professional face to the agencies we serve.

Our Unique Capabilities

Amateurs should emphasize the unique "decentralization" characteristic of the amateur service. Radio amateurs are already geographically dispersed throughout the areas to be affected by disaster. We are found in just about every community and neighborhood across the country. We're already everywhere that relief agencies would like to be, but can't,

At the Salvation Army Team Emergency Network (SATERN) communications center in New York City, Jim Wingate, WA2EIU (standing), and Michael Gomez, N2WGC, review field reports from canteen and feeding locations before forwarding them to the Salvation Army logistical officer. This operation supported the relief efforts after the September 11, 2001, terrorist attacks. (*SATERN photo*)

because of the obvious limitations. We need to reaffirm this unique characteristic in selling ourselves to the served agency community.

Expand the Client Base

Expanding our client base with new agencies to serve will maximize opportunities for Amateur Radio. If we lose the opportunity of serving some agencies as a result of our being displaced by new technology, we can hedge our bets for the future by expanding our client base; i.e. by drafting new and possibly nontraditional entities to serve. Looking for new clients to serve, some have been working with district schools in establishing an emergency communication network, with a permanent station at district HQ.

Other sectors for expanding our client base: public works departments, utility companies, transportation companies, hospitals, convalescent centers, senior citizen homes, and child care centers.

Summary

If we work to adapt to our served agency's new needs, and keep up our public service record, established more than 85 years ago, intact, we can continue to count on the valuable returns. Such support from our served agencies is priceless and we must do everything we can to safeguard it.

MAJOR DISASTERS

On September 11, 2001, Amateur Radio operators mobilized within minutes of the first attack of the World Trade Center in New York City, then responded magnificently in the Washington, DC, area and in western Pennsylvania. On September 11, 2001, and in the times since, Amateur Radio operators have demonstrated their readiness, perhaps as never before.

While ARES and RACES training might not have readied them to fully comprehend the terrible events of that day, Amateur Radio operators were among the first to volunteer their stations, their skills and themselves. Providing emergency communications tops the list of reasons that validate Amateur Radio in the eyes of the Federal Communications Commission. Given the ubiquity of cellular phones these days, some may have predicted this particular mission would evaporate. When the terrorists struck in New York City and Washington, DC, on September 11, however, commercial telecommunications systems — wired and wireless — were severely compromised. In the immediate aftermath of the crisis, telephone lines were jammed, and cell systems were overwhelmed.

Amateur Radio played a role in helping to restore order. "Never have I felt more strongly about what a great privilege it is to be part of the extraordinary global community of Amateur Radio," declared former ARRL President Jim Haynie, W5JBP, as amateurs sprang into action to do their part.

Nature relentlessly concocts severe weather and natural calamities that can cause human suffering on a large scale, and create needs which victims cannot alleviate without assistance. The Hurricane Katrina disaster of 2005 is a prime example.

Amateur Radio operators, specializing in communications, are involved in a variety of these situations. Here are several typical categories in which Amateur Radio operators play a role:

- Severe-weather spotting and reporting
- Supporting evacuation of people to safe areas
- Shelter operations
- Assisting government groups and agencies
- Victim rescue operations
- Medical help requests
- Critical supplies requests
- Health-and-Welfare traffic
- Property damage surveys and cleanup

There are several major disaster networks that come into play during large scale events: The SATERN Net (Salvation Army Team Emergency Radio Network) provides emergency communication support to the Salvation Army and populations at large, during disasters. They hold high profile nets on 20 meters during major incidents, and have a long history of excellence, discipline and service. SATERN members handle traffic in tornados, floods, hurricanes, fires, aircraft accidents, bombings, earthquakes, and more. See the SATERN website at **www.satern.org**.

The Maritime Mobile Service Net is composed of hams who serve and assist those in need of communications from foreign countries and on the high seas. According to its website, **www.mmsn.org**, the primary purpose of the net is for handling traffic from maritime mobiles, both pleasure and commercial, and overseas deployed service personnel. They also assist missionaries and persons working abroad. The Net meets every day from 12 PM until 9 PM Eastern Standard Time, and from 12 PM until 10 PM Eastern Daylight Time, on 14.300 MHz. They cover the entire Atlantic

At left, the eye of Hurricane Irene, as seen from the International Space Station. (*NASA photo*). Sean Kutzko, KX9X — part of the HQ Emergency Response Team — helped staff W1AW during the hurricane and passed area weather reports to the National Weather Service office in Taunton, Massachusetts. (*KI1U photo*)

Ocean, Mediterranean Sea, Caribbean Sea and the eastern Pacific Ocean.

The network is recognized by the United States Coast Guard with whom it has an excellent working relationship. The MMSN has handled hundreds of incidents involving vessels in distress, medical emergencies in remote locations and passing health and welfare traffic in and out of areas affected by natural disasters.

Another major player is the Hurricane Watch Net, which is described below under the heading "Hurricanes."

Severe Weather Spotting and Reporting

Nasty weather hits somewhere every day. Long ago, amateurs exchanged simple information among themselves about the approach and progress of storms. Next, concerned hams phoned the weather offices to share a few reports they thought might be of particular interest to the public. National Weather Service forecasters were relying on spotters: police, sheriff, highway patrol, emergency government and trained individuals who reported weather information by telephone. But when severe weather strikes, professional spotters may be burdened with law enforcement tasks, phone lines may become overloaded, special communication circuits might go out of service or, worse yet, there can be a loss of electrical power. Because of these uncertainties, weather center officials welcomed amateur operators and encouraged them to install their battery-powered radio equipment on site so forecasters could monitor the weather nets, request specific area observations and maintain communications in a serious emergency.

Those first, informal weather nets had great potential to access perhaps hundreds of observers in a wide area. Many Meteorologists-in-Charge eagerly began to instruct hams in the types of information needed during severe-weather emergencies, including radar interpreting. Eventually, Amateur Radio SKYWARN operations developed as an important part of community disaster preparedness programs. Accurate observations and rapid communications during extreme weather situations now prove to be fundamental to the NWS. Amateur Radio operators nationwide are a first-response group invaluable to the success of an early storm-warning effort. Weather spotting is popular because the procedures are easy to learn and reports can be given from the relative safety and convenience of a home or an auto.

Weather reports on a severe-weather net are limited to drastic weather data, unless specifically requested by the net-control operator. So, most amateurs monitor net operations and transmit only when they can help.

Weather forecasters, depending on their geographical location, need certain information.

During the summer or thunderstorm season report:
- Tornados, funnels or wall clouds
- Hail
- Damaging winds, usually 50 miles per hour or greater
- Flash flooding
- Heavy rains, rate of 2 inches per hour or more

During the winter or snow season report:
- High winds
- Heavy, drifting snow
- Freezing precipitation
- Sleet
- New snow accumulation of 2 or more inches

Here's a four-step method to describe the weather you spot:
1) *What*: Tornados, funnels, heavy rain and so on
2) *Where*: Direction and distance from a known location; for example, 3 miles south of Newington
3) *When*: Time of observation
4) *How*: Storm's direction, speed of travel, size, intensity and destructiveness. Include uncertainty as needed. ("Funnel cloud, but too far away to be certain if it is on the ground.")

Alerting the Weather Net

The Net Control Station, using a VHF repeater, directs and maintains control over traffic being passed on the Weather Net. The station also collates reports, relates pertinent material to the Weather Service and organizes liaison with other area repeaters. Priority Stations, those that are assigned tactical call signs, may call any other station without going through net control. The NCS might start the net upon hearing a National Oceanic and Atmospheric Administration (NOAA) radio alert, or upon request by NWS or the EC. The NCS should keep in mind that the general public or government officials might be listening to net operations with scanners.

Here are some guidelines an NCS might use to initiate and handle a severe-weather net on a repeater:
1) Activate alert tone on repeater.
2) Read weather net activation format.
3) Appoint a backup NCS to copy and log all traffic — and to take over in the event the NCS goes off the air or needs relief.
4) Ask NWS for the current weather status.
5) Check in all available operators.
6) Assign operators to priority stations and liaisons.
7) Give severe weather report outline and updates.
8) Be apprised of situations and assignments by EC.
9) Periodically read instructions on net procedures and types of severe weather to report.
10) Acknowledge and respond to all calls immediately.
11) Require that net stations request permission to leave the net.
12) During periods of inactivity and to keep the frequency open, make periodic announcements that a net is in progress.
13) Close the net after operations conclude.

At the Weather Service

The NCS position at the Weather Service, when practical, can be handled by the EC and other ARES personnel. Operators assigned there must have 2 meter handheld radios with fully charged batteries. The station located at the NWS office may also be connected to other positions with an off-the-air intercom system. This allows some traffic handling without loading up the repeater. Designate a supplementary radio channel in anticipation of an overload or loss of primary communications circuits.

If traffic is flowing faster than you can easily copy and relay, NWS personnel may request that a handheld radio be placed at the severe weather desk. This arrangement allows them to monitor incoming traffic directly. Nevertheless, all traffic should be written on report forms. If a disaster should occur during a severe-weather net, shift to disaster-relief operations.

Repeater Liaisons

Assign properly equipped and located stations to act as liaisons with other repeaters. Two stations should be appointed to each liaison assignment. One monitors the weather repeater at all times and switches to the assigned repeater just long enough to pass traffic. The second monitors the assigned repeater and switches to the weather repeater just long enough to pass traffic. If there aren't enough qualified liaison stations, one station can be given both assignments.

Weather Warnings

NWS policy is to issue warnings only when there is absolute certainty, for fear of the "cry wolf" syndrome (premature warnings cause the public to ignore later warnings). Public confidence increases with reliable weather warnings. When NWS calls a weather alert, it will contact the local EC by phone or voice-message pager, or the EC may call NWS to check on a weather situation.

Hurricanes

A hurricane is declared when a storm's winds reach 75 miles per hour or more. These strong winds may cause storm-surge waves along shores and flooding inland.

A Hurricane *Watch* means a hurricane may threaten coastal and inland areas. Storm landfall is a possibility, but it is not necessarily imminent. Listen for further advisories and be prepared to act promptly if a warning is issued.

A Hurricane *Warning* is issued when a hurricane is expected to strike within 24 hours. It may include an assessment of flood danger, small-craft or gale warnings, estimated storm effects and recommended emergency procedures.

Amateurs in the 4th and 5th call areas in particular can

Ground Truth

"The National Weather Service calls ham radio operators its eyes and ears — volunteers with federally licensed radio transmitters in their vehicles who provide 'ground truth' about severe weather that the forecasters can see only on their radar and computer screens.
...'They tell us whether warnings need to be extended or allowed to expire,' weather service meteorologist Larry Eblen said. '[Without them] it'd be like losing an arm.'"
— *American-Statesman*, April 5, 2004

spot and report the approach of hurricanes well ahead of any news service. In fact, their information is sometimes edited and then broadcast on the local radio or TV to keep citizens informed.

The Hurricane Watch Net on 14.325 MHz, for example, serves either the Atlantic or Pacific during a watch or warning period and keeps in touch with the National Hurricane Center. Frequent, detailed information is issued on nets when storms pose a threat to the US mainland. In addition to hurricane spotting, local communicators may announce that residents have evacuated from low-lying flood areas and coastal shore. Other amateurs across the country can help by relaying information, keeping the net frequency clear and by listening.

Tornados

A tornado is an intensely destructive whirlwind formed from strongly rising air currents. With winds of up to 300 miles per hour, tornados appear as rotating, funnel-shaped clouds from gray to black in color. They extend toward the ground from the base of a thundercloud. Tornados may sound like the roaring of an airplane or locomotive. Even though they are short-lived over a small area, tornados are the most violent of all atmospheric phenomena. Tornados that don't touch the ground are called *funnels*.

A Tornado *Watch* is issued when a tornado may occur near your area. Carefully watch the sky.

A Tornado *Warning* means take shelter immediately, a tornado has actually been sighted or indicated by radar. Protect yourself from being blown away, struck by falling objects or injured by flying debris.

"Tornado alley" runs in the 5th, 9th and 10th US call areas. Amateurs in these areas often receive Tornado Spotter's Training and refresher courses presented by NWS personnel.

Amateur Radio's quick-response capability has reduced injuries and fatalities by giving early warnings to residents. Veteran operators know exactly how serious a tornado can be. They've seen tornados knock out telephone and electrical services just as quickly as they flip over trucks or destroy homes. Traffic lights and gas pumps won't work without electricity, creating problems for motorists and fuel shortages for electric generators.

After a tornado strikes, amateurs provide communications in cooperation with local government and relief agencies. Welfare messages are sent from shelters where survivors receive assistance. Teams of amateurs and officials also survey and report property damage.

Floods, Mud Slides and Tidal Waves

Floods occur when excessive rainfall causes rivers to overflow their banks, when heavy rains and warmer-than-usual temperatures melt excessive quantities of snow, or when dams break. Floods can be minor, moderate or major. Floods or volcanic eruptions may melt mountain snow, causing mud slides. A tidal wave or tsunami is actually a series of waves caused by a disturbance that may be associated with earthquakes, volcanoes or sometimes hurricanes.

Don't wait for the water level to rise or for officials to ask for help; sound the alarm and activate a weather net immediately. Besides handling weather data for NWS, enact the response plans necessary to relay tactical flood information to local officials. Assist their decision making by answering the following questions:

1) Which rivers and streams are affected and what are their conditions?

2) When will flooding probably begin, and where are the flood plain areas?

3) What are river-level or depth-gauge readings for comparison to flood levels?

Mobile operators may find roads flooded and bridges washed out. Flood-rescue operations then may be handled by marine police boats with an amateur aboard. If power and telephones are out, portable radio operators can help with relief operations to evacuate families to care facilities where a fixed station should be set up. The officials will need to know the number and location of evacuees. As the river recedes, the water level drops in some areas, but it may rise elsewhere to threaten residents. Liaisons to repeaters downstream can warn others, possibly through the federal Emergency Alert System, of impending flooding. Property-damage reports and welfare traffic will usually be followed by disaster relief and cleanup operations.

Winter Storms

A Winter Storm *Watch* indicates there is a threat of severe winter weather in a particular area. A Winter Storm *Warning* is issued when heavy snow (6 inches or more in a 12-hour period, 8 inches or more in a 24-hour period), freezing rain, sleet or a substantial layer of ice is expected to accumulate.

Freezing rain or freezing drizzle is forecast when expected rain is likely to freeze when it strikes the ground. Freezing rain or ice storms can bring down wires, causing telephone and power outages.

Sleet consists of small particles of ice, usually mixed with rain. If enough sleet accumulates on the ground, it will make roads slippery.

Blizzards are the most dangerous of all winter storms. They are a combination of cold air, heavy snow and strong winds. Blizzards can isolate communities. A Blizzard *Warning* is issued when there is considerable snow and winds of 35 miles per hour or more. A *Severe Blizzard Warning* means that a heavy snow is expected, with winds of at least 45 miles per hour and temperatures 10° F or lower.

Travelers advisories are issued when ice and snow are expected to hinder travel, but not seriously enough to require warnings. Blizzards and snowstorms can create vehicle-traffic problems by making roads impassable, stranding motorists or drastically delaying their progress.

In some areas, local snowmobile club members or four-wheel-drive-vehicle enthusiasts cooperate with hams to coordinate and transport key medical personnel when snowdrifts render roads almost impassable. They may also assist search teams looking for motorists.

Brush and Forest Fires

A prolonged period of hot, dry weather parches shrubs, brush and trees. This dry vegetation, ignited by lightning, arson or even a helicopter crash, can start a forest fire. The fires quickly become worse when winds spread the burning material.

An amateur who spots a blaze that has the potential of growing into a forest fire can radio the Park Service and ask them to dispatch a district ranger and firefighting equipment. When fires are out of control, hams help with communications to evacuate people, report the fires' movement or radio requests for supplies and volunteers. ARES groups over a wide geographical area can set up portable repeaters, digital links or ATV stations.

Amateurs in the 6th and 7th US call areas in particular should get adequate safety training, including fire line safety

When an ice storm struck central Kentucky, local ARES volunteers helped with communications in the Emergency Operations Center for more than a week. (*Rob Neuzel photo*)

Amateur Radio operators in New Mexico supported the activities of responding agencies when four wildfires broke out within a few miles of each other after a warm, dry winter. (*W5EJ photo*)

and fire shelter deployment. Even then, travel to a fire operation only upon receiving clear dispatch instructions from a competent authority. If you don't have proper training, inform whoever is in charge of your lack of training to prevent being given an inappropriate or dangerous assignment.

Fire safety rules are of special importance in an emergency, but also should be observed every day to prevent disaster. Since most fires occur in the home, even an alert urban amateur can spot and report a building on fire. Fires are extinguished by taking away the fuel or air (smother it), or by cooling it with water and fire-extinguishing chemicals. A radio call to the fire department will bring the needed control. The Red Cross generally helps find shelter for the homeless after fires make large buildings, such as apartments, uninhabitable. So even in cities, communications for routing people during and after fires may be needed.

Earthquakes and Volcanic Eruptions

Earthquakes are caused when underground forces break and shift rock beneath the surface, causing the Earth's crust to shake or tremble. The actual movement of the earth is seldom a direct cause of death or injury, but can cause buildings and other structures to collapse and may knock out communications, telephone service and electrical power. Most casualties result from falling objects and debris, splintering glass and fires.

Earthquakes strike without warning, but everyone knows that the quake happened. Amateurs should first ensure that the immediate surroundings and loved ones are safe, and then begin monitoring the ARES frequencies. Amateurs are often the first to alert communities immediately after earthquakes and volcanic eruptions occur. Their warnings are definitely credited with lessening personal injuries in the area.

Amateurs may assist with rescue operations, getting medical help or critical supplies and helping with damage appraisals. There will be communications, usually on VHF or UHF, for Red Cross logistics and government agencies. After vital communications is handled, the rest of the world will be trying to get information through Health and Welfare traffic.

Shelter Operations

A shelter or relief center is a temporary place of protection where rescuers can bring disaster victims and where supplies can be dispensed. Many displaced people can stay at the homes of friends or relatives, but those searching for family members or in need are housed in shelters.

Whether a shelter is for a few stranded motorists during a snowstorm, or a whole community of homeless residents after a disaster, it is an ideal location to set up an Amateur Radio communication base station. An alternate station location would be an ARES mobile communications van, if available, near the shelter.

Once officials determine the locations for shelters, radio operators can be assigned to set up equipment at the sites. In fact, the amateur station operators could share a table with shelter registration workers. Make sure you obtain permission for access to the shelter to assist and do not upset the evacuees. Use of repeaters and autopatches allows Welfare phone calls for those inside the shelters to inform and reassure friends, families and relatives.

Health and Welfare Traffic

There can be a tremendous amount of radio traffic to handle during a disaster. This will free phone lines that remain in working order for emergency use by those people in peril.

Shortly after a major disaster, Emergency messages within the disaster area often have life-and-death urgency. Of course, they receive primary emphasis. Much of their local traffic will be on VHF or UHF. Next, Priority traffic, messages of an emergency-related nature but not of the utmost urgency, are handled. Then, Welfare traffic is originated by evacuees at shelters or by the injured at hospitals and relayed by Amateur Radio. It flows one way and results in timely advisories to those waiting outside the disaster area.

Incoming Health and Welfare traffic should be handled only after all emergency and priority traffic is cleared. Don't solicit traffic going to an emergency because it can severely overload an already busy system. Welfare inquiries can take time to discover hard-to-find answers. An advisory to the inquirer uses even more time. Meanwhile, some questions might have already been answered through restored circuits.

Shelter stations, acting as net control stations, can exchange information on the HF bands directly with destination areas as propagation permits. Or, they can handle formal traffic through a few outside operators on VHF who, in turn, can link to NTS stations. By having many NTS-trained amateurs, it's easy to adapt to whatever communications are required.

Property Damage Surveys

Damage caused by natural disasters can be sudden and extensive. Responsible officials near the disaster area, paralyzed without communications, will need help to contact appropriate officials outside to give damage reports. Such data will be used to initiate and coordinate disaster relief. Amateur Radio operators offer to help but often are unable to cross roadblocks established to limit access by sightseers and potential looters. Proper emergency responder identification will be required to gain access into these areas. In some instances, call-letter license plates on the front of the car or placards inside windshields may help. It's important for amateurs to keep complete and accurate logs for use by officials to survey damage, or to use as a guide for replacement operators.

Accidents and Hazards

The most difficult scenarios to prepare for are accidents and hazardous situations. They are unpredictable and can happen anywhere. Generally, an emergency *autopatch* is used only to report incidents that pose threats to life or personal safety, such as vehicle accidents, disabled vehicles or debris in traffic, injured persons, criminal activities and fires.

Using the keypad featured on most modern VHF handheld and mobile radios, the operator activates a repeater autopatch by sending a particular code. The repeater connects to a telephone line and routes the incoming and outgoing audio accordingly. By dialing 911 (or another emergency number), the operator has direct access to law enforcement agencies.

Vehicle Accidents

Vehicle accident reports, by far the most common public service activity on repeaters, can involve anything from bikes, motorcycles and automobiles, to buses, trucks, trains and airplanes. Law enforcement offices usually accept reports of such incidents anywhere in their county and will relay information to the proper agency when it pertains to adjacent areas.

Here's a typical autopatch procedure:

1) Give your call and say "emergency patch."

2) Drop your carrier momentarily.

3) Key in the access code.

4) Dial the emergency number (usually 911).

5) Wait for police or fire operator.

6) Answer the questions that the operator asks.

7) After operator acknowledges, dump the patch by keying in the dump code.

8) Give your call and say "patch clear."

9) Don't transmit continuously! Talk in short sentences, releasing your push-to-talk switch after each one, so the operator can ask you questions.

When you report a vehicle accident, remain calm and get as much information as you can. This is one time you certainly have the right to break into a conversation on a repeater. Use plain language, say exactly what you mean, and be brief and to the point. Do not guess about injuries; if you don't know, say so. Some accidents may look worse than they really are; requesting an ambulance to be sent needlessly could divert it away from a bona-fide accident injury occurring at the same time elsewhere. And besides, police cruisers are generally only minutes away in an urban area.

Here's what you should report for a vehicle accident:

1) Highway number (eg, I-43, SR-94, US-45).

2) Direction of travel (North, South, East, West).

3) Address or street intersection, if on city streets, or closest exit on highway.

4) Traffic blocked, or if accident is out of traffic.

5) Apparent injuries, number and extent.

6) Vehicles on fire, smoking or a fuel spill.

Example: "This is WB8IMY, reporting a two-car accident, I-94 at Edgerton, northbound, blocking lane number two, property damage only."

The first activities handled by experts at a vehicle accident scene are keyed to rescue, stabilize and transport the victims. Then they ensure security, develop a perimeter, handle vehicle traffic and control or prevent fires from gasoline spills. Finally, routine operations restore the area with towing, wrecking and salvage.

The ability to call the police or for an ambulance, without depending on another amateur to monitor the frequency, saves precious minutes. Quick reaction and minimum delay is what makes an autopatch useful in emergencies. The autopatch, when used responsibly, is a valuable asset to the community.

Freeway Warning

Many public safety agencies recommend that you do not stop on freeways or expressways to render assistance at an accident scene unless you are involved, are a witness or have sufficient medical training. Freeways are extremely dangerous because of the heavy flow of high-speed traffic. Even under ideal conditions, driver fatigue or inattentiveness, high speeds and short distances between vehicles often make it impossible to stop a vehicle from striking stationary objects. If you must stop on a freeway, pull out of traffic and onto distress lanes. Exercise extreme caution to protect yourself. Don't add to the traffic problem. Instead, radio for help.

Search and Rescue

Amateurs helping search for an injured climber use repeaters to coordinate the rescue. A small airplane crashes, and amateurs direct the search by tracking from its Emergency Locator Transmitter. No matter what the situation, it's reassuring to team up with local search-and-rescue organizations who have familiarity with the area. Once a victim is found, the hams can radio the status, autopatch for medical information, guide further help to the area and plan for a return transportation. If the victim is found in good condition, Amateur Radio can bolster the hopes of base-camp personnel and the family of the victim with direct communications.

Even in cities, searches are occasionally necessary. An elderly person out for a walk, gets lost, and doesn't return home. After a reasonable time, a local search team plans and coordinates a search. Amateurs take part by providing communications, a valuable part of any search. When the missing person is discovered, there may be a need to radio for an ambulance for transportation to a nearby hospital.

Hospital Communications

Hospital phones can fail. For example, a construction crew using a backhoe may accidentally cut though the main trunk line supplying telephone service to several hundred users, including the hospital. Such major hospital telephone outages can block incoming emergency phone calls. In addition, the hospital staff cannot telephone to discuss medical treatment with outside specialists.

Several handheld-radio equipped amateurs can first handle emergency calls from nursing homes, fire departments and police stations. They can also provide communications to temporarily replace a defective hospital paging system. Next, they can help restore critical interdepartmental hospital communications and, finally, communications with nearby hospitals.

Preparation for hospital communications begins by cooperating with administrators and public relations personnel. You'll need their permission to perform inside signal checks, install outside antennas or set up net control stations in the hospital.

Amateurs in Arkansas provided support for search and rescue operations following a flash flood that claimed 20 lives. (*W5LED photo*)

Working with local hospitals doesn't always involve extreme situations. You may simply be asked to relay information from the poison control center to a campsite victim. Or you may participate in an emergency exercise where reports of the "victim's" condition are sent to the hospital from a disaster site. One typical drill involved a simulated crop-duster plane crash on an elementary school playground during recess. The doctors and officials depended on communications to find casualties who were contaminated by crop-dusting chemicals. Again, never give the names of victims or fatalities over the air; this information must be handled only by the proper agency.

Toxic Chemical Spills and Hazardous Materials

A toxic-chemical spill suddenly appears when gasoline pours from a ruptured bulk-storage tank, a water supply is unexpectedly contaminated, or a fire causes chlorine gas to escape at an apartment swimming pool. On a highway, a faulty shut-off valve lets chemicals leak from a truck, or drums of chemicals fall onto the highway and rupture. Amateur communications have helped in all these situations.

Caution: don't rush into a Hazardous Materials (HAZMAT) incident area without knowing what's involved, or you may well become a victim yourself. Vehicles carrying 1000 pounds or more of a HAZMAT are required by Federal regulations to display a placard bearing a four-digit identification number. From a safe distance radio the placard number to the authorities and they will decide whether to send HAZMAT experts to contain the spills.

Follow directions from those in command. Provide communications to help them evacuate residents in the immediate

The Long Beach (California) ARES/RACES communications van is ready to go at a moment's notice. (*WB6GXS photo*)

RVs as Emergency Communications Vehicles

When volunteers flock to a disaster (and the larger the disaster, the larger the flock) there is an additional burden placed on the relief agencies to support them with food, water, and shelter. One of the great benefits of RV-owner hams is that they are already experienced in being self-sufficient for long periods of time, limiting impact to local agencies since RVers have their own food, water, shelter, fuel, power, antenna platform, mobile command post/operating location and restroom and shower facilities.

The Colorado Disaster Response Team that supported relief operations in Mississippi and Louisiana in the wake of Hurricane Katrina would not have been deployed without the knowledge that they could support themselves with the essentials — which in turn enabled them to support others. — *Jeff Ryan, KØRM* area and coordinate between the spill site and the shelter buildings. Hams also assist public service agencies by setting flares for traffic control, helping reroute motorists and so on. We're occasionally asked to make autopatch calls for police or fire department workers on the scene as they try to determine the nature of the chemicals.

The National Transportation Safety Board, the Environmental Protection Agency and many local police, fire, and emergency government departments continue to praise ARES volunteers in their assistance with toxic spills.

MUTUAL AID (ARESMAT) CONCEPT

Most disasters are local and of relatively short duration, which is why the traditional county and Section-based ARES approach is appropriate most of the time. However, disasters do not conform to state and ARRL Section boundaries. Disasters that are truly national-level catastrophes require national-level coordination. Regional disasters of less magnitude than, say, the 2005 Gulf coast hurricanes, do not require national coordination but may need well-organized responses from several adjacent ARRL Sections.

At the present time, relatively few ARRL Sections have formal, written agreements with neighboring Sections spelling out how emergency communications cooperation would be structured and managed. The ARRL National Emergency Response Planning Committee (NERPC) recommended that Section Managers should consider developing such agreements with one or more neighboring Sections, depending on the disaster hazards likely in their parts of the country. These agreements would become appendices to existing Section emergency plan documents.

The NERPC suggested that the following points should be among those considered in the mutual aid planning process and the development of formal agreements:

1) Share current phone numbers, postal addresses and e-mail addresses for the Section Manager, Section Emergency Coordinator and Section Traffic Manager in each adjacent section.

2) List major likely hazards in each Section.

3) List available resources Sections have that can be used to assist adjacent Sections. If ARESMAT are available, then list locations, points of contact, and capabilities.

4) If ARESMAT resources are needed, then Section leadership should be familiar with and utilize ARESMAT information and requirements in the PSCM.

5) List the major served agencies in each Section, whether or not a written support agreement exists, and the point of contact for each. Identify any volunteer insurance coverage, credentialing, and expense reimbursement which may be available from these agencies.

6) Describe the activation authority and the process for requesting and providing out-of-Section mutual assistance in each Section.

7) List or summarize Section currently-installed emergency communications capabilities and points of contact.

8) List Sections' major VHF and HF routine, operations and traffic net frequencies.

9) List Sections' website addresses.

10) It is suggested that the agreement should specify that mutual assistance can be invoked only by Section Managers, Section Emergency Coordinators, or specific designees.

11) It is recommended that the agreement should require certain documentation be kept when the agreement has been invoked. For example: daily documentation and logbook for SITREPS (situation reports), after-action reports, and notes on future needs.

12) It is recommended that the agreement should require each Section Manager who requests or provides mutual assistance to prepare a written after-action report which summarizes each mutual assistance activation. This report should be sent to the involved SMs and to ARRL HQ no later than 30 days following the stand-down from each mutual assistance activation.

13) Plans should be reviewed by each SM, SEC and STM annually, and updated as necessary.

Distress Calling

An amateur who needs immediate emergency assistance (at sea, in a remote location, etc.) should call MAYDAY on whatever frequency seems to offer the best chance of getting a useful answer. MAYDAY is from the French *m'aidez* (help me). On CW, use SOS to call for help. The distress call should be repeated over and over again for as long as possible until answered.

The amateur involved should be prepared to supply the following information to the stations who respond to an SOS or MAYDAY:

■ The location of the emergency, with enough detail to permit rescuers to locate it without difficulty

■ The nature of the distress

■ The type of assistance required (medical aid, evacuation, food, clothing)

■ Any other information that might be helpful in the emergency area or in sending assistance

This procedure has been used in events such as the earthquakes in Haiti, Japan and New Zealand.

INTERNATIONAL EMERGENCY COMMUNICATIONS

Many disaster situations transcend national boundaries, and that is especially true in this hemisphere. Emergency communications radio amateurs are often involved in such international scenarios. The International Amateur Radio Union Region 2 (comprising the Americas) Emergency Coordinator (abbreviated as EMCOR) is an international coordinating, planning and organizational position who is familiar with the international organization of emergency management and communications, and the emergency communications structure of his/her nation. He/she is also aware of the emergency communications structure and resources of the various Region 2 countries through continuing liaison with the Member Societies.

The EMCOR's objective is to develop compatible international norms and standard operating procedures and ensure their acceptance and adherence by all Region 2 Member Societies, which includes the US and ARRL. The Region 2 EMCOR is supported by an Emergency Coordination Advisory Group (ECAG), which has a representative from each of the Areas of Region 2. The purpose of this group is to aid and support the EMCOR in his/her work and to represent him/her as liaisons within each group member's Area, in order to support the emergency organizations of the Member Societies.

A Quick-Deploy Portable 3-Band Station-In-A-Box and Antennas

We all hope that we are never called to deploy in real emergency situations. But, if we are called, are we ready? It's a relatively simple thing to operate and provide emergency communications locally if all we need is some VHF/UHF systems. Most of us can manage this with a handheld or a mobile FM radio operating off of a battery pack or car power system. But if the situation calls for HF operations, or if we need to set up a fixed station covering all three spectrum regions HF/VHF/UHF, the problems and challenges can multiply. For rapid deployment and operability, we need radios and power supplies in a compact, portable to-go box, and an easily transportable, quickly erectable antenna system for all three frequency regions. Here are some ideas.

My solution is to incorporate the radios and power supplies into a standalone box, pre-wired for power, with two coax antenna connections and a fan for ventilation to reduce heat. Although my box is constructed of wood in a flat configuration, other materials and plans would work as well. Our flat layout provides some separation of the radios, allowing for ease of operation by two operators if desired.

The box contains a Kenwood TS-450S HF transceiver with built-in antenna tuner, a Yaesu FT-7800 dual band VHF/UHF FM radio, a 13.8 V/29 A switching power supply, fuses, power and fan switches, and an LED light.

If 120 V ac power is available, it can be used through the power supply. If there is no ac power available, direct connection for 12 V from a battery is provided. Ground connections in the box are wired to a rear panel terminal for a ground rod connection. RF and AC connectors for both antennas are also found on the back panel of the box.

Antennas

The two antennas are mounted on a single, heavy duty 12 foot tripod. The tripod is secured with tent stakes on grass, or anchored with weights (I use old brake drums) on hard surfaces. The first antenna is a J-pole for VHF/UHF, mounted vertically up the center support. The second antenna is an HF inverted-V design, with its apex

The station-in-a-box offers quick and easy deployment and efficient operability. (*AA2NI photo*)

at the center of the vertical support. A telescoping pole or other support could also be used. The center connector of the "V" is a 1:1 balun, and the two wire arms are each connected to a reel of wire mounted on wheeled supports. The proper lengths for various frequencies are marked on the reels, which are self-supporting. Enough wire is available to allow for 80 meter operation if desired.

On arrival at the operating location, the box is set out, the antenna tripod is erected, the HF antenna is set for the proper operating frequency, and power is applied. From start of setup to on the air: about 15 minutes. The unit and antennas have been road-tested during recent Field Day operations. — *Niko Gershon, AA2NI*

REFERENCES

General ARRL Resources

Public service: **www.arrl.org/public-service**
Amateur Radio Emergency Service: **www.arrl.org/ares**
ARES e-mail newsletter: **www.arrl.org/ares-e-letter**
Media resources:
www.arrl.org/media-and-public-relations

Training

ARRL training courses:
www.arrl.org/emergency-communications-training
Red Cross training: **www.redcross.org/takeaclass**
FEMA training courses: **training.fema.gov**
FEMA National Incident Management
System: **www.fema.gov/nims/**
IARU Emergency Communications:
www.iaru.org/emergency/

Major Amateur Radio Emergency Communications Nets

Hurricane Watch Net: **www.hwn.org**
Maritime Mobile Service Net: **www.mmsn.org**
Salvation Army (SATERN) Net: **www.satern.org**
Waterway Net: **www.waterwayradio.net**

VoIP SKYWARN/Hurricane Net: **www.voipwx.net**

Served Agencies and Other Organizations

ARRL/Served Agency Memoranda of Understanding:
www.arrl.org/served-agencies-and-partners
National Volunteer Organizations Active in Disaster:
www.nvoad.org
American Red Cross: **www.redcross.org**
National Weather Service: **www.nws.noaa.gov**
Department of Homeland Security — Citizen Corps, FEMA:
www.citizencorps.gov, **www.dhs.gov**, **www.fema.gov**
Association of Public-Safety Communications
Officials — International: **www.apcointl.org**
National Communications System: **www.ncs.gov**
National Association of Radio and Telecommunications
Engineers: **www.narte.org**
Salvation Army: **www.salvationarmyusa.org**
Society of Broadcast Engineers: **www.sbe.org**
Quarter Century Wireless Association: **www.qcwa.org**
Radio Emergency Associated Communication Teams:
www.reactintl.org
SKYWARN: **www.skywarn.org**

Chapter 5   Maria Evans, KT5Y

Traffic Handling — Getting the Message Through

For just pennies a day, you can protect yourself and your family from all sorts of catastrophic illnesses with the Mutual of Podunk health care policy...

Yes, at the amazing low price of $9.95, you can turn boring old potatoes, carrots, and okra into culinary master-pieces with the Super Veggie-Whatchamadoodler — a modest investment for your family's mealtime happiness...

Tired of all that ugly fat on your otherwise pristine body? Our Exer-Torture home gym will trim those bulges in 30 days or your money back...

Ah, those pitches. Everybody is trying to sell something — even participants in the specialty modes of Amateur Radio. Our eyes light up thinking about all those wondrous gizmos that digitize, packetize and equalize. Those kinds of specialty modes are easily remembered and can quickly gain popularity. Most people, though, forget about the oldest specialty mode in Amateur Radio — traffic handling.

Admittedly, it's hard for traffic handlers to compete with other specialty modes because it just doesn't look exciting. After all, tossing messages from Great Uncle Levi and Grandma Strauss sure doesn't put you on the leading edge of our high-tech hobby, does it? Yet, hundreds of nets are members of the ARRL

National Traffic System (NTS), probably one of the most highly organized special interests of Amateur Radio. Today's traffic handlers are at this very moment setting new standards for traffic handling via digital modes — as well as using traditional modes. If you enjoy emergency preparedness, traffic handling is for you. Sure, it's true that over 90% of all messages handled via Amateur Radio are routine — certainly not life-and-death stuff. But consider this: Your local fire department often conducts drills without ever putting out a real fire, your civil defense simulates emergencies regularly, and some department stores hire people to come in and pretend to be shoplifters to check the alertness of their employees. Similarly, when real emergencies rear their ugly heads, traffic handlers just take it all in stride and churn messages out as they always do.

Traffic handling is also an excellent way to paint a friendly picture of Amateur Radio to the non-amateur public. What sometimes seems to be unimportant to us is seldom unimportant to that person in the address block of a message. Almost every traffic handler can relate stories of delivering a Christmas message from some long-lost friend or relative that touched the heart of the recipient such that they could hear the tears welling up at the other end of the phone. Those

Handling traffic is a valuable skill that you'll need to know when an emergency arises. Whether you operate SSB, CW or digital modes, there are plenty of opportunities for you to join in and learn.

How to be the Kind of Net Operator the Net Control Station (NCS) Loves

As a net operator, you have a duty to be self-disciplined. A net is only as good as its worst operator. You can be an exemplary net operator by following a few easy guidelines.

1) Zero-beat the NCS. The NCS doesn't have time to chase all over the band for you. Make sure you're on frequency, and you will never be known at the annual net picnic as "old so-and-so who's always off frequency." Double-check that RIT control if your radio has one.

2) Don't be late. There's no such thing as "fashionably late" on a net. Liaison stations are on a tight timetable. Don't hold them up by checking in 10 minutes late with traffic.

3) Speak only when spoken to by the NCS. Unless it is a bona fide emergency situation, you don't need to help the NCS unless specifically asked. If you need to contact the NCS, make it brief. Resist the urge to help clear the frequency for the NCS or to advise the NCS. The NCS, not you, is boss.

4) Unless otherwise instructed by the NCS, transmit only to the NCS. Side comments to another station in the net are out of order.

5) Stay until you are excused. If the NCS calls you and you don't respond because you're getting a cold one from the fridge, the NCS may assume you've left the net, and net business may be stymied. If you need to leave the net prematurely, contact the NCS and simply ask to be excused ("QNX PSE" on CW).

6) Be brief when transmitting to the NCS. A simple "yes" (C) or "no" (N) will usually suffice. Shaggy dog tales only waste valuable net time.

7) Know how the net runs. The NCS doesn't have time to explain procedure to you while the net is in session. After you have been on the net for a while, you should already know these things.

8) Before the net begins, get yourself organized. Have at hand all the materials you will need to receive traffic. If you have messages to send, have them grouped by common destination according to the procedure of the net you're participating in. Nothing is more frustrating to the other operators — especially the one waiting to take your traffic — than being told, "Wait a minute, I've got it here somewhere."

9) When receiving traffic and you have a question about the accuracy of anything passed in the message, don't tie the net up with discussions about ZIP codes, telephone area codes, etc. Just tell the NCS that you would like to discuss message number 123 with the sending station after the net, or request to be allowed to move off frequency to clear up the matter. Remember, only the originating station can change the message — with the exception of the word count — between the number and the signature. Any suggested changes can be added as an Op Note if necessary.

10) Download a current copy of the *Public Service Communications Manual* from **www.arrl.org** and read it.

11) Don't freelance your traffic. Wait your turn to pass your messages as directed by the NCS.

happy recipients will always mentally connect Amateur Radio traffic handling with good and happy things, and often this is the most satisfying part of this hobby within a hobby.

Next time you go to a hamfest, see if you can spot the traffic handlers. They are almost always reveling in a big social cluster, sharing stories and enjoying a unique camaraderie. Traffic handlers look forward to the next hamfest, because it means another chance to spend time with their special friends from the airwaves. These friendships often last a lifetime, transcending barriers of age, geographical distance, background, and gender or physical ability.

Young or old, rural or urban, there's a place reserved for you on the traffic nets. Young people often can gain respect among a much older peer group and obtain high levels of responsibility through the traffic nets, which is good preparation for job opportunities and scholarships. "Nine-to-fivers" on a tight schedule can still manage to get a regular dose of Amateur Radio in just 15 to 30 minutes of net operation — a lot of hamming in a little time. Retired people can stay active in an important activity and provide a service to the general public.

Even if you live in the sticks, where you rarely get a delivery, you can still perform a vital function in NTS as a net control station (NCS) or as a representative to the upper echelons of NTS. You don't have to check in every night (a popular myth about traffic handling — if you can donate time just once a week you are certainly welcome on NTS). You don't need fancy antennas or huge amplifiers, and you don't even need those ARRL message pads. For the cost of a pad or paper and a pencil, you can interface with a system that covers thousands of miles and consists of tens of thousands of users. A world of fun and friendship is waiting for you in traffic handling. You only have to check into a net to become part of it.

MAKING THE BIG STEP: CHOOSING A NET AND CHECKING INTO IT

Checking into a net for the first time is a lot like making your first dive off the high board. It's not usually very pretty, but it's a start. Once you've gotten over the initial shock of hitting the water that hard, the next one comes a lot easier. But, like a beginning diver, you can do a little advance preparation to get you emotionally prepared for your first plunge.

Before you attempt to interface with the world of NTS, you need the right "software." Go online and find the ARRL Net Search page from the links at **www.arrl.org/arrl-net-directory-search**. While you're visiting the ARRL site, download two free ARRL operating aids — FSD-3, the list of ARRL numbered radiograms, and FSD-218, the "Amateur Message Form" that also includes Q signals for nets and other useful information. These are available via **www.arrl.org/public-service-field-services-forms**. The *Public Service Communications Manual* (*PSCM*) is also recommended reading (**www.arrl.org/public-service-communications-manual**. After you have a basic understanding of the materials, you're ready to pick out a net in your ARRL Section/state that suits you.

Go through the net listings and match up your time schedule with the nets in your Section/state. Your Section/state slow-speed CW net is a good choice (or your neighboring Section, if yours doesn't have one). But if you still don't have the confidence to try the big CW Section net, don't feel embarrassed about checking into a slow-speed net. Slow-speed nets are full of veterans that help with net control and NTS duties, and they're willing to help you, too. Perhaps you'd like to try the Section phone net or weather net or a local 2 meter net. At any rate, you are the sole judge of what you want to try first.

Once you've chosen a net, it's a good idea to listen to it for a few days before you check in. Although this chapter will deal with a generalized format for net operation, each net has its own special style of operation, and it's best to become acquainted with it before you jump in. If you have a friend who checks into the net, let your friend tell you about the ins and outs of the net.

When the big day arrives, keep in mind that everybody on that net had to check into the net for the first time once. You aren't doing anything different from the rest of them, and this, like your first QSO, is just another rite of passage in the ham world. You will discover that it doesn't hurt, and that many other folks will be pleased, even happy, that you checked in with them. (See accompanying sidebar for general recommendations on how to make your NCS love you!)

On CW

First, we'll pay a visit to a session of the Missouri CW Net, not so long ago, on an 80 meter frequency not so far away. Peter, KØSI is calling tonight's session, using that peculiar CW net shorthand that we aren't used to yet.
KØSI: MCWN MCWN MCWN DE KØSI KØSI KØSI QND QNZ QTC? K

(Translation: Calling the Missouri CW Net, calling the Missouri CW Net. This is KØSI. This is a directed net, zero-beat me. Any traffic? Over.)

In the meantime, John, NDØN, Geo, K2ONP and Letha, WØOUD are waiting in the wings to check in. Since each is an experienced traffic handler, each listens carefully before jumping in, so as to not step on anyone.
NDØN: N
KØSI: N

(Notice that NDØN just sent the first letter of his suffix, and the NCS acknowledged it. This is common practice, but if you have the letter E or T or K as the first letter of your suffix, or if it is the same as another net operator's first letter, you might use another letter. It's not a hard-and-fast rule.)
NDØN: DE NDØN GE PETE QTC SOUTH CORNER 1 AIØO 1 K

(NDØN has one piece of traffic for South Corner, and one for Rob, AIØO.)
KØSI: NDØN DE KØSI GE JOHN R A̅S̅

(Good evening, John, roger [I acknowledge] your traffic list. Wait/standby.)
K2ONP: M
KØSI: M
K2ONP: DE K2ONP GE PETE TEN REP QRU K

(K2ONP is representative to the NTS Tenth Region Net tonight, and he has no traffic.)
KØSI: K2ONP DE KØSI HI GEO TU A̅S̅
WØOUD: BK
KØSI: BK
WØOUD: DE WØOUD GE PETE QRU K
KØSI: WØOUD DE KØSI GE LETHA QNU TU A̅S̅

(Good evening, Letha, the net has traffic for you. Please stand by.)

(Since Letha lives in South Corner, the NCS is going to move WØOUD and NDØN off frequency to pass the South Corner traffic.)
KØSI: ØN?
NDØN: HR

(HR [here], or C [yes] are both acceptable ways to answer the NCS, who will usually use only your suffix from here on out to address questions to you.)
KØSI: OUD?
WØOUD: C
KØSI: NDØN ES WØOUD QNY UP 4 SOUTH CORNER K

(Go up 4 kHz and pass the South Corner traffic.)
NDØN: GG (Going)
WØOUD: GG

(When two stations go off frequency, the receiving station always calls the transmitting station. If the NCS had said WØOUD QNV NDØN UP 4 GET SOUTH CORNER, WØOUD would have called NDØN first on frequency to see if she copied him. This is done often when conditions are bad. If they don't make connection, they will return to net frequency. If they do make connection, and pass the traffic, they will return as they are done.)
AIØO: O
KØSI: O
AIØO: DE AIØO GE PETE QRU K

ARRL QN Signals for CW Net Use

QNA*   Answer in prearranged order.
QNB*   Act as relay Between_____ and _____.
QNC   All net stations Copy.
         I have a message for all net stations.
QND*   Net is Directed (controlled by net control station.)
QNE*   Entire net stand by.
QNF   Net is Free (not controlled.)
QNG   Take over as net control station.
QNH   Your net frequency is High.
QNI   Net stations report In.
         I am reporting into the net. (Follow with a list of traffic or QRU.)
QNJ   Can you copy me?
QNK*   Transmit messages for_____ to_____.
QNL   Your net frequency is Low.
QNM*   You are QRMing the net. Stand by.
QNN   Net control station is _____.
         What station has net control?
QNO   Station is leaving the net.
QNP   Unable to copy you.
         Unable to copy _____.
QNQ*   Move frequency to _____ and wait for _____ to finish handling traffic. Then send him traffic for _____.
QNR*   Answer_____ and Receive traffic.
QNS   Following Stations are in the net.*
         (Follow with list)
         Request list of stations in the net.
QNT   I request permission to leave the net for _____ minutes.
QNU   The net has traffic for you. Stand by.
QNV*   Establish contact with _____ on this frequency. If successful, move to _____ and send him traffic for _____.
QNW   How do I route messages for ___?

QNX   You are excused from the net.*
         Request to be excused from the net.
QNY*   Shift to another frequency (or to __ kHz) to clear traffic with _____.
QNZ   Zero beat your signal with mine.

*For use only by the Net Control Station.

Notes on use of QN Signals

The QN signals listed here are special ARRL signals for use in amateur CW nets only. They are not for use in casual amateur conversation. Other meanings that may be used in other services do not apply. Do not use QN signals on phone nets. Say it with words. QN signals need not be followed by a question mark, even though the meaning may be interrogatory.

These "Special QN Signals for New Use" originated in the late 1940s in the Michigan QMN Net, and were first known to Headquarters through the then head traffic honcho W8FX. Ev Battey, W1UE, then ARRL assistant communications manager, thought enough of them to print them in QST and later to make them standard for ARRL nets, with a few modifications. (Note that the original holders of W8FX and W1UE are Silent Keys and the call signs have been reassigned.) The original list was designed to make them easy to remember by association. For example, QNA meant "Answer in Alphabetical order," QNB meant "Act as relay Between ...," QNC meant "All Net Copy," QND meant "Net is Directed," etc. Subsequent modifications have tended away from this very principle so that some of the less-used signals could be changed to another, more needed, use.

Since the QN signals started being used by amateurs, international QN signals having entirely different meanings have been adopted. Concerned that this might make our use of QN signals with our own meanings at best obsolete, at worst illegal, ARRL informally queried FCC's legal branch. The opinion then was that no difficulty was foreseen as long as we continued to use them only in amateur nets.

KØSI: AIØO DE KØSI GE ROB QNU UP 4 AIØO WID NDØN AFTER WØOUD THEN BOTH QNX 73 K

(Good evening, Rob, the net has traffic for you. Please go up 4 kHz and get one for you from NDØN [WID means "with"] after he finishes with WØOUD. Then, when you are both finished, you and NDØN are both excused from the net. 73!)

AIØO: 73 GG

As you can see, it doesn't take much to say a lot on a CW net. Now that all the net business is taken care of, the NCS will start excusing other stations. Since K2ONP has a schedule to make with the Tenth Region Net, he will be excused first.

KØSI: K2ONP DE KØSI TU GEO FER QNI NW QRU QNX TU 73 K

K2ONP: TU PETE CUL 73 DE K2ONP S̄K̄

WØOUD: OUD

(Letha is back from receiving her traffic.)

KØSI: OUD TU LETHA NW QRU QNX 88 K

WØOUD: GN PETE CUL 88 DE WØOUD S̄K̄

Now, the NCS will close the net.

KØSI: MCWN QNF [the net is free] GN DE KØSI CL

When you check into a CW net for the first time, don't worry about speed. The NCS will answer you at about the speed you check into the net. You will discover that everyone on a CW net checks in with a different speed, just as everyone has a different voice on SSB. It's nothing to be self-conscious about. As the saying goes, "We're all in this together." The goal is to pass the traffic correctly, with 100 percent accuracy, not burn up the ether with our spiffy fists. Likewise, don't hesitate to slow down for someone else. Remember, when handling traffic, 100 percent accuracy is the minimum acceptable performance level!

On SSB

Now, let's tune in a session of the Missouri Single Sideband Net.

As we look in on KØPCK calling tonight's session, keep in mind these few pointers:

1) The net preamble, given at the beginning of each session, will usually give you the information you need to survive on the net. Method of checking in varies greatly from net

Who Owns the Frequency?

Traffic nets sometimes have difficulties when it comes time for the call-up and a ragchew is taking place on the published net frequency. What to do? Well, you could break in on the ragchew and ask politely if the participants would mind relinquishing the frequency. This usually works, but what if it doesn't? The net has no more right to the frequency than the stations occupying it at net time, and the ragchew stations would be perfectly within their rights to decline to relinquish it.

The best thing to do in such a case is to call the net near, but not directly on, the normal frequency — far enough (hopefully) to avoid causing interference (QRM), but not so far that net stations can't find the net. Usually, the ragchewers will hear the net and move a bit farther away — or even if they don't, the net can usually live with the situation until the ragchew is over.

It is possible to conceive of a situation, especially on 75 meter phone, in which the net frequency is occupied and the entire segment is loaded with ongoing QSOs. In any case, it is not productive to argue about who has the most right to a certain frequency. Common courtesy says that the first occupants do, but there are many extenuating circumstances. Avoid such controversies, especially on the air.

Accordingly, net frequencies should be considered approximate, inasmuch as it may be necessary for nets to vary their frequencies according to band conditions at the time. Further, no amateur or organization has any preemptory right to any specific amateur frequency.

---

to net. For instance, some section nets have a prearranged net roll, some take check-ins by alphabetical order, or some even take check-ins by geographical area. Don't feel intimidated by a prearranged net roll call. Those nets will always stand by near the end of the session to take stations not on the net roster.

2) As you listen to a net, you will find that on phone, formality also varies. Some SSB nets are strictly business, while others are chattier. However, don't always confuse lack of formality with looseness on a net. There is still a definite net procedure to adhere to.

3) Once, on a close play, the catcher asked umpire Bill Klem, "Well, what is it?"

"It ain't nothin' till I call it," he growled.

By the same token, you need to keep in mind that the NCS is the absolute boss when the net is in session. On CW nets, this doesn't seem to be much of a problem to the tightness of operation, but on phone nets, sometimes a group of "well-meaners" can really slow down the net. So don't "help" unless NCS tells you to.

Since net time is upon us, let's get back to the beginning of the Missouri Single Sideband Net.

"Calling the Missouri Single Sideband Net, calling the Missouri Single Sideband Net. This is KØPCK, net control.

The Missouri Single Sideband Net meets on 3963 kHz nightly at 5:45 PM for the purpose of handling traffic in Missouri and to provide a link for out-of-section traffic through the ARRL National Traffic System. My name is Ben, Bravo Echo November, located in Toad Lick. When I call for the letter corresponding to the first letter of the suffix of your call, please give your call sign only."

"Any low-power, mobile or portable stations wishing to check in?"

(wait 5 seconds)

"Any relays?"

(wait 5 seconds)

"This is KØPCK for the Missouri Sideband Net. Do we have any traffic?"

"KØORB traffic"

"KØORB, good evening Bill. List your traffic, over."

"Good evening, Ben. Two out-of-state."

"Very good. Who is our Tenth Region Rep tonight?"

"Good evening, Ben. This is NIØR, Ten Rep."

"NIØR, this is KØPCK. Hi, Roger. Please call KØORB, move him to 3973 and get Bill's out-of-state traffic."

"KØORB, this NIØR. See you on 73."

"Going. KØORB."

Now, let's sit back and analyze this. As you can see, the format is pretty much identical except that it takes more words. Oh, yes, one other difference...you may have noticed that not one single Q signal was used! Q signals should not be used on phone nets. Work hard at avoiding them, and you will reduce the jargon barrier, making it a little less intimidating for a potential new check-in.

Two Special Cases

HF digital operations are almost identical to CW nets, except for the method of transmission, but you need to remember this: It is always important to zero-beat, but here it is crucial!

The other exception to the rule is the local 2 meter FM net. Many 2 meter nets are designed for ragchewing or weather spotting, so often if you bring traffic to the net, be prepared to coach someone in the nuances of traffic handling.

A few other things to remember:

1) Unlike a "double" on CW or SSB, where the NCS might get both call signs if two stations call at the same times, a double on an FM repeater either captures only one station, or makes an ear-splitting squealing heterodyne. Drag your feet a little before you check in, so you are less likely to double.

2) Be especially aware to wait for the squelch tail or courtesy beep. More people seem to time out the repeater on a net than at any other time!

3) Remember that a lot of people have scanners, many with the local repeater programmed on one of the channels. Design your behavior in such a way that it attracts non-hams to Amateur Radio. In other words, don't do anything you wouldn't do in front of the whole town!

MAKING IT, TAKING IT AND GIVING IT AWAY: MESSAGE HANDLING AND MESSAGE FORM

By this stage, you have probably been checking into the net for a while, and things have started to move along quite smoothly on your journey as a traffic handler. But in the life of any new traffic op, the fateful day comes along when the NCS points RF at you and says those words that strike fear in almost every newcomer: "Go up four, get Cornshuck Hollow."

Now what? You could suddenly feign "rig trouble" or a "power outage" or a "telephone call," or just bump your dial and disappear. After all, it has been done before, and everyone that didn't do it sure thought of it the first time they were asked to take traffic! Of course, there is a more honorable route — go ahead and take it! Chances are you will be no worse than anyone else your first time out.

To ease the shock of your first piece of traffic, maybe it would be a good idea to go over message form by the book — namely, the ARRL message form.

ARRL Message Form — The Right Way, and the Right Way

A common line of non-traffickers is, "Aw, why do they have to go through that ARRL message form stuff? It just confuses people and besides, my message is just a few words or so. It's silly to go through all that rigamarole."

Well, then, let's imagine that you are going to write a letter to your best friend. What do you think would happen to your letter if you decided that the standardized method the post office used was silly, so you signed the front, put the addressee's address where the return address is supposed to go, and stamped the inside of the letter? It would probably end up in the Dead Letter Office.

An amateur message follows a structured form that is standardized so it will reach its destination speedily and correctly. It is very important for every amateur to understand correct message form, because you never know when you will be called upon in an emergency. Most non-hams think all hams know how to handle messages, and it's troublesome to discover how few do. You can completely change the meaning of a piece of traffic by accident if you don't know the ARRL message form, and as you will see later, this can be a real problem. Learn it the right way, and this will never happen.

If you will examine the sample message in **Figure 5.1**, you will notice that the message is essentially broken into four parts: the preamble, the address block, the text and the signature. The preamble is analogous to the return address in a letter and contains the following:

1) The number denotes the message number of the originating station. Most traffic handlers begin with number 1 on January 1, but some stations with heavy volumes of traffic begin the numbering sequence every quarter or every month.

2) The precedence indicates the relative importance of the message. Most messages are Routine (R) precedence — in fact, about 99 out of 100 are in this category. You might ask, then why use any precedence on routine messages? The

Checking Your Message

Traffic handlers don't have to dine out to fight over the check! Even good ops find much confusion when counting up the text of a message. You can eliminate some of this confusion by remembering these basic rules:

1) Punctuation (X-ray, Query) counts separately as a word. ("X-ray" signifies a period and "Query" signifies a question mark.)

2) Mixed letter-number groups (1700Z, for instance) count as one word.

3) Initial or number groups count as one word if sent together, two if sent separately.

4) The signature does not count as part of the text, but any closing lines, such as "Love" or "Best wishes" do.

Here are some examples:
- Charles J McClain — 3 words
- W B Stewart — 3 words
- St Louis — 2 words
- 3 PM — 2 words
- SASE — 1 word
- ARL FORTY SIX — 3 words
- 2N3904 — 1 word
- Seventy three — 2 words
- 73 — 1 word

Telephone numbers count as 3 words (area code, prefix, number), and ZIP codes count as one. ZIP + 4 codes count as two words. Canadian postal codes count as two words (first three characters, last three characters).

Although it is improper to change the text of a message, you may change the check. Always do this by following the original check with a slash bar, then the corrected check. On phone, use the words "corrected to."

Book Messages

When sending book traffic, always send the common parts first, followed by the parts not common to all messages. For example:

R NØFQW ARL 7 BETHEL MO SEP 7 B̄T̄

ARL FIFTY ONE BETHEL SHEEP FESTIVAL
LOVE B̄T̄
PHIL AND JANE B̄T̄

NR 107 TONY AND LYN CALHOUN ĀĀ
160 NORTH DOUGLAS ĀĀ
SPRINGFIELD IL 62702 B̄T̄

NR 108 JOE WOOD AJØX ĀĀ
84 MAIN STREET ĀĀ
LAUREL MS 39440 B̄T̄

NR 109 JEAN WILCOX ĀĀ
1243 EDGEWOOD DRIVE ĀĀ
LODI CA 95240 N

Before sending the book traffic to another operator, announce beforehand that it is book traffic. Say "Follows book traffic." Then use the above format. On CW, a simple HR BUK TFC will do.

reason is that operators should get used to having a precedence on messages so they will be accustomed to it and be alerted in case a message shows up with a different precedence. A Routine message is one that has no urgency aspect of any kind, such as a greeting. And that's what most amateur messages are — just greetings.

The Welfare (W) precedence refers to either an inquiry as to the health and welfare of an individual in a disaster area or an advisory from a disaster area that indicates all is well. Welfare traffic is handled only after all emergency and priority traffic is cleared. The Red Cross equivalent to an incoming Welfare message is a Disaster Welfare Inquiry (DWI).

The Priority (P) precedence is getting into the category of high importance and is applicable in a number of circumstances: (1) important messages having a specific time limit, (2) official messages not covered in the emergency category, (3) press dispatches and emergency-related traffic not of the utmost urgency, and (4) notice of death or injury in a disaster area, personal or official.

The highest order of precedence is EMERGENCY (always spelled out, regardless of mode). This indicates any message having life-and-death urgency to any person or group of persons, which is transmitted by Amateur Radio in the absence of regular commercial facilities. This includes official messages of welfare agencies during emergencies requesting supplies, materials or instructions vital to relief of the stricken populace in emergency areas. During normal times, it will be very rare.

3) Handling Instructions are optional cues to handle a message in a specific way. For instance, HXG tells us to cancel delivery if it requires a toll call or mail delivery, and to service it back instead. Most messages will not contain handling instructions.

4) Although the station of origin block seems self-explanatory, many new traffic handlers make the common mistake of exchanging their call sign for the station of origin after handling it. The station of origin never changes. That call serves as the return route should the message encounter trouble, and replacing it with your call will eliminate that route. A good rule of thumb is never to change any part of a message.

5) The check is merely the word count of the text of the message. The signature is not counted in the check. If you discover that the check is wrong, you may not change it, but you may amend it by putting a slash bar and the amended count after the original count. See the "Checking Your Message" sidebar for additional information on the message check.

Another common mistake of new traffickers involves ARL checks. A check of ARL 8 merely means the text has an ARL numbered radiogram message text in it, and a word count of 8. It does not mean ARRL numbered message no. 8. This confusion has happened before, with unpleasant results. For instance, an amateur with limited traffic experience once received a message with a check of ARL thirteen. The message itself was an innocuous little greeting from some sort of fair, but the amateur receiving it thought the message was ARRL numbered message thirteen — "Medical emergency situation exists here." Consequently, he unknowingly put a family through a great deal of unnecessary stress. When the smoke cleared, the family was on the verge of bringing legal action against the ham, who himself developed an intense hatred for traffic of any sort and refused to ever handle another message. These kinds of

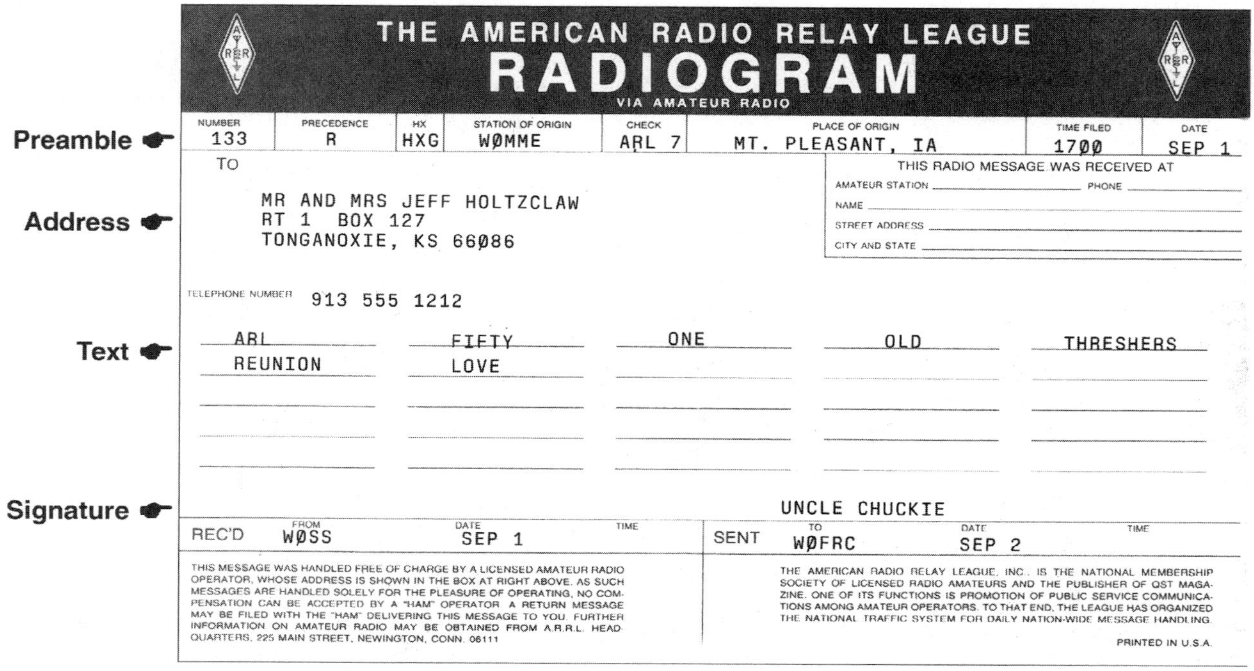

Figure 5.1 — Example message properly entered on the ARRL message form.

episodes certainly don't help the image of Amateur Radio!

6) The place of origin can either be the location (City/State or City/Province) of the originating station or the location of the third party wishing to initiate a message through the originating station. Use standard abbreviations for state or province. ZIP or postal codes are not necessary. For messages from outside the US and Canada, city and country is usually used.

7) The filing time is another option, usually used if speed of delivery is of significant importance. Filing times should be in UTC time.

8) The final part of the preamble, the date, is the month and day the message was filed — year isn't necessary.

Next in the message is the address. The more items included in the address, the better its chances of reaching its destination. To experienced traffic handlers, ZIP codes and telephone area codes can be tip-offs to what area of the state the traffic goes, and can serve as a method of verification in case of garbling. For example, all ZIP codes in Minnesota start with a 5. Therefore, if a piece of traffic sent as St Joseph, MO, with a ZIP of 56374 has been garbled along the way, it conceivably can be rerouted. So, when it comes to addresses, the adage "the more, the better" applies.

The text, of course, is the message itself. You can expedite the counting of the check by following this simple rule — when copying by hand, write five words to a line. When copying with a keyboard, or when sending a message via a digital mode, type the message 10 words to a line. You will discover that this is a quick way to see if your message count agrees with the check. If you don't agree, nine times out of 10 you have dropped or added an X-ray (a break), so copy carefully. Another important thing to remember is that you never end a text with an X-ray — it just wastes space and makes the word count longer.

When counting messages, don't forget that each X-ray (period), Query (question mark) and initial group counts as a word. Ten-digit telephone numbers count as three words; the ARRL-recommended procedure for counting the telephone number in the text of a radiogram message is to separate the telephone number into groups, with the area code (if any) counting as one word, the three-digit exchange counting as one word, and the last four digits counting as one word. Separating the telephone number into separate groups also helps to minimize garbling. Also remember that closings such as "love" or "sincerely" (that would be in the signature of a letter) are considered part of the text in a piece of amateur traffic.

Finally, the signature. Remember, complimentary closing words such as "sincerely" belong in the text, not the signature. In addition, signatures such as "Dody, Vanessa, Jeremy, Ashleigh, and Uncle Porter," no matter how long, go entirely on the signature line.

At the bottom of our sample message you will see call signs next to the blanks marked "sent" and "received." These are not sent as the message, but are just bookkeeping notes for your own files. If necessary, you could help the originating station trace the path of the message.

Keeping It Legal

In the FCC rules under the Prohibited Transmissions heading (§97.113), it states that no amateur station shall transmit "Communications for hire or for material compensation, direct or indirect, paid or promised, except as otherwise provided in these rules."

The FCC rules also have a section directly addressing traffic handling — §97.115, "Third party communications," which reads as follows:

(a) An amateur station may transmit messages for a third party to:

(1) Any station within the jurisdiction of the United States.

(2) Any station within the jurisdiction of any foreign government when transmitting emergency or disaster relief communications and any station within the jurisdiction of any foreign government whose administration has made arrangements with the United States to allow amateur stations to be used for transmitting international communications on behalf of third parties. No station shall transmit messages for a third party to any station within the jurisdiction of any foreign government whose administration has not made such an arrangement. This prohibition does not apply to a message for any third party who is eligible to be a control operator of the station.

(b) The third party may participate in stating the message where:

(1) The control operator is present at the control point and is continuously monitoring and supervising the third party's participation; and

(2) The third party is not a prior amateur service licensee whose license was revoked or not renewed after hearing and re-licensing has not taken place; suspended for less than the balance of the license term and the suspension is still in effect; suspended for the balance of the license term and re-licensing has not taken place; or surrendered for cancellation following notice of revocation, suspension or monetary forfeiture proceedings. The third party may not be the subject of a cease and desist order which relates to amateur service operation and which is still in effect.

(c) No station may transmit third party communications while being automatically controlled except a station transmitting a RTTY or data emission.

Note that emergency communications is described in §97.403 as providing "essential communication needs in connection with the immediate safety of human life and immediate protection of property when normal communications systems are not available."

It's self-explanatory. Every amateur should be familiar with these rules. Also, while third-party traffic is permitted in the US and Canada, this is not so for most other nations. A special legal agreement is required in each country to make such traffic permissible, both internally and externally (except if the message is addressed to another amateur). More information about these third-party agreements may be found at **www.arrl.org/third-party-operating-agreements**.

Handling Instructions

HXA — (Followed by number.) Collect landline delivery authorized by addressee within _____ miles. (If no number, authorization is unlimited.)

HXB — (Followed by number.) Cancel message if not delivered within _____ hours of filing time; service originating station.

HXC — Report date and time of delivery (TOD) to originating station.

HXD — Report to originating station the identity of station from which received, plus date and time. Report identity of station to which relayed, plus date and time, or if delivered report date, time and method of delivery.

HXE — Delivering station get reply from addressee, originate message back.

HXF — (Followed by number.) Hold delivery until_____ (date).

HXG — Delivery by mail or landline toll call not required. If toll or other expense involved, cancel message and service originating station.

An HX prosign (when used) will be inserted in the message preamble before the station of origin, like this: NR 207 R HXA50 W1AW 12 . . . (etc.).

If more than one HX prosign is used, they can be combined if no numbers are to be inserted, like this: NR 207 R HXAC W1AW . . . (etc.).

If numbers are inserted, the HX should be repeated: NR 207 R HXA50 HXC W1AW . . . (etc.).

On phone, use phonetics for the letter or letters following the HX, to ensure accuracy.

Such third-party agreements specify that only unimportant, personal, nonbusiness communications be handled — things that ordinarily would not utilize commercial facilities. (In an emergency situation, amateurs generally handle traffic first and face the possible consequences later. It is not unusual for a special limited-duration third-party agreement to be instituted by the affected country during an overseas disaster.) The key point here is, particularly under routine day-to-day nonemergency conditions, if we value our privileges, we must take care not to abuse any regulations, whether it be on the national or international level.

Some Helpful Hints for Receiving Traffic

1) Once you have committed the format of ARRL message form to memory, there's no need to use the official message pads from ARRL except for deliveries. Traffic handlers have many varied materials on hand for message handling. Some just use scrap paper. Many buy inexpensive tablets available at stationery stores.

2) Don't say "QSL" or "I roger number . . . " unless you mean it! It's not "roger" unless you've received the contents of the message 100%. It's no shame to ask for fills (repeats of parts of the message). Make sure you have received the traffic correctly before going on to the next one.

3) Full (QSK) or semi-break-in can be very useful in handling traffic on CW. If you get behind, saying "break" or sending a string of dits will alert the other op that you need a fill.

4) You can get a fill by asking for "word before" (WB), "word after" (WA), "all before" (AB), "all after" (AA) or "between" (BN).

Sending the Traffic

Just because you've taken a few messages, don't get the notion that being good at receiving traffic makes you a good sender, too. Good traffic operators know they have to learn the nuances of sending messages as well as getting them. Your ability to send can make or break the other operator's ability to receive traffic in poor conditions. You must be careful to send your traffic at a comfortable speed for the receiving op, and use standardized protocol (standard ARRL message form). As you will see, protocol is slightly different for phone and CW, with even a couple of other deviations for HF digital or packet operations.

Sending the Traffic by CW

Someone once remarked, "The nice thing about CW traffic handling is that you have to spell it as you go along, so you don't usually have to spell words over." Also, the other main difference in CW traffic handling is that you tell someone when to go to the next address line or message section by use of the prosigns $\overline{AA}$ or $\overline{BT}$. Keeping this in mind, let's show how our sample message would be sent:

NR 133 R HXG WØMME ARL 7 MOUNT PLEASANT IA 1700Z SEP 1
MR MRS JEFF HOLTZCLAW
ROUTE 1 BOX 127 $\overline{AA}$
TONGANOXIE KS 66086
TEL 913 555 1212 $\overline{BT}$
ARL FIFTY ONE OLD THRESHERS REUNION LOVE $\overline{BT}$
UNCLE CHUCKIE $\overline{AR}$ N (if you have no more messages) or $\overline{AR}$ B (if you have further messages)

Now, let's examine a few points of interest:

1) You don't need to send preamble words such as "precedence" and "check." The other operator is probably as familiar with standard ARRL form as you are (maybe more!).

2) The first three letters of the month are sufficient when sending the date.

3) In the address, always spell out words such as "route" and "street."

4) Do not send dashes in the body of telephone numbers; it just wastes time.

5) Always, always, always spell out each word in the text! For example, "ur" for "your" could be misconstrued as the first two letters of the next word. Abbreviations are great for ragchewing, but not for the text of a radiogram.

6) Sometimes, if you have sent a number of messages, when you get to the next-to-last message, it's a good idea to send $\overline{AR}$ 1 instead of $\overline{AR}$ B to alert the other station that you have just one more.

7) If the other operator sends a string of dits to get your attention, stop sending and wait for the last word received by the other side. Then, when you resume sending, start up with that word, and continue through the message.

Becoming a proficient CW traffic sender is tough at first, but once you've mastered the basics, it will become second nature — no kidding!

Sending the Traffic By Phone

Phone traffic handling is a lot like the infield fly rule in baseball — everyone thinks they know the rule, but in truth few really do. Correct message handling via phone can be just as efficient as via CW if and only if the two operators follow these basic rules:

1) If it's not an actual part of the message, don't say it.

2) Unless it's a very weird spelling, don't spell it.

3) Don't spell it phonetically unless it's a letter group or mixed group, or the receiving station didn't get it when you spelled it alphabetically.

Keeping these key points in mind, let's waltz through our sample message. This is how an efficient phone traffic handler would send the message:

"Number one hundred thirty three, routine, Hotel X-ray Golf, WØ Mike Mike Echo, ARL SEVEN, Mount Pleasant, Iowa, seventeen hundred Zulu, September one."

"Mr and Mrs Jeff Holtzclaw, route one, box twenty seven, Tonganoxie, T-O-N, G-A-N, O-X, I-E, Kansas, six six zero eight six. Telephone Nine one three, five five five, one two, one two. Break." You would then let up on the PTT switch and give the operator any fills needed in the first half of the message.

"ARL FIFTY ONE Old Threshers Reunion Love Break Uncle Chuckie. End, no more" (if you have no more messages), "more" (if you have more messages).

Notice that in phone traffic handling, a pause — or with difficult addresses, "next line" — is the counterpart for AA.

Also notice the lack of extraneous words. You don't need to say, "check," or "signature," or "Jones, common spelling." (If it's common spelling, why tell someone?) You only spell the uncommon. Most importantly, you speak at about half reading speed to give the other person time to write. If the receiving operator types, or if you have worked with the other op a long time and know his capabilities, you can speak faster. Always remember that any fill slows down the message more than if you had sent the message slowly to begin with!

Oh, Yes...Those Exceptions

Once again, HF digital and FM provide the exceptions to the rules. Digital traffic is very much like CW traffic. Use three or four lines between messages. This allows you to get four or five average messages on a standard sheet of paper.

When sending a message over your local repeater, remember that you often will be working with someone who isn't a traffic handler. It may be necessary to break more often (between the preamble and the address, for instance). Also, always make sure they understand about ARL numbered radiogram texts, and if they don't have a list, tell them what the message means. (The complete list of ARRL numbered radiogram texts is part of FSD-3 mentioned at the start of this chapter.) FM is a quiet mode, so you can get away with less spelling than you do on SSB.

If you yourself are already into traffic, don't try to force-feed correct traffic procedure in the case of someone just starting out; ease the person into it a little at a time. You will give a more positive impression of traffic handling and may even make someone more receptive to joining a net. After all, our goal as traffic handlers is to have fun while being trained in accurately passing message traffic.

DELIVERING A MESSAGE

Up to now, all our traffic work has been carried out on the air. All of this changes, though, when we get a piece of traffic for delivery. Now we're tasked with contacting the general public with this message. Unfortunately, many hams don't realize the importance of this action and miss an opportunity to engrave a favorable impression of Amateur Radio on non-hams. It's ironic that many hams can chat for hours on the air, but can't pick up the telephone and deliver a 15-word message without mumbling, stuttering or acting embarrassed. Delivering messages should be a treat, not a chore.

Let's go through a few guidelines for delivery, and if you keep these tips in mind, you and the party on the other end of the phone will enjoy the delivery.

1) Introduce yourself. Don't you hate phone calls from people you don't know and don't bother to give a name? Chances are they're trying to sell you something, and you brush them off. Most people have no idea what Amateur Radio is about, and it's up to you to make a good first impression.

2) Ask for the person named in the message. If he or she is not home, ask the person on the phone if they would take a message for that person.

3) Tell who the message is from before you give the message. Since the signature appears at the end of the message, most hams give it last, but you will hold the recipients attention longer if you give it first. When you get letters in the mail, you check out the return addresses first, don't you? Then you open them in some sort of order of importance. Likewise, the party on the phone will want to know the sender of the message first.

A good way to start off a delivery is to say something such as, "Hi, Mr/Mrs/Miss So-and-So, my name is Joe Amateur, and I received a greeting message via Amateur Radio for you from wherever from such-and-such person." This usually gives you some credibility with your listener, because you mentioned someone they know. They will usually respond by telling you that such-and-such is their relative, college friend, and so forth. At that point, you have become less of a stranger in their eyes, and now they don't have to worry about you trying to sell them some vinyl siding or a lake lot at Casa Burrito Estates. Make sure you say it's a greeting message, too, to allay any fears of the addressee that some bad news is imminent.

4) When delivering the message, skip the preamble and just give the text, avoiding ARL text abbreviations. Chances are, Grandma Ollie doesn't give two hoots about the check of a message, and thinks ARL FORTY SIX is an all-purpose cleaner. Always give the translation of an ARL numbered text, even if the message is going to another ham.

5) Ask the party if they would like to send a return message. Explain that it's absolutely free, and that you would be happy to send a reply if they wish. Experienced traffickers can vouch that it's easy to get a lot of return and repeat business once you've opened the door to someone. It's not uncommon for strangers to ask for your name or phone number once they discover Amateur Radio is a handy way to communicate with friends and relatives.

6) Notices of death and/or serious injury should only be handled as communication between emergency preparedness, Red Cross, Salvation Army or other relief agency officials and only in the absence of alternate commercial facilities. Radio amateurs should never, repeat never, be responsible for notifying individuals, third-party or otherwise, of death or serious injury. These should always be handled through the appropriate relief agencies.

To Mail or Not to Mail

Suppose you get a message that doesn't have a phone number, or the message would require a toll call. Then what? If you don't know anyone on 2 meters that could deliver it, or Directory Assistance is of no help, you are faced with the decision of whether or not to mail it. There is no hard-and-fast rule on this (unless, of course, the message has an HXG attached). Always remember that since this is a free service, you are under no obligation to shell out for a stamp or track someone down just because you accepted the message.

Many factors may influence your decision. If you live in a large urban area, you probably have more deliveries than most folks, and mail delivery could be a big out-of-pocket expense that you're not willing to accept. If you live out in the wide-open spaces, you may be the only ham for miles around, and probably consider mail delivery more often than most. Are you a big softie on Christmas or Mother's Day? If so, you may be willing to use a few stamps during those times of the year when you wouldn't otherwise. At any rate, the decision is entirely up to you.

Although you may be absolved from the responsibility of mailing a message, you don't just chuck the message in the trash. You do have a duty to inform the originating station that the message could not be delivered. A simple ARL SIXTY SEVEN followed by a brief reason (no listing, no one home for three days, mail returned by post office, and so forth) will suffice. This message always goes to the station of origin, not the person in the signature. The originating station will appreciate your courtesy.

Join the MARS Team

The Military Auxiliary Radio System (MARS) is a United States Department of Defense sponsored program consisting of Amateur Radio operators who provide military communications support in time of need. The MARS program is broken down into separate Army, Navy/Marine and Air Force branches.

MARS volunteers are issued military call signs with three-letter prefixes (example: AAA9AC) for their MARS operations. To join the MARS team you must:
■ Be 17 years of age or older. (Signature of parent or legal guardian is required when an applicant is under 18.)
■ Be a United States citizen or resident alien.
■ Possess a valid Amateur Radio license issued by the Federal Communications Commission.
■ Possess a station capable of operating on MARS HF and/or VHF frequencies, and on required modes.

MARS frequencies are outside the amateur bands, but many transceivers are MARS-capable, or can be modified accordingly. Check with transceiver manufacturer.
■ Agree to accept strict monthly or quarterly requirements for on-air participation.

Requirements vary a bit among the MARS branches. See these MARS websites for more information:
Army: **www.netcom.army.mil/mars/**
Navy/Marines: **www.navymars.org**

Air Force MARS is organized into Divisions around the US, but a good overview may be found at the USAF MARS North Central Division website, **www.afmars.org**.

MARS is enhancing its emergency communication capabilities and incorporating the latest technology in its operations. Check it out! — *Bill Sexton, N1IN*

NOW THAT YOU'RE MOVING UP IN THE WORLD

By now, you are starting to get a grasp of the traffic world. You've been checking in to a net on a regular basis, and you're pretty good at message form. Maybe you've even delivered a few messages. Now you are ready to graduate from Basic Traffic 101 and enroll in Intermediate Traffic 102. Good for you! You have now surpassed 80 percent of your peers in a skillful specialty area of Amateur Radio. However, there's still a lot to learn, so let's move on.

Book Messages

Over the years, book messages have caused a lot of needless headaches and consternation among even the best traffic handlers. Many hams avoid booking anything just because they think it's too confusing. Truthfully, book messages are fairly simple to understand, but folks tend to make them harder than they actually are.

So, just what are book messages? Book messages are merely messages with the same text and different addresses. They come in two categories — ones with different signatures, and ones with the same signatures. Often you will see book messages around holiday times and during fairs or other public events.

Oh, yes...one other thing about book messages. When you check into a net with a bunch of book messages, give the regular message count only. Don't say, "I have a book of seven for Outer Baldonia." Say instead, "Seven Outer Baldonia." Then, when you and the station from Outer Baldonia go off frequency to pass the traffic, tell him that it is book traffic. When he tells you to begin sending, give common parts first, then the parts that are not common to every message (addresses and possibly signatures.) By following this procedure, you will avoid a lot of confusion.

Suppose you get a book of traffic on the NTS Region net bound for your state, but to different towns. When you take them to your section net, you will not be able to send them as a book, since they must be sent to different stations. Now what? Simply "unbook" them, and send them as individual messages. For instance, let's say you get a book of three messages for the Missouri section from the region net. Two are for Missouri City, and one is for Swan Valley. Simply list your traffic as Missouri City 2 and Swan Valley 1, for a total count of 3. Books aren't ironclad chunks of traffic, but a stepsaver that can be used to your advantage. They can be unbooked at any time. Use them whenever you can, and don't be afraid of them.

Are You a Type-NCS Personality?

As net control station (NCS), it pays to remember that the net regulars *are* the net. Your function is to preside over the net in the most efficient, businesslike way possible so that the net participants can promptly finish their duties and go on to other ones. You must be tolerant and calm, yet confident and quick in your decisions. An ability to take things as they come is a must. Remember that you were appointed NCS because your Net Manager believes in you and your abilities.

1) *Be the boss, but don't be bossy.* It's your job to teach net discipline and train new net operators (and retrain some old ones!). You are the absolute boss when the net is in session, even over your Net Manager. However, you must be a benevolent monarch rather than a tyrant. Nets lose participation quickly one night a week when it's Captain Bligh's turn to call the net. If the net has a good turnout every night but one, that tells something about its NCS.

2) *Be punctual.* Many of the net participants have other commitments or nets to attend to; liaison stations are often on a tight schedule to make the NTS region or area net. If you, as NCS, don't care when the net starts, others will think it's okay for them to be late, too. Then traffic doesn't get passed in time, and someone may miss his NTS liaison. In short, the system is close to breaking down.

3) *Know your territory.* Your members have names — use them. They also live somewhere — by knowing their locations you can quickly ascertain who needs to get the traffic. As NCS, it's your responsibility to know the geography of your net. You also need to understand where your net fits into the scheme of NTS.

4) *Take extra care to keep your antennas in good shape.* An NCS can't run a net with a puny signal. Although you don't have to be the loudest one on the net, you do have to be heard. You will discover that the best way to do this is to have a good antenna system. A linear amplifier alone won't help you hear those weak check-ins!

5) *The NCS establishes the net frequency.* Just because the ARRL Net Search lists a certain frequency doesn't give you squatters rights to it if a QSO is already in progress there. Move to a nearby clear frequency, close enough for the net to find you. QRM is a fact of life on HF, especially on 75/80 meters, so live with it.

6) *Keep a log of every net session.* Just because the FCC dropped the logging requirements doesn't mean that you have to drop them. It's a personal decision. The Net Manager may need information about a check in or a piece of traffic, and your log details can be helpful to him in determining what happened on a particular night.

7) *Don't hamstring the net by waiting to move the traffic.* Your duty is to get traffic moving as quickly as possible. As soon as you can get two stations moving, send them off to clear the traffic. If you have more than one station holding traffic for the same city, let the "singles" (stations with only one piece for that city) go before the ones with more than one piece for that city. The quicker the net gets the traffic moved, the sooner the net can be finished and the net operators can be free to do whatever they want.

BECOMING NCS AND LIVING TO TELL ABOUT IT

Some momentous evening in your traffic career, you may be called upon to take the net. Perhaps the NCS had a power failure, or is on vacation, or perhaps a vacancy occurred in the daily NCS rotation on your favorite net. Should this be the case, consider yourself lucky. Net Managers entrust few members with net control duties.

Of course, you probably won't be thinking how lucky you are when the Net Manager says "QNG" and sticks your call after it. Once again, just like your first check-in or your first piece of traffic, you will just have to grit your teeth and live through it. However, you can make the jump easier by following these hints long before you are asked to be a net control:

1) Become familiar with the other stations on the net. Even if you never become NCS, it pays to know who you work with and where they live.

2) Pay close attention to the stations that go off frequency to pass traffic. What frequencies does the net use to move traffic? Which stations are off frequency at the moment? You will gain a feel for the net control job just by keeping track of the action.

3) Try to guess what the NCS will do next. You will discover many dilemmas when you try to second-guess the NCS. Often different amounts of traffic with equal precedence appear on the net, and a skillful NCS must rank them in order of importance. For instance, if you follow the NCS closely, you will discover that traffic for the NTS rep, such as out-of-state traffic, gets higher priority than one for the NTS rep's city. Situations such as these are fun to second-guess when you are standing by on the net and will better prepare you for the day you might get to run the net.

Should that day arrive, just keep your cool and try to implement the techniques used by your favorite net control stations. After a few rounds of NCS duties, you will develop your own style, and who knows? Perhaps some new hopeful for NCS will try to emulate you some day! See the accompanying sidebars for further hints on developing proper net control methods.

Handy Hints for Handling Traffic at Fairs or Other Public Events

1) Although you may only be there a day or two, don't compromise your station too much. Try to put up the most you can for an antenna system because band conditions on traffic nets in the summer can really be the pits! Usually, you will be surrounded by electrical lines at fairs, so a line filter is a must. An inboard SSB or CW filter in your rig is a definite plus, too, and may save you many headaches.

2) Don't huddle around the rigs or seat yourself in the back of the booth. Get up front and meet the people. After all, your purpose is to show off Amateur Radio to the general public.

3) Most people will not volunteer to send a piece of traffic, nor will they believe a message is really free. It's up to you to solicit business. Be cheerful.

4) Always use plain English language when explaining Amateur Radio to non-hams. Say "message," not "traffic." Don't ramble about the workings of NTS or repeaters; your listener just wants to know how Aunt Patty will get the message. "We take the message and send it via Amateur Radio to Aunt Patty's town, and the ham there will call her on the phone and deliver it to her," will do.

5) Make sure your pencils or pens are attached to the booth with a long string, or you will be out of writing utensils in the first hour!

6) Make sure there are plenty of instructions around for hams not familiar with traffic handling to help them get the hang of the situation.

7) Make sure your booth is colorful and attractive. You will catch the public's eye better if you give them something to notice, such as this suggested poster idea.

HANDLING TRAFFIC AT PUBLIC EVENTS

A very special and important aspect of message handling is that of how to handle traffic at public events. If the event is of any size, such as a state fair, it doesn't take long to swamp a group of operators with traffic. Only by efficient, tight organization can a handful of amateurs keep a lid on the backlog.

No matter what size your public event, the following points need to be considered for any traffic station accessible to the public:

1) Often, hams who don't handle traffic will outnumber traffic handlers in the booth. This means your group will have to lay out a standard operating procedure to help those not familiar with traffic handling assist the experienced ops.

Jobs such as meeting the public, filling out the message blanks, sorting the "in" and "out" piles, and keeping the booth tidied up, can all be performed by people with little or no traffic skill, and is a good way to introduce those people into the world of traffic.

2) If you plan to handle fairly large amounts of traffic, the incoming traffic needs to be sorted. A good system is to have an in-state pile, an in-region pile, and an area pile for the three levels of NTS. After the traffic has been sent, it needs to be stacked in numerical order in the "out" pile. Keeping it in numerical order makes it easier to find should it need to be referred to.

Since your station will be on for a number of hours, plan to check into your region and area nets as well as your Section net. Another good idea is to have helpers on 2 meters who can also take some of your traffic to the region and/or area net. These arrangements need to be worked out in advance.

3) Make up your radiogram blanks so that most of the preamble is already on them, and all you need to fill in is the number, check and date. In the message portion, put space for only about 20 words to discourage lengthy messages. Try to convince your customer to use a standard ARL text so you can book your messages.

A real time- and headache-saver in this department is to fill out the message blank for the sender. This way, you can write in the X-rays and other jargon that the sender is unaware of.

4) Most importantly, realize that you sometimes have to work at getting customers as much as if you were selling something! Most people have no concept of Amateur Radio at all, and don't understand how message handling, works. ("How can they get it? They don't have a radio like that," is a very common question!)

Use posters to make your booth appealing to the eye. Make sure one of the posters is of the "How your message gets to its destination" variety, such as the one shown in this section. Don't go over someone's head when answering a question — explain it simply and succinctly.

Finally, don't be afraid to solicit business. Get up in front of the booth and say hi to folks. If they say hi back, ask them if they would like to send a free greeting to a friend or relative anywhere in the US (grandparents and grandchildren are the easiest to convince!). Even if they decide not to send a message, your friendliness will help keep our image of "good guys in white hats" viable among the general public, which is every bit as great a service as message handling.

THE NATIONAL TRAFFIC SYSTEM — MESSAGE HANDLING'S ROAD MAP

Although you probably never think about it, when you check into your local net or section net, you are participating in one of the most cleverly designed game plans ever written — the National Traffic System (NTS). Even though the ARRL conceived NTS way back in 1949, and it has grown from one regular cycle to two or more, NTS hasn't outgrown itself and remains the most streamlined method of traffic handling in the world. (During this discussion, please refer to the accompanying Section/Region/Area map in **Figure 5.2**, the NTS Routing Guide in **Table 5.1** and the NTS Flow Chart in **Figure 5.3**.) More resources are available online at **www.arrl.org/nts** and in Section II of the *Public Service Communications Manual*.

Actually, the National Traffic System can trace its roots to the railroad's adoption of Standard Time back in 1883, when radio was still only a wild dream. Three of the Standard Time Zones are the basis for the three NTS areas — Eastern Area (Eastern Time Zone), Central Area (Central Time Zone) and Pacific Area (Mountain and Pacific Time Zones). Within these areas are a total of 12 regions. Why not just break it up into 10 regions, one for each US call sign district? Ah, but

check the map. You will discover that NTS not only covers the US, but our Canadian neighbors as well. Then, of course, the region nets are linked to Section/local nets.

The National Traffic System includes four different net levels which operate in an orderly time sequence to effect a definite flow pattern for traffic from origin to destination. A message flows through the National Traffic System in a manner similar to an airline passenger who starts out in a small residential town with a destination across the continent in another small town. He or she has to change carriers many times in the process, starting with a local ground conveyance to a feeder airline, to a transcontinental airline, to another feeder airline, then local transportation for delivery to the final destination. In a very similar manner, the transcontinental message starts with the originating station in a local net, is carried to the section net, the region net, the area net, via Transcontinental Corps (TCC) to a distant area net and then back down the line to delivery.

Of course the message, like the passenger, can "get on" or "get off" at any point if that's the origin or destination. Thus, a message from, say, New York to Detroit would never

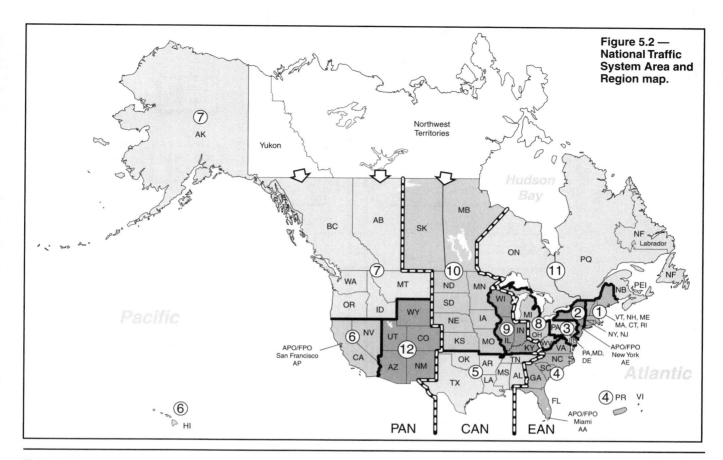

Figure 5.2 —
National Traffic
System Area and
Region map.

Table 5.1
National Traffic System Routing Guide

State/Province	Abbrev.	Region	Area	State/Province	Abbrev.	Region	Area
Alaska	AK	7	PAN	New Brunswick	NB	11	EAN
Alabama	AL	5	CAN	New Hampshire	NH	1	EAN
Alberta	AB	7	PAN	New Jersey	NJ	2	EAN
Arizona	AZ	12	PAN	New Mexico	NM	12	PAN
Arkansas	AR	5	CAN	New York	NY	2	EAN
British Columbia	BC	7	PAN	Newfoundland	NF	11	EAN
California	CA	6	PAN	North Carolina	NC	4	EAN
Colorado	CO	12	PAN	North Dakota	ND	10	CAN
Connecticut	CT	1	EAN	Nova Scotia	NS	11	EAN
Delaware	DE	3	EAN	Ohio	OH	8	EAN
Dist. of Columbia	DC	3	EAN	Oklahoma	OK	5	CAN
Florida	FL	4	EAN	Ontario	ON	11	EAN
Georgia	GA	4	EAN	Oregon	OR	7	PAN
Guam	GU	6	PAN	Pennsylvania	PA	3	EAN
Hawaii	HI	6	PAN	Prince Edward Is.	PEI	11	EAN
Idaho	ID	7	PAN	Puerto Rico	PR	4	EAN
Illinois	IL	9	CAN	Quebec	PQ	11	EAN
Indiana	IN	9	CAN	Rhode Island	RI	1	EAN
Iowa	IA	10	CAN	Saskatchewan	SK	10	CAN
Kansas	KS	10	CAN	South Carolina	SC	4	EAN
Kentucky	KY	9	CAN	South Dakota	SD	10	CAN
Labrador	LB	11	EAN	Tennessee	TN	5	CAN
Louisiana	LA	5	CAN	Texas	TX	5	CAN
Maine	ME	1	EAN	Utah	UT	12	PAN
Manitoba	MB	10	CAN	Vermont	VT	1	EAN
Maryland	MD	3	EAN	Virginia	VA	4	EAN
Massachusetts	MA	1	EAN	Virgin Islands	VI	4	EAN
Michigan	MI	8	EAN	Washington	WA	7	PAN
Minnesota	MN	10	CAN	West Virginia	WV	8	EAN
Mississippi	MS	5	CAN	Wisconsin	WI	9	CAN
Missouri	MO	10	CAN	Wyoming	WY	12	PAN
Montana	MT	7	PAN	APO New York	APO NY	2	EAN
Nebraska	NE	10	CAN	APO San Francisco	APO SF	6	PAN
Nevada	NV	6	PAN				

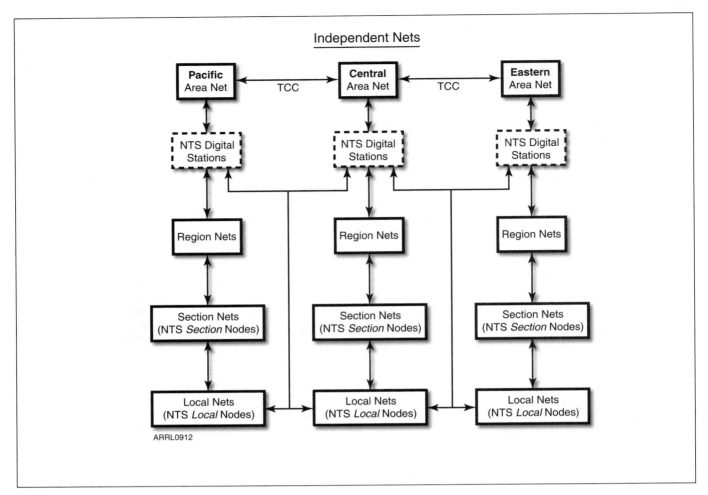

Figure 5.3 —National Traffic System flow chart.

get on TCC, but would get off at area level. A message from San Francisco to Los Angeles would not go beyond region level, and one from Syracuse to Buffalo would remain inside the Section net.

Messages may also be passed through NTS-affiliated local and Section traffic nodes that employ digital modes with store-and-forward capabilities and bulletin board operations. Long hauls can be made by NTS Digital Relay Stations at HF, which interface with Section traffic nodes, and the traditional nets of the system.

The interconnecting lines between the boxes on the flow chart in Figure 5.3 represent liaison stations to and from each level of NTS. The liaisons from area net to area net are the Transcontinental Corps (TCC). In addition to the functions shown, TCC stations also link the various cycles of NTS to each other.

The clever part about the NTS setup, though, is that in any given cycle of NTS, all nets in the same level commence at approximately the same local time. This allows time for liaisons to the next level to pick up any outgoing traffic and meet the next net. In addition, this gives the TCC stations at least an hour before their duties commence on another area net or their schedule begins with another TCC station.

The original NTS plan calls for four cycles of traffic nets, but usually two cycles are sufficient to handle a normal load of traffic on the system. However, during the holiday season, or in times of emergency, many more messages are dumped into the system, forcing NTS to expand to four cycles temporarily. The cycles of normal operation are Cycle Two, the daytime cycle, which consists primarily of phone nets, and Cycle Four, the nighttime cycle, made up mostly of CW nets. In addition, Cycle One has been implemented in the Pacific Area and Cycle Three in the Eastern Area. Now that the rudiments of NTS have been covered, let's see where you fit in.

Digital Stations

The handling of traffic among sections, regions and areas can also be accomplished alternatively, on a supportive/cooperative basis, through liaison with the traditional aspects of the system, by the set of NTS Digital Relay Stations across the country. These stations, certified by their respective Area Digital Coordinators, handle traffic by digital modes at HF. The system structure is more loosely defined than is the traditional system. They serve to supplement the existing system, providing options and flexibility in getting traffic moved expeditiously across the country, especially in overload conditions.

Fame and Glory: Your Traffic Total, PSHR Report and Appointments

Even if you handle only one message in a month's time, you should send a message to your ARRL Section Traffic Manager (STM) or ARRL Section Manager (SM) reporting your activity. Your report should include your total originations, messages received, messages sent and deliveries.

An origination is any message obtained from a third party for sending from your station. If you send a message to Uncle Filbert on his birthday, you don't get an origination. However, if your mom or your neighbor wants you to send him one with her signature, it qualifies (it counts as one originated and one sent). The origination category is essentially an extra credit for an off-the-air function. This is because of the critical value of contact with the general public and to motivate traffickers to be somewhat more aggressive in making their message-handling services known to the general public.

Any formal piece of traffic you get via Amateur Radio counts as a message received. Any message you send via Amateur Radio, even if you originated it, counts as a message sent. Therefore, any time you relay a message, you get two points: one received and one sent.

Any time you take a message and give it to the party it's addressed to, on a mode other than Amateur Radio, you are credited with a delivery. (It's okay if the addressee is a ham.) As long as you deliver it off the air (eg, telephone, mail, Internet/e-mail, in person), you get a delivery point.

Your monthly report to your STM, if sent in radiogram format, should look something like this:

NR 111 R NIØR 14 ST JOSEPH MO NOV 2
BLAIR CARMICHAEL WBØPLY

MISSOURI STM
FULTON MO 65251
OCTOBER TRAFFIC ORIG 2 RCVD 5 SENT 6
DLVD 1
TOTAL 14
73
ROGER NIØR

If you have a traffic total of 500 or more in any month, or have over 100 originations-plus-deliveries in a month, you are eligible for the Brass Pounders League (BPL), even if you did all that traffic on SSB! Make sure you send your traffic totals to your STM or SM.

Another mark of distinction is the Public Service Honor Roll (PSHR). You don't have to handle a single message to get PSHR, so it's a favorite among traffickers in rural areas. You can receive points for activities such as checking into public service nets, participating in public service events and handling emergency traffic. Candidates for PSHR need to report their monthly PSHR point total to their STM or SM. See the *QST* Public Service column for particulars or **www.arrl.org/public-service-honor-roll**.

If you are an ARRL member, you can also become eligible for an Official Relay Station appointment in the ARRL Field Organization. (For details concerning the ARRL Field Organization, see **www.arrl.org/field-organization**.)

The local radio amateur community and your section leadership officials are ready to help you get involved in traffic handling. To contact your Section Manager, see the list near the front of any recent issue of *QST* or visit the information page for your Section on the ARRL website (**www.arrl.org/sections**).

NTS and You

Before the adoption of NTS, upper-level traffic handlers worked a system called the "trunk line" system, where a handful of stations carried the burden of cross-country traffic, day in, day out. Nowadays, no one has to be an "iron man" or "iron woman" within NTS if they choose not to. If each liaison slot and TCC slot were filled by one person, one day a week, this would allow over 1000 hams to participate in NTS! Unfortunately, many hams have to double and triple up duties, so there is plenty of room for any interested amateur.

An NTS liaison spot one day (or night) a week is a great way to stay active in the traffic circuit. Many hams who don't have time to make the section nets get satisfaction in the traffic world by holding a TCC slot or area liaison once a week. If you would enjoy such a post, drop a note to your Section Traffic Manager or Net Manager. They will be happy to add another to their fold.

However, remember that the area and region net are very different from your Section or local net in one aspect. The function of the Section or local net is to saturate its jurisdiction, so the more check-ins, the better. On the upper-level nets, though, the name of the game is to move the traffic as quickly and efficiently as possible. Therefore, additional check-ins — other than specified liaisons and stations holding traffic — only slow down the net. (If you are a station holding traffic to be moved, you can enter NTS at any level to pass your traffic, even if you've never been on an upper-level net before. Entering the system at the Section or local level is preferred.)

If you are interested in finding out more about the workings to NTS, get a copy of the *Public Service Communications Manual*, available online as described at the beginning of this chapter. Every aspect of NTS is explained, as well as information about local net operating procedure, RACES and ARES operation. The *PSCM* will also orient you with net procedure of region and area NTS nets. It takes a little more skill and savvy to become a regular part of NTS, but the rewards are worth the effort. If you have the chance, go for it!

So There You Have It

Although this chapter is by no means a complete guide to traffic handling, it should serve as a good reference for veterans and newcomers alike. If you've never been involved in message handling, perhaps your interest has been piqued.

Should that be the case, don't put it off. Find a net that's custom-made for you and check into it! You'll find plenty of fine folks that will soon become close friends as you begin to work with them, learn from them, and yes, even chat with them when the net is over.

The roots of traffic handling run deep into the history of Amateur Radio, yet its branches reach out toward many tomorrows. Our future lies in proving our worth to the non-ham public, and what better way to ensure the continuance of our hobby than by uniting family and friends via Amateur Radio? Sure, it takes some effort, but a trafficker will tell you he stays with it because of the satisfaction he gets from hearing those voices on the other end of the phone say, "Oh, isn't that nice!" We've plenty of room for you — come grow with us!

The following ARRL NTS Officials helped with the revision of this chapter: Bill Thompson, W2MTA, Jim Leist, KB5W, Robert Griffin, K6YR, and Nick Zorn, N4SS.

DXing — Contacting Those Faraway Places

What is DX? An abbreviation for "distant station" or "signal from a distant station," DX is at the core of Amateur Radio. The excitement of contacting ever more distant stations has attracted amateurs of all types from the very earliest days of radio. The goal of spanning larger and larger distances has driven many technological advances. Whether DX means to you, as it does to HF DXers, a contact somewhere outside your own country, or to VHF+ DXers, a faraway grid square or hilltop, all of us get a thrill out of pushing the limits of our own skill and equipment. That's what "DXing" really means — extending your radio range and abilities.

Most amateurs don't begin their ham radio activity as a DXer. We start by making local contacts with friends and club members and gradually become aware of radio's broader possibilities. Even experienced hams have discovered DXing after years of local and regional contacts. The spark may be a visit to a DXer's station or seeing a presentation on DX, but is most likely to be an unexpected contact over a long distance. Perhaps a DX station answers your CQ one evening or you encounter an unexpected call sign while tuning the band. Even bringing up your favorite repeater while far from home on a hike or drive is DXing! This is the "magic of radio" writ large and it has been known to take hold of one's ham radio interests with a lifetime's tenacity.

DXing is even more fun if you become skilled at it! That's the purpose of this chapter — to introduce beginners to DXing and help those with some experience at the DX game get better at it. The sections cover Beginning and

Steve, GW4BLE, is a well-known call on the HF bands from Wales. Steve hands out a lot of first-ever GW QSOs on the HF bands.

Intermediate DXing, followed by a section on DX activities. Propagation, so important to DXers, is covered on a band-by-band basis. DXpeditions and QSLing conclude the chapter. See you in the pileups!

BASIC DXING

If you've made a few DX contacts (or would like to) and are interested in making DX a part of your regular ham radio diet, you've come to the right place! In many ways, this is the most exciting part of your DX career. Every time you turn on the radio, you'll experience something new and every contact is as exciting as it can possibly be! Enjoy this time and make it fun, as it lays the foundation for everything that follows.

Let's set a timeline of one year for you to learn the

basics of DXing. What should you have learned during that one trip around the Sun? Why one year? You'll get to know HF or VHF+ propagation during all of the seasons and have a chance to work numerous DXpeditions and contests. This translates to invaluable experience that you wouldn't have had a year before. You'll have a year of practice in your log, along with a bunch of exotic calls and QSLs on the wall.

As a beginning DXer, you will have the exalted title of

"Little Pistol." Even if you have a lot of fancy equipment, you'll still be learning the ropes and getting used to the techniques and procedures of DXing. This section assumes that if you will be engaging in HF DXing, you have a General, Advanced or Amateur Extra license.

Basic DXing Equipment

Relax! You don't have to take out a second mortgage to get into the world of DXing! In fact, you may have most of the gear already. You may be surprised to learn that most of the DX stations you encounter on HF will be using equipment very similar to yours. It's how you operate it that will make the difference. For entry-level HF DXing, you'll need equipment similar to that described below.

HF Transceiver

Almost any modern 100 W HF transceiver (160-10 meters) less than 10 years old will give perfectly adequate performance. If your radio doesn't use DSP (digital signal processing) for IF filters, the receiver should be equipped with both SSB (2.0 or 2.4 kHz) and CW (400 or 500 Hz) crystal or mechanical filters. You should invest in a comfortable set of communications-quality (200 to 4000 Hz is sufficient) headphones — you'll be wearing them a lot — and a high-quality microphone. Headphones with an attached boom mike (called a *boom set*) are a good choice. The radio should support computer control. Radios with a second receiver are quite useful for DXing. The transceiver will have at least two VFOs (usually shown as VFO A and VFO B) you should learn to access and select. If you are

The combination of headphones and lightweight microphone makes extended hours of operating a breeze. Choosing a microphone element designed for maximum intelligibility and proper positioning of the boom really makes a difference on the other end of the QSO.

just learning CW, learn to use a *paddle* with your rig's internal keyer or use an external electronic keyer.

HF Antennas

For the "high bands" above 10 MHz, dipoles at least 20 feet off the ground will get you started. A multiband vertical (with plenty of radials for ¼-wavelength ground-plane antennas) will also work. On the low bands below 10 MHz, a vertical wire antenna (such as an inverted L), dipoles at heights of 40 to 50 feet or more, or multiband verticals will do the job. A copy of the *ARRL Antenna Book* with its many antenna designs and information on antenna systems is an invaluable addition to your station reference materials. ARRL's *Simple and Fun Antennas for Hams* offers a variety of real-world, practical antennas. For a wide selection of antenna projects, the series of antenna *Classics* books published by the ARRL has proven designs for wire antennas, verticals and beams. (All of the ARRL publications are available online from the ARRL Store — **www.arrl.org/shop**.)

Dipoles generally work best with both ends at about the same height although an inverted V configuration is acceptable. They may also be mounted in a sloping position, with one end much higher than the other. This is often done for DXing on 40, 60, 80 and 160 meters. Many variations on the dipole and other similar wire antennas may be found in the ARRL book *ON4UN's Low-Band DXing* by John Devoldere, ON4UN.

If a ground-mounted vertical is used, at least 16 radials should be installed — more if possible. If the vertical is elevated, such as on a roof or mast, it is best to provide at least four radials for each desired band. Excellent references for installation of radial systems for verticals may be found in the *ARRL Antenna Book* and *Vertical Antenna Classics* (available from the ARRL).

Use low-loss coax, such as RG-8 or RG-213 and trim the antennas to resonance near the bottom end of the General frequency allocations. If impedance matching is required, invest in good quality equipment.

Computer and Software

You'll find a lot of resources on the Internet, so you should be able to make use of your computer at the same time you're on the air. Most ham programs are not "resource hogs" so you won't need a top-of-the-line computer.

The computer should have at least one USB or serial port available to connect to your radio's control port. The majority of ham programs are *Windows*-based, but there is software available for *Linux* and Macintosh users too.

As you begin logging DX stations, it's a good idea to start a computerized logbook. There are a number of programs available — ask other local hams, particularly DXers, what they are using. A DXer will want features like QSL label printing, award status

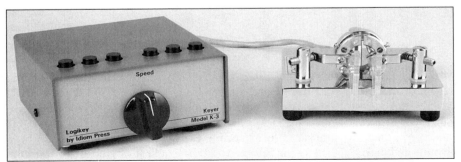
Learn to use a paddle and keyer to raise your code speed while dramatically reducing the effort required to send CW.

tracking, and the ability to export log data as ADIF formatted files for electronic QSLing. The major programs have websites to explain the program features and functions. It is not recommended that you write your own software or use a spreadsheet or word processor, since your log won't be compatible with other common programs.

VHF+ Equipment

On VHF+, one of the many fine 50 W or higher "all-band" rigs is more than sufficient to get you started. You will be primarily operating on 6 and 2 meters. A CW filter is a "nice to have" on the VHF+ bands but not critical. For antennas, you can get started with dipoles or loops but there are many inexpensive 2- or 3-element 6 meter antennas available. For 2 meters, a Yagi with five or more elements is easy to mount and rotate and will yield much better results than an omnidirectional antenna. You can try building your own antenna from the plans in *VHF and UHF Antenna Classics* or try some of WA5VJB's "Cheap Yagi" designs at **www.wa5vjb.com**.

Use horizontally polarized antennas because that is the standard on VHF+. Low-loss coax is a must — every dB lost in the feed line is very hard to make up! And a higher antenna is usually a better antenna.

Height is important on VHF+ to increase the distance to your radio horizon. If you aren't in an advantageous location, consider an effective portable or "rover" installation that you can drive to a nearby hilltop — even the roof of a parking garage will do!

Basic DX Operating

As you begin to take DXing seriously, the most important thing is not to learn how to transmit but how to listen! Listen, listen, listen! Even in this age of computer networks and instantaneous worldwide connections, there is no substitute for being able to tune the band, understanding what you hear. As you become more experienced you'll learn what the bands sound like when they're open. You'll get to know the characteristic sound of a signal that originated far away, what a pileup sounds like, how to hear the DX station under all that interference, and so forth. If you jump right in and start transmitting you'll never

John, KF5BFG, is shown operating the well-laid-out low-power HF station of Jim, WØUO during a recent ARRL DX Phone contest. Notice that all of the main station controls — keyboard, radio, display — are directly in front of him and easy to see. The wrap-around style of shelving makes auxiliary equipment easy to operate as well. (*K5ANR photo*)

The availability of all-band, all-mode rigs like the IC-7000 shown here make it easy to operate mobile or portable in HF or VHF+ contests.

get a chance to learn. The oldest DX saying in the book is, "You can't work 'em if you can't hear 'em!" The moral of that story is that if you want to make your transmissions count, learn how to receive.

Another important aspect of learning any activity is to have reasonable expectations. After all, if you begin an exercise program you don't expect to start winning races right away, do you? It's important to expect you'll have successes — savor them! Expecting too much — such as working 200 different countries in a month or working more DX than the local Big Gun — is a sure recipe for disappointment. What DX you can expect to work depends a great deal on where you live and solar conditions. If you keep your expectations modest you'll find DXing will continue to be enjoyable day after day.

In line with reasonable expectations, it's also unreasonable to start DXing with too little power. A 100 W transceiver will generate a solid, mid-level signal capable of working many DX stations. QRP (5 W output or less on CW) places a premium on the operator skills that you are trying to acquire, so avoid the frustrations of QRP for the time being. Once you are more skilled, turn the power down and enjoy the pleasant challenges of QRP operating.

Timely and up-to-date information is even more important than signal power. There are a few tools and references that every DXer should have close at hand:

- ARRL DXCC List and ITU call sign prefix reference. You can find this information in *The ARRL DXCC List* booklet or online at **www.arrl.org/dxcc**. As you spend time on the bands you'll gradually memorize the common prefixes, but special and unfamiliar ones will keep you guessing for a while. Keep this list handy and consult it often.

- World map showing CQ zones, DXCC entities, and most common prefixes. Mount it on the wall so that you can see it easily from your operating position. An azimuthal equidistant map centered on your location will also tell you the direction to each country at a glance. The ARRL offers nice wall maps of the world and of North America.

- Weekly ARRL propagation bulletins and monthly propagation predictions. These are available at no charge to ARRL members via W1AW, by email, or from the ARRL web page at **www.arrl.org/propagation**.

By having these three pieces of reference information close at hand you will learn how to predict what you will hear on the air and understand what you hear. For example, if the propagation bulletin predicts good conditions to Japan at a certain time of day, the map also lets you know to listen for signals from UAØ (Asiatic Russia), HL (Korea), BY (China), and so forth. If you are fortunate to hear a station with the JD1 prefix, the DXCC List confirms that this station is from Ogasawara or Minami Torishima. Both are considerably less common than mainland Japanese stations and possibly a "New One" — a DXCC entity you haven't yet worked!

What about CW? This is also a great time to start learning CW if you don't already use it. As a Little Pistol, you'll want to maximize the effectiveness of your station, and CW allows you to do just that. Veteran DXers will confirm that it is a lot easier to make a contact on CW than on phone, regardless of power level. CW signals pack their power into a narrow bandwidth instead of spreading it out over a couple of kilohertz. This allows you to "get through" when conditions aren't good or noise levels are high, as they often are on the lower bands. Start now and you'll be knee-deep in the CW pileups before you know it!

Collecting Information

Gathering information is as important to a DXer as any other facet of operating, because knowledge really is power. In fact, it's *better* than power because it doesn't matter how strong your signal is if you're operating on the wrong frequency or at the wrong time!

A DX newsletter, such as *Daily DX* or *QRZ DX*, really helps the DXer in the search for new stations. A DXer or DX club may set up a website and begin keeping a chart of the activities of DX operators by using QSN (heard on ___ kHz) reports. For example, you may note that a VP8 station in the Falkland Islands is beginning to show up on a certain band on or near a certain frequency and usually around the same time of day. Further charting may show that this occurs on the same day but every other week. If you are there at the right time on the next likely day, you'll have a good chance of making a VP8 contact!

Keep track of national holidays and customs in your area of interest. Know when the DXer from other lands might be taking a cup of coffee (or whatever) into the shack to enjoy a few minutes of radio before or after work. Read a newspaper or web news service with a good international section to keep

Using Spotting Networks

Once (and still) simply referred to as "packet," DX spotting networks have become a significant force in DXing. Since the early days of DXing, local DXers have banded together to share information about what stations are on the air. Before packet radio, DXers listened on a VHF frequency (usually on 2 meters) that was kept quiet except for announcements about DX stations. For example, you might hear, "TZ6ZZ is on 14024, listening up two, K6ABC clear." Helping each other has a long and honorable history in DXing.

Packet radio became popular in the early 1980s and DXers naturally migrated to it. Bulletin board systems appeared, based on similar systems used over landline computer networks. Soon PacketCluster software adapted the bulletin board to the DX-centric format used today. Local stations connected via VHF or UHF and stayed connected, receiving a steady stream of information that could be stored and reviewed, if so desired. Instead of a voice announcement, the example above might have looked like "1530Z K6ABC TZ6ZZ 14.024 QSX up 2."

As the Internet became ubiquitous, the packet radio link gave way to a network connection. By that time, the format for data and commands for PacketCluster operating were in widespread use and so were replicated on web-based versions. Today, a worldwide system incorporates users linked by packet radio, TELNET, or web-based interfaces. If desired, you can sit in your shack and watch a steady stream of DX station information and announcements flow by, posted by stations from all over the world!

This is a "good news, bad news" situation. The good news is, of course, that there is so much information for DXers. More DX QSOs and entities are being logged by

more DXers than ever. What could be wrong with that? The bad news is that there is so much information that the need to actually tune the band yourself is reduced. Without putting your ears to work, you lose the opportunity to gain hard-won personal knowledge of propagation and band characteristics. You will also find that the posted information is not 100% reliable, as well, leading to the "busted call" or dreaded "not in the log" result.

DX spots also create the original version of a "smart mob," known as a "packet pileup" to DX operators. As information about the DX station filters out across the world's spotting networks, dozens to literally hundreds of DXers can descend on a single frequency, hoping for a QSO! It's important to remember that a DXer relying on spotting information to do his or her tuning will *never* be the first to find a DX station on the bands!

Nevertheless, as long as an appropriate amount of caution is applied and you remember that spotting networks are an aid and not an end in themselves, the information can be a great boon. Learn as much as you can about the spotting system you choose to use. Use the information to help you find the DX first instead of rushing madly about as spots pop up on your computer screen.

You can find local spotting networks by inquiring of your local or regional DX club. A list of spotting systems worldwide, Internet spotting sites and many other useful spot-related links is available at **www.dxcluster.info** and at **www.ng3k.com**. Once connected, be sure to use the Help functions of the system to find out how to operate it correctly. Remember that the information you post will likely be seen around the planet within a few minutes!

track of world events that may affect DXing.

DX spotting networks are another important tool. In fact, it has been said that many owe their DXCC Honor Roll plaques to them. (A "DX spot" is a short message that a particular station is being heard on a specific frequency — see the sidebar "Using Spotting Networks.") Add spot filtering software that alerts the operator if a needed station comes on the air, and you have a most formidable tool.

The DX spotting network now stretches around the world through Internet connections. It's possible to see what's being worked in Italy or Japan. This is actually more useful than you may think. First, it's possible to know that stations from certain areas are actually on the air. It's also possible to identify these stations and even request schedules. Sometimes, depending on propagation, spots from another area of the country can be useful. Spots can help you work stations at times that you would not have even listened and spots have tipped operators to band openings not thought possible before. Some sites allow you to search past spots to help determine the best bands or times to try.

Real-time spotting is probably the most superior method of intelligence gathering currently in use for ongoing operations. It is a truly amazing system and the hybrid radio/Internet system is one of the best forms of useful ham ingenuity.

Receiving and Transmitting

In previous editions of this book, Bill Kennamer, K5NX, offered some advice on operating that is just as pertinent today as it was a few years ago. Let's follow Bill as he grabs a cup of coffee and heads for the DX bands for a typical morning of DXing during a part of the sunspot cycle when the sunspots are low to moderate, just as they are in early 2012. For these conditions, the band of choice would be 20 meters…

Begin on SSB near the bottom of the band. You do have your headphones on, don't you? Remember now, we're just listening, so it doesn't matter where we are in the band. Of course, when transmitting it will be necessary to be in the part of the band authorized for your license class.

Tune slowly up the band. Listen to the QSOs going on. If the signals are steady and the speaker sounds like a local station, pass it up at this time and move slowly up the band. A signal is heard speaking in accented English. Stop here and listen. The signal may be strong and steady or it may be strong but occasionally dipping in strength. This may well be a DX station. Stick around long enough for them to send a call sign or otherwise give a clue as to location. If it is a European, then you know the band is open in that direction, for example.

Determine the style of operating. If the DX is in a QSO, record the frequency and call signs. Don't call until the contact is definitely finished. To do otherwise would be rude and only lids are rude. You can check back in a few minutes.

Keep moving up slowly. Be sure to pay attention to weak signals. Many times they are passed over because people either can't hear them through their speakers (but you're wearing headphones, remember?) or think they're too weak to be workable. More than once a rare DX station has appeared on the band, called a few CQs with no response and gone away. With 100 W and a simple antenna it's to your advantage to try to find stations before anyone else is calling and the pileup starts. It's likely that the DX station may be running 100 W to a dipole, sometimes even an indoor dipole. If you can hear the DX, they can most likely hear you, too, especially if no one else is calling.

The important thing while you're tuning is to listen to as many different DX stations as possible. Notice the sound, the accents, the audio quality. With a little practice, you can tune the band quickly, and immediately identify the DX stations. Later, you will be able to do the same thing on CW.

Now it's time to begin calling some of the DX stations you've been hearing. You hear the DX station sign off. You know the call sign. Now call! If it's a station that has been working short QSOs, give their call one time only (they *know* their call!), and yours twice, using standard phonetics. Then wait. If you're lucky, the DX will come back to you! If the DX comes back to someone else, wait patiently until the contact is finished. DXing is a game of patience. Turn off your VOX while waiting! Tripping your VOX while waiting on the frequency is the behavior of a lid.

You're lucky!! The DX station came back to you! You're now in QSO with the DX station. The first QSO with a DX station can be somewhat like dancing. They lead, you follow. As a rule, on your first transmission work by a formula. Give your name, state and signal report. A good form would be, "My name is Bill in the state of Arkansas. Your report is 5 by 9. Over." The DX station's English may be limited, they may be working many stations, or may be waiting on frequency for a schedule. In any case, the next transmission will determine whether they will say 73 or want to have an hour's discussion of the state of the fishing where you live. Just follow the DX station's lead and enjoy the QSO, no matter how long or short. Yes, you'll want to QSL. We'll talk about that later.

Many times you'll hear DX stations running stations at a fairly high rate. They'll answer each station with call sign and signal report then go on to the next station. When calling a running station sign your call sign *one time* using phonetics. If you're beaten in the pileup, wait until the next opportunity and call again. Don't ask the station for QSL information in this type of pileup — listen until it's given or look it up on the Internet or in a newsletter.

Operating Split

There are two kinds of pileups, transceive (or simplex) and split frequency. These are exactly what their names imply — transceive means working stations on the same frequency for both transmit and receive. Split means using one frequency for transmitting and another for listening. Both are easily manageable if proper technique is used. For medium to large-sized pileups, split is actually quite preferable because it's easy for everyone to hear the DX station clearly. It's important to listen and see how other operators apply that technique from either end of the pileup!

If you don't hear anyone coming back to the DX station yet the signal reports keep on coming, the DX station is probably working split with the callers transmitting on a different frequency. This is when a rig with a sub-receiver (a second independent receiver) pays for itself. Split frequency operation can be, and is, done most frequently by alternating between two VFOs but can be even more effective when done with two receivers. On CW, start looking for the stations calling about 1 kHz up. Tune higher from the DX station until the calling stations are found. The pileup may be as much as 5 to 10 kHz away and is almost always higher in frequency. Once you've found the pileup, start tracking the stations that are working the DX station to see how far, and in which direction, they are tuning between QSOs.

While you're listening to the pileup and trying to find the frequency at which the DX station is working callers, you'll notice many stations just seem to call over and over, never standing by to listen. Why do they do that? Others respond to the DX station, no matter what the call sign of the requested station. Why do they do that? No one really knows, but it certainly slows down the operation, doesn't it? Certainly, it makes it impossible for them to find where the DX station is listening and dramatically reduces their chances of getting in

the log. Don't be a pileup lid — respond only when the DX station is calling for a call sign close to yours. Spend your time listening and you'll be able to say, "Got 'em in just one call!"

Goals for the Little Pistol DXer

The world of DXing can be overwhelming at first. There is so much to learn and so much to do! All around are experienced veterans who have been DXing seemingly since the days of spark and who have worked everything dozens of times. To cut the problem down to size, set five modest goals for your first stage of DXing and accomplish them. Here are five suggestions for the Little Pistol:

- Learn to operate your transceiver well.
- Learn to tune the bands and find propagation opportunities — don't get hooked on DX spots.
- Learn how to operate split and how to find the DX station's transmit frequency.
- Start computer logging and register for Logbook of the World (see the section on QSLing later in this chapter).
- Work 75 or more different DXCC entities or VUCC grids.

Pirates and Police, Lids and Jammers

By Bill Kennamer, K5NX

The DXer does encounter a few problems in the pursuit of his or her avocation. Those nefarious denizens named in the title of this sidebar are not there to make life easier for the DXer. However, all DXers will ultimately have in common the fact that they have overcome and persevered through the jungle created by the antics of these creatures of the ether. These cretinous individuals should not diminish the pleasure of the DXer but be a point of pride, overcoming the obstacles posed by such miscreants.

Pirates have been with us always. We can't be sure if Marconi heard one when he first fired up but certainly the first signal received across the Atlantic by Godley was one. Probably the most famous pirate was named Slim. At a time when a volcanic island had popped up out of the sea near Iceland, Slim turned up from Cray Island as 8X8AA, claiming that the island had just popped up in the North Atlantic and would qualify for a new country. He held forth for several days, then disappeared forever. Since then, many pirates over the years have been tagged as Slim. So if an operation comes onto the air and it's so improbable as to be suspect, it may be Slim back for another run.

One thing the DXer must do when encountering suspected pirates: *Work Them!* Yes, always work them because sometimes the improbable is true. The rule is *Work 'em First, Worry Later (WFWL)*. Two things are accomplished by doing so: first, the DXer can practice pileup technique and second, if it is for real, it's in the log. If it's suspect, the QSL need not be sent until later. But if it's not in the log it's hard to get a QSL! Some pirates and bootleggers do QSL, so it's not unusual to get cards rejected for awards credit. Everybody experiences this, so it's best to continue working stations until a QSL counts.

Every pileup will have police and jammers. The police

may be well-meaning souls but they really are in the same category as the jammers. They just do it in a less sophisticated way. The DX is calling and working a hundred an hour by split frequency. Meanwhile, on the DX operator's transmit frequency, the lids, police, and jammers may be all heard at once, each pursuing DX infamy. The lid will start with "Who's the DX?" or "Where's he listening?" or the inevitable, "Is the frequency in use?" All these questions could be answered by listening a little but either the lid's time is too valuable or intelligence level is too low to think of that.

This is, of course, an excuse for the police to jump in with varying responses. Ten police will, one after the other (never in unison) give all the information anyone would care to know about the DX station, meanwhile totally obliterating the DX station and stopping the pileup in its tracks. This is immediately followed by 10 more who attack the lid, questioning his parentage or intelligence level. Finally come the last 10 who are telling the previous ones and the lid to just shut up. Ah yes, the musical chaos of the pileup!

Did we say music? That must be the cue for the jammer to appear, as broadcasting music is one form of jamming. Recording someone calling and replaying it on the DX frequency is also a frequently used technique. Most jammers these days are not that sophisticated. Now it's mostly just tuning up or calling CQ on the DX frequency or running a couple of minutes of white noise onto the air. One of the easiest ways for the jammers to enjoy themselves is to just ask who the DX is and get the police started.

Meanwhile, the DXers can rejoice in the fact that although all these obstacles are placed in the way they are still working the DX! So let the others moan and groan, let them complain to the utmost. The fact remains, those who learn their skills well will succeed.

BEYOND THE BASICS

When can you graduate from being a Little Pistol? Whenever you want! You'll know when you've become a "Medium Gun" because you feel confident on the bands, you have enough contacts for an award or two (even if you choose not to apply for them), and you begin to recognize the sounds of DXing. You can discern the bands opening and closing, identify the characteristics of DX signals, and know how to make DX QSOs.

This is the busiest period of any DXer's "career" because there are plenty of "New Ones" to put in the log. You're now skilled enough to be successful on a regular basis, but not so experienced that you don't get surprised now and then! Enjoy being a Medium Gun, because it's fun!

Eventually you'll approach some rarefied air — 300 DXCC entities or 200 grids or band-mode-zone totals that seemed unattainable not so long ago. Remember? You've become a Big Gun! As such, you should be writing this chapter, congratulations! Don't forget what it was like to be a Little Pistol and the magic spell of even the most garden-variety DX QSO. Your assignment? Be an Elmer and a friend to an up-and-coming Little Pistol so that they will become a Big Gun someday, just like you!

DXing Equipment — The Next Step

As a DXer with some experience in the log, you'll have used your station enough to have found some of its weak spots and have a list of features you need. Now's the time to upgrade, including obtaining the Extra class license for the extra frequencies that are prime DX territory! Before you begin changing your equipment, make a list of what your station can and cannot do. Get the advice of more experienced DXers to see if you're missing something important or are yearning for a feature or gadget that really doesn't make much difference.

A cautionary note — there is no substitute for being on the air! All the gear in the world and all the Internet bandwidth won't put your call in the DX log. It's easy to get lost in the gadgetry of DXing. As you improve your station's capabilities, build for reliability. A fancy, but broken, amplifier or antenna doesn't make any QSOs! Your goal should be to put out a solid signal every time you operate and to get plenty of "chair time."

HF Transceiver

A transceiver with 100 W of RF output remains adequate. Upgrade to one of the rigs that uses advanced DSP technology to create the IF filters or purchase a complete set of filters for your radio. Cascaded crystal filters (one in each IF stage) can be a very powerful listening tool! Other DSP functions, such as several levels and styles of noise reduction and auto-notch filters will be useful, as well. The second or sub-receiver is no longer an option — you'll definitely want to have one while chasing DX stations with large pileups.

Accessories, such as the microphone and paddle, should be selected to fit your operating preferences. Evaluate different types of microphone elements on the air to find the one that gives you punchy but crisp and clear audio. For DXing, high and low frequency response is secondary to intelligibility over difficult paths and in pileups. As your CW competency and speed increase you may want a paddle with a lighter touch. An external keyer with message buffers may make operating more convenient. Don't be afraid to start trying different styles of these very important interfaces between you and the radio!

As you pursue rarer DX over more difficult paths, obtaining an amplifier will prove to be a good step. It needn't be a top-of-the-line, 1500 W continuous-duty model. Amps that put out 1000 W or so are perfectly adequate. There are lots of used amplifiers that will give plenty of good service. A footswitch will help you avoid excessive wear and tear on the amplifier's transmit/receive relay.

HF Antennas

You'll want to consider some sort of tower and beam antenna. This is a great investment, one of the best the DXer could ever make. A small *tribander* (a rotatable antenna that operates on 20-15-10 meters) at 40 to 50 feet will provide a noticeable improvement over wire antennas on both transmit and receive. Wires may still be used for the low bands or the tower itself may be fed as a vertical.

The 30, 17 and 12 meter bands become increasingly important as the DX becomes rarer. Be sure to at least have wire antennas for these bands, particularly for 30 and 17 meters. If you can obtain a beam antenna for 17 and 12 meters, it will make a big difference because those bands often provide a contact with a DXpedition or rare station when 20, 15 and 10 meters are too crowded.

Pay particular attention to your feed lines and associated accessory equipment. Don't throw away your hard work and expense by using inferior cable, connectors, or construction techniques. Pay attention to the details and "do it right." Individual fractions of a dB saved by careful assembly of station components can add up to significant differences on the air. Proper assembly reduces station down time, too!

VHF+ Equipment

The biggest bang for your ham radio buck at this stage is to install bigger antennas mounted higher above ground. Propagation is often marginal on 6 and 2 meters, particularly after you've worked all of the nearby grids and those common on sporadic-E or whatever tropospheric propagation is common in your area. Antennas with longer booms and more elements — for example, a 4 or 5-element Yagi on 6 meters and 10 elements or more on 2 meters — often make the crucial difference in being heard when signals are weak and openings very brief.

Power amplifiers and mast-mounted preamps on the higher bands will pay dividends by increasing your ability to take advantage of marginal openings. You'll also begin to hear and work weaker stations, increasing the number of

Optimizing Your Receiver

While operating a transmitter is certainly important, the success of a DXer more often depends on the ability to get the most out of a receiver on crowded and noisy bands where weak DX signals lurk. Your rig's operating manual will tell you a lot about what the various controls do, but not a lot about the effect using them will have on what you hear. It's worth repeating the old adage, "You can't work 'em if you can't hear 'em!" Here's how to hear 'em better.

Let's start with passband tuning, IF shift, variable bandwidth or similar controls. All of these allow you to avoid interference by shifting the receive filter frequency without changing the VFO or filter bandwidth. Because the different manufacturers often implement these features slightly differently, read the radio's manual and experiment with the controls to observe their effect.

Digital signal processing (DSP) is standard technology in modern rigs, allowing tremendous flexibility in selecting filter shape and width. Noise reduction and notch-filtering features also help remove annoying noise, tones, and carriers. Learning how to use the DSP functions effectively is crucial for obtaining top performance from your receiver.

You might be surprised to learn that your RF gain control is not locked in the full-on position! Maximum RF gain makes your receiver very sensitive, but also leaves your IF (and sometimes the RF) amplifiers susceptible to overloading by strong signals common on the DX bands. Experiment with reducing RF gain to see if it improves your receiver's performance in a strong signal environment. Even during casual operating, backing off the RF gain can dramatically reduce background noise. Experiment with changing the AGC settings. You can even turn AGC off and use the RF gain control manually to control volume. Use the minimum amount of receiver gain necessary to really clean up what comes out of the headphones or speaker!

The attenuator can be your biggest friend when dealing with strong nearby signals. It's surprisingly easy for a strong signal to overload a receiver's RF amplifier or mixers, creating spurious distortion products that can mask weaker signals. As you add attenuation you may find that interference drops dramatically when your receiver is no longer being overloaded. Using 10 dB of attenuation cures a surprising number of ailments at the cost of just a couple of S units of signal strength. Remember that the goal is to maximize signal-to-noise ratio, not necessarily absolute signal strength.

Two receiver functions actually make strong-signal performance *worse* when they are activated. The biggest villain is the noise blanker (not noise reduction — a DSP function). Most operate by sensing wide-bandwidth pulses from the entire band, not just what is coming through the narrow filters further along the receiver's signal path. As a result, a strong nearby signal can confuse a noise blanker to the point of nearly shutting down a receiver or causing what sounds like severe overmodulation over many kHz. Unless you have really strong local line noise or mobile ignition noise, turn your noise blanker off. If the band is full of strong signals, noise blankers are useless or worse.

The second villain is the preamplifier (preamp). It's rarely useful on the lower HF bands and only occasionally of use on 12 and 10 meters. Preamps are much more useful at VHF and higher frequencies. By increasing the incoming signal strengths, it becomes much easier to overload a receiver as described above. Keep the preamp off unless absolutely necessary to hear the desired signal.

By effectively using the capabilities of a modern receiver, you will surely find that the band is quieter and nearby signals less disruptive. In fact, you will find yourself making better use of your receiver's controls every day!

The following description of receiver characteristics was written by ARRL Lab Engineer Mike Gruber, W1MG. A full description of receiver performance tests is included in recent editions of *The ARRL Handbook*. The regular transceiver product reviews in *QST* show how to compare specifications from radio to radio.

CW and SSB Sensitivity

One of the most common sensitivity measurements you'll find for CW and SSB receivers is *minimum discernible signal* (MDS). It indicates the minimum signal level that can be detected with the receiver (although an experienced operator can often copy somewhat weaker signals). MDS is the input level to the receiver that produces an output signal equal to the internally generated receiver noise. Hence, MDS is sometimes referred to as the receiver's "noise floor."

You'll find MDS expressed in most spec sheets as µV or dBm. The lower the number in µV, or more negative the number in dBm, the more sensitive the receiver. (For example, a radio with an MDS of −139 dBm (0.022 µV) is more sensitive than one with an MDS of −132 dBm (0.055 µV).)

When making sensitivity comparisons between radios, keep in mind that more is not always better. Atmospheric and other radio noise on the band (not the receiver noise) often sets the practical limit below 20 MHz. If the receiver can hear external noise, greater sensitivity simply amplifies it. Also, too much sensitivity may make the receiver more susceptible to overload and decrease dynamic range.

Your receiver is one of the most important tools in your DXing toolkit. Learn all you can about the various controls and adjustments, and don't be afraid to crack open the manual and experiment.

A typical modern HF transceiver has an MDS of between −135 and −140 dBm (or 0.0398 to 0.0224 µV). You can easily make a dB comparison between two radios if the MDS is expressed in dBm. Simply subtract one MDS from the other. If, for example, one has an MDS of −132 and the other −139 dBm, the latter radio has a sensitivity that is 7 dB better than the first — if both measurements are made at the same receive bandwidth.

Dynamic Range

Dynamic range is a measure of the receiver's ability to tolerate strong signals outside of its passband. Essentially, it's the difference between the weakest signal a receiver can hear and the strongest signal a receiver can accommodate without noticeable degradation in performance. Two types are considered in *QST* product reviews: blocking dynamic range (BDR) and third-order intermodulation distortion dynamic range (IMD DR).

Blocking dynamic range (also called blocking gain compression) describes a receiver's ability to not become desensitized by a strong undesired signal on a different frequency while tuned to a desired signal. IMD dynamic range, on the other hand, is an indication of a receiver's ability to not generate false signals as a result of the two strong signals on different frequencies outside the receiver's passband. Both types of dynamic range are normally expressed in dB relative to the noise floor.

As in the case of our hypothetical receiver, the IMD DR is usually 20 dB or more below the BDR. This means false signals will usually appear well before sensitivity is significantly decreased. It's not surprising that IMD DR is often considered to be one of the more significant receiver specifications. It's generally a conservative evaluation for other effects that may or may not be specified. Meaningful dynamic range comparisons can only be made when the unwanted signals are equally spaced from the desired signal. Wider spacings generally result in better (higher) DR figures.

Third Order Intercept Point

Another parameter used to measure receiver performance in *QST* product reviews is the third-order intercept point (IP3). This is the extrapolated point (specified in dBm) at which the desired signal and the false signals caused by third-order IMD become equal in strength. Higher levels for IP3 indicates better receiver performance.

Second Order IMD Dynamic Range and Intercept Point

Second-order IMD distortion dynamic range, like third-order products, also are generated within a receiver. Strong signals (f1, f2) cause the offending products at frequencies of f1 ± f2. In today's busy electromagnetic environment, they can create severe interference under certain conditions.

Consider the case of two strong shortwave stations, on two different bands, that sum to the frequency of the weak DX you're trying to copy. If their intermodulation product is strong enough, you may not be able to copy the station through the interference. As an example, a high seas coast telephone station on 4400 kHz might combine with a shortwave broadcast station on 9800 kHz to produce an intermod product on 14200 kHz.

IF and Image Rejection

A station transmitting at a receiver's IF frequency can also create interference if its signal is strong enough and the radio's IF rejection is insufficient. The station will then be heard on all frequencies no matter where the receiver is tuned! Be sure to consider IF rejection when considering a receiver if a nearby transmitter is located on its IF frequency.

Because mixers create output signals at both the sum and difference of the input frequencies, there are two frequencies for which a signal at the IF can be created. If a signal at the undesired frequency — usually outside of an amateur band — is strong enough, its resulting mixing product — called an image — interferes with signals of the desired frequency. The ability of the receiver to filter out or otherwise reject signals that cause images is called image rejection.

When testing IF and image rejection, we first measure the level that causes the unwanted signal to be received with a strength equal to the MDS. The difference between the unwanted signal's strength and the MDS is then the IF or image rejection in dB.

stations available for you to contact. Feed line and connector quality is crucial for VHF+ DXing, so don't scrimp. Ask for advice from veteran VHF+ DXers.

Taming the Pileup

You've learned the basics by now. DX signals are recognized by their sound and tuned in quickly. You are comfortable competing with other stations and have learned the appropriate timing of making your call. The bands feel like home to you. Now it's time to tackle the most difficult DXing task — the pileup. Once again, Bill Kennamer, K5NX, has some valuable lessons to impart, useful on HF or VHF+.

Tuning the band, a DX station is heard passing out rapid-fire QSOs — signal reports only or grid squares. As a rule, you should listen for a moment or two to see who it is. If needed, great, get ready to make your call. If not, stick around for some time to listen. The pileup builds, almost to the point of getting unmanageable. Notice who's getting through and who's not.

The stations transmitting just part of their call signs or just their last two letters on phone seem to be having a more difficult time. That's because many DX stations these days give priority to a full call sign. Even with a good signal, sending the "last two" leads to spinning your wheels to some degree. Full calls are always best. On CW this isn't much of a problem.

Jacek, SP5DRH, operated as H4ØKJ from remote Pigeon Island in the Solomon Islands Temotu Province for two weeks during 2011. Temotu is only reachable with a 50-mile open-water trip by boat!

Notice that occasionally you will hear a station sending a call sign while another station is sending extraneous information to the DX station like name or location in a busy pileup. This is a technique called *tailending*. Although it is a good technique if you get the timing right, you need to listen to a few good practitioners of the art, for it is an art, before trying it. Otherwise it can cause QRM and make you sound like a lid.

Notice that often the calling station is on a slightly different frequency and uses a different speed on CW. Sometimes the station is weaker when tailending. Some practitioners of the art actually turn off their amplifier before trying it because that avoids being obnoxious. Notice also that if the station trying the technique tries it once or twice and it doesn't work, it isn't tried again. To continue could annoy the DX station, who may be deliberately not responding to tailenders when they call, but one or two calls later just to keep everyone from trying it at once. A pileup can quickly turn into bedlam if two or three tailenders are taken in a row and everyone starts calling.

Continue listening to the pileup and see where callers are positioning themselves in the pileup. On CW, they may be sending higher by 100 to 200 Hz from where the last caller was worked, to make their signal stand out. Sometimes slower speed is better if everyone else is fast. This also works somewhat on phone. By adjusting the XIT (transmitter incremental

tuning) on SSB, it's possible to make your voice take on a different pitch that may cut through the pileup. Listen to see if tailenders are getting through (easier to do while split than transceive). Do the same thing on SSB if it's a phone pileup.

Listen carefully to what the DX station is saying. If you can't hear, don't call until you can. Surprisingly, when these pileups get really loud and poorly behaved, the DX station will often call out a specific frequency where no one is calling. Those who are listening will catch it. Those who don't hear will continue to call in vain. Look also for operators who operate at or below the edge of the announced calling frequency range. Sometimes DX stations will announce something like "200 to 210." At that moment, they may have tuned down to 200 to start tuning up again. Often a caller at 199.5 can get the QSO because of the difference in pitch, or because sidebands from the signal make it difficult to hear on 200. This only works once. If the DX moves away from 200, then it's back to square one. Find and follow, then get ahead.

Have you heard the operator at the DX club who comes into the discussion on the latest big DXpedition? "Yep, worked them with one call." You'll can almost bet that a half hour or more was spent using these techniques to set up that one call.

Goals for the Medium Gun DXer

Now is the time to develop "DX muscles" by expanding your expertise and building up your station to work the rarest DX reliably. You will begin your quest for the top echelons of DXCC or VUCC. These goals will take time and effort to achieve, but the journey is its own reward. Your QSL collection will begin to swell with numerous cards from around the world. Don't ignore the social aspects of the hobby — take in a DX convention or two and meet some of those faces behind the signals you hear (and compete against) in the pileups! They'll be glad to meet you, too, and maybe a few lifelong friendships will begin.

- Improve your station capabilities to reach another level of DX stations or grids.
- Study unusual propagation opportunities or propagation on an unfamiliar band.
- Hone your pileup technique in large and difficult pileups.
- Log DXpeditions on as many bands or from as many grids as possible.
- Start working toward 5BDXCC and 5BWAZ. On VHF+, keep logging new grids and investigate new modes.

DX AWARD PROGRAMS AND CONTESTS

It is completely natural to take an interest in extending your station's range. Getting the most out of your equipment and personal skills delivers a well-deserved sense of accomplishment. DXing can be treated as a casual activity focused on making overseas friends or as competitive as you wish. Many DXers enjoy a relaxed chat with someone in a different country just for the sheer pleasure of establishing contact. You may elect to work DX and never submit an award application or submit a DX contest log — that's fine! Or you may try to reach #1 DXCC Honor Roll by verifying contacts with every entry on the DXCC List. Find your DX comfort level and enjoy!

To encourage and reward improved operating and station construction, many organizations sponsor DX-oriented awards. The ARRL, *CQ* magazine, the Radio Society of Great Britain (RSGB), and many other organizations sponsor DX award programs for both HF and VHF+. There are literally thousands of awards! Let's take a brief look at some of the most popular award programs. (Look for more information in the **Operating Awards** chapter of this book.)

WAC and WAS

WAC (Worked All Continents) and *WAS* (Worked All States) are the gateway to DXing for many hams. Complete information on these two awards is available at **www.arrl.org/wac** and **www.arrl.org/was**, respectively.

WAC is a great "first" HF DX certificate to hang on the wall, signifying contact with each of the six main continents: North and South America, Europe, Asia, Africa and Oceania. WAC is available on VHF+ bands, too — a real achievement!

WAS on HF often requires both high- and low-band contacts to complete, along with a pair of "real" DX countries: Hawaii (KH6) and Alaska (KL7). Completing a QSO with your "last" state will be an unforgettable thrill! WAS on VHF+ is much harder because of the limits of propagation above the HF bands.

Both programs offer endorsements for completing the required contacts on multiple bands, too. Depending on solar conditions, the multiple band WAC or WAS can be a worthy challenge. Once you've qualified for WAC or WAS, you're well on your way to DX adventures.

DXCC Program

Undoubtedly the premier DX award program on either HF or VHF+, *DXCC* was initiated in the 1930s when amateur equipment and techniques were just beginning to enable regular intercontinental contacts. (The first transatlantic QSOs were made in 1923.) After World War II, the program was restarted and modern DXing began in earnest. Through the years, DXCC (**www.arrl.org/dxcc**) has come to be the standard for DX achievement around the world. In fact, to become a full member of some DX clubs, the applicant must have achieved DXCC!

The DXCC award is based on the *DXCC List* of recognized "entities" that may or may not be countries in the traditional sense. Currently 340 entities count for DXCC credit as of early 2012. Some are "regular" countries like France or Japan while some are tiny islands far from the beaten track or geographical oddities tucked away in obscure corners of the world.

The DXCC program recognizes many different types of operating. Along with single and multiple-band endorsements, the program recognizes CW, Phone, and Digital DXCC — even DXCC from contacts via amateur satellites! Serious DXers can also pursue the five-band *5BDXCC* award and participate in the *DXCC Challenge*, working DX entities on every band they can. The ARRL sponsors special challenges from time to time, such as the *Diamond DXCC Challenge* for working all of the original DXCC entities during 2012, in celebration of the 75th anniversary of DXCC.

The DXCC Challenge award encourages DXers to expand their capabilities to all bands. The basic award is for 1000 entities worked on a combination of bands.

CQ DX Award Program

CQ magazine (**www.cq-amateur-radio.com**) has promoted DXing for many years and sponsors a number of popular DX awards along with an active HF and VHF+ contest program. These complement DXCC very well, and most DXers participate in both *CQ* and ARRL awards programs. The list of CQ DX Awards includes:

- *CQ DX* — similar to DXCC with its own *CQ DX Country List*.
- *CQ DX Marathon* — a yearly competition for contacting *CQ* Countries and Zones
- *CQ DX Field* — based on Maidenhead Grid Fields around the world.
- *CQ iDX* — recognizes contacts made via Voice Over Internet Protocol (VOIP) systems.
- *WAZ* (Worked All Zones) — contact all of the 40 zones recognized by *CQ*.
- *WPX* (Worked Prefixes) — counts different call sign prefixes worldwide.

VUCC

VHF+ DXers think of grid locators in the way HF DXers think of countries and entities. The ARRL's *VUCC* (VHF-UHF Century Club) award (**www.arrl.org/vucc**) is based on contacts with the 2° by 1° Maidenhead grid locators (**www.arrl.org/grid-squares**) anywhere in the world. There are 32,400 of these regions, many rarely traveled, so it is unlikely anyone will "work 'em all" any time soon.

As with the DXCC award, the VHF+ DXer must contact 100 grid locators, or "grids" as they're called, on the air. With modest equipment, VUCC takes about the same amount of effort as DXCC for an HF DXer.

IOTA and US Islands

It's a rare DXer that hasn't imagined operating from a deserted island under a tropical sun with the whole world calling in! The *Islands On the Air* program, sponsored by the RSGB (**www.rsgbiota.org**) caters to that imaginative impulse. Island groups are identified by continent, such as NA-001 or OC-050. There are 18 separate IOTA awards,

The Islands On the Air program (www.rsgbiota.org) has grown to become one of the world's most popular DXing awards programs. Focusing on saltwater islands, IOTA chasers have a nearly never-ending supply of New Ones to put in the log. (Another program, the US Islands program, includes inland and river islands. See www.usislands.org.)

beginning at making contact with 100 different island groups.

Where IOTA only counts "saltwater" islands, the US Islands program (**www.usislands.org**) includes all of the islands in the United States. As you might imagine, some of these can be as difficult to contact as rare DXCC entities!

There are a number of special island award programs around the world. Links to the appropriate website can be found by entering "ham radio island awards" into an Internet search engine.

DX Contests

Occasionally you will turn on the radio to find the band crammed full of loud signals from all over the planet. Operators will be exchanging short messages, such as a

DXing, DXpeditioning and . . . Contesting!

By Wayne Mills, N7NG

*Wayne has been a DXer and contester for over 40 years. He is currently at the top of the DXCC Honor Roll and holds WAZ and 5BDXCC awards as well. After participating in contests for many years from home, Wayne began his ventures to offshore locations in the late 1980s. Since then he has been involved in numerous world-class contest operations, including several world records in multioperator classes, and has a single operator world record as well. He has participated in numerous major DXpeditions to every continent of the world, including ZA1A — the operation that launched the Amateur Radio service in Albania, and significant operations from Myanmar, Pratas Island, Scarborough Reef and the Temotu Province of the Solomon Islands. Wayne was elected to the CQ DX Hall of Fame in May 1999. More information can be found in the **Contesting** chapter of this book.*

This chapter offers excellent insight into how to become a seasoned DXer. Learning, however, is best accomplished by doing. Practice with the lessons of this chapter can be obtained by participating in contests. Contesting offers a great opportunity to practice DXing skills. Contesting can also point to ways to improve your station. DXing is an art, which requires considerable skill, skill that often is acquired only after years of practice, practice and more practice. The more you work at it, the more proficient you will become. Contesting can help the DXer gain important operating skills and increased station effectiveness.

Many years of experience as a DXer and contester convinces me that this is true. My contesting experiences began shortly after I began DXing. Contests

Not all DXpeditions focus solely on HF — or even the Earth! The recent 3B8EME operation activated Mauritius on moonbounce using 144 and 432 MHz and worked 340 stations — a new record! PA3CEE and PE1L are shown here with the array of 144 MHz long Yagis.

created many opportunities to practice chasing relatively non-rare DX in a short period of time. The skills acquired in the course of many contest efforts have made DXing easy for me. Emulating the contester who is successful leads to greater efficiency on your part. Listening is a particularly important ability. Paying attention to what is happening and deciding how to approach a pileup is particularly important. Is the DX working split? Is there a distinctive listening pattern? Where and when should I call next? In major pileups, it is easy to spot those who lack the techniques to be successful. I credit contesting with teaching me the timing, placement and rhythm to be a successful DXer.

From home, contesting offers many opportunities to snag a rare DX station in a major-league pileup. You may be competing with some of the largest stations in the country, so it's not necessarily easy. However, this is great practice for getting through to the very rare DX, and it's also a good gauge of your abilities and your station's capabilities. At the same time, pileups in a contest are not always as large and as unruly as those on the rarest of DX stations. Because there are so many DX stations in a contest, many DXers are off chasing one or the other, leaving this one for you.

Elementary contesting is often learned at a local club's ARRL Field Day site. Field Day includes many of the elements of contesting and DXpeditioning. For many hams, the ARRL Field Day is their introduction to contesting. The ARRL Sweepstakes contest is a great next step, since good results can be had with a smaller station and antenna system. For the DXer, the ultimate experience is the DX contest. In addition to providing DXing experience, DX contests can add many counters to your DX total. Success in these contests may require bigger signals and more skill, but good results can still be had with a modest station.

Success in contests requires a high-quality station. The stronger signal you can deliver to the DX station, the better your chance to bust the pileup. Big power isn't always necessary, and good antennas are often better than

power, as antenna gain improves receiving as well as transmitting. Knowledge of propagation often substitutes for high power. Calling when propagation favors your area will likely result in success. All of these factors, which are crucial to successful contesting, will make you a better DXer.

When you feel comfortable participating in contests from home, you may be ready to graduate to participating in contests outside the 48 states. At some point, many DXers wonder what it would be like to operate at the other end of a pileup. With travel to distant points on the globe easier than ever before, the opportunity to operate at "the other end" is a reality for many DXers. If you would like this type of activity, why not take your spouse on a vacation to the Caribbean and spend a weekend working a DX contest? You will probably find yourself inundated with callers in a way you have never experienced!

Read some of the literature before the trip, though. Such an effort will give you experience in logistics, licensing, and travel as well as DXpedition operating. Setting up a station in a remote hotel accommodation can be an experience. This can be a low-pressure affair designed to give you a real DXpedition experience. Have you learned the basics? When the action starts, you will soon find out!

Want to learn DXpeditioning? Just what exactly do you need to know to be a DXpeditioner? One of the best places to start learning is in a DX contest. Contesting offers the opportunity to operate on the other end of the pileup. As a DXpeditioner, you need to learn how to dig call signs out of big pileups while maintaining control and minimizing the impact on the band. You need to know how to work specific regions when everyone from everywhere is calling you. Stamina, you'll need *lots* of stamina! Most successful DXpeditioners are also well-known contesters.

DXpeditioning requires different types of ability. Rather than putting your signal in the right place at the right time, you must identify signals in that huge mess we call a pileup. You must not only pick out a call, but you must do it quickly, with a predictable pattern and rhythm. DXpeditioning is mostly about operating. To some extent, the name of the game is *rate*. How many stations can you work in an hour? For rare locations, it may also be about how to work as many different stations as possible. At the operating position of a DXpedition, you will usually find a DXer who is also a contester. Contesters have the operating skills required to be successful DXpeditioners. For DXpeditioning, you must also set up a station in some far-off place, often with few resources. Everything is done "Field-Day style." Logistics and planning are very important. Most of all, however, you must be familiar with working a pileup. This is DXpeditioning.

If you are getting the idea that contesting can help in developing your DXing and DXpeditioning skills, you are right. There are two steps in contesting that can help develop these skills. The first is simply to become familiar with contest-style operating by participating in contests from home. Many of the skills required can be learned by observing how it is done. This experience will greatly enhance your DXing skills. The second step, which is the easy and fun way to learn DXpeditioning, is to actually participate in contests from a location "off shore." Contesting offers a condensation of DXing opportunities into a number of short but highly concentrated operating periods throughout the year. For intense experience, practice in breaking pileups and developing DXing skills, try contesting!

CQ Hall of Fame members Roger, G3SXW, and Nigel, G3TXF, are seen here as they depart to French Guyana (FY) for another of their many DXpeditions. (*G3SXW photo*)

signal report, contact number or location codes. What's this? It's a DX contest! Some DX contests are of an "everybody works everybody" format — truly a worldwide DX event! Others restrict contacts to those with a specific country, region, or continent. Most focus on a single mode such as CW or phone. (That means the portion of the band for the "other" mode is relatively quiet if you prefer a more relaxed radio environment.) These competitions are almost always open to all operators and encourage contacts with stations that aren't in the competition directly. Listen a little to get a feel for what information is being exchanged and then jump in!

DX contests are a terrific way to make a lot of short QSOs with DX stations, particularly for beginning DXers. For more information on contesting, check out the **Contesting** chapter in this book.

PROPAGATION

DXing is an activity that can span several sunspot cycles. The bands will change dramatically as the solar conditions change. While you may eventually discover a "favorite band," the DXer should know how each band works in order to take advantage of what is offered. After all, there's DX to be worked on at least one of the bands almost all the time, whether there are 50 spots on the Sun's disc or none at all. The choice is not whether to chase DX, but on which bands to chase it! Three excellent websites for radio propagation information are **www.hfradio.org**, **www.spaceweather.com**, and **www.rsgb.org.uk/psc**.

While it's important to understand the effects of solar phenomena, the key is to be on the air to find DX signals and put them in your log, no matter if the conditions are good or poor. After all, the DXpedition is going to be on the air and the DX contest will begin regardless of how the bands sound. Read and learn as Bill Kennamer, K5NX, takes us on a tour of each DX band in the following sections.

10 Meters

If you're new to the HF bands, you may be wondering why there is such a fuss about 10 meters. As the sunspot cycle progresses toward a peak, as it is while this book is being written in early 2012, 10 meters can quickly change from hibernating to open worldwide. That's why it is necessary to know all its propagation well. Of all the HF bands, 10 meters has more propagation modes than any other. Each has its place depending upon the time of year, time of the sunspot cycle or time of day.

During low sunspots, 10 meters often opens with *sporadic E* as RF-reflecting E layer clouds form rather quickly and often break up just as fast. While sometimes intense enough to even provide propagation on 20 meters, sporadic E propagation is most noticeable on 10 and 6 meters. Openings can be from 1500 to 3000 miles, depending upon whether the cloud is formed well enough to permit one or two hops. Sporadic E often occurs during the summer, and sometimes in mid-winter. Openings can last as long as 24 hours. When this occurs, it's likely to be open all night long. Summertime openings can provide openings to Europe or the Pacific, and can occur at either low or high sunspot numbers. The best season in the Northern Hemisphere is May through early August, followed by a weaker season in December.

Scatter is another form of 10 meter propagation. Using high power and high antennas, stations from 400 to 800 miles away can be worked, albeit with weak signals. Occasionally the ping of a meteor can be heard or an airplane may be positioned just right, as signal strengths jump suddenly, then fall. Scatter occurs during high sunspot or low sunspot periods.

Another form of scatter involves beaming away from the desired direction. Often called *sidescatter* or *skew path*, this propagation mode can be used by beaming southeast in the morning and southwest in the afternoon. During the early stages of a sunspot cycle, this is a main propagation path to Europe, opening when the direct path never does. It will sometimes seem that all signals come from this one direction. When in doubt about which way to point the beam, this is the mode to try. Don't hesitate to try directions other than the direct path to the DX station!

Backscatter is still another of the scatter modes that can be useful. Sometimes 10 meters is an extreme long distance band. At times like that, it's often difficult to work close-in stations. Backscatter can be used for these situations. To use this mode, *both* stations should point their antennas in the *same* direction. The stations then receive each other's signals as they are reflected from the ground or from the ionosphere itself. The band needs to be somewhat quiet for this to occur. As an example, suppose a station in Texas wants to work a station in Mexico. The Mexican station is working the East Coast or Europe. The Texan's best chance is to turn the antenna in the direction of the stations being worked by the Mexican station.

During periods of high sunspots, the preferred propagation mode is via the F layer. This produces the best long distance propagation of all. Due to the nature of 10 meters and the long skip involved, there is less interference from stations on the same frequency. This can be deceptive, as the DXer is often beaten in pileups by stations that can't be heard at all! Still, this is preferable to hearing the pileup hammer one's ears, and it makes hearing the DX station a lot easier.

As sunspot Cycle 24 continues its upward climb, there will be more and more 10 meter openings. Near the peak of the cycle, during a contest it may well be impossible to find a clear frequency from 28.300 MHz all the way to 29.000 MHz! Band openings during these periods are incredible, although worldwide band openings are somewhat more rare. Yet it is possible to cover the world with low power when conditions are right.

North-south transequatorial propagation is available at almost any time in the sunspot cycle. From North America, it is possible to work Africa, New Zealand, Australia or South America at almost any time of the sunspot cycle. Paths south of 90° or 270° are open weakly throughout most of the sunspot cycle.

With its unique characteristics, 10 meters gets attention from amateurs of all interests. When 10 meters is open, DX stations will tend to operate here to take advantage of the opening.

12 Meters

As you might expect, 12 meters closely resembles 10 meters. It is lower in frequency, so it is open more often than 10, but slightly less often than 15 meters. If 15 is open, it is worthwhile to try 12. As the sunspot numbers continue to climb, 12 meters will become increasingly popular.

15 Meters

This is somewhat of a transition band. It has many of the characteristics of 20 meters at times, including possible long-path openings, in addition to some of the characteristics of 10 meters. It often provides very long distance openings, and would be a good choice for working Africa and the Pacific in the afternoon during times of moderate to good solar activity. At times of low sunspots it may not open at all on east-west paths, but is usually open to the south.

Typically, 15 opens after sunrise — if it is going to open. At the bottom of the sunspot cycle, openings are likely to be of very short duration. During cycle peaks, openings are likely to last from sunrise to long after sunset. Propagation moves noticeably from east to west, with absorption around local noon often making signal levels drop for a while, only to return later in the afternoon. The band will begin to open to the west as the Sun moves across the Pacific.

At times of high solar activity, 15 meters will provide openings to Asia as late as local midnight. However, at times of low solar activity, the band isn't likely to open to Asia at all unless the DXer happens to live on the West Coast. When the bands are open, no band provides more access to exotic DX than 15 meters.

17 Meters

Sandwiched between 15 and 20, 17 meters has many of the characteristics of 15 meters. It's lower in frequency, so it's open more often and for longer periods, especially during times of low sunspots. Again, look for morning openings from the east and evening openings to the west. Tuning down the bands, you will begin to notice more atmospheric noise as you move from 15 to 17 meters.

20 Meters

The undisputed king of the DX bands is 20 meters, which supports long distance propagation at any time of the sunspot cycle. During low sunspots, it's likely to be the *only* band open for DX during the daytime. At sunspot maximums, 20 will be open to somewhere almost 24 hours each day. Almost every form of propagation can be found here.

During the winter, 20 will open to the east at sunrise. The opening will last until stations at the eastern end of the path are past sunset. In the early afternoon, the opening will extend to the south and to the southwest. Early evening should find the band opening to the west to northwest.

In the spring and fall, long-path propagation exists with openings to the east coming from a southwesterly to westerly path just after sunrise and lasting for several hours. In the evening, long-path opens to the southeast. It is not unusual to find long-path openings to areas of the world that are actually stronger than the short-path opening.

Summertime often finds openings to the Far East in the mornings while European openings continue through the early evening and on into the night. There is always a southern path extending well into the night after other paths have closed. The band may seem to close, then open up again later around midnight on certain paths.

This single band is so productive that more than a few serious DXers restrict their antenna choice to one large monoband 20 meter antenna. All DX operates on 20 meters at some point; it's impossible to be a truly effective DXer without it.

30 Meters

If ever there was a DX band that provided 24-hour DXing at any stage of the sunspot cycle, 30 meters would be it. It shares many of the characteristics of 20 and 40 meters with long nighttime openings while providing DX throughout most of the daytime as well. Propagation is hard to describe as 30 meters can almost be open to anywhere at any time as the seasons change. The DXer should check this band frequently for some pleasant surprises.

40 Meters

If 20 meters is the king of DX bands, then 40 meters surely must be the queen. While affected by many of the same conditions as 80, absorption by the D layer is reduced because of the shorter wavelength, and it becomes possible to work intercontinental DX during the late afternoon. In fact, at the sunspot minimum it's possible to hear DX all day long and some of it may be worked if your signals are not too severely absorbed.

In the late afternoon, the band is likely to provide good long-path openings to the southeast. Openings are again basically toward the east until well after eastern sunrise. Afterward, the opening will swing south, then toward the west as sunrise approaches. An opening to the southwest is very common in the morning, and stations that would normally be found with a northwest great circle path will be found there with no opening at all to the northwest! An example of this is the USA-to-Hong Kong path, which will often be open at a heading of 210-225° rather than the expected 330°.

DXing on 40 meter phone can be difficult because of interference from shortwave broadcast stations located outside ITU Regions 1 and 2. These megawatt transmitters make sharing the band difficult, if not impossible. This situation began changing in 2009 as broadcasters started to vacate their 40 meter frequencies, creating a worldwide allocation for amateurs from 7 to 7.2 MHz. Region 3 broadcasters are still found in the amateur allocation, however, and split operation on phone remains common.

60 Meters

Just as 30 meters shares the characteristics of both 20 and 40 meters, 60 meters features aspects of its adjacent bands, 80 and 40 meters. Restricted to five fixed-frequency channels, DX is found on this band more and more as additional countries grant their amateurs access. The amateur allocation in the US is secondary to government stations, so be careful when transmitting so as not to create unnecessary interference to the primary users! The ARRL has published information on the 60 meter band at **www.arrl.org/60-meter-faq**. Check this page for updates in regulations and band planning.

80 Meters

Propagation on 80 meters shares many characteristics with 160 meters, described below. Auroral zones, D layer absorption, and thunderstorm activities all have limiting effects on this band. It usually begins to open in the early afternoon. The band opening is to the east and will continue until after sunrise at the eastern end of the path, then to the south, finally ending with westerly openings as sunrise approaches.

DXing on 80 meters is seasonal, with better conditions in the wintertime but with DX still available in the summer. In times of low sunspots, 80 (or 75, as the phone part of the band is commonly called) becomes the prime nighttime phone band as 20 and 40 both close. While used less often in times of high sunspots, it's still open although usually later in the evening.

Aficionados of the bands below 20 meters keep a copy of _ON4UN's Low-Band DXing_ handy at all times. It contains detailed information on antennas, propagation and operating for these challenging but rewarding bands.

160 Meters

Often called the "Top Band," 160 offers one of the great DX challenges. Openings are sometimes very short in duration, and usually provide shorter distance openings than other bands. During high sunspot levels the band is open, but the Sun's activity causes an increase in noise level and absorption of signals increases as the D layer, forming at sunrise and dissipating at sunset, is more intense in years of high solar activity. This effect is somewhat lessened during times of low sunspot activity but for the most part, 160 meters is still a

nighttime band. There is even an e-mail reflector dedicated to 160 meter operation: **lists.contesting.com/mailman/listinfo/ Topband**. It deals exclusively with 160 meter information such as DXing, antennas, propagation and band conditions.

Propagation on 160 begins in the late afternoon to early evening, in the direction of the approaching darkness. As stations in the east approach their sunrise, there will likely be a short but noticeable increase in their signal strength, called the _dawn enhancement_. This is your opportunity to span the longest distances. Propagation continues to flow east to west, as the DXer follows the Sun. As the Sun rises, the DXer can expect to work stations to the west until they finally sink into the noise as the D layer begins to absorb the signal again.

Also worth more than a little mention are the auroral zones, ring-shaped regions centered on the magnetic poles. Charged particles from the Sun follow the Earth's magnetic field and are guided to the magnetic poles. Along with creating the visual displays known as aurora, the particles flowing down through the ionosphere create a vertical region that attenuates signals passing through it. The longer the wavelength, the greater will be the attenuation. Thus, low band signals are affected more than others by the auroral zones. This will be apparent on northerly paths, as stations in the Yukon and Alaska often report one-way propagation where they can hear stations to the south, yet are not able to be heard by them.

Shorter periods of sunlight and less thunderstorm activity make 160 meter propagation better in the fall and winter. Don't overlook possible openings to the Southern Hemisphere in the summer, as the seasons are reversed and those in the Southern Hemisphere are experiencing their best propagation of the year.

The VHF DX Bands

6 Meters

A DX band? Yes! As the nickname "The Magic Band" attests, 6 meters can provide some of the most exciting DXing of any band. Again, many modes of propagation are available, but sporadic E is probably the most common. Occurring in the spring and early summer and again in December, sporadic E can provide DX contacts up to 4000 miles and sometimes more. At the peak of the solar cycle, 6 meters provides intercontinental contacts via the F layer.

This band is the lowest practical frequency for EME (moonbounce) operations. Stations utilizing four or more high gain antennas and high power have been able to communicate internationally even though the band is closed for other propagation modes. No longer a curiosity, 6 meters is a legitimate DX band. Many stations have DXCC totals well over 100 on this band.

2 Meters

Two meters is also a DX band. Through the use of meteor scatter, many Europeans have earned credits for their Mixed DXCC on 2 meters. However, most DXers who have earned DXCC on 2 meters have done so through the use of moonbounce (EME).

Pick a Band — From 160 to 2

This is not a scientific guide to propagation on the DX bands. It is only to alert the DXer to the possibilities of the DX bands and how to use them. The DXer should note the time of day, solar activity, the direction of the DX, and make a band choice that may provide an opportunity to find the DX. No attempt has been made to fully explain any phenomenon, only to point out that it does exist, and the DXer should plan for the various possibilities. For example, you may have to calculate the Sun's position at the other end of the desired path in order to make a band choice. The important thing to remember is that the DXpedition doesn't usually sit at home waiting for the Sun. Get on the air and use whatever propagation exists!

Special Propagation

Beacons

Any guide to propagation can only educate so much. The final test is to listen for yourself whenever you can. Don't just watch DX spots roll in off the Internet — tune for yourself! There are many beacon stations around the world that transmit low-power carriers and CW identification to alert stations to band openings.

The best known set of beacons is the Northern California DX Foundation/International Amateur Radio Union International Beacon Project operating on the 20, 17, 15, 12 and 10 meter bands. Each beacon operates in sequence at a series of power levels so that you can gauge the conditions. Complete information on the beacons is available at **www.ncdxf.org** along with tutorial information about them.

There are also many beacon stations on the 10 meter band between 28.190 and 28.225 MHz. When solar flux is low, such as at the bottom of the sunspot cycle, beacons are very useful propagation tools. Listings of 10 meter beacon stations are available on the Ten-Ten website (an organization that promotes activity on 10 meters) at **www.ten-ten.org**.

Long-Path Propagation

Any of the HF bands can support long-path propagation at some point during the sunspot cycle. Because of the extra distance involved, signals are generally weaker and the openings much shorter. Making contacts via the long-path is exciting and worth the extra effort.

The conditions that support long-path propagation vary depending on the band. For the "low bands" (those below 10 MHz), long-path most often occurs along the gray line (see below) near sunrise and sunset. The openings are short — often just a few minutes. Because of atmospheric noise on these bands, working DX long-path usually requires a good location and capable station. Above 10 MHz, long-path requires solar illumination instead of darkness so that the MUF (maximum useable frequency) is high enough to support propagation all the way along the route. Watch for long-path openings to the southeast in the morning and to the southwest in the afternoon.

Long path most often occurs over paths that pass over the oceans because the lower losses of reflection by salt water keep signal strengths usable at longer distances. A special form of long path is *round-the-world* (RTW) propagation. If you hear an echo of your signal delayed by about 1/7th of a second, your signal may be traveling completely around the Earth!

Gray Line Propagation

Because the D layer is the lowest layer of the ionosphere, it remains non-illuminated for longer than the higher layers. Thus, it forms after all the other layers and is the first one to dissipate. The result is a region along the *terminator* — the dividing line between light and dark areas — in which absorption from the D layer is reduced. Propagation along the terminator is called *gray-line* propagation. Gray-line propagation may be especially useful at the beginning of an opening. A good antenna system and output power will maximize the success of gray-line contacts. Use your favorite Internet search engine to locate information on software that generates gray-line maps for the different seasons.

Tropospheric Propagation

Although unknown at HF, tropospheric propagation, or "tropo," can be a regular source of DX QSOs on the VHF+ bands. Most common at 2 meters and shorter wavelength bands, propagation can occur along discontinuities and weather features in the atmosphere. The two most common sources of tropo are weather fronts and temperature inversions. You can watch for tropo by monitoring the FM broadcast band for signals from distant stations.

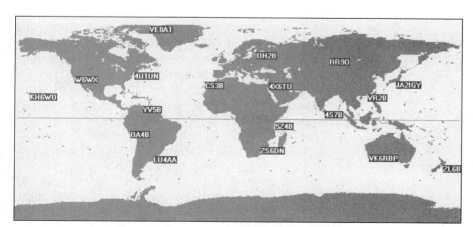

The beacons of the NCDXF/IARU beacon network allow HF DXers to check conditions on the 20, 17, 15, 12 and 10 meter bands from anywhere in the world.

DXPEDITIONS

These short-term operations have been mentioned several times so far in this chapter. From the DXer's perspective, they provide an exciting change to the everyday bands. Suddenly there are big pileups on different bands and modes — everyone wants a contact before they shut down! Their QSLs are often spectacular, and there may be a video or convention presentation to enjoy. With radios and antennas more compact and efficient than ever, there are more DXpeditions on the air than ever, too! While most active on HF, more and more DXpeditions take gear for 6 meters, even moonbounce!

And what DXer could resist daydreaming about being on "the other end" of the pileup? Hundreds of stations calling, pileups around the clock day and night, thousands of contacts logged at high rates. This could be you! What's to stop you from putting together a small station and hopping on the next

Bill, N7OU/T3ØOU, (L) and Bob, W7YAQ/T3ØYA, (R) make regular DXpeditions to the islands of the Pacific. During their 2011 trip to Tarawa in Western Kiribati, they made more than 20,000 contacts, mostly using CW.

plane for somewhere with sandy beaches and not much radio activity? Not much, actually!

This section talks about DXpeditions from both ends — how to work them and the basics of going on one. They are a big part of the spice of DXing — bringing geography home in a way a textbook simply can't.

Working DXpeditions

You won't be able to work DXpeditions unless you know they're on the air. Furthermore, you may have to make arrangements to be on the air at the right time for propagation to your area. After all, the expeditioners aren't going to wait for you to get home from work! Most DXpeditions are 24/7 operations, following the bands with the Sun.

The first thing is to learn about the trip and who is taking it. This is where newsletters and DX websites are most helpful. They'll alert you to upcoming expeditions and answer questions such as, when will the operation begin and end? Who are the operators? What bands and modes will they use?

Will they be using specific frequencies or will you need to be looking for them? It's a good thing that there are websites and newsletters to provide the information. Write down all the necessary information on paper and post it at your station for easy reference. You might also want to let other family members know that you'll be operating at odd times in pursuit of these rare birds!

You'll find that there is a wide variety in the capabilities of DXpeditions. Some are one-operator holidays with operating time, bands and modes limited to the interests and schedule of the individual taking the trip. At the other end of the scale is the "mega" DXpedition with a dozen operators or more, lots of equipment, continuous operation, and loud signals wherever they choose to tune. These big operations, so to speak, often have supporting resources such as on-line logs and pilot stations that provide feedback and guidance to the expeditioners.

Once the expedition is on the air, listen to the pileups and decide on a strategy. If your station has strong capabilities in that part of the world, you might enjoy jumping in at the beginning. If not, take the opportunity to listen and learn the operating styles being used. You can wait until the pile thins out or try to catch them as they change bands or modes. The risk of waiting is, of course, that something might go wrong — generator failure or a storm — and cause an early shutdown. Toward the end of even the largest expeditions, however, the pileups thin out and it becomes easier to make contact.

Medium Gun DXers may take as a goal to have a single, solid contact in the DXpedition's log on each band and mode in which they have an interest. It's usually not necessary to make several "insurance" QSOs to be sure of having one good one. If the DX sent your call clearly and you were able to hear the entire QSO without confusion as to timing, you should be in the log. If not, make a second QSO. Avoid being one of the "DX hogs" who make duplicate QSOs just because they can. It denies other stations an opportunity to make possibly their first QSO with the expedition and maybe the first ever with that entity! On-line logs that are available during the operation are particularly helpful in this regard. Once your call is confirmed, you can relax.

After the expedition is over, be sure to QSL according to the directions of the operators or their QSL manager. Manage your expectations for a quick confirmation. Most DXpeditions give their logs a careful check before responding to QSL requests. Gear has to be unpacked, cleaned, and sorted or shipped. The expedition members have to get their personal lives back in order. QSLs have to be printed. It may be weeks or more likely months before your QSL request is processed. If patience is difficult to come by, get on the air and work some more DX!

During the days of chasing an elusive DXpedition QSO, you may become frustrated. The operators may switch to another area just as propagation to yours is building. They may operate on bands with poor propagation to you or spend time on your favorite mode. There may be times when the operator has a hard time controlling the pileup or working stations at a decent rate. At times like this, don't let your frustrations get the better of you. The expeditioners are likely operating under stress. They're hot, cold, thirsty, smelly, being bitten by insects or crabs, and wondering why it was that they sailed, flew, or drove all the way to whatever bizarre location it is. It's your relatively easy job to remain calm and follow their instructions. Give them the benefit of the doubt, since they have gone to great lengths for your benefit.

Going on a DXpedition

It's a rare DXer indeed who hasn't listened to a DXpedition and imagined being at the "other end" with the headphones on, picking out calls one by one from a sandy beach or mountaintop location. Surely, we've all thought, "I could do that!" as we listen to contacts stream by. The answer is that you can certainly give it a try! There is no guarantee of success, of course, but it's a lot easier to be the DX than you might think.

You need to start simple, of course. Good practice is surprisingly easy to come by — operate from an IOTA island or operate from a portable location in the next contest. Read articles or websites about the experiences of other DXpedition operators. Learn what gear you require and develop a package of equipment that works. Get used to operating away from your comfortable shack. Become skilled at packing,

A Microlite Penguin Point of View on DXing

By Lew Sayre W7EW/W7AT for the Microlite Penguins

There is no substitute for the excitement and thrill of tuning a band, hearing a weak signal, realizing it was real DX and then working that station! We want that type of experience to remain active for as long as hams are able to propagate their calls around the world.

What is different about the Microlite Penguin philosophy of DXing? We think that the onus for working a DX station should be squarely upon the shoulders of the ham who is looking to make the DX contacts. The DX is not responsible for the contact — the ham at home should be responsible! Technology has made it very easy for a radio operator to get on the Internet, scan the spotting systems and see what is currently being spotted. Then that ham can use the computer interface to drive the radios, amplifiers, tuners and antennas to QSO the DX for another step on the DXCC ladder.

How easy is that? Way too easy, in our opinion. This shift to technology makes the operating skill factor much less relevant. Why tune and listen to figure out the DX station's pattern, when you can simply punch the computer button to spread your call repeatedly over the pile-up so that you might get into the DX log?

Human nature places a higher value on something that you have to work for rather than something you are given. Developing the DXing skills, and then applying them to snag that

rare DX makes a QSO much more valuable than working a massive DXpedition signal that anyone could work.

The Microlite Penguin philosophy celebrates simple antennas such as verticals and dipoles. We typically use 100 W. That is enough to put a workable signal into any corner of the Earth. We'll use 500 to 800 W on the very low bands because of the nasty QSB and QRM that are prevalent on those frequencies. We are experienced operators who tend to work the weak ones first and the strong ones last. We try not to give advance notice when we embark on a Microlite DXpedition. In short, we appreciate the skills it takes to make contact with the DX station and wish to encourage the advancement of the art of DXing.

The rising cost of transportation will make major DXpeditions less frequent. Compared to large, pre-announced expeditions, Microlite Penguins carry much less gear — no beam antennas or multiple amplifiers. This means we are much more likely to be putting on a spot rare in the DXing world, as compared to different types of DXpeditions where they do everything except turn on your radio for you.

If you've worked VP8ORK, VP8THU, VP8GEO, FT5XO or ZL8R you've utilized the philosophy and skills of the Microlite Penguins. Developing your skills as a DXer provides better enjoyment and satisfaction during your Amateur Radio activities.

The Microlite DXpedition team landed on the South Orkneys in 2012. The team travels with small radios and lightweight antennas, relying on the ears of DXers to pull their signals through. (L-R) W3WL, Microlite mascot Pete the Penguin, 9V1YC, VE3EJ, N6MZ, N1DG, WB9Z, KØIR, K6AW, N4GRN, K9ZO, W7EW, ND2T and EY8MM. (*EY8MM photo*)

transporting, deploying, and repacking your equipment.

Once you're ready to become "real DX," choose a reasonable first location. You wouldn't want to try for a really difficult destination on the first time out. Difficulty can mean transportation or licensing. Remember that you'll need all the proper permissions for your operation to count for most award programs! It's best to start with an easier location where licensing and transportation and accommodations are not a problem. After a couple of "shakedown cruises" you can set your sights higher. Is your passport up to date? Let's go then!

There are a number of websites that can assist you in finding the necessary information. The ARRL website has a good section on international licensing at **www.arrl.org/international-operating** and the DX Zone website (**www.dxzone.com/catalog/DX_Resources/**) has quite a number of links to ham-friendly rental destinations. Although the DX Holiday website (**www.dxholiday.com**) is not maintained regularly, it still contains quite a bit of information on the mechanics of DXing and important travel links. Don't overlook operators who have operated from your chosen location before. Most are quite willing to help you out by answering questions and even making recommendations or introductions. Soon you'll have airline tickets and your gear packed for the trip!

An alternative to figuring it all out on your own is to join forces with a group making a trip of their own. If one of your club members has gone on DXpeditions, that's a good place to start your inquiries. They may be planning another trip, or know someone who is, and be willing to make an introduction. You can also contact DXpedition operators from teams that have made recent trips, perhaps by approaching them after a presentation. If you're enthusiastic and keep at it, you should be able to eventually find a team in need of another operator. Here's where your practice trips will come in handy as experience the group will value. You'll have to fit in with their plans and style, contributing and assisting as requested. Nevertheless, the experience will be invaluable to you.

Describing the process of conducting a DXpedition is well beyond the scope of this book. Every trip is different, but all require a lot of detailed and painstaking effort to be successful. Start small, work your way up, soak up information from every source available, and someday we'll see your face on the cover of our favorite magazine with a weathered but happy smile!

Supporting DXpeditions

As you will find out if you go on a DXpedition, they can be expensive undertakings! To put a team of operators on a rock in the middle of the ocean or on an ice floe near one of the Earth's poles — and get them back home again safely — requires a lot of resources and planning. Recent DXpeditions to some of the rarest islands have operating budgets of more than $100,000! Needless to say, not all of this expense is borne by the operating team. Sponsors are required. Manufacturers often donate or loan equipment to DXpeditions, but that won't pay for a boat!

DXers are encouraged to support the DXpedition by making a donation as requested and encouraging your DX club to do the same. While it is most helpful to donate before the DXpedition hits the airwaves, it is also acceptable to make a donation with your QSL request.

The following are just a few of the organizations that raise money to support DXpeditions and who are themselves supported themselves by the donations of individual DXers: European DX Foundation (EUDXF, **www.eudxf.de**); German DX Foundation (GDXF, **www.gdxf.de**); INDEXA (**www.indexa.org**); Northern California DX Foundation (**www.ncdxf.org**).

Operating Permission and Documentation

Once a DXpeditioner starts to get off the beaten track, the issue of operating permission becomes more important. That's particularly true for uninhabited locations that may be under some kind of access restriction, such as a wildlife preserve. In many cases, operating permission consists only of the necessary landing permits. For example, some French and American possessions have limited access but no need for a special license. These destinations will require special landing permission, and it must be in writing from the proper agency. This may be a difficult task but it is not insurmountable, as proven by the fact that it has been done before. It may take many letters and a few visits before the goal is accomplished. By definition, nothing difficult is ever easy!

The copies of operating and landing permissions will document that the DXer had permission to be there for the purpose of Amateur Radio. There is a need, however, to further document presence at the location. Documents may consist of transportation receipts, ship's logs or certifications signed by the captain, and pictures of the operators at known locations. Postcards mailed to the DXCC desk from the location, or if that's impossible, from the nearest port, also help document the operation. If there is any doubt as to what constitutes the appropriate documentation for a DXpedition, contact the administrator of the appropriate awards program and find out!

CONFIRMING THE CONTACT — QSLING

For DXers who are pursuing awards, confirming the contact is almost as important as the contact itself. The paper QSL has been a part of Amateur Radio and DXing for as long as radio itself has existed. Electronic confirmation systems, such as ARRL's Logbook of the World, complement paper QSLs. In either case, they provide the confirmation that actually proves the contact. After all, without a confirmation, the DXer might never know that he or she had worked a pirate or a bootlegger!

Electronic QSO Confirmation

Why, in this 21st century age of instantaneous communication and digital information, are there not systems to confirm a QSO electronically? Why, there are! The two most-used systems are eQSL (**www.eqsl.cc**) and the ARRL's Logbook of the World (LOTW, **www.arrl.org/lotw**). Both systems require a registration process and that you upload an electronic copy of your logbook.

Not all awards programs yet accept electronic QSLs. For example, the ARRL does not accept eQSL confirmations for its awards, while Logbook of the World confirmations are accepted for its major awards. Each system publishes a list of awards for which electronic QSLs are accepted. There are complete instructions for using the system and descriptions of how the system works on their respective home pages.

Most DXpeditions eventually upload their logs to LOTW so your QSOs can be automatically confirmed. If you want a paper QSL, you'll have to request that separately by using one of the methods described below. The electronic LOTW confirmation may be used for ARRL awards and other award programs are being added to LOTW. As of early 2012, LOTW supports DXCC, VUCC, WAS and the CQ WPX

Hamad, 9K2HN is one of many DXers around the world using the Logbook of the World electronic contact confirmation system. Hamad has uploaded more than 300,000 QSOs made over many years.

award program. Check the LOTW website to see what other award programs are being supported.

Electronic QSLs are unlikely to ever completely replace paper QSLs because the experience of exchanging QSLs remains very enjoyable. A collection of paper QSLs built up over a lifetime contains many beautiful souvenirs. It is likely that DXers will continue to exchange a paper card for initial contacts and use electronic QSLing for subsequent confirmations and for contest QSOs.

Online QSL Request System (OQRS)

Many DXpeditions have started using the Online QSL Request System (OQRS) created by Bernd Koch, DF3CB in 2003. This system allows you, the DXer, to request a paper QSL and also make supporting donations to the expedition. This frees the expedition from handling all of your cards — which they rarely need for any reason — and allows you to cover postage and handling costs completely online. No stamps, envelopes, postal delays (or worse), and you still get a card!

Each expedition operates its own OQRS independently — there is no central OQRS. This allows each expedition to tailor their QSLing practices as required. You'll need to follow the expedition's instructions for requesting a QSL and supporting the expedition.

Paper QSLs

It's important to realize that a DX station receives a lot more incoming cards than he or she really needs. Therefore, it's really important for DXers to make it easy for their cards to be answered.

First, the card itself should be designed for the convenience of the DX station or QSL manager. Having to process literally tens of thousands of QSLs, it's easy to understand how a manager could get a little upset with having to hunt for information around the card or on both sides. QSL card design doesn't make the chore totally painless, but prevents the manager or DX station from learning the DXer's call sign in a negative context! So the QSL card should have all the information on one side only. It should be easy to read and in a logical order.

There is certain information required on a QSL card that is to be submitted for DXCC credit, the standard for DX awards programs. Confirmation for two-way communication must include the call signs of both stations, the DXCC entity, mode, date, time and the frequency band used. For VUCC, the station's grid square should be included. Desirable information includes the county and, if the DXer lives on an island, an Islands on the Air (IOTA) identifier. This way, if DX stations happen to be pursuing awards, they will be able to use the DXer's QSL card for their own purposes.

The card should have the information printed plainly on the card. Avoid optical illusion cards or ones with overly embellished lettering. Save them for non-DX purposes. Plain lettering on a plain card is much better. If a picture card is desirable, it may be better to have the picture on the front and the information in plain print on the back. Print your call on *both* sides of the card. That way the card can be displayed by the DX station, but processed rapidly as well.

There are three ways to get a card to its destination: By bureau, by QSL service and direct mail. Each has its advantages, although there are some differences in the speed. There are also some differences in how a DX station will handle them. The method the DXer uses depends upon his or her own personal requirements.

The ARRL Outgoing QSL Service (see the end of this chapter) provides economical service to the countries that have incoming bureaus. While slow, with turnaround time sometimes exceeding a year or more, still this may be considered an efficient and cost-effective method for QSLing. This is especially true when compared with postal pilferage of direct QSLs in some parts of the world. The disadvantages of the bureau system are that in some countries served by bureaus, only the cards of members are delivered. The bureau system is highly recommended when QSLing to countries with large populations of hams. The new GlobalQSL system (**www.globalqsl.com**) bypasses a great deal of the paperwork by allowing you to upload your log directly to their service. Paper QSLs are then printed from your log data and sent to bureaus and managers directly. This is slower (and cheaper) than direct mailing individual cards, but faster (and more expensive) than the bureau system.

Another QSL forwarding service is the WF5E QSL Service (**www.qsl.net/wf5e**). For a small amount per card, the QSL service will forward your cards to the bureau, by direct mail, or to a manager. Cards are returned via the DXer's own incoming bureau unless special arrangements are made. The DXer will notice the cards coming back this way, as they are usually marked with the service's stamp.

Turnaround time via QSL services like this is reduced as cards are sent to bureaus in smaller quantities and cards are sent to managers with return postage. In most cases, it isn't even necessary to know the manager, as the QSL service keeps track of managers and will get the card to the right place. The success rate of using a QSL service is very good.

Direct QSLs

Direct QSLing is used by many DXers. QSLing direct isn't cheap, so be prepared to spend some money if this method is used. Presentation is worth a lot when QSLing direct, so carefully prepare the card and envelopes to maximize the chance of a response. The bureau is often more convenient for amateurs who are permanent residents.

Direct QSLing starts with a good address. Sometimes the station will give a complete address over the air. If not, then one of the call sign lookup sites on the Internet or available by CD-ROM may have the information. Try entering "qsl route" or something similar into your favorite search engine, or visit **www.ac6v.com/callbooks.htm**. The Internet sites often have newer addresses for stations that have recently been active. It is best to get the complete name of the operator, as it is always best that call signs *not* be placed on the envelope.

The envelopes themselves are important. Other countries do not use the same envelope sizes that are commonly found in the United States. This means that using a standard US #10 envelope will create the undesirable situation of sending something through the mail that attracts unwanted attention and possible theft. It is far better to obtain the proper size envelope for the job at hand rather than trying to make do. The best size is a 4¾ × 6½-inch outer air mail envelope, and a 4½ × 6¼-inch inner air mail envelope for returns. If possible, the addresses should be typed directly on the envelope, or printed labels. It is important to remember that *no* call signs should go on the outside of any envelope, again, to avoid unwanted attention. The envelope should look as ordinary as possible.

Inside the flap of the return envelope the DXer should put their call and date, time, and mode of the QSO. In the event the card gets separated from the return envelope, it is still possible for the manager to look up the QSO and send the card. Also, either cards or a list of all QSOs made with the station, if a DXpedition, should be sent so that the manager won't have to guess about whether to provide cards for all QSOs found in the log. Chances are the manager *won't* if not asked!

Return Postage

The old saying "The final courtesy of a QSO is a QSL" should be changed to "It is discourteous to send a QSL card *without* return postage provisions." QSL cards aren't cheap

these days, with even the cheapest around 5 cents each. As this is written, inside the United States it costs 45 cents for mailing in an envelope or 32 cents as a postcard. Multiply this by a thousand, and you'll find that QSLing could easily cost $400 to $500! Make it air mail and the price jumps even further. Then consider that United States postal rates are among the cheapest in the world, which could put the tab for a thousand QSLs without return postage well over $1000! That's a lot of money for something the DX station likely doesn't need! It should be easy to see why there is poor or no response to cards received without return postage. A word to the wise: If you really want that QSL card, be sure that return postage is provided in whatever form is necessary.

A popular way of providing return postage remains the International Reply Coupon (IRC). They may be obtained from a Post Office and are redeemable for the lowest air mail rate in any Universal Postal Union (UPU) country. IRCs can often be obtained from a QSL manager in the DXer's own country. IRCs purchased this way trade somewhere between the value of new IRCs and the redemption value.

Be aware that in some countries, the lowest air mail rate won't provide enough postage to return an envelope and QSL card. Sometimes it takes two. For example, until recently, Germany's lowest air mail rate provided for less weight than the average QSL card and envelope. So it became necessary to go to the next highest rate, and it takes two IRCs to provide enough postage.

Another way to provide return postage is by sending unused stamps of the country of the DX station or QSL manager with sufficient value to provide return postage. This allows the manager to fill out the card and put it in the envelope without converting money or redeeming IRCs. Purchase postage and affix it to the envelope. It also removes the temptation to keep the IRCs or money, returning the card later, if at all. If this method is used, it's best to put the postage on the return envelope so that it may only be used for returning the DXer's cards.

Some DXers prefer to provide return postage by sending a ubiquitous "green stamp," the United States one dollar bill. There are several problems associated with using green stamps, not the least of which is mail pilferage. Even mail passing through the US is not immune to it and in some countries, if the envelope is identified as going to an Amateur Radio operator, it is almost certain to disappear. In addition to exchange problems at the country of destination, there are some countries around the world where hard currency is so controlled it is illegal to have US currency.

In other countries, green stamps trade much like IRCs; that is, they are not exchanged at all, but traded for the amateur's own QSLing needs. They are often sent with visitors from the US back to the States to buy US postage and forward the cards on from there. One green stamp no longer will buy sufficient postage in many countries. So two are required if the DXer expects to get a return. Green stamps are used mostly for convenience, but the price paid may well be loss of the card.

Preparation is Key

With the QSL card, return postage in whatever form, and envelopes, the DXer is ready to prepare the QSL for mailing. First be sure the QSL is completed properly, with all QSOs made with the station listed on the card. The card should then be inserted into the envelope, which should have the DXer's return address typed or printed on it. Be sure that the country name is the bottom line of the return address. If a green stamp or IRC is used, insert that into the return envelope. The idea is to make as flat a package as possible.

If the card is going to an area of high humidity, putting a piece of waxed paper under the return envelope flap can prevent it from sticking together before it is used. All this should then be placed into the outer envelope and sealed. Remember, no call signs or references to Amateur Radio should be on the outer envelope. With some luck, the DXer will see a desired rare QSL coming back in a few weeks or months.

One word about QSL turnaround: Many DXers have far too high expectations of how quickly they should receive QSLs from DXpeditions. It depends upon the operation and whether a special effort is put into quick turnaround, but six months is very reasonable for QSL return. Whereas the larger DXpeditions may have a small army of helpers to complete the QSLing, most smaller DXpeditions depend upon one individual. If an operation made 10,000 QSOs,

Danilo IZ1KHY, operated from Mario Zucchelli Station, II0MZ, during Antarctic Activity Week. The Worldwide Antarctic Program offers several awards for contacts with stations from the most-southern of the continents. (*I1HYW photo*)

allowing 3 minutes per card for opening, finding and checking the log entry, writing or attaching a label to the card, inserting the card and sealing the envelope, and obtaining and affixing stamps, figure on the manager handling 100 cards per day. That's five hours per day for 100 days without a break! If the manager also had a full-time job and family, you can see where a little time off from this routine would be desired. Allow a minimum of at least six months before even thinking about a second QSL, even if friends are receiving theirs. A card may just have been near the bottom of the pile.

Also, the DXer shouldn't send a request via the bureau at the same time as sending the direct card. QSL managers note all cards received and sent in the log. When they find a DXer using this practice, they make a note of the call sign and that DXer's next card often goes out with the last batch mailed or through the bureau.

THE ARRL OUTGOING QSL SERVICE

Note: The ARRL QSL Service *cannot be used* to exchange QSL cards within the 48 contiguous states. QSLs from the 48 states to and from Alaska and Hawaii may be sent through the ARRL QSL Service. All prices in this section are current as of April 2012. For the latest information on this service, check **www.arrl.org/qsl-service** or via e-mail to **buro@arrl.org**

One of the greatest bargains of ARRL membership is being able to use the Outgoing QSL Service to conveniently send your DX QSL cards to overseas QSL Bureaus. You just need to provide proof of ARRL Membership and include payment following the fee schedule below. The potential savings over sending direct QSL cards with return postage are huge. Your cards are sorted promptly by the Outgoing Service staff, and cards are on their way overseas usually within a week of arrival at HQ. Approximately one million cards are handled by the Service each year!

QSL cards are shipped to QSL Bureaus throughout the world, which are typically maintained by the national Amateur Radio Society of each country. In the case of DXpeditions and/or active DX stations that use US QSL managers, a better approach is to QSL directly to the QSL manager.

How to Use the Outgoing QSL Service

1. Presort your DX QSLs alphabetically by parent call sign prefix (AP, CE, DL, ES, EZ, F, G, JA, LY, PY, UN, YL, 5N, 9Y and so on). Canadian and Australian cards should be sorted by numerical call sign (VE1, VE2, VE3 & VK1, VK2, VK3 etc). Note: Some countries have a parent prefix

and use additional prefixes, i.e. G (parent prefix) = M, 2E, 2I, 2M, 2W... When sorting countries that have multiple prefixes, keep that country's prefixes grouped with the parent prefix in your alphabetical stack. Addresses are not required.

2. Do not separate the country prefixes by use of paper clips, rubber bands, slips of paper or envelopes.

3. Please enclose proof of your current ARRL membership. This can be in the form of a photocopy or cutout of the address area from your current copy of *QST*. You can also write the information from the label on a slip of paper and use that as proof of membership. A copy of your current membership card is also acceptable.

4. Members, including foreign, QSL Managers or managers for DXpeditions, should enclose payment. Rates vary depending on the quantity of cards you are sending and are subject to change with changes in postal rates. Check the ARRL website (**www.arrl.org/outgoing-qsl-service**) for current rates.

5. Please pay by check (or money order) and write your call sign on the check. Send cash at your own risk. Don't send postage stamps or IRCs. Please make checks payable to: "The ARRL Outgoing QSL Service." If you would like to know that your cards were received at the ARRL QSL Bureau, enclose an SASE in with your cards and that will be returned to you as a receipt.

6. DXCC credits cannot be used toward the QSL Service fee.

7. Include only the cards, proof of membership, an SASE (if desired) and the appropriate fee in the package. Wrap the

Table 6-1

DXCC Entities Not Served by the ARRL Outgoing QSL Service

A3	Tonga	SØ	Western Sahara	ZA	Albania
A5	Bhutan	S7	Seychelles	ZD7	St. Helena
A6	United Arab Emirates	S9	Sao Tome & Principe	ZD8	Ascension
C2	Nauru	ST	Sudan	ZD9	Tristan da Cunha
C5	Gambia	SU	Egypt	3B	Agalega, Mauritius, Rodrigues
C6	Bahamas	T2	Tuvalu		
CN	Morocco	T3	Kiribati	3CØ	Pagalu Island
D2	Angola	T5	Somalia	3CØ	Equatorial Guinea
D4	Cape Verde	T8	Palau	3DA	Swaziland
E3	Eritrea	TJ	Cameroon	3W	Vietnam
E5	North & South Cook Islands	TL	Central African Republic	3X	Guinea
HH	Haiti	TN	Congo	4J	Azerbaijan
HV	Vatican	TT	Chad	4W	Timor-Leste
J5	Guinea-Bissau	TU	Cote d'Ivoire	5A	Lybia
J8	St. Vincent	TY	Benin	5R	Madagascar
KG4	Guantanamo Bay	V3	Belize	5T	Mauritania
KHØ	Mariana Island	V4	St. Kitts & Nevis	5U	Niger
KH1	Baker & Howland Islands	V6	Micronesia	5V	Togo
KH4	Midway Island	V7	Marshall Islands	7O	Yemen
KH5	Palmyra & Jarvis Islands	VP2E	Anguilla	7P	Lesotho
KH7K	Kure Island	VP2M	Montserrat	7Q	Malawi
KH9	Wake Island	XU	Cambodia	8Q	Maldives
KP1	Desecheo Island	XW	Laos	9L	Sierra Leone
P2	Papua New Guinea	XZ	Myanmar	9N	Nepal
P5	North Korea	YA	Afghanistan	9U	Burundi
PZ	Suriname	Z2	Zimbabwe	9X	Rwanda

package securely and address it to the ARRL Outgoing QSL Service, 225 Main Street, Newington, CT 06111-1494.

8. Family members may also use the service by enclosing their QSLs with those of the primary member. Include the appropriate fee and indicate "family membership" on the primary member's proof of membership.

9. Blind members who do not receive *QST* need only include the appropriate fee along with a note indicating the cards are from a blind member.

10. ARRL affiliated-club stations may use the service when submitting club QSLs by indicating the club name. Club secretaries should check club affiliation on the ARRL web site to ensure that their affiliation is current. In addition to sending club station QSLs through this service, affiliated clubs may also "pool" their members' individual QSL cards for an even greater savings. Each club member using this service must also be an ARRL member. Cards should be sorted "en masse" by prefix and a proof of membership should be enclosed for each ARRL member.

Recommended QSL Card Dimensions

The efficient operation of the worldwide system of QSL Bureaus requires that cards be easy to handle and sort. Cards of unusual dimensions, either much larger or much smaller than normal, slow the work. Most cards fall in the following range: Height, 2¾ to 4¼ inches and width, 4¾ to 6¼ inches. Cards in this range can be easily sorted, stacked and packaged. Cards outside this range create problems. Larger cards often cannot be handled without folding or otherwise

damaging them. IARU Region 2 (which includes the US) has suggested that 3½ inches height and 5½ inches width are optimum.

Entities Not Served By the Outgoing QSL Service

Approximately 225 DXCC entities are served by the ARRL Outgoing QSL Service. As noted previously, cards are forwarded from the ARRL Outgoing Service to a counterpart Bureau in each of these entities. In some cases, there is no Incoming Bureau in a particular entity and cards therefore cannot be forwarded. However, QSL cards can be forwarded to a QSL manager, for example, ZB2FX via G3RFX. The ARRL Outgoing Service cannot forward cards to the entities shown in **Table 6-1**.

The QSL bureaus in some countries will only forward QSL cards to members of that country's national radio society. That restriction applies to cards bound for Denmark, France, Germany, Hungary, Italy, Japan, Monaco, Norway, Poland, Portugal, Russia, South Africa, Sweden and Zambia.

Additional Information

When sending cards to non-US QSL managers, be sure to clearly indicate the manager's call sign and sort the cards according to the manager's call sign, rather than the station worked. Short Wave Listening (SWL) cards can be forwarded through the QSL Service. The Outgoing QSL Service cannot forward stamps, IRCs or cash to the foreign QSL bureaus.

THE ARRL INCOMING QSL BUREAU SYSTEM

Within the US and Canada, the ARRL DX QSL Bureau System is made up of numerous call area bureaus that act as central clearing houses for QSLs arriving from other countries. These incoming bureaus are staffed by volunteers. The service is free and ARRL membership is not required. (Canadian amateurs can use the Radio Amateurs of Canada's incoming QSL bureau.)

How it Works

Most countries have "outgoing" QSL bureaus that operate in much the same manner as the ARRL Outgoing QSL Service. The members send cards to the outgoing bureau where they are packaged and shipped to the appropriate countries.

A majority of the DX QSLs are shipped directly to the individual incoming bureaus where volunteers sort the incoming QSLs by the first letter of the call sign suffix. An individual may be assigned the responsibility of handling one or more letters of the alphabet.

With the many vanity calls on the air, what bureau should you use? The answer is to use the bureau that handles QSLs for the district represented by the number in your call sign. If your call is NØAX, use the tenth district bureau no matter where you operate from. If you operate portable or mobile from another district, QSLs will still be sent to your home district's bureau — don't use the "portable" bureau. If you operate from an entity outside the US and it has a bureau, make the necessary arrangements for your QSLs to be mailed to you, otherwise they may be discarded.

Claiming Your QSLs

Check with your incoming bureau to see what procedure they follow. Some incoming bureaus prefer that you send them a supply of self-addressed, stamped envelopes (SASEs), while others prefer that you send money, which will be used for envelope and postage credits. Check with your bureau for the preferred method.

In the absence of instructions to the contrary, SASEs should be 5 × 7.5 or 6 × 9 inches. Neatly print your call sign in the upper left corner of the envelope. Place your mailing address on the front of the envelope. A suggested way to send envelopes is to affix First Class postage for 1 ounce and clip extra postage to the envelope. Then, if you receive more than 1 ounce of cards, they can be sent in a single package. (Check with your local post office for the correct rates.)

Helpful Hints

Good cooperation between the DXer and the bureau is important to ensure a smooth flow of cards. Remember that the people who work in the area bureaus are volunteers. They are providing you with a valuable service. With that thought in mind, please pay close attention to the following DOs and DON'Ts.

Do

- Do keep self-addressed 5 × 7½ or 6 × 9 inch envelopes or money credit on file at your bureau, with your call sign in the upper left corner, and affix at least one unit of first-class postage.
- Do send the bureau enough postage to cover SASEs on file and enough to take care of possible postage rate increases.
- Do respond quickly to any bureau request for SASEs, stamps or money. Unclaimed card backlogs are the bureau's biggest problem.
- Do notify the bureau of your new call sign as you upgrade. Please send SASEs with your new call, in addition to SASEs with your old call.
- Do include your call sign on any correspondence with the bureau.
- Do include an SASE with any information request to the bureau.
- Do notify the bureau in writing if you don't want your cards.
- Do notify the bureau of a change of address.

Don't

- Don't send domestic US to US cards to the various call area bureaus.
- Don't expect DX cards to arrive for several months after the QSO. Overseas delivery is very slow. Many cards coming from overseas bureaus are over a year old.
- Don't send your outgoing DX cards to your call area bureau.
- Don't send SASEs to your "portable" bureau. For example, NUØX/1 sends SASEs to the WØ bureau, not the W1 bureau.
- Don't send SASEs or money credits to the ARRL Outgoing QSL Service.
- Don't send SASEs larger than 6 × 9 inches. SASEs larger than 6 × 9 inches require additional postage surcharges.

Incoming QSL Bureau Addresses

The incoming bureaus occasionally change managers or addresses or web addresses. Their requirements and services may change. For this reason, you should check the ARRL website at **www.arrl.org/qsl-service** for the latest information and addresses for each incoming bureau.

DXing HISTORY

For a DXer to truly appreciate the awards and achievements of the DXing community, it is necessary to also appreciate the long history of DXing with the Amateur Radio tradition.

With the explosion of interest in ham radio during the 1950s came a corresponding interest in DX. Sunspot Cycle 19 peaked in 1959 — the most intense cycle on record. Hams were working DX with a few watts and a bit of wire thrown out the window! With all that DX to be worked came legendary call signs still discussed in reverent tones today. As a beginning DXer, you will enjoy knowing more about these ham radio icons, all Silent Keys. Here is a little information (only a little!) about these historic figures. Entering their call signs into an Internet search engine will provide hours of entertaining reading — perfect while waiting for that New One to appear on the bands!

■ **Gus Browning, W4BPD**: Gus hailed from South Carolina and activated quite a number of rare countries in the early and mid-1960s. He is best known for being the first to activate Bouvet Island (LH4C in 1962), but was a legendary solo DXpeditioner.

■ **The Colvins: Lloyd, W6KG and Iris, W6QL**: The Colvins traveled extensively through the 1960s, 1970s and 1980s, operating from well over 100 DXCC entities! Their QSL collection numbered well over one million cards. Lloyd and Iris set up the YASME Foundation (**www.yasme.org**), whose mission is to further Amateur Radio DXing.

■ **Bob Dennison, W0DX/VP2VI**: At one time an ARRL President and indisputably the father of the DXpedition, Bob started with an expedition to the Bahamas in 1948 as VP7NG. He was the first to activate Clipperton Island (FO8X) and other previously inactive countries.

■ **Ernst Krenkel, RAEM**: That's no error in the call sign, Ernst was the only amateur ever to hold a personal call sign without a number. He received that call as recognition for his efforts as the radio operator of a Russian polar expedition in 1938, saving the lives of more than 100 explorers adrift on an ice floe. It is for Ernst that the RAEM series of contests and awards are named.

■ **Charlie Mellen, W1FH**: Mellen was the first to achieve DXCC after WWII, obtaining Mixed-Mode and Phone certificates #1. His competition with Don Wallace W6AM (see below) to stay atop the DXCC listings ran for decades. He had the highest total of DXCC entities worked of any operator.

■ **Katashe Nose, KH6IJ**: An operator of extraordinary skill, Katashe was for many years the best-known and most-heard station from the central Pacific. He was a dominant figure in DXing and DX contesting through the 1980s.

■ **Stew Perry, W1BB**: 160 meters was considered too local a band for DXing but W1BB demonstrated that it was just a matter of education and technique. Stew (for whom the Stew Perry Topband Distance Challenge contest is named) almost single-handedly opened up the 160 meter band and coined the phrase "The Gentleman's Band."

■ **Don Wallace, W6AM**: It was Don who made the rhombic antenna famous with his 120-acre "farm" of 16 full-sized rhombics, each usable in either direction. Second only to W1FH (see above), Don set the standard for DXing from the West Coast.

■ **Danny Weil, VP2VB**: While sailing around the world, Danny activated many rare DXCC entities and made over 100,000 contacts up until his final expedition to Wallis Island (FW8FW) in 1963. It is his sailboat, *Yasme*, for whom the YASME Foundation is named.

For more historic information on DXing, you are encouraged to read Clinton DeSoto's *200 Meters and Down*. DeSoto created the concept of the DXCC program in the 1930s. To learn more about post-WWII DXing, *YASME — The Danny Weil and Colvin Radio Expeditions* by Jim Cain, K1TN, is an excellent source of biographical information about some of the major figures on the DX scene through the 1980s. Cain also annotates all of the W6KG/W6QL and VP2VB expeditions. If you can find a copy, *Don C. Wallace, W6AM, Amateur Radio's Pioneer* by Jan Perkins, N6AW, bridges the gap between DeSoto and Cain quite nicely and includes many color plates of antique and rare QSLs from the W6AM collection.

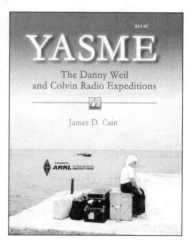

The adventures of Danny Weil, VP2VB, as he sailed the *Yasme* around the world are chronicled in this detailed book by Jim Cain, K1TN. Sponsored by the YASME Foundation, Jim also tells the story of the Colvins (Lloyd, W6KG, and Iris, W6QL), two very famous call signs in DX history.

DX Is! What It's All About

By Bill Kennamer, K5NX

"DX Is!" (Hugh Cassidy, WA6AUD)

If it were not for the desire to send a signal over the hill, then over the water, then across the oceans, and around the world, Amateur Radio or even wireless itself would probably have been dismissed as a useless laboratory phenomenon. But that first DXer, Guglielmo Marconi, put the signals over the hill, across the oceans, and around the world, and the world hasn't been the same since. It isn't an overstatement to say that worldwide communication owes everything to DXing and to Marconi, the original DXer and DXpeditioner.

The history of DXing is long and varied. Of course it starts with those early efforts of Marconi, who very early turned to commercial development. It continued with amateurs whose experimentation allowed them to work stations farther and farther away. But the real dream was to bridge the oceans. The ARRL had a part in that dream. At the Board of Directors meeting at the first National Convention in Chicago in 1921, Traffic Manager Fred Schnell presented a plan that would give the best possible chance for radio signals being heard across the Atlantic. For the transatlantic receiving test scheduled in the late fall, Paul Godley, 2XE, considered to be the foremost receiving expert in the United States at the time, and a member of the ARRL Technical Committee, was dispatched across the Atlantic with his best receiving equipment. Setting up in a tent on the coast of Scotland, Godley began his tests. By December 7, 1921, he was ready. Tuning across the bands, he began to hear a spark signal on 270 meters. The operator's call sign, 1AAW, was clearly heard! (But 1AAW turned out to be a pirate! Even at the beginning, pirates were one of the hazards of DXing.) The signals of more than 30 American amateurs were heard during this series of tests, waiting only for a two-way contact to be completed.

Even then, the experimenting and modernization spurred by a desire for better DX performance was apparent. Godley reported that of the signals heard, over 60% had used CW rather than spark and with less power. The death knell for spark had been sounded and the future of tube transmission was ensured — all because of the desire for DX.

In late 1921 and early 1922, Clifford Dow, 6ZAC, located in Hawaii, heard signals from the western United States. He announced this in a letter to *QST* and said if he could get some transmitting equipment, he believed he could make it across the Pacific. A group from the West Coast sent him the needed transmitter and two-way contact was established on April 13, 1922, between

The birthplace of Guglielmo Marconi is now the home of the Guglielmo Marconi Foundation station IY4FGM. While never licensed as an amateur, Marconi keenly appreciated and understood their drive to span ever greater distances via radio.

Dow and 6ZQ and 6ZAF in California. Thus was yet another tradition of DXing established, that of providing equipment to activate a "new one."

Léon Deloy, 8AB, of France had participated in the transatlantic tests of early 1923. His signal had been one of several heard by US amateurs but no two-way communication resulted. During the summer, he studied American receiving methods and even came to Chicago for the National Convention. He returned to France with American receiving equipment, determined to be the first to make the transatlantic crossing.

After setting up and testing, by November Deloy was

Not for nothing is tiny Scarborough Reef (BS7H) known as "Scaffold Reef!" Bob W6RGG is shown operating from one of the four exposed rocks during the 2007 BS7H expedition, giving many DXers the QSO they need to have "worked 'em all!" (*photo courtesy W6RGG*)

ready. He cabled ARRL Traffic Manager Schnell that he would transmit on 100 meters from 9 to 10 PM, beginning November 25. He was easily heard. By November 27, Schnell had secured permission for use of the 100-meter wavelength at 1MO and the station of John Reinartz, 1XAM. The two of them waited for Deloy.

For an hour Deloy called and sent messages. Then he signed. The first DX pileup began as Schnell and Reinartz both called. Deloy asked Reinartz to stand by, and worked first Schnell and then Reinartz for the first transatlantic QSOs. The age of DXing had finally truly begun.

From these small beginnings to the later exploits of such as Bob Denniston, Danny Weil, Gus Browning, Martti Laine, and groups that travel to lonely islands and mountain kingdoms, DXing has grown. While the early days were marked by exploration and discovery, we now recognize that we have the equipment, power and antennas to hear a pin drop on the other side of the world and respond to it. While some discovery is still involved, and that mostly on the VHF/UHF bands, for most of us DXing takes the form of radiosport at its zenith, a ritual of great importance to some, and a source of friendship and occasional enjoyment to others. DX Is!. . .no doubt about it, the essence of Amateur Radio.

RESOURCES FOR DXERS

Books and Magazines

- The ARRL Store (**www.arrl.org/shop**) offers a number of books and videos on DX and DXing — just enter "DX" into the search window for a list of available items.
- *The Complete DXer* by Bob Locher, W9KNI is an excellent tutorial to turn a Little Pistol into a Medium Gun. Bob's *A Year of DX* recounts his adventures pursuing the CQ DX Marathon's top spot over the course of a year. Both are available from the ARRL Store or Idiom Press, **www.idiompress.com**.
- *Up Two!* and *Contesting in Africa* by Roger Western, G3SXW — funny, engaging stories by G3SXW of his many one- and two-man DXpeditions to rare spots around the globe. Also available from Idiom Press.
- *DX Magazine* (**www.dxpub.com**) is a storied bi-monthly publication with a long history of stories about recent DXpeditions, large and small.
- DX columns are included each month in *QST*, *CQ* and *WorldRadio Online* magazines.

DX Clubs

- A list of links to DX club websites around the world is available at **www.ac6v.com**.
- To find local or regional DX clubs affiliated with the ARRL, check **www.arrl.org/find-a-club**.

DX Awards

- For a comprehensive list of links to Amateur Radio awards, primarily DX-oriented, visit **www.ac6v.com**.
- A website devoted to awards, including K1BV's directory of more than 3000 Amateur Radio awards, can be found at **www.dxawards.com**.

DX News Services

- *The Daily DX,* **www.dailydx.com**
- *QRZ DX* and *DX Magazine,* **www.dxpub.com**
- *425 DX Bulletin,* **www.425dxn.org**
- *OPDXA Bulletin,* **www.papays.com/opdx.html**
- New Jersey DX Assn *DX Reflector,* **www.njdxa.org**

Chapter 7

Contesting — Competitive Wireless

Tuning across forty meters, a just-finishing QSO slides into the filter's passband — "...R TKS VE4 ES SWEEP" Wow! Manitoba is the last section the tuner needs for a first-ever Clean Sweep in the annual November Sweepstakes. Sure enough, the station resumes calling, "73 ES CQ SS VE4YU VE4YU SS" and suddenly fumbling fingers reach for the paddle to send the call once, twice, over — listening in anticipation...

From nowhere, fragments of call signs begin to appear, building to a crescendo in seconds as a sporadic E cloud forms miles above the Earth in the late afternoon. You can sense dozens of Yagis swiveling to hunt for the best path as 6 meters — the "Magic Band" — opens between the station-rich northeastern states and the Midwestern plains. Quickly, logs fill with new grid squares in groups that bloom across the map. Then, like a summer thunderstorm, the cloud moves on, leaving only CQs bobbing in its wake as stations wait like surfers for the next big wave...

Slowing to round a curve on the blacktop, driver and passenger strain to see in the late afternoon shadows. "There it is!" exclaims the passenger, spotting a small green sign off the right-hand shoulder proclaiming "Entering Adair County." Watching for traffic, the driver pulls off the road to a small gravel area straddling the border. As he pulls the emergency

Showing the concentration of top operators, the team of Chris, KL9A, and Dan, N6MJ, operated in several major contests to get ready for the 2010 World Radiosport Team Championship (WRTC). This photo was taken at the K3LR station during ARRL DX CW. *(NØAX photo)*

brake, she is already calling, "CQ Missouri QSO Party from the Sullivan-Adair County line..."

BZZZZZZ...the alarm clock goes off and a heavy hand rises from a temporary ham shack cot to fumble toward the OFF button. Nap over, the operator rises and pours a cup of coffee from the thermos, peeking outside to confirm the first lightening of the eastern sky. Turning toward the rig — it's time to hit the low bands and pick off some juicy multipliers during the dawn enhancement to the west. Soon the Sun will rise and the operator will be moving up, up, up in frequency — following the MUF and the growing pileups but now it's time to listen deep into the night...

A fluttery double-horned signal warbles in the headphones, crossed-ellipses on the tuning display buried in noise and fading. Anxiously the operator waits for the RTTY decoder to lock on to the signal, scanning for a call sign in the characters tumbling out across the display. What's that? Once, twice... D2QMN? Yes! A double-click and out goes the call and exchange — to Angola! Sure enough, here comes the return exchange and an all-time RTTY New One goes in the log for a goose-pimple-raising moment of excitement! But there's no time to lose — there must be more DX out there tuning through the bands, so "TKS CQ RU..."

Contesting History

Contests have their genesis in the early days of message handling when the ability to relay messages quickly and accurately was the hallmark of a good operator. Even in the days of spark, there were a number of exercises that attempted to move messages across the country as quickly as possible. The signature of message handling is writ large across contesting today. Many of today's top operators got started as traffic handlers in the National Traffic System (NTS). If you look at the information exchanged during the ARRL Sweepstakes — number, category, call, check and section — you'll recognize the header of an ARRL Radiogram. The characteristics of a good traffic handler remain the attributes of a top contester: accurate, efficient, flexible, capable.

The first formal on-the-air competition was the 1927 International Relay Contest, sponsored by the ARRL as an extension to the annual "tests" in which stations attempted to make contact with stations outside the US and Canada. This event has changed names several times, growing into the ARRL International DX Contest we know and love today. The need also grew for a *domestic* contest emphasizing shorter distances within the North American continent. The result was the creation of the ARRL Sweepstakes contest in 1930. Contesting on the VHF and higher bands got its start in 1948 and the first radioteletype contest was held in 1957.

Contest History Who's Who

W9IOP, Larry LeKashman — In the late 1950s and early 1960s, ARRL Sweepstakes was the contest and W9IOP's call sign was never far from first place (as was W2IOP in previous years). Later a president of ElectroVoice, W9IOP is also famous for his pre-PC "Second Op" operating aid.

W4KFC, Vic Clark — His yearly Sweepstakes battles with W9IOP were the stuff of legend. Vic was a master contester and pioneered the use of two separate sets of equipment to make better use of available time. A past president of the ARRL (1982-83), Vic was also a Big Gun in DXing.

K2GL, Buz Reeves — Buz single-handedly created the multi-operator, multi-transmitter category of operating with a superb station and a crack team of operators. For years, K2GL was the standard setting station, inspiring present-day operations such as KC1XX, K3LR and W3LPL.

W7RM, Rush Drake — W7RM brought competitive multi-multi operating to the Northwest, building a station at Foulweather Bluff known not only for signal strength but the ability to hear well. His teams of operators include many top West Coast contesters active today.

LU8DQ, Jorge Humberto Bozzo — Widely considered one of the best CW operators of all time and certainly the best ever from South America, Jorge held four world records and had won every major contest at least once.

There are many reasons to engage in ham radio contests (also known as *radiosport*). Just as there are many levels of athletes, from the occasionally engaged to the devoted aficionado, so does contesting attract many types of entrants. For some hams, contesting is their primary interest. They build highly capable stations, travel thousands of miles to desirable locations or assemble a skilled team of master operators. Most contesters, whether they are on the air for an hour or a weekend, operate just for the pleasure of reaching out and touching so many other hams in so many other places so quickly.

Along with the most common phone and CW contests, there are a growing number of digital-mode events. There are also plenty of specialty contests intended to foster interest and activity from a particular region, in a specific mode, or as a style of operating. There is a contest featuring every state (these are usually called "QSO Parties"). Other contests feature the VHF+ bands above 30 MHz, and even here some specialty contest themes include moonbounce and meteor scatter. On the HF bands, there are contests for contacting everything from islands to lighthouses to countries. On both VHF+ and HF, short contests known as *sprints* are becoming more popular all the time.

Contests are held throughout the year. Looking to work some DX to build up your totals? The major DX contests are the ARRL RTTY Roundup in January, the ARRL International DX Contest with a CW weekend in February and Phone in March; the IARU HF World Championships in July; and the CQ World Wide DX and WPX Contests offering CW, Phone, and RTTY weekends from March through November. If you are chasing states for your Five-Band WAS award, check out the North American QSO Parties in January and August, the ARRL November Sweepstakes held on the first (CW) and third (Phone) weekends, and the ARRL's 160 Meter and 10 Meter Contests in December.

Why Contest?

By Dan Henderson, N1ND

Why does it seem there is always a contest on the air? Almost every IARU national society sponsors at least one event during the year. Generally intended to achieve the same goals as ARRL contests, they promote activity among the licensed amateurs in those countries and encourage the development of operating skills. You can also find listings of upcoming contests monthly in *QST*, linked from the ARRL Contest Branch homepage (**www.arrl.org/contests**) and at the on-line contest calendars listed in the Resources section of this chapter.

What inspires normally mild-mannered hams to develop a "warrior" mentality during contest weekends? There are no cash prizes or awards. What causes even casual operators to join the crowd during certain times of the year? What motivates otherwise normal operators to plan a year in advance to build and erect new antennas, add station equipment and clear time to participate in these on-the-air events?

Thousands of hams in the US and around the globe spend some time during the year contesting. Why go to the effort? The answers to that are as varied as the operators. There is no single reason, but most responses will fall into one of several categories.

Honing Operator Skills

Contesting is a great way to develop and hone operating skills. Contests require accuracy on both the sending and receiving side. Contest stations are among the best equipped — from reliable transceivers and effective antennas to computer technologies and frequently emergency power. Experienced contesters have developed their knowledge base about propagation and what bands are most effective over what distances at particular times of the day. Their contest performance depends on being able to get the message through with accuracy and thoroughness — extremely useful skills when operating in disaster relief. Where do you find these operators in emergencies? They can be found using their experience and stations to assist with emergency traffic and communications. Some of the top contesters hold ARRL Field Organization appointments, placing their talents at the disposal of communities in crisis.

Demonstrating Use of Amateur Frequencies

Contesting, especially on the VHF, UHF and microwave bands, is a valuable means of demonstrating the use of our frequencies and the need to preserve allocation of those parts of the radio spectrum. In today's age of frequency auctions and increasing commercial demand for spectrum, activity on the higher amateur bands provides a good argument for protecting and preserving our allocation. By encouraging the use of microwave bands during contest periods and providing an increased, concentrated period of activity during contest weekends, contesting increases both our use and knowledge of this valuable radio spectrum.

Advancing Amateur Technological Development

Contesting has been the inspiration for some of the technological advances during recent years. Many hams today use spotting networks as a regular part of their daily station operation. From spotting rare DX to putting out the word about band openings on 6 and 2 meters, these networks are an important part of amateur activity. But how many hams know that the original PacketCluster was created to allow contesters to "spot" contest multipliers? From antenna designs and station enhancements to integration of computer technology in the shack, you can see the work of members of the contest community in many areas of technological improvements in the hobby.

It's Fun!

Despite the value of technological advancements and developing operating skill, maybe the best reason amateurs contest is the simplest: it's FUN! Whether they are running stations at a rate of 120 per hour during the ARRL International DX Contest or experimenting with earth-moon-earth communications during the annual ARRL EME Competition, or experimenting with how well the new 6 meter beam works during a VHF contest, thousands of hams annually use contesting as their outlet to enjoy the hobby. The invested hours of study to earn your license and the dollars you spend in building and improving your shack and equipment come back to you with the rewards of enjoying a successful contest — and are valuable when called upon to assist in times of need. After all, there is no better way to develop your skills than to actively use them!

COOPERATION

Every contest has something for all levels of hams and something unique in almost all of sport — cooperation! To succeed in contesting, participants must cooperate with each other as they make contacts. Even archrivals need to put each other in the log! The best contesters are those who have figured out how to cooperate most effectively with the largest number of other hams. It is not enough to have just the strongest signal or the fastest fist. The tension between competing and needing to cooperate makes radiosport difficult enough to be interesting but not so difficult that strategy and skill can't win the game.

That richness of possibilities brings a wide variety of operators to the ham bands during a contest. During an hour's tuning or calling you'll encounter every level of ham from one just getting started to an expert who has been at the top of the heap for 50 years or more. Browsing the scores takes you to every corner of the Earth and from grade-schoolers coached by a parent in Kids Day to old-timers startling the operator at the other end by sending a Sweepstakes check (the year first licensed) in the 1930s. So it doesn't matter that you're not super skilled or just getting started. Jump in and discover the possibilities of competitive wireless!

Coexisting With Contests

Is contesting allowed everywhere on the amateur bands? Sometimes it sure sounds like it! In reality, there are plenty of kilohertz without contest activity. On the HF bands, by general agreement there is no contest activity on 60, 30, 17 or 12 meters. On the VHF+ bands, almost all contest activity takes place in the so-called "weak signal" segments at the lower edge of the bands.

Of the larger contests, most restrict operation to one mode so you'll just find normal or even lighter activity on the other portions of the bands. Even though there may be more than one contest scheduled during a weekend, most are small enough that activity is clustered around a handful of frequencies. If you choose not to participate, tune around or change bands and you'll likely be able to avoid contest activity. Just as planning ahead in real life avoids frustration, there are plenty of contest calendars to check for potential conflicts with your favorite non-contest activity.

Jordan, KF7LUA, operated in the 2011 ARRL Rookie Roundup and submitted the highest score for the 7th call district in the April 2011 contest. (*KF7LUA photo*)

It is a tradition on Aruba (P4) that after the contest, all of the visiting operators gather for dinner and relaxation. From the smiles, there are a lot of QSOs in the logs of (L-R) P49V, P4ØA, P4ØP, P4ØYL, P43C, P43A, and P49Y. (*KK9A photo*)

Just because a contest is going on doesn't mean other contacts can't be made, either! Even during the biggest contests, you'll hear non-contest QSOs taking place — how do they manage so well? The key is to make the most of your station's capabilities, primarily the receiver. Most receivers are very sensitive — too sensitive for a band full of big contest signals. Turn down the RF gain, turn off the preamp and noise blankers and maybe add a little attenuation. Help your receiver operate linearly and you may be surprised at how clean the band sounds as a result! (See the sidebar "Optimizing Your Receiver" in this book's "DXing" chapter.)

If you have a rotatable antenna, you may be able to point it in a direction that minimizes QRM but leaves plenty of signal for a comfortable QSO. Remember, you're trying to maximize the ratio of signal to noise plus interference, not necessarily the absolute signal level. Choosing frequencies toward the high end of the band segment, away from the lower portions where signals are stronger, will also help. There are usually plenty of opportunities to coexist with a contest.

CONTESTING BASICS

So what is a contest anyway? If you encounter someone calling "CQ Contest" on the air, what should you do? If you've found a contest that looks interesting, how can you determine the proper way of operating? Let's start with the basics.

The Contest QSO

A contest is a competition between stations to make as many contacts as possible according to the theme of the contest within the time period defined by the contest rules. Each contact will be as short as possible while still satisfying the rules of contest. Remember, this is a competition so what constitutes a contact is different from during regular day-to-day operating. During a contest, include a minimum of non-contest information.

Each contact consists of five steps that are just like a regular contact but greatly abbreviated:

■ One station calls CQ (CQing is known as *running*).

■ A caller responds to the CQ.

■ The CQing station responds with the call sign of calling station then sends the required information.

■ The caller acknowledges receiving the information and sends information back in return.

■ The CQing station acknowledges receiving the caller's exchange and ends the contact.

At any point, should one of the stations not receive a call sign or exchange properly, the information is repeated until received correctly. We'll go over that process later in this section.

The Contest Exchange

During each contact, specific information must be exchanged and logged. This information is called your *exchange*. In some contests, the exchange is very simple.

For example, in the North American QSO Party contests the exchange is your name and state, province, or country. (Because "state, province, or country" is so commonly used in contesting, it is often abbreviated SPC or S/P/C.) ARRL November Sweepstakes, mentioned earlier, has a lengthy exchange. Most contests keep the exchange simple, beginning with signal report (RST) and adding other information in line with the contest's theme. Here are some common types of information you'll find in contest exchanges:

■ *ITU or CQ Zone* — there are 88 ITU (**www.iaru.org/ituzonesc.gif**) and 40 CQ Zones (go to **www.cq-amateur-radio.com** and look for the CQ WAZ Award page).

■ *Serial number* — the number of the contact in the contest. For your fifth contact, your serial number would be 5 (sometimes sent as 05 or 005 for clarity).

■ *Name* — just your first or most common name. Nicknames are acceptable.

■ *Member number* — in contests sponsored by an organization this is the membership number of the control operator.

■ *Power* — up to three digits specifying your transmitter power ("KW" or "kilowatt" is sometimes sent instead of "1000"). Some operators don't add the "W" in kW since that is understood.

■ *Location code or abbreviation* — for contests that target a specific country or region, this is an abbreviation (such as "TN" for Tennessee in contests that use states) or numeric identifier. It can also be an abbreviated county name, ARRL section or a grid square in VHF+ contests. The contest sponsor website will define these exactly.

There are other types of information that might be needed in a contest exchange but these cover most contests. When in doubt, check the contest sponsor's website.

If you encounter a contester calling CQ but don't know the exchange information ask, "What do you need?" or on CW or digital, "INFO?" The CQing station will respond with something like, "I need your number and ARRL section" or on CW "PSE NR ES ARRL SEC." If it's your first contact in the contest and you live in the Pittsburgh, Pennsylvania area, you would respond with, "You're my number 1 in Western Pennsylvania" or on CW "NR 1 WPA." That's it! Contesters want and need your QSO so don't hesitate to ask them for help.

One common question from new contesters is, "Why are signal reports always 59 or 599?" During a non-contest QSO, accurate signal reports help both stations gauge the clarity of communications during the QSO. Since contest QSOs are so short, typically 10 seconds or less, there is little need for an accurate report. If the contester can hear you, 59 or 599 is just as good as any other report and removes uncertainty from what is sent. It also cues you to mentally prepare to copy the rest of the exchange. On CW, most contesters send 599 as 5NN. The "N" is a form of *cut number* where an abbreviation for a numeral is sent to save time. Other common cut numbers are "A" for 1 and a dash ("T") or "O" for zero. You are expected to convert the cut number character to a real numeral when you enter it into your log, even a computer log.

Contest Scoring

Your final score is a combination of the total number of contacts and the number of contacts with different locations or attributes, according to the theme of the contest. The usual calculation begins with adding up points from each contact, called *QSO points*. The total is then multiplied by the sum of the different locations or attributes, called *multipliers*. Since each contest has a different system (*vive la différence!*), check the sponsor's rules to compute your score.

All contacts may have the same QSO point value or the points may vary by band or distance or mode. Here are some examples:

■ *North American QSO Party* — each contact counts for 1 point.

■ *ARRL 10 Meter Contest* — phone contacts count for 2 points and CW or digital contacts 4 points. Contacts with Novice or Technician stations on CW count 8 points.

■ *CQ World Wide DX* — contacts between stations on different continents are worth 3 points. Contacts between stations in different countries on the same continent count for 1 point, except contacts between stations in different North American countries count for 2 points. Contacts within one's own country do not count for points but can count for multiplier credit.

■ *Stew Perry Topband Distance Challenge* — points for each contact are calculated based on the distance between the stations.

Multipliers are really the spice of the contest! If contesting were just about working a large number of stations it would be a rather simple game and quickly lose its novelty. Adding the requirement to make contacts with special stations or locations makes things really interesting! For example, a station might have a "pipeline" to Japan. If all of the contacts count for the single JA country multiplier, would it be better to work stations from Europe at a slower rate but pick up many more country multipliers? Is it better to call CQ in the ARRL 160 Meter Contest and hope that stations from the different ARRL and RAC sections respond or should you go looking for them? There are many aspects to consider, with the capabilities of one's station and propagation being the most important.

Check the rules for each contest to find out how multipliers are defined and then go hunting! You'll want to know if each multiplier counts only once or whether you can count multipliers from each band or mode. For example, in the ARRL Sweepstakes each section is counted once and only once — you can work a maximum of 80 section multipliers. In the ARRL DX Contest, though, each different DXCC entity counts as a separate multiplier on each band. There may be different types of multipliers besides locations. The IARU HF Championship also recognizes stations operating from IARU radio society headquarters as multipliers.

Along with QSO points and multipliers some contests offer special bonus points or power multipliers. Many state QSO parties (contests that require contacts with a specific state or states) have bonuses for working the sponsor's club or other special stations. Power multipliers are applied after the basic score is calculated but before bonuses are added. The QRP Amateur Radio Club International contests, for example, multiply the score by 10 if the output power is 1 W or less! As always, check the sponsor's rules for the exact scoring.

Typical Rules

Now that you're familiar with the basic ideas behind contesting, let's take a close look at a typical contest rule summary that might be found in a newsletter or on a website. Here's a typical listing for the 2012 CQ WPX SSB Contest, held at the end of March every year with reference numbers ([#]) added:

CQ WW WPX Contest — SSB, sponsored by *CQ* Magazine from **[1]** 0000Z Mar 24 - 2400Z Mar 25 (CW is May 26-27). Frequencies: **[2]** 160 - 10 meters. Categories: **[3]** SOAB, SOSB, SO-Assisted, HP, LP and QRP; MS (10-min rule), M/2, MM; SO-Rookie, SO-Tribander-and-Single-Wire. **[4]** SO operate 36 hours max with off times at least 60 min. Exchange: **[5]** RS(T) + serial number. QSO Points: **[6]** with different continents — 3 pts (14-28 MHz) and 6 pts (1.8-7 MHz), within North America — 2 pts (14-28 MHz) and 4 pts (1.8-7 MHz), with own country — 1 pt. Score: **[7]** QSO points × prefixes worked (ie, N8, KA1, HG73, JD1) counted only once. For more information: **[8]** www.cqwpx. com. Logs due **[9]** Apr 18 (CW, Jun 20) to ssb@cqwpx.com (cw@cqwpx.com).

[1] The time period is always specified in UTC. No contest QSOs outside these times are counted.

[2] The contest will be held on all HF bands, except 60, 30, 17 and 12 meters as noted previously. Smaller contests often specify a list of frequencies to concentrate activity so that participants can more easily make QSOs. Unless otherwise noted, you can work stations on all bands and modes permitted by the contest.

[3] If you are unfamiliar with the abbreviations, check the sponsor's rules for exact definitions. For example, SOAB means "single operator, all-band."

[4] There may be special rules about required breaks or restrictions on changing bands.

[5] This is the information to be exchanged in each contact.

[6] The rules carefully spell out the value of each contact.

[7] This is the formula for calculating your score. Note that the multipliers (call sign prefixes) are counted only once during the contest, not once on each band.

[8] Check the website for complete rules, since a summary leaves out details and conditions that affect how you should operate.

[9] Logs must be sent to the sponsors by this date or they may be used as *checklogs* that are used for log checking but without a score listed in the final results.

This information can also be used "in reverse" to find out in which contest a station is participating. For example, let's say that one October Saturday you turn on the radio and hear a station calling "CQ Contest" on CW. The exchange seems to be a signal report and some kind of state-number combination, such as "WA060." Turning to *QST* and looking

in the "Contest Corral" contest calendar you find six contests listed for that date — not an unusual number for a fall weekend. They are the Illinois QSO Party, US/VE Island QSO Party, QRP Fall QSO Party, Worked All Germany, JARTS RTTY Worldwide and Delaware Valley FM contests. Rule out the RTTY and FM contests right away. Of those remaining, all allow CW contacts and the exchange includes RST. The Illinois QSO Party exchange includes a county or SPC abbreviation. QRP contest QSOs require power and member number. Worked All Germany participants exchange a serial number or a DOK code (like a US Zip code). Clearly, the station must be calling from a US or Canadian island and is giving out a state or province abbreviation followed by the island designator! This sort of confusion is a good reason to include a contest name or abbreviation in your CQ!

Making a Contest QSO

You're ready to make a few contest QSOs! How about an example to show how it's done? Let's start with a typical QSO in the Washington State QSO Party (also known as "The Salmon Run"). In this example, we'll assume you are operating from W1AW in Connecticut.

On voice, the contact sounds like this:
W7DX: CQ Washington State QSO Party from Whisky Seven Delta X-ray
[W7DX is making the contest clear.]
W1AW: Whiskey One Alpha Whiskey
[Just give your call once, phonetically.]
W7DX: W1AW you're five nine in Chelan county
[This identifies the caller and gives the exchange.]
W1AW: Thank you, you're five nine in Connecticut
[You acknowledge that you've received W7DX's information and give yours — no repeat is needed unless requested by W7DX.]
W7DX: Thank you, CQ Salmon Run from W7DX
[This acknowledges receiving W1AW's information and starts the cycle again. See how easy it is?]

Here's the same contact on CW:
W7DX: CQ SR DE W7DX
["SR" stands for Salmon Run; it could also be WAQP for Washington QSO Party.)
W1AW: W1AW
[Again, just your call sign. No K or BK is required.]
W7DX: W1AW 5NN CHE
[Note the use of the cut number N to abbreviate 9. "CHE" is the abbreviation for Chelan County. Most state QSO party sponsors publish a list of approved abbreviations to make sure the contact is scored correctly.]
W1AW: R 5NN CT
[A simple "R" confirms that you received the information; then send yours. Again, no BK or repeat are needed.]
W7DX: TU CQ SR DE W7DX
[The TU acknowledges receiving W1AW's information and starts the cycle again.]

That's pretty snappy operating! No wasted characters or

Field Day — Not a Contest?

First held in 1933 as an emergency exercise, Field Day is a *non-contest* in a contest-like environment. It incorporates all modes, including satellite communications and both HF and VHF/UHF bands — the only ARRL on-air event to touch so many parts of ham radio. More US licensed amateurs participate in Field Day annually than any other on-the-air operating event. It allows contacts with any station worldwide, on any mode and on all bands (except 60, 30, 17 and 12 meters). Even diehard non-contesters seem to enjoy participating in this all-inclusive operating event.

Field Day occupies a special place in the hearts of many contesters because it is during these outings that many get their first taste of competitive operating. Perhaps at the elbow of a more experienced operator, logging and listening, inexperienced operators gain valuable experience during a single operating shift.

If you are new to contesting, take advantage of Field Day's smorgasbord to sample different styles of operating. Make sure to listen as a contest veteran tunes the bands or holds a frequency. Take a turn yourself! If you're an experienced ham, be sure to return the favor of those that taught you by showing a new contester "how it's done". You'll make a lifetime friend and help keep radiosport going!

Field Day isn't a contest but you can't tell it from the focus of the night-time operators! Filling the logs in the HF tent at the St Charles Amateur Radio Club, KOØA Field Day operation are (front to back) WØLON, KDØEIA, KE5WXD, and KDØIGO. (*NØAX photo*)

unnecessary information. If this were emergency traffic isn't that how you would want it to flow? Remember that even in a small contest, efficiency is important. You can ragchew with the station some other day although it's perfectly okay to quickly say hello if you know the operator. Just don't launch into a conversation in the middle of a contest QSO!

There is more to making contest QSOs than this simple example but that format will get you started. If you'd like to know more, the following sections are an introduction to real contest operating.

OPERATING BASICS: YOUR FIRST CONTESTS

You may have happened upon several contests and even made a few contest QSOs. It was fun, wasn't it? Are you ready to try entering one for real? Let's go! Your QSOs will be welcomed by everyone, especially the serious participants. They are always looking for additional contacts and, unless there are many callers, will be glad to guide you through your first contest QSOs.

Choosing a Contest

Contests generally fall into three categories, each having a different group of stations you should work. Contests that only allow point credit for working stations in the same country or region are called *domestic contests*. For an ARRL domestic contest, stations may work other stations in the US or Canada (known in contest lingo as W/VE.). The ARRL November Sweepstakes is an example of a W/VE domestic contest. In contrast, a European domestic contest limits QSOs to those between European stations.

There are two types of *DX contests*. Targeted DX contests require that contacts be between a specific region or DXCC entity and stations located elsewhere. Contacts in the ARRL International DX Contest, for example, must be between the contiguous 48 US states or a Canadian province and stations outside W/VE, including KH6, KL7 and US possessions. Non-W/VE stations cannot contact each other in this contest. Some targeted DX contests do allow contacts between stations in the targeted area. Check the rules to be sure.

The other type of DX contest is called *everybody-works-everybody* where all QSOs are allowed for some amount of credit. The ARRL 10 Meter Contest, IARU HF Championship, CQ WPX and CQ World Wide (WW) contests are all examples of this type of contest. As you might imagine, these are the largest contests of all, attracting thousands of participants worldwide.

Remember to check the rules for mode of operation. Some contests, such as the ARRL November Sweepstakes and ARRL International DX Contest have separate weekends

You don't have to leave the US to be rare! George, K5KG, traveled to North Dakota during the ARRL CW Sweepstakes and operated from the NØUD club station, setting a new section record! (*K5KG photo*)

for CW and phone operation. For the ARRL 10 Meter Contest and IARU HF World Championships, you work both CW and phone during the same weekend. In the ARRL RTTY Roundup, you can operate using any digital mode, from Baudot to packet to PSK31. ARRL VHF/UHF contests allow QSOs on any mode — CW, phone or digital — during the same event.

For your first few contests, assess your personal and station capabilities as well as what type of contacts you'd like to make. If you have a modest station and are just beginning, look for the state QSO parties. These low-key events are great opportunities to get your feet wet and chase the Worked All States award. Sponsored by groups and clubs in the various states, the goal is to encourage activity among the hams of that particular state. Some state QSO parties offer interesting prizes. Be a winner in the California state QSO party and you may find yourself with a bottle of vintage California wine for your efforts. Top scoring stations in another state QSO party may receive jams, apples or even smoked salmon (as well as some beautiful certificates to hang on the wall).

If you would rather try for some DX contacts, the ARRL DX Contest, IARU HF Championship and CQ WPX or WW contests put lots of loud signals on the band that you can probably work in a few calls. Don't be afraid to jump into almost any contest you find. You will pick up the rhythm and techniques quickly.

Read the Rules

To find a contest and be ready to operate, check the "Contest Corral" contest calendar in a current issue of *QST* for available contests and pick one that looks interesting. Check the sponsor's website for the complete rules and more information about the contest, including awards and special operating requirements. Being familiar with the rules will make operating more comfortable, smooth and enjoyable.

Knowing the rules also will help you plan your operating times. You should know when the event starts and how long you are allowed to operate. Does the contest require *off-times* during the event? Is it a 12-, 24- or 48-hour contest? Not knowing the rules beforehand could require you to delete multipliers and QSOs worked late in a contest because you exceeded the maximum permissible operating time.

After you choose a contest, learn the exchange. This is the most important thing to know for every contest you enter, no matter how much experience you have. By memorizing the exchange it becomes so automatic you'll find you can do other things while sending it. That ability will become valuable in future contesting. After you've learned the exchange, you're ready to go on the air!

Search and Pounce Technique

What a great term! *Search and Pounce* (S&P) describes exactly the technique of tuning up and down a band for new stations (searching) then working them (pouncing). As you tune, you'll hear some stations calling "CQ Contest" or simply "CQ Test." To get up to speed, just listen for a while. Observe how the louder, busy stations do it, making each call quickly and crisply. They send the exchange smoothly without extra syllables, words or characters and without unnecessarily repeating information.

If you find it helpful, prepare by writing the contest exchange on "cheat sheets" to guide you through each QSO without getting flustered. (This is also helpful when mentoring a new operator or a youngster making the first QSOs.) Practice giving your exchange along with a QSO being made on the air but without transmitting. Here's a tip: In a phone contest take a full breath before replying to a station. Give all of your exchange the same way every time in a single, uninterrupted statement. Your voice will be natural and unforced — you'll sound and feel much more confident.

Once you're ready, how do you give yourself the best chance of getting through? What's the best way to call? On phone, make the most of your transmissions by speaking clearly and distinctly. Speak briskly without rushing or mumbling. Use standard phonetics that are easy to speak (remember, you'll be saying them a lot!) and easy to understand. If you're unsure about your technique, practice with a friend on a quiet band. On CW, send your call cleanly with the characters spaced properly. Using a computer program or CW keyer is a good way to send your call correctly every time. Send at a speed you'll feel comfortable receiving.

Give your full call one time and one time only, using phonetics on phone. Why the full call? Because sending only a partial call (such as the poor practice of giving only the "last two" letters) requires at least one extra set of transmissions to get your complete call sign. This slows down the running station — a breach of contest etiquette. And why only one time? Because if you're heard, you'll get through with only one call. If you're not heard, the extra calls are just interference. Listen for the running station's response and respond appropriately. If another station is called, wait until the contact is completed and try again. Or if you think too many other stations are calling, store the frequency in one of your rig's VFOs or memories or even write the frequency and call on paper so that you can come back later and try again.

Stick with standard or commonly used phonetics. You should eventually learn up to three common sets because in marginal conditions it pays to be able to change to a more easily understood word for better comprehension.

Another problem for operators new to contesting is keeping up with the speed at which contacts are conducted. A running station may only listen for two seconds before starting another CQ. You have to start your call during that short window to be heard. Don't put the microphone down or take your hand off the key! By the time you get ready to transmit, it will be too late. Be ready to transmit as soon as the running station's transmission ends. You don't have to send your entire call in two seconds because the running station will pause as soon as your transmissions are heard. It's only important that you start in time to be heard. Just think of contesting as "DXing speeded up" and you'll quickly adapt.

Efficiency is the name of game in contesting. There's no need to give the running station's call before yours — after all, the other operator already knows his or her call! Don't append information to your call unless it's necessary to identify your station. Don't add "/QRP" or your location, for example. It adds nothing to identify you and just creates more work for the station you're calling.

If the running station hears you, be ready to copy the response. Most contacts will happen just as shown in the example given earlier. What happens if there is QRM, QRN, QSB or any number of other problems that cause errors? What if the running station gets your call sign wrong?

Let's start with correcting your call sign. The best time to fix it is as soon as the running station responds to you. Don't give your exchange — implying your acceptance of the incorrect call — until your call is given correctly by the running station. Here's an example (imagine that both stations are using phonetics in this phone example):

The World Radiosport Team Championship (WRTC) is held every four years, bringing together top contesters from around the world for an Olympics-style competition. Operating Field-Day style around Moscow, Vlad, RW1AC, and Alex, RA1AIP, took first place in WRTC2010. WRTC2014 will return to the US to be held in New England (www.wrtc2014.org). (*EY8MM photo*)

OH8X: CQ contest from OH8X
KD8ABC: KD8ABC
OH8X: KD8APZ you are 59 15
[OH8X has the call wrong and gave you the exchange 59 zone 15. Usually you don't say "zone" — it's understood.]
KD8ABC: KD8ABC KD8ABC
[Just say your call sign, phonetically, no exchange yet.]
OH8X: KD8ABZ?
KD8ABC: KD8ABC, last letter is C
[Here's your chance to try a different phonetic for the difficult letter.]
OH8X: KD8ABC QSL, 59 15
KD8ABC: Thank you, 59 4
[Now that OH8X has your call sign and you have OH8X's exchange, give your exchange. KD8ABC is in zone 4.]
OH8X: Thank you, CQ contest OH8X

What if part of the exchange is lost? Request a repeat immediately, before giving your information as shown in this CW example for a VHF+ contest:

W8ABC: KD8ABC [static crash]
KD8ABC: GRID?
W8ABC: KD8ABC EM99
KD8ABC: R EN81

There are many variations on making corrections. The important thing is to let the other station know there is a problem before sending information back to them. If you implicitly accept the incorrect information by responding with your exchange, it's confusing and takes longer to correct the error.

As you give your exchange information, don't add any extra words or phrases. Just give the information in the same order used by the running station. There is no need for phrases such as "please copy" or "you are" or to name each bit of information. Do not repeat the exchange you've received. Just rattle off your information in one string and the running station will be perfectly happy.

Don't say or send anything twice. Don't repeat any information unless requested or you are absolutely sure the running station won't copy everything on the first try — you might be surprised! Just send your information — once — as smoothly and as efficiently as possible. You will be pleased with how effective this technique is and how it builds your confidence.

If you are asked for a repeat, give only the information requested. If you are asked for your prefix, give only your prefix. If asked for your suffix or any letter of your call sign or report, give only what is asked. The receiving station already has most of the information or will confirm a full call sign after getting all of it. To send anything extra may cause confusion under marginal receiving conditions.

Now that you have all of the information, log the QSO time and date in UTC, the band, and the complete exchange. Then continue to tune for more contest contacts. There's still a lot to learn but the basic fun of contesting has begun!

INTERMEDIATE CONTEST OPERATING

After you find out how easy it is to have fun in a contest, you may want to get a little more serious about participating. You don't have to go all-out as a serious contester to enjoy some success but it will take a little effort to get good results. You'll want to submit a log to the sponsors, see your standings in the final results and possibly even contribute your score to a contest club. This is good stuff! Even if you never get more serious about radiosport than casual contesting, it will be amazing how much you learn about operating and propagation while simultaneously extending your station's capabilities.

Part of being successful lies in managing your expectations. Unreasonable expectations lead to frustration that can really diminish your enjoyment of contesting. Don't expect to place in the national Top Ten until you've spent some time gaining experience. If your QTH is challenging — such as a valley location, a high noise area or limited by antenna restrictions — it will be difficult to make a big score from home. In any case, plan an operating strategy by which you could reach some reasonable goals. Get creative to develop your radio skills! Operating from a portable location or mobile is an option getting more popular every year.

Roving — operating on the move or from several choice locations — has become a very popular operating style for VHF+ contesters. John, W1RT, is giving his rover antennas some "hands-on" attention from atop Mohawk Mountain in grid FN31 during the ARRL September VHF QSO Party. (*K1RA photo*)

Be prepared to handle the QRM that comes naturally in a contest. The bands will be much more crowded than during a normal weekday. Don't expect quiet, clear frequencies in the middle of the activity. This is where your listening skills become very important. Contesting develops an operator's ability to copy information through noise, fading and interference from nearby signals. How you handle contest QRM is one of the most important contest skills.

Calling CQ

You may have tried an occasional CQ in a contest as a beginner but as a more serious participant you'll want to CQ or *run* as much as possible. Experienced contesters know that if they have a good signal, the overall rate at which they can make contacts will be as good or better than tuning the band. More importantly, they also know that the multipliers will eventually tune by *them*. Learning to call CQ and hold a run frequency is an important contest skill.

To decide whether or not to call CQ you have to decide whether your signal is strong enough in the target area. One way to find out is to tune the band searching and pouncing. If you are working stations on the first call, you're probably loud enough to get answers to a CQ. You can also ask stations that you work about your signal strength. If you decide you're loud enough, the next step is to find an unoccupied frequency.

A good way to find a frequency is to tune from one end of the band (usually the high end) and look for "holes" between stations calling CQ. When you find one, ask if the frequency is in use (send your call once on CW to avoid unidentified transmissions, although just "?" is common) and listen for responses. On phone, you will need to be at least 1.5 kHz from adjacent stations. On CW, at least 300 Hz. Don't expect a channel without QRM in a big contest. If you can hear just the high frequency crackle or low-frequency rumble of nearby signals, that's about as good as you can expect.

Assuming you got no response to your inquiry (and remember to listen for non-contest QSOs), it's time for a CQ. Think of each CQ as casting a fishing lure into a lake with fish swimming by. Your lure has to be in the water if a fish is going to bite, so keep the channel occupied with short listening periods between calls. On phone or CW, leave two to three seconds between CQs. Short CQs work best on busy bands — too long a CQ and impatient contest stations will tune right by.

Here are some examples of reasonable contest CQs on phone. Note the use of phonetics at least once in each CQ:
"CQ Contest CQ Contest from Whiskey One Alfa Whiskey, Whiskey One Alfa Whiskey, Contest"
"CQ CQ Contest this is Kilo Delta Seven Foxtrot Yankee X-ray, KD7FYX"
And on CW:
CQ TEST VE7SV VE7SV TEST
CQ SS CQ SS K4RO K4RO SS (SS is for Sweepstakes)
TEST K1TO (if QSOs are really moving along quickly)

Instead of "Contest" you can substitute the name of the contest if you are participating in one of the smaller contests. That attracts the attention of stations tuning by.

Each CQ should be brisk and crisp, not slurred or

tentative. Think of each CQ as a small advertisement for your station that makes another operator want to answer you. Your voice should be friendly but businesslike.

As long as we're on the subject, calling CQ is an excellent reason why contest audio is so important. While you tune the bands, make note of stations with good and bad audio. What is it about the good audio that got your attention? It was probably punchy with crisp mid-to-high frequency response, just enough low frequencies, and not noisy or distorted. Strive for those qualities. Get together on a dead band with a friend between contests and adjust your mic gain and speech processor settings for that same quality of audio. If you use a voice keyer, do the same for its messages. You'll recall some stations whose audio is so distorted, over-compressed or contaminated with background noise that they're hard to understand. Why make it difficult for your audience to understand you?

Let's assume that you find a frequency and you're calling CQ. If you get a steady stream of callers, there's nothing better in contesting! Be consistent and smooth in your responses. Give directions or make requests calmly — no need to shout! Make sure of the other station's call sign and exchange before calling CQ again.

Improve your running rate by learning to get the full call sign sent to you the first time, every time. Repeats not only take time but stations waiting to work you may move on. Learn to receive a call sign phonetically and give it back to the other station without phonetics. This only works, however, when you're absolutely, positively sure that you have the call sign correct. Remember that contest sponsors remove points for incorrect call signs.

What if you don't get many callers? How long should you continue to call CQ? There is no set answer but you should be doing whatever maximizes your contact rate. Most contesters will try a reasonably clear frequency for two or three minutes without callers before tuning away. If in the past hour you were able to work stations at a rate of 30/hour (most contest logging software will display your "last hour" rate), then calling CQ should be expected to generate that rate or better. If you get a stream of callers that eventually dries up, a good rule of thumb is to continue calling CQ for at least twice the interval between your S&P QSOs. For example, if your S&P rate was 30/hour or one station every two minutes, you should call CQ for four minutes before deciding to return to S&P. This is not a hard and fast rule. As you gain experience, your intuition will begin to tell you when to CQ and when to tune.

If you're not getting answers to your calls or are being asked for repeats a lot, think about why this might be. Are you sending too fast on CW? Are you transmitting clean audio on SSB? Either can prevent you from making QSOs, so it's counterproductive to have poor audio or to send too fast. On CW, it's often more productive to slow down late in the contest when you've already worked most of the active contesters. Remember, you cannot win many contests by working only the hardcore, experienced contesters. You have to also work casual operators who turn on their radios, make a

few contacts, then go off to enjoy other pursuits. Temper your voice or keying speed to what you're trying to accomplish at that minute. If you have a large pileup, go fast so callers will know they have a chance and stick around. If you're getting only one or two calls per minute, be slower and friendlier.

If you have multiple or directional antennas, don't forget to try different directions or antennas. As bands open and close, the vertical and horizontal angles at which signals arrive can change dramatically. An antenna that was hot as a pistol when the band first opened may be the wrong one an hour later. The band may also open to another area. For example, from the Midwest in a domestic contest such as Sweepstakes, fading rate to the 1-2-3 districts is a cue that it's time to aim your antennas west.

You might also lose your frequency to another station. Two stations in each other's skip zones can call CQ right on top of each other without ever hearing the other station! You can tell this is happening when stations seem to be calling but the timing isn't "right." You may also hear the other station faintly via backscatter. When this happens, if you feel you're the louder station, you might want to stay and battle it out. If you think sticking around will hurt your contact rate too badly, by all means look for another frequency.

Occasionally another station will ask if the frequency is in use, not hear your reply and proceed to call CQ. You can try to convince them to move or your can move yourself. It depends on your interpersonal skills and signal strength. Another station may try to squeeze in between you and the next station up or down the band when there really isn't room. You'll just have to decide whether to hold your ground, slide up or down the band a little bit to accommodate the newcomer, or look for a new frequency. In any of these cases, don't lose your temper and get into an argument or worse, intentionally interfere with the other station. Life is too short for that stuff — if you're arguing with another station, you're not making QSOs!

Advanced Search and Pounce

As a more serious competitor, you'll want to make better use of the time you spend tuning around the band. A good operator can work stations at a rate of 60/hour on a "fresh" band with lots of stations calling CQ. This requires a radio with two VFOs and bandstacking registers and either a good personal memory or a pencil and paper. Practicing this technique or some variation of it can make a big improvement over tuning up the band one station at a time.

Start at one end of the band on VFO A. Tune until you find a station and call them. If you work them right away, keep tuning. If you don't, set VFO B = VFO A and tune to the next station and call them. You now have two running stations in the two VFOs. Alternate between the VFOs until one station is worked, then keep tuning with that VFO. Flip back to the other VFO and call that station at the end of a contact. By alternating between the VFOs you can be in two pileups at once all the way down the band! If the pileup on a station is just too big, store the frequency in a band-stacking register or a memory and make a note of the call and frequency. Revisit

Single Operator Assisted: Using Spotting Networks for Higher Scores

By Charles Fulp, K3WW

Many contests have added a Single-Operator Assisted (SOA) or Unlimited (SOU) category. We'll just call it SOA here. This category usually has the same rules at the Single-Operator category with one major exception. The entrant may use spotting networks such as the DX clusters and the Reverse Beacon Network (**www.reverse-beacon.net**). Spotting networks have opened up a whole new world for many contesters, allowing access to information about band conditions and stations and multipliers available during the contest as never before.

The SOA category allows operators who enjoy monitoring their spotting network for new countries to participate in contests without missing anything. Other operators like working cooperatively with their friends while operating contests. Still others feel that the use of spotting networks can help them score more points for their club by increasing their multiplier totals. Being part of the network can keep some operators motivated to push on to bigger scores. Being "connected" in many ways makes SOA closer to a multi-op category than single-op.

The only special equipment necessary to participate in the SOA category is a link to a spotting network. Originally, the links were by VHF packet radio to central stations using PacketCluster software. Later, contest software was developed to integrate VHF packet networks. Today, it is most common to connect by the Internet. Many of the remaining VHF PacketCluster systems are connected to the Internet, as well. Most logging programs will accommodate packet and Internet connections and will interact with the radio, computer and logging in such a way that getting to a spot is only a mouse click or keystroke away.

SOA Station Setup

If you decide to try to make the best scores you can, some station design features can help you and make SOA much more fun. The first thing you should have is a transceiver that can be controlled by your contest logging program. This allows you to move quickly to work new multipliers and back to your original frequency, where you can resume your tuning or calling CQ.

If you choose to use high power, an auto-tuning amplifier and automatic antenna switch allow you to quickly jump from one band to another. Some operators just bypass the amplifier when making a quick contact on another band.

As in the Single-Op category, the use of a second radio can improve your performance as an SOA entrant. If your station is capable of running at good rates on some bands, you can use the second station to study spots. When the opportunity is right, make quick contacts between answers to your CQ. Since many SOA stations are not the biggest on the bands, being able to stay on a frequency and catch some extra multipliers without leaving for more than a few seconds at a time can help you get the most out of your station. Having a second radio also decreases the importance of auto-tuning amplifiers and rapid band change antenna switching. Of course the more automated everything is, the more flexible your station can be.

Too Much Information

Historically the top Single-Op entrants usually outscore the top SOA. There are several reasons for this. Traditionally the top operators with stations capable of winning at the highest levels enter the Single-Op category. After competing in the SOA category for a few years and watching the performance of other participants, I coined the term "Single-Op Distracted."

There are many elements involved in building a big score and access to spotting information is only one. Being distracted by all the spots is the biggest nemesis of the serious SOA entrant. If you are actually trying to make the best score you can, reverting to being a DXer can ruin your effort. In order to chase spots, it is usually necessary to give up some of the other activities that can build a big score. Even if you work every spot with one call, you will lose running time chasing them.

Most operators will find it difficult to hold a run (CQ) frequency and simultaneously enter a lot of large pileups. It is very easy to become distracted by all of the information available on the spotting networks and end up forgetting to do all the other things that Single-Ops do to make big scores. At some point, you must be able to ignore exotic, hard-to-work multipliers and concentrate on making lots of easy-to-make contacts. On the other hand, you may set a goal of working the most multipliers possible and not be concerned about optimizing your score.

Knowing your objective, regardless of your entry category, is important in establishing a game plan for any category. If you want to work some new countries or make a clean sweep, monitoring the spotting nets can improve your chances. If you want to make more points for your club, you will need a different strategy. Here's the most effective game plan for the SOA entrant: Do everything that you would do as a Single-Op, while judiciously picking up extra multipliers without detracting

the frequency in a few minutes and you'll often find a big pileup is now a little pileup and get right through. Watching skilled operators S&P their way across a band this way is quite an experience as they hop from frequency to frequency.

Don't just tune from loud signal to loud signal. Listen carefully where there seems to be a small gap or a weak signal. Stations with small antennas, such as temporary setups by operators on vacation or operating Field Day-style, may have weak signals and be unable to attract a large pileup. They can probably hear you just fine, however — if you don't tune past them!

Many logging programs offer a feature called a *band map*. This is a linear scale along one edge of the display showing call signs and frequencies. Call signs are added to

Chas, K3WW, operates from this well organized ham shack. You can count on him to finish in the Top Ten in the Single-Op Unlimited category.

from your most efficient practices.

Calling CQ is still the fastest way to build a large QSO total for most operators. When we can't run effectively, searching and pouncing can produce good QSO totals. With spotting, S&P can be even more effective. As you tune the band, you can skip over duplicates quickly and the spots may help in identifying some of the stations you come to.

Making the Best Use of Spots

It pays to tune in an orderly manner, even if you do run off to a different portion of the band or even to another band to grab a new multiplier. Most software now displays a band map, which lets you see many of the calls as you tune your radio. This visual display permits you to know who you can probably skip and who you probably need to work. You can click your mouse and go to new multipliers directly from the band map as well as from the window that lists the most recent spots.

Early in the contest I tend to just display new multipliers but use the band map to make tuning on my second radio while running on my primary radio a quicker job. Later in the contest it may be more productive to work through the band map jumping from one needed station to the next, especially if you cannot hold a good run frequency.

Listen carefully to be sure the spots are accurate! If

you have already worked a lot of QSOs, the ones that show up as "needed" may well be bad calls. If you only have one radio but it has two receivers, you can still try to maintain a run and listen on the second radio to the spots in your band map. I find this more efficient than trying to tune the second receiver on the same band that I am running with no help from the spotting network.

On some bands you will find stations working split. An unfortunate complication of spotting networks is that many stations now announce their listening frequency less often. For the SOA operator this information is often available from the network, making it faster to work these stations while Single-Ops have to wait for the DX station to announce the listening frequency.

Another situation involves stations that do not identify very often. There is a strong temptation to assume that the spot is correct and work these stations without ever hearing the call. This is a risky proposition as a fair percentage of spotted calls are incorrect. Even when they are correct, sometimes a different station is on the frequency when you arrive.

Information from the spotting network will let you know which bands are most active and should allow you to choose the best band at any given time. Nothing replaces knowledge of what is going on around you.

It is important to be patient, especially early in the contest when there are large numbers of spots for stations that will be active throughout the weekend and much easier to work later in the contest. Unless you especially like the challenge of entering pileups with many of the biggest stations in your area, you may find it easier to wait for the smoke to clear before you go after a new multiplier.

If a station in an area where you have long periods of propagation is spotted early and the pileup is large, don't waste time unless you have an incredible signal. Even if you do, it may be more productive to wait until later to pick up many of these stations.

Technology keeps changing — the VHF spotting voice nets gave way to PacketCluster, which has to a large degree been replaced by Internet-based DX clusters. The Reverse Beacon Network now provides more accurate spots almost the instant a station begins to call CQ on a new frequency. This has permitted extended opportunities to chase spots at rates that often approach the rates of a typical run.

If you want to maximize your enjoyment of the entire contest experience, give the Single-Op Assisted category a try.

the band map as you work them, by manually entering them into the band map or automatically from a spotting network. It's usually possible to configure the band map to show only multipliers, only stations not yet worked or even all stations. As you tune, some programs will even put the call of a station on the band map at the current frequency into the call window, ready for you to give your call and work them!

As you develop these quick-tuning skills, you'll find a quick scan of the band to be a valuable way to grab points quickly as you change bands or between periods of CQing.

Spotting Networks

As an intermediate contester, you'll be using your computer for contest logging as explained in the sidebar,

CW Skimmer

CW contesting recently added a new operator — this one doesn't transmit though because it is completely automated! Alex, VE3NEA has developed the *CW Skimmer* (**www.dxatlas.com/CwSkimmer**) that can decode up to 700 CW signals simultaneously (!) using the output of a wide-band receiver.

The output of *CW Skimmer* is both a visual window showing where the stations are calling and also decoded call signs and frequencies that can be used as the input to your logging software or to send spots to the world-wide spotting networks.

Having this automated capability has been "turned around" by the Reverse Beacon Network or RBN (**www.reversebeacon.net**) into a "who's being heard where" service that listens to the HF and VHF+ bands continually. The RBN monitors the output from "skimmers" located around the world, displaying the call signs and signal strengths of stations calling CQs that are heard and decoded by the skimmers. To find out if you're being heard and how well, get on the air and call CQ a few times — unless your signal is really weak, within a minute your call sign will appear in the list.

Needless to say, this has had an impact on CW contesting! By reducing the need to tune the band looking for stations, more stations find the CQers. The bad news is that so many stations can tune to the CQer's frequency so quickly that the pileups can quickly become too unwieldy to handle. In the words of Yogi Berra, "Nobody goes there anymore — it's too crowded!" So use *CW Skimmer* wisely — don't let it substitute for the radio "know-how" you need to become a skilled operator.

"Computers in Contests." Besides automating many of the housekeeping functions of logging, the computer can also connect you to information from other contesters. This requires you to enter the Single Operator Assisted (SOA) category as described in the sidebar. (In some events it's called the Single Op Unlimited category.) The rules differ from the single operator category in one way — the entrant may use information from DX spotting networks (also called "packet" because the original computer-based spotting networks used *PacketCluster* software running over packet radio links). To be clear, with few exceptions, getting such information from *any* source other than your own ears — whether from packet or 2 meter voice nets — *requires* you to submit your log in the SOA category. (In contests without an SOA category, you usually — but not always — have to enter in a multioperator category if you use spotting assistance.)

Connecting your computer to the Internet and your radio is a powerful combination used through two features of the logging software, the *announce window* and the *band map*. The band map was introduced in the Advanced Search and Pounce section. Logging software can use information from the spotting network to populate the band map automatically, filling it with stations spotted around the world. It's like having the whole world tuning for you! As you tune, the computer senses the new frequency and scrolls the band map along with your receive frequency.

The announce window shows each spot individually. This is important because additional information may be posted by the spotter, such as "listening up 2" or "QSX 7167" for a DX station on 40 meter phone who is transmitting below 7100 kHz and listening in the US phone band. The band map and announce window features can usually be configured to show only stations you haven't yet worked or only those that are new multipliers. It may be able to show the different types of information in different colors, to help you quickly make sense of it.

You will find that spots from stations far away from your location are often not much use in contests since propagation is probably quite different in that location. Even spots from the other side the US are often of no value. Learn how to use the spotting network filters to prevent unworkable spots from cluttering up your band map and spot windows. It's easy to remove spots from bands and modes not included in your current contest. Some systems can also filter spots based on the location of their origin. Programs like VE7CC's *CC Cluster* act as a "smart" spotting network client with special filtering and display functions.

Spotting networks have had a big effect on intermediate contesting — not all good. The fun side of spotting is that casual participants have more fun by finding more stations to work. This increases their score, as well as their club's aggregate score, and they may work some new stations toward an award. The problem arises when the spotting information begins to *replace* tuning and operating skill instead of *assisting* the operator.

The rush of stations to work a newly spotted station creates what are known as "packet pileups." DX operators know instantly when they've been "spotted" as their pileup grows suddenly from a handful of callers to dozens or more. The sudden rush of stations is confusing to everyone, causing the pileups to get out of sync with the DX station, reducing contact rate for everyone. Don't contribute to the mob mentality — if you grab a spot to work a station, wait until you can hear them before calling and use good pileup discipline. Sometimes it's more productive to wait a while before chasing a spot, giving the packet pileup a chance to subside.

Don't become dependent on spotting network assistance. Use it to aid you and your own abilities. Make sure that you copy each call sign you work. Spots are helpful but the call signs given may be — and frequently are — wrong or *busted*. By not copying the call sign and exchange for yourself, and simply trusting the spotting network, you run the risk of having the incorrect QSO removed from your log, along with a penalty!

CONTEST STRATEGY

As an intermediate contester, you have progressed from struggling to tune the bands and work stations one by one to being able to quickly search and pounce your way through a thicket of stations. You're probably even calling CQ and holding your own! You're ready to start thinking about strategy.

Pre-Contest Preparation

Start by making sure you know the contest rules well enough to perform properly during the contest. This includes knowing whom to work during the contest and how the scoring system works. All of these will play a part in strategic planning for the contest. The exchange should be memorized to the point that you could send the exchange while concentrating on some other contest chore, such as logging, checking multipliers or equipment conditions. You should know your grid square, CQ zone, ITU zone, state, county, section

Scott, ZF2SC, combined a vacation with some contest operating in the ARRL 10 Meter Contest. From the right location a simple station can make a lot of contacts! (*ZF2SC photo*)

or anything else required for any contest you might enter. A seasoned contester knows the exchange for all of the major contests.

Develop an operating plan, even if just a simple one. Without some kind of plan, it is difficult to be successful in any contest. While there are some experienced contesters who seem to never have a plan, that's not really true. It's just that their experience is such that before the contest starts they can estimate where they will be at various points along the way, what multipliers they will need, and what kind of QSO totals will be required.

Select an operating category based on your station limitations, operating time available and personal capabilities. If propagation is good, you might want to try QRP or leave the amplifier off for the weekend and try low power. Single-band categories are often a great way to really learn about propagation and pursue single-band DXCC or other single-band awards. If you are a serious certificate collector, you may find little competition in the more obscure categories.

Even if the category is one where you do not think you will win, you should still have some sort of plan and goals set before the contest. Find the results of last year's contest and see what it took to win your section, division or call area. Then see what the leaders in your chosen category did in last year's version of the contest. Evaluate this year's expected propagation. For example, on HF when sunspots are rising, expect 10 meters to be better than the year before. As sunspots decline, expect 10 meters to be worse. The other bands should see an increase or decrease in activity based upon what 10 meters will do. Most single-operator, all-band (SOAB) participants will naturally migrate to the highest band open.

Along with evaluating the probable propagation on each band, check previous contest *breakdowns* of other stations in your category — the number of multipliers and QSOs on each band. A *rate sheet* will show the number of QSOs on each band during each clock hour, giving you a picture of which hours were busy and slow. It's best to pick a station near to you and with similar equipment for this evaluation. Breakdown information can be found on the 3830 e-mail reflector archives at **www.contesting.com** or in the detailed online contest results from ARRL and other contest sponsors. Make an estimate for QSOs and multipliers for each band. It's good to have goals, even though things will likely change during the contest.

Breakdowns from last year's contest can be used to prepare for this year's contest. Use those breakdowns to set goals for this year's contest. It's often helpful to compare the rate from the previous year to find out where you were and what you were doing as the contest progressed, especially if you made a wrong move last year.

By studying the band breakdowns and looking at your own goals, you can determine the probability of meeting them and make an educated guess as to what to do if you need to correct something in your operation. You should strive to stay ahead of last year's score, even to the point of computing how much you want to be ahead in this year's contest. Watching last year's rate sheet will keep you on track for an increased performance. Improvement is always the name of the game in contesting and results analysis will help get you there.

Finally, make the necessary plans to prevent interruptions to your contest effort. Be ready to go at the start of the contest period and stay at the station as much as possible during the contest. As described later in this chapter, food preparation should be such that there is sufficient food available but you should not plan on having a sit-down dinner during the contest. Try to get as much rest as possible in the days leading up to the contest. Sleep time will be minimal and the sleeping area should be close by and comfortable. Be sure to have a good alarm clock (or two!) and be able to motivate yourself to get out of bed when it goes off.

Getting a Fast Start

Beginning on the highest band expected to be open at the start of the contest is the best thing to do. Getting some success by working stations in the first few minutes of the contest is important to your overall success. While you can't win a contest in the first few minutes, getting off to a good start will have a positive effect on your attitude for the whole weekend.

If you start by doing search-and-pounce, don't sit on a frequency waiting to be someone's first QSO unless you're in contact as the contest begins. There are probably others lurking on frequency trying to do the same thing and you'll find yourself in a big pileup right away. You'll have better results by making a quick sweep through the band to make a few contacts before settling in. Make a band map as you go and then get down to business. After the first 30 minutes of the contest, you'll settle down and the band will even out as everyone finds a comfortable rhythm. You may have to make a couple of band changes right away to find the best band for making contacts.

You may decide to start by trying to establish a run frequency. This is a good strategy if you know you have a good signal where the band is open. Unless you're a Big Gun, aim for higher in the band where the crowding won't be so intense. Although the adrenaline will be flowing, don't start at extremely high speed. Work a few stations and assess what the conditions and activity will bear. Don't be too impatient for a high rate because it takes everyone a little while to get rolling.

QSO Rate Versus Multipliers

Any contest should be considered as something similar to a scavenger hunt. The object is to collect a lot of something (QSOs in this case) while also acquiring as many items from a list (multipliers) as possible. Each contest has a different theme (list) with different strategies as a result. For example, in working a DX contest from the US the most active, available multipliers are in Europe. In the eastern US, the most QSOs will also be found in Europe. Thus, if you live in the eastern US, you would concentrate your operating hours on Europe. If you live in the western US, you are likely to work the most QSOs in Asia which fewer active multipliers. So you would try to work European multipliers but plan on making a lot of QSOs by working Asia. This requires an entirely different operating strategy.

In some contests, you may make most of your QSOs by S&P. That means the time you spend calling in a pileup is important. The less time required per QSO the better and big pileup is harder to crack than a small one. Remember that a G or JA multiplier has the same value as the much rarer P29 station. The G or JA will have a smaller pileup so you'll log the multiplier quickly. Remember, the object is to work as many countries *and* QSOs as possible on each band, not to work the rarest ones. All multipliers are equal!

If your goal is to achieve a certain score, you should try for a reasonable balance between QSOs and multipliers. For example, you can score 50,000 points in the CQ WW contests with 300 three-point QSOs and 55 multipliers spread across several bands. This score is a reachable goal for most stations.

If you work a station that would be a multiplier on another band and you think propagation would support a QSO on that band, you can ask the station to move to that band for a quick contact. This is called *moving multipliers* and can make a dramatic improvement in your score. It's probably not a good idea to ask stations to move if they are busy but this technique can be effective when things are slow.

If the station prefers not to move or if propagation is not good on other bands at the moment, try making a schedule for later in the contest. If you overhear another station making a schedule or moving a juicy multiplier to another band, try to follow the move or show up on schedule and work the multiplier, too. Always be listening and thinking during the contest.

Whether you decide to S&P, call CQ, or change bands will depend on how far along the contest is. If it's the first day and other bands are open, you might want to S&P on another band, especially if you're running low power or the band is too crowded for you to hold a run frequency. The decision of when to chase multipliers or to stay with calling CQ largely depends on both the contact rate and the point value of a new multiplier. Ellen White, W1YL, in a 1955 *QST* article, stated a formula that still works well today. This formula can help determine whether it's more worthwhile to work a multiplier or a new QSO. The formula is: Value of Multiplier (in equivalent QSOs) = Number of Contacts Worked ÷ Number of Multipliers worked + 1.

As an example, in a DX contest, 20 QSOs ÷ 10 Mults + 1 = 3, so 1 new multiplier is equivalent to 3 QSOs. In another example, 1200 QSOs ÷ 350 Mults + 1 = 4.4, so the multiplier is equivalent to 4.4 QSOs. As you can see, the further into the contest you go, the greater value of a multiplier. You can also calculate how much time can be spent in pursuit of one multiplier versus continuing to work QSOs. In the second example, if your contact rate was 30/hour (one every 2 minutes), you could spend 2 × 4.4 = 8.8 minutes chasing the new multiplier and keep your score increasing at the same rate. Many contest logging programs will do this calculation for you in real-time.

Band Planning

Band plans are hour-by-hour strategies for operating on different bands to different areas. To make a band plan, spend some time with a propagation prediction program and logs from other similar contests at the same time of year and look for openings to the various areas of the world. This is a good time to ask experienced contesters for help. They will tell you how much planning is useful and what part of the plan is the most important. As you build experience, it will be helpful to have some guidelines throughout the contest to remind you to check other bands, look for openings and maintain a balance between CQing and tuning for multipliers.

Although you may have a general feel for propagation, the wide variability of propagation with the seasons and solar conditions require a custom plan for each contest. Even then, it could all go out the window on any given weekend if conditions and participation don't cooperate. The good contest operator develops a strategic awareness of what is happening during the contest and changes strategy as necessary. This is where experience comes into play and helps you adapt.

Many operators have gone into a contest with a game plan and stubbornly stayed with it even if it wasn't working. During the contest you must be flexible. If 15 meters was your band plan choice and nothing is happening for you there, go to 10 or 20 or possibly even lower. If 10 meters works best, don't try to force 15. Check the other bands from time to time to be aware of how propagation is changing. Either a marked lessening of your rate or a lack of new stations to work is a sign that you need to change to a different band.

Considering Population

A reliable strategy requires determining where the populations centers are for the contest of interest and maximizing efforts to reach those centers. For a DX contest from the East Coast of the US, the most important population center is Europe. For the West Coast, the most reachable population centers are in Asia and Oceania but some time must be devoted to working Europe. The Mid-South often has opening to both but with shorter openings to either. For domestic contests, the object is to work the population centers of the eastern seaboard while getting multipliers from the west, and running California when possible. This even applies to eastern stations that often devote more time to lower bands. Fix your strategy on contacting the population centers. If you need help deciding which population centers are most important, check out past contest results and see where the entries come from.

By the same token, pointing your antennas away from a population center for extended periods of time will not increase your contest scores. Yet valuable multipliers often come from less-populated directions. The best solution to that problem is determining when there is a high likelihood of working a station in that direction, devoting a few minutes to the pursuit of multipliers and returning to the primary direction. As an example, 10 meters often opens for Northern Hemisphere stations in a southerly direction around local noon, even in low sunspot years.

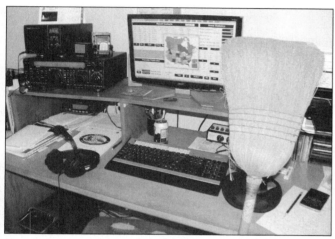

The broom signifies a Clean Sweep of all 80 sections in the 2010 ARRL Sweepstakes by Chris, N4KIT. Beginning in 2012, there will be 83 sections — can you work them all? (*N4KIT photo*)

AFTER THE CONTEST

You've put a lot of effort into making contacts and working multipliers — don't sell yourself short by not submitting your log to the contest sponsors! If you're a contest club member, you will want to be sure your club receives credit for your score, as well. Even if you've just entered the contest casually and made a handful of QSOs, go ahead and submit a log. The sponsor will appreciate your efforts and it allows them to more accurately gauge contest activity.

As soon as the contest is over, start the log preparation process by making a backup copy of the log file before you do anything else. You're probably tired and anxious to relax — this is when mistakes happen, so be careful about naming and storing the file! There is no feeling worse than losing your just-completed contest log.

If you're really tired, go no further! Wait until you're fresh to submit your computer log. Make any changes you've noted on paper during the contest. For example, if you made a mistake in copying a station's exchange and made a note to yourself to fix it, now is the time. Many logging programs allow the operator to embed notes in the log. Collect all of your notes and make any necessary log changes. Most operators will also review the log for typos, such as entering double or extra characters. Finding typographical errors is the responsibility of the contest operator, not the contest sponsor. Remember, the log you submit is the log that will be checked.

What about duplicate QSOs — should they be removed? Assuming you are submitting your log via e-mail or the web, leave them in the log. The sponsor's software will only count

The Contest Club

If you've tried a contest or two and liked it, you might want to consider rubbing shoulders with like-minded individuals. One of the most important resources available to today's amateur is the contest club. While such clubs have been around for many years, the formation of new clubs has been on the upswing. What better way to improve your operating and contesting skills, to learn the tricks of the trade or to gain knowledge and experience in contesting than by joining together with other amateurs with the same interests? In every region of the country you will find solid contest clubs, all working toward a similar goal: being the best at what is called in some parts of the world *radiosport*.

Meetings of a contest club, such as the Yankee Clipper Contest Club shown here, are excellent opportunities to pick up valuable operating and technical information, as well as providing the opportunity to meet other contesters from your area. (*K1IR photo*)

Just as different hams have different interests, you will find a wide variety of contest clubs, each with a special focus. Some clubs concentrate their efforts on VHF, UHF and microwave events. These clubs often form portable multi-op expeditions or seek to have rover stations active during the contest. They can often provide technical assistance, perhaps helping you to get on a new microwave band for the contest.

Other clubs concentrate on HF events and possibly have DXing as an additional focus of the group. Some of these clubs specialize in DX contests, while others specialize in domestic contests. More than a few of these clubs also sponsor some specialty contests of their own, such as state QSO parties. Meeting programs often show new and simple ideas for improving station or operator capabilities.

Club Competition

What challenges these clubs to compete? The ARRL sponsors affiliated club competition in seven major operating events: the January VHF Contest, the International DX Contest, the June and September VHF Contests, the November Sweepstakes, the 160 Meter Contest and the 10 Meter Contest. Each year dozens of clubs — in Local, Medium or Unlimited categories depending on their size — enlist their members to "win one for the club." If your club isn't already competing, check out the criteria for the ARRL Affiliated Club Competition published on the ARRL website. Clubs may also compete against one another in other major contests, such as the CQ World Wide DX Contest.

Join the Group, Improve Your Score

At meetings of the contest club, you'll have the opportunity to meet individuals at all experience levels. Many clubs have some sort of program for helping new contesters. Most clubs have one or more multi-operator stations that need a supply of operators. It's valuable to get onto a multi-op crew to learn contesting from experienced individuals. Camaraderie in a contest club makes the contester feel like part of the group, and sharing contest experiences at meetings (official and otherwise) helps bring the contester along to new heights.

Many clubs also run some sort of intra-club competition to help foster higher club scores. This allows contesters within a club to compete for awards that might not be available on a national level and provides motivation for sticking with it. For example, the club award program may reward certain score levels, numbers of QSOs or even time operated — anything to encourage club members to "stay in the chair" and contribute to the club score. The value of a contest club to the individual contester cannot be denied and it is rare that anyone is found in the Top Ten of any contest who is not a member of a recognized contest club.

You can find local and regional contest clubs by using the ARRL Club search web page at **www.arrl.org/find-a-club**. Enter "contest" in the keyword window. You can also contact your ARRL Division's representative on the Contest Advisory Committee (**www.arrl.org/arrl-staff-vuac-cac**).

---

one of the QSOs automatically. You won't be penalized for duplicate QSOs because the sponsor calculates QSO points for you. If you are submitting a paper log, leave the QSOs in the log file but enter zero for QSO points or note them as duplicates and do not count them as part of your claimed score.

You will need to use the proper forms or electronic files the sponsor requires for an official entry. Each contest has a submission deadline found in the rules announcement on the sponsor's website. It's usually not more than 30 days and sometimes much less, so submit your log as soon as possible after the contest ends so you won't miss the deadline or forget. The amount of work involved in processing and verifying your contacts is considerable so contest sponsors are strict about meeting the log submission deadlines. Make certain that your entry is either e-mailed or postmarked by the deadline date.

Ethics — To Edit or Not to Edit

Before editing your log after the contest there are ethical considerations to be weighed. How much editing is appropriate? What should you do if the information you've logged "looks" wrong? These questions (and more) are addressed in the ARRL's "HF Contesting — Good Practices, Interpretations and Suggestions" at **www.arrl.org/hf-operating-guidelines**. Here's what it says about log editing:

"It's possible to 'sanitize' a log after the contest...but the contest is over at the time the rules say it's over. Examples of post-contest log manipulation include editing times, correcting band changes, checking calls against the call book, checking against…spots, looking through logs from other contesters, confirming calls and exchanges with your buddies, reading DX and contesting reflectors for news about rare calls and even posting questions like, 'did anyone get QSL info for that VQ0?'

"There are wide ranging opinions about the acceptability of editing your log after the contest. The most conservative and always acceptable answer is that no editing of any sort is permissible. Some feel you have until the log submission deadline to do anything you want to the log. Most contesters would agree that if you made a note during the contest about an error, it's OK to fix it afterwards. Furthermore, it is generally OK to make a quick pass through the log immediately after the contest looking for 'obvious' typos such as entering

CT as CTT or changing 'o' to '0' — in fact, most logging software does such a check before creating the final log file. Correcting syntax errors reported by a log acceptance robot, such as improper dates or multiplier abbreviations is also acceptable. Once you step over the line into making changes to what you think you 'should' have logged, that's going too far.

"Reviewing your log is completely appropriate to help improve your operating accuracy and look for ways to improve strategy — in the *next* contest. In fact, many top operators regularly review their logs and even record parts of contests in order to review and improve their operating practices. For example, when you get your log-checking report, you can go back to review busted calls and see what the other station really sent. This is an excellent way to discover where your weak spots are. A quick scan of last year's log will refresh your memory about when and where you worked those rare multipliers, too!"

LOG SUBMISSION

When you are satisfied with your log, prepare a copy for the contest sponsor. The rules will usually specify the format in which the log should be submitted. The log format is the arrangement of information in the submitted computer file. The most common is known as *Cabrillo* and most logging software can create log files in this format. Again, carefully check the rules to see what types of files are accepted. If you don't send the right one, chances are your log won't be accepted and your score won't show up in the results.

Cabrillo: A Contest Log Standard

The most common file format used by contest sponsors is Cabrillo. (Pronounced ca-BREE-oh, the name refers to Cabrillo College near the home of Trey Garlough, N5KO author of the Cabrillo format specification.) *All* electronic files for ARRL (and many other) contests *must* be in the Cabrillo format. All of the major contest logging programs will generate a valid Cabrillo file.

Cabrillo files are composed of ASCII characters, and the log information is in fixed-position columns. See the example in **Figure 7.1**. Cabrillo also adds a number of standardized "header" lines that contain information about the log, such as the operator's name, call and location, contest category, power and so forth. The Cabrillo format allows sponsors to automate the process of log collection, sorting and checking even though entrants use many

different programs to generate the submitted log files. The Cabrillo log file should be named **yourcall.cbr** or **yourcall.log** (for example, **n0ax.cbr** or **n0ax.log**). You can read up on Cabrillo at **www.arrl.org/cabrillo-format-tutorial**.

If you have created an electronic Cabrillo format log file for submission, the next step is to e-mail it to the sponsors. The rules will provide the address to use. Attach your log to an e-mail with the subject line containing just the call you used during the contest, nothing else. The e-mail may be processed by a human or by a software "robot" program that automatically scans the received log files. Before sending the

```
START-OF-LOG: 2.0
ARRL-SECTION: NH
CALLSIGN: K1RO
CATEGORY: SINGLE-OP 160M LOW CW
CLAIMED-SCORE: 47320
CLUB:
CONTEST: ARRL-160
CREATED-BY: WriteLog V10.43F
NAME: Mark Wilson
ADDRESS: 77 Anderson Rd
ADDRESS: Newport, NH 03773
OPERATORS: K1RO
SOAPBOX:
QSO:  1836 CW 2006-12-02 0043 K1RO        599 NH     K0TV        599     NH
QSO:  1839 CW 2006-12-02 0045 K1RO        599 NH     K4ZA        599     MDC
QSO:  1840 CW 2006-12-02 0045 K1RO        599 NH     AA1SU       599     VT
QSO:  1805 CW 2006-12-02 0047 K1RO        599 NH     N8II        599     WV
QSO:  1806 CW 2006-12-02 0048 K1RO        599 NH     VE3MIS      599     ON
QSO:  1809 CW 2006-12-02 0049 K1RO        599 NH     K1EO        599     EMA
QSO:  1810 CW 2006-12-02 0050 K1RO        599 NH     N2MM        599     SNJ
QSO:  1812 CW 2006-12-02 0052 K1RO        599 NH     K1GU        599     TN
QSO:  1814 CW 2006-12-02 0052 K1RO        599 NH     K3ZO        599     MDC
QSO:  1815 CW 2006-12-02 0053 K1RO        599 NH     N4IR        599     TN
QSO:  1817 CW 2006-12-02 0053 K1RO        599 NH     W3BGN       599     EPA
QSO:  1864 CW 2006-12-02 0056 K1RO        599 NH     K1EP        599     EMA
QSO:  1860 CW 2006-12-02 0057 K1RO        599 NH     W4PM        599     VA
QSO:  1859 CW 2006-12-02 0057 K1RO        599 NH     NB1B        599     EMA
```

Figure 7.1 — The header and first few QSOs from a typical Cabrillo file ready for submission to the contest sponsor. The header contains all the information that the sponsor needs to include the entry in the right category and send awards if earned. Each QSO is reported on a separate line in a consistent format. Because the Cabrillo format is the same no matter which logging program was used during the contest, log data can easily be loaded into a master database for crosschecking.

Table 7.1
ARRL Contest Log E-mail Addresses

10 GHz and Up Contest	10GHZ@arrl.org
ARRL 10 Meter Contest	10Meter@arrl.org
ARRL 160 Meter Contest	160Meter@arrl.org
August UHF Contest	AugustUHF@arrl.org
ARRL International DX CW Contest	DXCW@arrl.org
ARRL International DX Phone Contest	DXPhone@arrl.org
International EME Contest	EMEContest@arrl.org
Field Day	Fieldday@arrl.org
IARU HF World Championships	IARUHF@iaru.org
January VHF Contest	JanuaryVHF@arrl.org
June VHF Contest	JuneVHF@arrl.org
RTTY Round-UP	RTTYRU@arrl.org
September VHF Contest	SeptemberVHF@arrl.org
November Sweepstakes CW	SSCW@arrl.org
November Sweepstakes Phone	SSPhone@arrl.org
Straight Key Night	Straightkey@arrl.org

e-mail, double-check the attached file to be sure it is the file you intended to send!

Where do you send the e-mail? Each ARRL contest has a specific e-mail address and only entries for that contest should be sent there (see **Table 7.1**). Other contests will have submission addresses in their published rules. The sponsor may offer a web page you can use to simplify the log upload process. The WA7BNM *Cabrillo Web Forms* web page at **b4h.net/cabforms** allows you to manually enter log data for many contests and e-mails it to the contest sponsor in Cabrillo format.

If a person handles your log file, you will probably receive an acknowledgement within a day or two. The sponsor may also add your call to a list of "Logs Received" on a website. If you don't receive an acknowledgement and your call doesn't appear on the list with other calls, resend the log and send a *separate* e-mail to the sponsors.

If a software robot accepts your log, it will scan the log immediately. The robot looks to be sure that it understands everything in the log. The robot does *not* perform any QSO crosschecks with other logs. The robot will tell you if your dates are wrong or if you've picked a category that doesn't exist for that contest or if your contest club isn't recognized, for example. You can then correct any problems in the log file, resubmit it to the robot and wait for the reply. You can send your log to the robot any number of times. Each subsequent version will overwrite the previous version.

When the robot is happy with the information in your log (remember, that doesn't mean your QSOs are okay, just that the information is properly formatted) you will receive a message that the log has been accepted and you may be given

a numeric "receipt" or confirmation number. Save the robot's e-mail and all confirmation numbers for possible later reference.

While all this sounds terribly complicated, logging software usually makes the process very simple. If there is not much log editing to be performed, it's not uncommon to have a complete log submitted to the sponsors within 15 minutes after the contest! This is a vast improvement from the Olde Days when it would take at least a week to go through the hand-written paper logs. Once you've walked through this process a couple of times, it won't be a problem.

Logs on Paper

If you logged contacts on paper log sheets during the contest, you should also get a copy of the official contest entry form known as a *summary sheet*. Summary sheets are a necessary part of your entry. Without them, the contest sponsor may not be able to determine how you intend to enter the contest. Don't rely on photocopies of forms you have from the same contest several years earlier. Contest rules change and those changes will be reflected on the summary sheets. Even though the number of paper logs is declining, they continue to be accepted by the sponsors of most contests. (See the note above about using WA7BNM's Cabrillo Web Forms page to convert paper logs to electronic form.)

Make certain you legibly complete the forms, including all information. If you don't complete the required forms, your entry is going to be difficult to process by the contest sponsor. If you don't include the little things, such as a correct entry category or power level, the sponsor may have no alternative but to assign your entry to default categories. For example, your failure to include the fact that you were QRP in the contest may mean your entry is treated as high power — and could cost you a chance at a certificate!

The mailing address for ARRL contest entries is: ARRL Contest Branch, 225 Main St, Newington, CT 06111. Please write the name of the contest on the outside of the envelope. You may also download summary sheets from **www.arrl. org/paper-log-entry-forms** and log sheets or rules from the contest's web page at **www.arrl.org/contest-rules**. Perhaps a friend or family member can download the files for you if you don't have Internet access.

While it is tempting, *don't* submit entries for more than one contest in the same envelope or e-mail. Contest sponsors are looking for a single entry in each envelope or e-mail. If you include more than one in a submission, it can be overlooked or stapled together as a single entry and misfiled. When the error is finally discovered, it could well be past the submission or publication deadline for one of the contests.

LOG CHECKING

What happens next varies from contest to contest but the overall process is more or less the same as in the following oversimplified description. Your log is inspected to be sure that it has all the necessary information, that the dates are correct, and so forth. The logs are then sorted by category and crosschecking begins.

If the contest is of small to medium size, crosschecking may be done manually and a detailed inspection only done on logs competing for awards. A committee of volunteers then makes the necessary corrections to scores and publishes the results. This may take from a few weeks beyond the submission deadline to several months.

For larger contests, including those sponsored by the ARRL, the automated process is much more thorough. All logs, once accepted by the robot or checked by hand, are combined into a master database. Special software then compares each of the submitted QSOs with the log of the corresponding station and looks for errors. If there are errors, the appropriate penalties are assessed. Following the crosscheck of all QSOs, the scores for all participants are then computed and compiled for the sponsor, who then publishes the results. The results for larger contests are generally available in a few months to a year.

The automated log checking process also generates a report for each log containing information on what the process found. This is called a *log checking report* (LCR) or a *UBN report*, where "UBN" stands for Unique, Busted or Not-In-the-Log. (See the Glossary at the end of this chapter.) Log checking reports are full of valuable information, generally containing complete information on every QSO in which errors were found.

Errors that can be attributed to you (miscopying calls or exchange information) will result in penalties defined by the sponsors. In general, you'll lose credit for the QSO including any multiplier credit claimed. (If you worked the multiplier again later in the contest, you'll still get credit for it.) Some contests also assess an additional penalty to discourage fast-but-sloppy operating. You're not being accused of cheating, just penalized for making a mistake to reward better performance next time!

Errors not attributed to you (the other station busting your call or information) are still valuable because they highlight possible shortcomings in your transmissions. For example, if a lot of stations are miscopying the H in your call as S or 5, you may not be sending your call cleanly. Even so, you are rarely penalized for errors by "the other guy."

Once the log checking is complete, the scores are compiled and the sponsor determines the winners. Results are usually published on the web and sometimes in magazines such as *QST* or *National Contest Journal* (*NCJ*). That the results are ready is generally made known through websites, e-mail reflectors, newsletters, and magazines. Awards and certificates are mailed after results publication.

Results Analysis

After the contest, results can be analyzed to see what might have been done differently. Comparing notes with friends is a good idea, as you will often find they did something totally different from you and it may come in handy to have the benefit of their experience in the future.

Assuming you used computer logging, you'll find that most programs have several post-contest features for use in log analysis. In addition, standalone log analyzer software such as *CBS* (**www.kkn.net/~k5tr/cbs.html**), *SH5* (**www.tr4w.com/sh5**), and KØRC's spreadsheet tools (**tinyurl.com/66szvjr**) can provide in-depth analysis of contest logs.

One of the best log analysis tools is the simple rate sheet described previously. It shows your hourly rate for each hour of the contest and the bands used during that hour. Log files often show the frequency used for each contact so you can tell if you were CQing (contacts on the same frequency) or using S&P. Other breakdowns will show the general area where the contacts came from, the first contact for a particular multiplier or how many contacts came from each individual multiplier.

A *points-per-hour sheet* may also be found as part of most analysis packages. Using this data, you can draw a graph to see how the score progressed hourly or which hours seem to be most productive. You will also notice that the score rises at a faster rate the farther into the contest you look. The more contacts, the more total point value to multiply and the score starts to increase geometrically. This is further graphic proof that it pays to keep working at making contacts.

CONTEST EQUIPMENT

Just as a knowledgeable driver can't win a race without a good car, the radiosport operator will find it hard to make a good score without solid radio gear. Start by purchasing good-quality equipment and work your way up, learning how to make the most out of every item. Step by step, you'll build your way to a capable, effective station.

Basic Equipment

A good receiver is needed for even the casual contester. Most modern radios have good receivers that can handle the big signals you'll encounter on contest weekends. High dynamic range is essential. (See the sidebar "Optimizing Your Receiver" in this book's chapter on DXing.) For non-DSP radios, install good-quality filters if they are available: 500 Hz for CW and 2.0 kHz for phone. Headphones are a must, as you just can't catch all of the weak calls in the QRM without them. Others near your operating position will appreciate their use too.

The transmitter should have a good, properly adjusted speech processor and the microphone should have a contest

RTTY Contesting

By Ed Muns, WØYK

Each year, participation in the major RTTY contests increases dramatically. New hams as well as veteran CW and phone contesters are jumping into the fun. Unlike RTTY operation a few decades ago, today you can set up this digital mode with a minimum of additional equipment beyond a basic CW/phone station. Transmitting and receiving can be easily done with most modern transceivers, an old PC and simple cables. Most contesters already have a computer integrated with their stations, so getting on RTTY can be very quick.

Gearing Up

The majority of RTTY contests use the traditional 60 WPM (45.45 Baud) 5-bit Baudot code consisting of sequences of "marks" and "spaces" that are simply two RF carriers 170 Hz apart. On receive the audio output of the receiver is connected to the sound card input on the PC where the RTTY demodulator software decodes it into text on the screen. Alternatively, the receiver audio can be connected to a hardware RTTY modem which in turn is connected to the computer via a standard RS-232 cable. If system ground loops cannot be easily eliminated, a "ground loop isolator" can be used between the receiver audio output and the PC sound card or RTTY modem.

To transmit, a standard serial keying interface cable is connected from the computer to the FSK input of the transmitter. If a hardware RTTY modem is being used instead, its output can connect to the transmitter's FSK input. A second transmitting alternative is to use AFSK (Audio Frequency Shift Keying) and connect the PC's sound card output (or hardware RTTY modem audio output) to the transmitter's mic input, using LSB mode. Again an audio isolation transformer may be needed to deal with hum from a ground loop.

More details of these connections can be found in the "Getting Started on RTTY" web page, authored by Don Hill, AA5AU at **www.aa5au.com/rtty.html**. He also developed and maintains a robust RTTY contesting website at **www.rttycontesting.com**. An experienced and successful RTTY competitor, Don gives an excellent overview of all aspects of RTTY contesting. Although his website is based on the *WriteLog* contest software, much of the information is equally applicable to setups using other programs. There are also links to many other sources of information for new and experienced RTTY contesters alike.

There are several choices for software, but most people starting out today choose *MMTTY*, a freeware RTTY PC program for receiving and transmitting. While the RTTY modulation and demodulation capability is superb, the contest logging aspect of *MMTTY* is far less capable than what most contesters will need. For RTTY contest logging, three programs are most popular: *Writelog*, *N1MM Logger* and *Win-Test*. *MMTTY* can be integrated with each of these so that RTTY encoding/decoding is available with contest logging in a single optimized package.

RTTY Operating Skills

In contrast to CW contesting where the operator's brain timeshares between decoding CW and other tasks, in RTTY contesting the computer does all the decoding for you. When a RTTY signal is properly tuned in on the receiver, the result is clear "printing" of the transmitted characters on the computer screen. The good news is that this frees up the operator to attend to other details of contest operation, including very effective use of SO2R (single-op, two-radio) operating. The bad news is that until the receiver is tuned very close to the correct frequency of the incoming signal, only gibberish is available on the screen. With practice, your ears will be able to help you tune in the signal to within a few hertz. RTTY decoding software and RTTY modems have tuning indicators to facilitate precise tuning of the signal.

In normal RTTY ragchewing with little or no QRM from nearby signals, wide IF filtering in the receiver works best because the RTTY decoding software typically provides optimal filtering. However, in the typical contest environment with heavy QRM, many RTTY contesters use a narrow 250-Hz IF filter. Starting out, you may want to use a 500-Hz filter until you are accustomed to quickly tuning in a RTTY signal.

Once you have basic RTTY receiving and transmitting working and integrated with your choice of contest logging software, you will want to focus on making your system as streamlined as possible for the most efficient RTTY contest operation. Basic to this are the message buffers used almost exclusively for all RTTY contest transmissions. While it is easy to go into "keyboard mode" and be able to type free text, it is far more efficient to use message buffers, just as in CW contesting. Message buffers should be kept as short as possible to reliably convey the necessary information. Each message should be preceded with a Line Feed and ended

element that emphasizes mid-range speech components. Some popular mikes have a switch for contest/DX use or casual conversation. Remember that overdriving your transceiver or amplifier is not only bad manners but also hurts your intelligibility on the air. It is important to have a crisp, clear signal.

A memory keyer or a computer with a keying interface is a must for CW. Configure the memories to send as much of the CQ and exchange information as possible. For digital mode contesting, use *macro* or *message* keys that send

pre-programmed information. Using the memories leaves you time for housekeeping chores, such as keeping up a band map, reviewing a multiplier table, or other things that contribute to raising your score while the computer or keyer does the work of sending CQs or your exchange.

Full sized antennas are preferred. A dipole at modest height gives great "bang for the buck" performance. If you can't install it up high, try sloping it from as high as possible on one end toward a preferred direction. If you use a vertical antenna, make sure you install a good ground system and

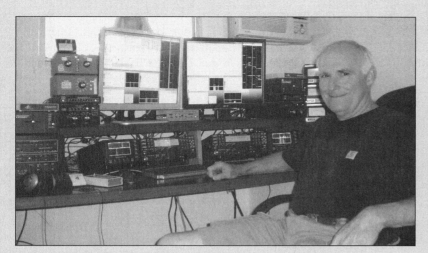

RTTY contesting is the most rapidly growing part of radiosport. Operators like Ed, WØYK/P49X are enjoying working many new calls, with over 3400 contacts logged in the 2012 ARRL RTTY Roundup!

with a Space. This sets off your transmission within the screen of the receiving station in the presence of gibberish characters generated from band noise.

You will soon learn that some "gibberish" is actually numbers that were falsely decoded as letters. For example, "TOO" becomes "599" when this occurs. If you suspect a letter group is really a number, as in a contest exchange, look at the keyboard and translate the letters to numbers by mapping the key above and to the left of each letter key.

Efficient RTTY contest operation for high rates also requires minimum keystrokes for each of (hopefully!) hundreds or thousands of contacts. Thus, it is important to study your logging software features to understand how to accomplish each phase of a RTTY contest QSO with the fewest keystrokes.

In many loggers, each phase can be achieved with a single keystroke. For example, software using a call sign database will capture and highlight valid call signs out of incoming transmissions. Properly configured, the logger will grab the most recent call sign that is a new multiplier or a new band-station, drop it in the call sign field of the entry window, call the station and send your exchange... all as a result of pressing a single key on the keyboard! As

the return exchange comes in, use the mouse to click on any part of the exchange that is not already pre-filled in the entry window. At the end of the station's transmission, you can press another key to send a TU, QRZ message.

Single Op, Two Radios

With the RTTY fixed speed of 60 WPM, it is quite feasible to achieve hourly QSO rates in excess of 120/hour with a properly configured and tuned SO2R RTTY contesting station. Because the operator does not need to expend brainpower on decoding the signal, more attention can be given to tuning and operating each radio. In fact, this characteristic leads veteran CW contester K5ZD to point out that RTTY contesting is the ideal training ground for SO2R skill development in general.

As with SO2R contesting in the other modes, there is a choice to be made. Do you use a single computer to control both radios and both sets of RTTY hardware/software, or do you use two networked computers, one for each radio/RTTY setup? Basically, this is a Multi-Two setup with transmit interlock to guarantee transmission by only one radio at a time. Currently, the majority of SO2R contesters use the single-computer system on all modes — CW, phone and RTTY.

There are a number of advantages to the two-computer model. With the ready availability of PCs suitable for ham applications these days, it is quite practical. Furthermore, in RTTY contesting very little typing actually need be done, so two mini-keyboards (full size, but minus the number pad area) and trackballs/mice can be conveniently arranged at the operating position along with two displays. As explained earlier, only two keystrokes and perhaps a trackball movement are all that is required for most contest QSOs in a properly configured RTTY contest station.

So jump in and have a blast with RTTY contesting! While there are many similarities to CW and phone contesting, there are also a number of unique differences. This can add diversity and excitement to your overall contesting experience. Be aware of direct comparisons to your current favorite mode of contesting and keep an open mind while learning RTTY contesting.

keep it clear of obstructions. Both antennas will probably work better than you'd expect — don't be afraid to call any stations you can hear. They'll probably hear you better than you can hear them. Tribanders (beams that operate on 20, 15 and 10 meters) and other gain antennas are more desirable.

Without recommending a specific type of antenna, one thing will always hold true: Proper installation is the key. Ultimately contesting is the true test of any station's potential. It doesn't do any good to have the best, highest antenna in the world if it's fed with a piece of junk coaxial cable and

unsoldered connectors. Make sure that the antenna is properly built and tuned, that you use good quality feed line, and all connectors are installed and waterproofed correctly.

Intermediate Equipment

As you become more engaged in contesting, take every opportunity to optimize the radio station as much as possible within your budget. A contest station can be as cheap or expensive as you want to make it but continue to purchase top quality equipment.

Contesters often talk in terms of "layers" of stations. Making an improvement is often intended to allow the station to reach a new group — or layer — of stations that are currently too weak to work effectively. By improving an antenna, receiver or transmitted signal those stations can be worked and you will find a lot of new calls in your log. Each layer seems to require approximately one S-unit's worth of improvement (6 dB, nominally) on receive *and* transmit. The other stations have to hear you and you have to hear them. When you plan upgrades — lowering a radiation angle, lowering a noise floor, or raising power — think in terms of layers of improvement.

Receiver improvements at this level revolve around better performance in crowded conditions, not necessarily more memories or wider coverage. You'll want to take every opportunity to listen to different receivers. Can the receiver clearly reproduce a weak signal squeezed in between two domestic titans calling CQ? If many stations are calling, does the receiver allow you to hear individual signals or do they merge into one big mess? How does the receiver sound when the DSP functions are operating? Most modern receivers are quite good and significant improvements are often subtle. Take the time to learn about them because you'll be using a receiver every time you're on the air!

The ability to hear through QRM makes the difference between good scores and great ones. The better you can hear, the better the results. Use the receive attenuator to prevent overload. A receiver's AGC can be overpowered by strong nearby signals — try reducing the RF gain as this often will help you hear weak signals through strong signals. Use the variable bandwidth or IF shift controls. Turn off the noise blanker. Experiment with the settings in the face of QRM but remember the original settings so that you can return to them.

DSP filtering is the norm in contest-grade radios and can be tailored to suit almost any conditions. Just remember that while you're messing around with the filter settings, you're not making QSOs!

For analog receivers, install multiple filters if available, especially for CW. There are two schools of thought on wide and narrow CW filters. One says that it is better to hear stations calling if they are not exactly on your frequency, while the other school feels that in crowded band conditions it's better to use the narrow filters. If you have both filters available, you can switch between them to suit the circumstances.

A contest-grade transceiver with dual receivers may be the ultimate weapon. The second receiver allows you to work two pileups simultaneously or search for multipliers while running stations. If you don't have such a transceiver, it's possible to use an outboard second receiver (perhaps your old rig?) with a two-port power divider coupled through the external antenna port of the main transceiver. Two receivers are effective for finding new stations to work on the same band or on different bands or for working split frequency pileups on 40 and 75 meter phone. Remember that you still have to listen for ongoing QSOs on the split transmit frequency before calling the other station!

Amplifiers

Adding an amplifier to a transceiver is definitely a way to reach a new level or two of stations. A small amplifier with 500 to 1000 W output will make a big difference in your signal and allow you to hold a frequency under challenging conditions. Going to a "full gallon" at 1500 W output is better yet. Remember that you may need to upgrade your antenna system and feed line components to handle the higher power level. You may also have to run a sufficiently heavy electrical service to the shack. It's generally unnecessary in contesting to require full break-in (QSK) capabilities of the amplifier but if you like that style of operating it may be worth the extra expense.

Amplifiers should be chosen for high duty cycle usage. Cooling is important, so don't expect the fan to be quiet. Whatever its output rating, a good amplifier for contest use should be able to loaf along at full rated output power because it's likely to be turned on for an entire contest — up to 48 hours at a time. If you are buying a used amplifier, check availability and price of the amplifier tubes and components that may need to be replaced, such as the TR relays.

HIGH BAND ANTENNAS

Antennas for serious contesting are usually bigger, higher and more efficient than for any other use in Amateur Radio. The antenna system is where more improvement can be made than anywhere else in the station.

This discussion will focus on the needs of the single-operator, all-band operator. Those needs are different from the single-band operator or multi-op station. For example, the single band or multi-multi operator needs antennas capable of getting through during band opening and closing times and marginal openings as well as providing good coverage during the peak band openings. The single-operator all-band operator needs antennas that provide good coverage during the peak band openings but not necessarily during the marginal band openings and closings. The single operator needs to be working lots of QSOs on an open band rather than chasing marginal openings.

Most intermediate contesters begin their high-band (20, 15 and 10 meter) antenna systems with a large Yagi antenna at least 60 feet in the air. These antennas should have at least three full-size elements active on each band, providing gain above that available from smaller or shortened three-element antennas. Front-to-back ratio will improve by an S-unit or more, which is helpful in reducing interference from nearby stations. A station using an amplifier and such an antenna in an average or better location should be able to hold a run frequency under most conditions.

Planning Your Antennas

To improve beyond this level requires some thought and planning so that money and effort are not wasted. The place to start in planning a contest antenna system is the *ARRL Antenna Book.* Information in the chapter on propagation helps you make use of the book's CD-ROM tables of radiation angles at which openings occur with maximum probability for most areas of the world. By using that information, you can develop an effective antenna building strategy for your location. For example, the path from Cincinnati, Ohio, to Europe on 20 meters always requires an arrival angle between 1° and 28°. However, 90% of the time, the angle is from 3° to 12°. The peak signal angle is 8°, which occurs 26% of the time, so an antenna system for working Europe on 20 meters should be designed to radiate at angles at or near 8°. This study can be carried out for each band of interest and antennas optimized to provide patterns within the range of angles specified in the tables for your area.

Choosing a site for your antenna is also important. If you are considering a move, use modeling to evaluate the new location as a candidate for hosting a contest station antenna farm. Even if you're working with an existing location, some properties are large enough that antenna placement could make a difference. Check out the chapter "Effects of Ground"

If you wondered why the Stanford University Radio Club, W6YX, does so well in contests it might have something to do with this dramatic location high above San Francisco Bay! (*N0AX photo*)

in the *ARRL Antenna Book.* There you will find information about site selection and the use of the *HFTA* program included in the book. Using this program, a USGS 7.5 minute topographical map of your QTH and the files of arrival angles for the various bands and regions, you can determine the most useful angles for propagation for your area. You can then apply those studies to generate ideas for your own antenna farm. If you can't choose a site, at least you can check the potential of your present site.

Returning to our Cincinnati example, a 20 meter antenna should provide a take-off angle of 8° for peak propagation to Europe on 20 meters. Using a profile for your terrain (and each QTH is different), you might find that for equivalent antennas at 100 feet your terrain is actually almost 2 dB better at 8° than flat terrain. Maybe the analysis shows that your terrain has a disadvantage, instead. Try moving the antenna to a different location on the site or adjusting the height of the antenna to change the antenna's radiation pattern to peak at the most favorable angle.

How High?

Higher is not always better. You may find that raising an antenna actually hurts performance! In the previous example, changing the antenna from 100 to 150 feet lowers performance at the optimum angle of 8° by about 1 dB and the overall pattern is hurt even more, with the introduction of higher angle lobes and suppression of radiation at some angles between 8° and 15°! On the other hand, a multi-multi or single-band station would want at least one antenna at this height or maybe even higher for use during band openings and closings, plus other antennas at different heights for use under other conditions.

Comparisons of antenna heights should of course be made based on the topography of the site. But what differences can one expect by changing antenna heights given the same terrain? Given a flat ground site, moving the antenna to 100 feet from 70 feet results in an advantage of about 2 dB at the optimum radiation angle. Similarly, the difference between 100 feet and 50 feet over flat ground can be almost 5 dB, and it's around 2 dB between 50 and 70 feet. That is not the case on all types of terrain. For example, it is possible to show that steeply sloping terrain in front of the antenna can provide such an advantage that a 50 foot high antenna will perform almost as well as a 100 foot high antenna. However, both will be outperformed by an antenna at 70 feet — exactly the perfect height for that terrain.

Antenna type also makes a difference in choice of heights. A dipole over flat ground at 70 feet would have a gain of approximately 7.7 dBi at 14°. A three-element beam at the same height would have a gain of 14.2 dBi at 14°. At the desired angle of 8°, the dipole's apparent gain would have dropped to 5.8 dBi, while the beam's gain would be 12.1 dBi. The beam has a substantial gain difference at the same height as the dipole and would equal it from a lower height. To have the advantage at 8°, the beam could be as low as 40 feet and still be marginally better than a dipole at 70 feet. However, a high dipole may be shown to be as good as a low beam. Using modeling programs and studying the angles can help with choice of antenna type.

Multiple Antennas

Stacked antennas are now almost standard equipment for the competitive contest station. A "stack" is two or more antennas for the same band placed at different heights on the tower. Usually they can be fed together or independently.

Not only do stacked antennas allow choices of height and direction, they also broaden the footprint of the transmitted signal and provide anywhere from 1 to 3 dB extra gain. For contest stations, "loud is good" (N2AA), so it's worth studying the possible gains available from stacked antennas. Look at different numbers of antennas (usually 2, 3 or 4) at varying heights when considering station improvements.

Many contest operators have successfully stacked tribander Yagis, so the limitations of using only monobanders no longer exists. Using stacked tribanders on a city lot will often increase the flexibility and competitiveness of smaller contest stations.

Obviously some compromises must be made in antenna selection and antenna heights but these choices should be made from an informed position and not without some understanding of the basic principles involved.

LOW-BAND ANTENNAS

The low bands (160, 80 and 40 meters) require just as much study as the high bands. You may, however, have fewer practical options because of the physical size of the antennas for these bands. Even if you're on a city lot rather than acreage out in the country, it is still possible to put out a decent signal if you pay attention to detail.

For 40 meters, the easiest solution these days seems to be the two-element shortened beam, often called the "shorty forty." Offered by several companies, these antennas work well at 70 feet or higher. Rotatable dipoles are often quite

VHF+ Contesting

By Jon Jones, NØJK

VHF+ contests offer an exciting and challenging experience for the HF contester. (Most of these events include VHF, UHF and microwave bands but they're mainly just called "VHF or VHF+ contests.") Single-band 10 meter and 160 meter contests are perhaps the most like VHF+ contests. At the solar minimum, 10 meters behaves a lot like 6 meters at the solar maximum. Iono-spheric F2 propagation can make an appearance in the ARRL's September and January VHF contests. E-skip, aurora, and meteor scatter are propagation modes used both on 10 and 6 meters. Working weak signals on the higher VHF bands is much like digging out weak DX amid the static on 160 meters.

Station Equipment

You may already have a transceiver that will get you started in VHF+ contesting. HF/VHF/UHF "all-band" radios such as the ICOM IC-706 series and IC-7000, the Kenwood TS-2000, and Yaesu's FT-847 and FT-897 allow casual participants to get their feet wet on 6 and 2 meters and even 70 cm with their current radios in the VHF contests. Even more radios offer 6 meter coverage along with HF, which will get you started in VHF+ contesting as a single-band 6 meter entry. For higher bands and 222 MHz, transverters are usually necessary. Several models are commercially available and require only a little special knowledge to set up and use.

Although you can start with a dipole or your 2 meter FM antenna, you'll quickly find that the contest is more fun with a horizontally polarized Yagi or loop of some sort. On 6 meters a dipole can work well, but a small 3-element Yagi is a significant improvement. The good news is that VHF/UHF antennas are compact so you can put them on a mast, roof tripod, or light-duty tower and turn them with a small rotator. You might even have some extra room in between your HF antennas. Be sure to use a good quality feed line — coaxial cables like RG-213 have quite a bit of loss at higher frequencies.

Portable operation is popular and encouraged in the VHF+ contests. For the antenna-restricted or apartment operator, the Single Operator, Portable and Rover categories let you operate on a competitive basis with many of the well-equipped home stations. A 10-W portable station on a mountaintop can be louder than a high power station down in a valley!

Multi-operator teams such as K8GP and W2SZ/1 set up high-power stations and large antennas for all bands on high mountaintops to extend their reach. They're like beacons, operating with big signals and sensitive receivers on several bands simultaneously and give many VHF+ operators their first far-away contacts.

Operating a VHF Contest

Grid locators, often called "grid squares," are usually the multipliers in VHF+ contests. Grid squares aren't actually square. They are 1° latitude by 2° longitude rectangles that measure approximately 70 × 100 miles in the continental US. A grid square is identified by two letters (the field) and numbers (the square). For example, the grid square for W1AW in central Connecticut is FN31. In most VHF+ contests, grid squares are the only information (other than call signs) that must be exchanged. (See **www.arrl.org/locate/gridinfo.html** or this book's chapter on VHF/UHF operating for more information on grid locators.) The VHF Sprints use a more precise "6-character" grid locator for more precision. My grid then becomes "EM28ix."

VHF contests are often casual when conditions are slow. Operators work at a leisurely pace and may take several tries to finish a contact with a weak station. Things change if the band opens, though. During a tropo or E-skip opening, the VHF+ bands can be as busy as effective at these heights and you can even load the boom of a large triband Yagi as a 40 meter dipole.

Phased verticals can also be used and a simple vertical radiator can be made from aluminum tubing or by using wire supported by a fiberglass mast. If your property has suitable trees, wire antennas such as an inverted L, a Bobtail curtain, or a wire Yagi are often excellent choices.

You'll find that 80 and 160 meters are similar — it's just the size of the antenna that's different. While three-element 80 meter beams are nice, many contesters are putting up phased verticals or *four-square* arrays on these bands. (A four-square is an array of four vertical antennas laid out in a square with switching circuitry to provide gain in several directions.) Another popular option is a switched array of sloping dipoles suspended from a tower. You can be competitive with well planned but simple arrays.

Again, take into consideration the desired wave angles, then do what it takes to maximize performance at the optimum angles. In most cases on the low bands, that's likely to mean vertical antennas but not always. You would do well to buy a copy of *ON4UN's Low Band DXing* written by John Devoldere, ON4UN, and published by ARRL. This book has everything you need to know about low-band transmit and receive antennas. The winning contester has a copy to study and you should, too.

VHF/UHF ANTENNA SYSTEMS

A beginning VHF+ contester likely has a beam of several elements for 2 meters and possibly a dipole or small beam on 6 meters. Unlike FM antennas, those used for SSB/CW operation and contesting are horizontally polarized. It is easy to improve antenna gain and pattern at VHF+ in ways impossible at lower frequencies.

Big improvements in gain are available simply by increasing the number of elements on a long-boom Yagi antenna. It's not unusual to see Yagis with 20 elements or more at 2 meters and higher frequencies nor are 7-element Yagis

40 meters on Saturday evening in the phone Sweepstakes! Several stations have reached more than 2000 contacts on 6 meters in a VHF contest, with peak rates of over 200 contacts per hour.

Strategy

Strategy is important to achieving a high score. Operating as many bands as possible and making sure to work stations on all available bands is the way to maximize your score. A 432-MHz QSO is worth twice as many points as one on 6 or 2 meters. On 1296 MHz a contact is worth 3 times as much plus the grids are counted as new multipliers on each band. This means you can increase your score dramatically by moving stations from band to band for new QSOs. This is common practice so be sure to ask if a station has other bands available.

Just as in an HF contest, balance your efforts between working new grids and making more QSO points to maximize your score. If a band is open to an unusual area, stick with it to expand your multiplier and QSO count. It may

not be open later. For example, operate on 6 and 2 meters in the ARRL June VHF Contest as long as they are open and work the higher bands at a later time. In the January VHF Contest, when 6 meters is often dead, changing bands frequently and moving stations to needed bands as you run across them is the way to maximize your score.

Always remember that on VHF and above, enhanced propagation can occur when you least expect it. For example, E-skip can appear in January — as it did in the 2007 and again in the 2012 VHF Contest. On Saturday evening of the 2007 contest, QRP ops KA6AKH and NØJK made 6 meter E-skip contacts with ease. In January 2012, I made over 200 contacts on 6 meters running 10 watts and a simple 2-element Yagi including DX to P43A in Aruba! When 6 meters is open, low power and a dipole or whip can make 1000-mile contacts. So stay alert and "expect the unexpected" in VHF+ contests — this is often what make them fun and interesting to operate in.

VHF+ contesters can go on expeditions, too! Jon, NØJK, traveled to Bermuda (VP9) for the June ARRL VHF QSO Party. From this location, E-skip (E$_s$) propagation is common into the Eastern seaboard and even across the US on 6 meters if conditions are good. Other VHF+ contesters head for the Caribbean, beaming northwest across the entire US and Canada.

Maintaining a top-notch contest station takes work! Here is past ARRL President, Joel W5ZN, doing some tower work a few hours before the ARRL June VHF QSO Party. Whatever he did seemed to work — the team won the Limited Multioperator division! (*NØAX* photo)

uncommon on 6 meters. These antennas can have more than 10 dB of gain in free space — the same as an amplifier! (Be careful around these antennas because of the increased levels of RF exposure at high power!)

Beyond simply increasing the boom length and number of elements, arrays of multiple long-boom Yagis create some truly awesome gain and pattern performance. They take some careful planning to get the mechanical and electrical details right but the results are impressive.

Another area of improved antenna system performance at VHF+ frequencies is in feed line loss. For a feed line run of 100 feet, changing to surplus hardline (½-inch or larger) can save several dB over the best flexible coax. This is a "free" improvement, requiring no rotator and no power supply. Losses are simply reduced — you'll hear better and be heard better.

One aspect of high-performance VHF+ antenna building not available to HF operators is for roving or portable operation. If you can't build a powerhouse antenna system at home, make one you can move and take it on the road! VHF+ antenna systems can be mounted on a vehicle or trailer and taken to a hilltop or other advantageous location — make your own propagation!

THE COMPUTER-RADIO HYBRID

Using software to log contacts, connect to worldwide networks, and control station equipment has taken a central role in contesting. This is a natural result of the power available in even low-end computers combined with low-cost or free software for day-to-day operating and special programs designed just for contesting.

Once just a tool for entering log information, the computer is integrated into nearly all phases of the modern contest station. The computer sends voice and CW messages. It reads and sets the operating parameters of the radio. Digital mode contesting is virtually impossible without it. Through interfaces, it can control nearly all of the station equipment. All this allows the operator to remain focused on making QSOs instead of fiddling with various pieces of equipment.

If you log DX and ragchew contacts on a computer or use a sound-card for digital mode operating, it's a short step to computer-based contesting, too. Based on the author's personal experience, after your first contest using a computer you'll wonder how you ever got along with paper and pencil — welcome to the 21st century!

Logging Software

If you are just getting started in contesting, you can

get along just fine with a simple program and manual radio control. Take advantage of the logging software's ability to handle the "paperwork" so you can focus on operating. When you can use the program without having to continually think about how to perform the basic functions, you're ready for an upgrade. You'll also notice yourself wishing that some functions like band-switching were automated and here again, you're ready for an upgrade.

You may be able to adapt your general-purpose logging program to contest operating and some programs can even generate the necessary Cabrillo-formatted files that you can submit to the contest sponsors. Most general-purpose software, however, isn't really designed for efficient contest operating — you should begin with one of the simpler contest logging programs or "loggers" and learn how it works. Contest-oriented programs can generate files for importing by your general-purpose program so all of your contacts are tracked for awards and QSLing.

Once you've entered a station's call sign in the logger's call entry window, the software will check to see if the station is a dupe or a possible new multiplier, whether the multiplier is needed on other bands, and provide similar call signs of active contest stations in case you're not sure of what you copied. Entering the other station's exchange is just as easy.

A logger program can send CW messages for you automatically, control a voice keyer or record and playback voice messages on phone, and both decode and send RTTY signals. Operating details can easily be automated this way to free up the operator to focus on accurate copy and thinking about competitive strategy.

If you want to take advantage of the worldwide spotting networks, your contest logging program can interact directly with those websites to both capture the calls and frequencies of stations in the contest and send out spots from your contacts. The calls can be displayed on *band maps* that show you where stations are operating — you can click on the call signs and control your radio to go right to that frequency!

After the contest, the logger will perform all of the tasks for you to submit your log to the contest sponsors, generating the correct files and forms necessary. Once your log is submitted, you can use the logger to go back through the log and generate useful statistics and information breakdowns for you to become a better operator in future contests.

Most contest logging software and accessory programs are written for the *Windows* operating system. (A complete list of standalone logging software is maintained on the Contest Wiki at **wiki.contesting.com/index.php/Logging** and on comprehensive websites such as **ac6v.com/logging. htm** and **www.dxzone.com/catalog/Software/Contesting**.) There are a few programs for the Macintosh and *Linus* user, as well. The new *In The Log* online service (**www. inthelog.com**) is an online logger that supports a number of contests and is accessed using a web browser on a computer or smartphone. Regardless of your personal operating system preference, if you want to operate at multi-op stations you should learn one or two of the popular *Windows*-based programs. Contest logging software is changing all the time so visit these sites often and keep your software upgraded to the latest version!

Older software that was developed for the *MS-DOS* operating system (*CT, NA, TR-LOG*) will run in a command-line window on versions through *Windows Vista* with most operators choosing to stay with *Windows XP*. This software will not run on *Windows 7* or later versions.

Selecting Logging Software

Start your selection process by asking other club members what logging programs they use and which ones they started with. (This would be a good time to join a contest club as the members have all gone through the same learning process.) Pick a contest in which you have a bit of experience and try out the software without trying to automate your station. Another strategy is to guest-operate at a station already running the software you're interested in. Note what you like and don't

like about it then go back to the club members with your questions. Most of the loggers have busy user's groups to help newcomers, test new versions, and share experiences.

After you've gotten a little experience with two or three programs, you'll have a pretty good idea of what you want and need. Upgrade to or purchase the latest version of the program and install it on your computer. Walk through the tutorial or practice sessions if the software offers them. Print out the user's manual or operating guide. Learn how to configure the software for your favorite contests — many loggers can store configuration files that can set up the program for specific contests individually.

After you use logging software a few times you'll develop preferences for how the software looks on the computer display. Programs that can open several windows for different functions allow you to resize and move the windows around the screen. Place the main contact entry window, call sign check window, and any spotting network windows (if you are going to operate in the Assisted or Unlimited categories) where you can see them without swiveling your head around or having to use the mouse or keyboard to bring them to the "front." Move lesser-used windows that display contact rate, general information, score summaries and so forth to the edges of the display. If you have a second display, this would be a good place to put the supporting windows.

There are a number of accessory programs that augment logging software. Propagation prediction and frequency maps can be very helpful in deciding when to change bands and look for secondary band openings. A gray-line program will remind low-band operators when to look for sunrise and sunset openings, for example. Some of these functions may be included in or accessible from the logging software. Decide which you want to run and experiment with placing their windows on your computer display.

A detailed discussion of using and configuring contest-logging software is beyond the scope of this book but you will find many, many articles and posts on computer logging

Antenna switching schemes can quickly become quite complex and difficult to operate properly. Automated accessories, such as the WXØB Six Pack, keep switching functions simply and less likely to be operated improperly.

both online and in magazines such as the *National Contest Journal*. Again, rely on the experiences of club members to help you over the rough spots and don't be afraid to sit in and watch a skilled operator use the computer during a contest.

Computer Requirements

Since the demands of contest operating are modest for a computer (how fast can you possibly work stations, anyway?) you don't have to use top-of-the-line hardware. Check the logging software's minimum requirements for what you need. The used and reconditioned computers available at your local computer recycler will probably work just fine and at a fraction of a new computer's cost. They will also have lots of older interface cards and adapters that may work just fine in a ham shack. Save your budget for antennas and radios!

Most stations use tower or desktop computers that can be placed on the floor or away from the operating position. If you choose to use a laptop, you may want to add an external display. To date, there has not been much use of tablet-style computers for contest logging but feel free to experiment. Mobile and portable logging requires laptops or smaller equipment.

It is important to have a full-size keyboard. The smaller keyboards of laptops and ultrabooks are more difficult to use. You should probably learn to touch-type, as well, since that will allow you to focus on the contact and not on where the keys are! If you plan on doing much digital mode operating, make room for an external mouse or trackball on your desktop. Remember that any input device you use will need to operate with a minimum of distraction to the operator.

If you plan on entering Assisted, Unlimited or Multi-operator categories, you'll need a full-time connection to the Internet-based spotting networks. The amount of data received is not great, so a dial-up connection is acceptable. You can even use instant messaging services to chat with other operators during the contest! As a pure single-op, you are still permitted to take advantage of propagation bulletins, weather information and other useful Internet services.

RFI to and from computers can be an issue. Make sure your computer has a metal enclosure (laptops and tablets are often designed to be less RFI-prone because of their plastic cases) and that interface cards and cable shields can be securely grounded to it. When you're shopping for cables, the extra expense for shielded cables is usually worthwhile. You should purchase a selection of ferrite snap-on cores and toroids, as well.

Don't scrimp on display quality — you'll be looking at it hour after hour. A mid-size display that you can place close to the operating position is more effective than a large display that you have to place further away.

Interfacing the Computer to the Station

Looking at photos and videos of competitive stations, you'll find a large display (or two!) front and center at the operating position with radios and accessory gear to the side. Behind the Top Ten operating position it's not uncommon to find more computer cables for audio, data and control than RF cables.

You'll need to connect the computer to the radio through its control port. The two standard radio control interfaces are RS-232 and ICOM's CI-V interface, a variation of RS-232. USB interfaces are beginning to appear in amateur transceiver as of early 2012. Ethernet interfaces are available on a handful of transceivers.

The data protocols used to control radios vary with manufacturer and model so be sure your logging software will support your radio and that your computer has the correct interface for it. Since most new laptop PCs do not have an RS-232 port, you'll have to use a USB-to-RS-232 adapter or get a computer-to-transceiver interface designed for USB operation.

Keying interfaces for CW are usually based on a COM port, even if implemented as a USB-to-RS-232 adapter. Due to timing issues within *Windows*, most contesters use an external *WinKey*-based keyer (**www.k1el.com**) as a standalone keyer or as part of a more comprehensive control interface. You can use a standalone keyer in conjunction with the logger-based keying by using a splitter at the radio key input jack

Audio and digital signal interfaces generally consist of transformer-isolation with limited level adjustments. The audio connection to the radio can be made through the microphone input or via an accessory connector. Some interfaces also support the connection of a regular microphone. Direct FSK and CW keying is sometimes supported through an optically isolated solid-state switch. There are many variations of these interfaces so it is best that you list all of your operating needs and then start shopping. This is another area in which your contest club can be very helpful and there are number of construction articles in magazines and online to build them yourself.

As the number of interface functions increased, several manufacturers have introduced *SO2R controllers* that bring many common functions into one piece of equipment — CW and voice keyers, audio switching, digital mode interfaces, accessory equipment control, etc. (SO2R stands for *single-operator, two radios* — a common technique for advanced contest operation.) If you find the number of accessory devices starting to get out of hand in your station, it is time to look into these integrated controllers. (For more information on SO2R, see K8ND's SO2R Resources website — **www.k8nd.com/Radio/SO2R/K8ND_SO2R.htm**.)

Station Control

The complexity of a full-blown contest station makes it very difficult for the human operator to control all of the equipment manually. There are multiple antenna switches, filters, stubs and amplifiers to be reset at every band change. If the operator is using two radios at once to CQ on one band and tune for mults on another, audio to the headphones needs to be switched as well.

Most of the information to make the necessary changes is available in the band and frequency information the radio can supply through its data and band ports. *Band decoders* are standalone devices that translate the band information generated by your radio into switch or relay closures that can

Two-Radio Contesting

The use of two radios in a single-operator station (SO2R or single-op, two-radios) has been around for many years but has spread significantly in recent years. Coupled with innovations in logging software, it is almost necessary for the winning single-op contester to use two radios.

This subject could almost be a book in itself. Design of a station capable of two-radio contesting is similar to the design of a multi-multi station. One transceiver might listen on one band while the second is transmitting on another. The use of band-pass filters and harmonic suppression stubs is necessary for successful high-power operation. If adequate separation is available between antennas, a two-radio station can be as simple as adding another transceiver and a dipole or vertical antenna.

There is an advantage to using the second station. The degree of the advantage depends on how well the operator is able to use the station.

The purpose of the second radio is to allow an operator who might be calling CQ on one band to be listening for activity or multipliers on another band. Once found, a multiplier may be called and worked on the second station during a listening period for the first station. Over the course of the contest, a neophyte to SO2R operation may add up to 100 QSOs. An accomplished operator can add as many as 400 QSOs, including multipliers that may not otherwise be worked. Needless to say, this is a tremendous advantage in close competitions. As with any contesting skill, effective SO2R operation requires practice. Until you learn how to do it well, trying to manage a second radio may actually slow you down when you should be concentrating fully on a high-rate run.

There are several ways to listen to the second radio. Some listen to one radio in one ear, the other in the other ear on a stereo headset. Others like to mix the audio into both ears but with one radio running a higher volume. A third and less confusing method is to shut off the monitor on the main radio and listen to the second radio only during transmit periods for the first radio. This can be done with a relay to switch the audio.

Designs for two-radio switching systems have appeared in the *National Contest Journal* in recent years. Several manufacturers offer "SO2R controllers" and there are numerous websites that provide information on operating with two radios.

You don't have to have a room full of equipment to be effective at single-operator, two-radio (SO2R) contesting. This compact and straightforward SO2R station is operated by Pete, N4ZR, in West Virginia.

control antenna switches, filters, and perform other station configuration tasks. Logging software can often read the radio's information and change antenna and filter settings through band decoders or other external interfaces. This is a good way to "offload" the operator.

The interfaces can be driven by the radio directly or by the station computer. The computer is assumed to be connected to the radio from which it acquires the band and frequency information. It is hard to add switch and filter control automation "halfway." If you are considering adding these functions to your station, it's best to do the whole job at once. The interface manufacturers provide a wealth of information

on their websites to assist you in designing your new system and selecting equipment. Articles in *National Contest Journal* and information in the *ARRL Antenna Book* and the *ARRL Handbook* show you how to build this equipment yourself, if you prefer.

Given the expense of repairing or replacing a blown filter, amplifier output or receiver input, automating station tasks is a good investment once complexity begins to exceed the operator's ability to keep track of all the settings. You can tell when it has become time for automated interface control when you find yourself making mistakes in the heat of the contest or become confused when tired or busy.

STATION ACCESSORIES

In addition to basic equipment like transceivers, amplifiers and antennas, most contest operators add accessories and tools that make operation more efficient.

Headphones and Microphones

Headphones are the only choice for the serious contester. Some prefer headphones with a restricted audio range, while others prefer hi-fi type phones with a good low frequency response for hearing low pitched CW signals. Some operators like to switch the audio in one ear so that it is out of phase with audio in the other ear, giving the signals a spatial quality of perception. You'll probably change your preference over time so experiment with different models. You will need stereo headphones if you have a dual channel receiver.

An important consideration: Headphones must be comfortable to wear for long periods of time. While some operators prefer the lightweight foam padded headsets, most prefer the full muff headsets that help reduce sounds from outside the radio. Sometimes it's a good idea to be able to change headphones when you feel like your head is in a vise or when a set rubs too long on one patch of skin.

A headset/boom microphone combination is best for SSB operation. Fatigue is always a factor in any contest and not having to keep your head in a certain position to use the microphone can provide great relief. Some prefer the freedom of movement that VOX control permits. Others rely on a footswitch so that they only transmit when they want, not whenever they talk or cough.

The information available from contest-grade transceivers allows the rig to control external devices such as filters and switches. To convert the rig's information into switch closures a decoder is required, such as the Top Ten device shown here.

Keyers and Paddles

If you choose to use a standalone keyer — a popular option to have a keying method independent of the computer — it is important for speed control and message selection to be very simple, preferably with control knobs and buttons. Menu-selections or key-sequences are not convenient during a contest. As described in the previous section, a *WinKey*-based keyer can often be interfaced to the computer logging program while still supporting an external paddle.

The choice of CW paddles is highly personal, but it is important that you be able to place the paddle near the keyboard to minimize the amount of hand and arm movement needed to use it. The paddle should also stay put on the operating desk and not slide around.

Stubs and Transmit Filters

As you build a more sophisticated station, you'll reach the point where you want to tune around for new stations and multipliers on one band while you're CQing on another. With the transmitting and receiving antennas in such close proximity, it's inevitable that noise and signals from the transmitter will challenge your ability to receive on another band at the same time. Most contest stations employ a combination of band-pass filters and transmission line stubs to clean up the transmitter and limit the signals the receiver has to deal with.

Band-pass filters are available in single-band or multi-band models. The multi-band models can be switched manually or automatically by an interface device connected to the radio. Most stations place filters between the transceiver and amplifier although the larger stations also build high-power band-pass filters that can handle the full amplifier output.

Stubs — resonant lengths of transmission line — are used to remove harmonics and out-of-band signals at specific frequencies. The *ARRL Antenna Book* discusses how to construct and apply stubs. An excellent reference on this topic is *Managing Interstation Interference* by George Cutsogeorge, W2VJN, available from International Radio (**www.inrad.net**). Stubs can provide 20 dB or more of attenuation at low cost and effort.

ERGONOMICS

Ergonomics is the study and practice of human engineering in station design. Simply put, if you're not comfortable, you won't stay in the chair and operate. If you don't stay in the chair, you won't be competitive. This section touches on some of the important aspects of station ergonomics but for more complete information and guidelines, read up on workplace ergonomics. The requirements are much the same as for a radio operating position. Enter "office ergonomics guidelines" into an Internet search engine for numerous references on placement of equipment, products, exercises and so forth. Over the course of a contest, ergonomics and the

comfort factor can make a big difference in your alertness and energy!

Speaking of chairs, what you sit on can make or break your weekend. Choose an office chair designed for someone who works at a computer keyboard all day. It should be firm but comfortable, adjustable for height and back support and sturdy enough to last. You'll find big, padded models too soft for long-term sitting. A firm, adjustable chair allows you to change positions for variety through the contest. Chairs have been a subject of discussion on the CQ-Contest e-mail reflector (**lists.contesting.com/mailman/listinfo/cq-contest**) and

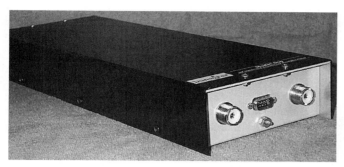

Multi-band bandpass filters, such as the Dunestar Model 600 shown here, help minimize interference and prevent receiver damage during SO2R or multi-operator competitions. Such filters are most effective when they are set up to switch automatically as the transceiver changes bands.

Don, NTØF, operates "barefoot" (without a linear amplifier) in RTTY contests using a 40-10 meter beam at 60 feet and dipoles for 160 and 80. Notice how the computer screen is the focus of the operating position, with the transceiver and accessories within easy reach. Since this photo was taken, he has added another transceiver to operate SO2R (single-operator, two radios). (*NTØF photo*)

you can search for those threads in the reflector's archives. You spent hundreds (or thousands) of dollars on your radio — don't scrimp on another piece of equipment you'll be using every minute the rig is on!

Arranging Your Operating Desk

The operating desk's surface should be large enough to hold all of your operating equipment, usually with multiple tiers for holding the various items in their most convenient locations. Arrange equipment so that everything used frequently during the contest is immediately at hand or in front of you. The keyboard, radio and monitor should be central, with all peripheral equipment surrounding the operator in accordance with how it will be used. Place the keyboard, radio and CW paddle short distances apart to minimize unnecessary hand and arm movement. In general, if you're uncomfortable while operating move the equipment around until you are comfortable. Place the computer case completely off the desktop since it shouldn't have to be touched during contest.

Your desk or table will usually be 29 inches high. That's the standard for office furniture in the US and an ideal height for a working surface. The standard height for a typing surface is 26 inches. That's the height you would want for a computer keyboard. It's important that the keyboard be lower to prevent repetitive motion injuries and to prevent fatigue from using a keyboard at the wrong height. To lower the keyboard, try attaching a keyboard tray or shelf underneath the operating surface. As a bonus, that gives you more room on the desktop. Remember to use a pad to support your wrists and forearms if the keyboard is on the desktop.

The computer is a major factor in today's contest operation. Place the computer display directly in front of the operating chair, since that's where you will be looking most of the time. Don't place the display to the side or so high that you have to raise your head to look at it. The display should be at the right distance for comfortable viewing. If you wear glasses, to reduce eye strain consider a pair of single-lens glasses specifically for watching a computer display at that distance.

Rotator control boxes and antenna switches should be easy to reach, although consideration should be given

to having these items controlled by the radio or computer. Rotator control boxes are available with preset controls that don't require a hand to be on them throughout rotation. It's tiring to hang onto a rotator control box throughout a contest, trying to remember when to release the switches while you're concentrating on making QSOs. Some antenna switches, such as for high/low or stacks, are probably best controlled by hand but the band-by-band switching of antennas can be performed by an interface controller driven by the radio or logging computer. Wattmeters should be placed in visual range so that you can monitor the functions of the transmitter and antennas during the course of the contest.

Unless your amplifier has automatic band switching, mark the dials so that you can quickly set the controls when you make band changes. Amplifiers should be placed where you can see the meters and indicator lights to check for proper operation and where you can reach the controls for occasional adjustments. Since the adjustments and band changes aren't made frequently, amps can be placed off to the side or above the radios and monitor. Make sure it is easy to see warning and overload indicators from your operating position.

Place a clock at the operating position, even though the computer clock will actually be the one used. The separate clock provides a reference for checking the computer time throughout the contest.

To save wear and tear on your voice, phone operators should definitely consider a voice keyer of some sort — particularly for calling CQ. The best option might be using the computer's sound card to record messages that can be replayed from the computer keyboard under control of the logging software. This integrates voice and logging functions so that your hands do not need to continually move back and forth between the keyer and keyboard.

PERSONAL PREPARATION

Whether you are just making contest QSOs now and then, for a few hours at a time or spending the whole weekend at it, you need to be alert and clear-headed to make and record QSOs accurately and operate your equipment properly. To do so means that you should also take care of that very important piece of equipment — the operator!

Sleep

The number one consideration to taking care of yourself during long contest weekends is getting enough sleep. Some contesters can "do 48 in the chair" but they have to prepare themselves first. They stock up on sleep throughout the week before the contest and often try to sleep during the hours just before the contest starts. That means no tower or antenna work on contest day! By building up a reserve of sleep they start the contest refreshed, making it a lot easier to get through that first 24 hours. The second night is tough for everybody and about impossible if you were running on empty during the first night.

How many operators actually operate all 48 hours? Not many! Look at the contest results to see if hours of operation are listed. Most of the top scorers in a 48 hour contest put in between 40 and 46 hours of operating time. They grab short periods of sleep during slow hours, trading the loss of a few QSOs for improved mental acuity the following day. Again, look at logs and ask other operators to find out when you should do the same.

How long should you sleep? The answer varies from person to person but there are a number of references that indicate the brain works best with a 90-minute sleep cycle. According to those researchers, sleeping for one such cycle leaves you more refreshed and satisfied than one hour or two hours. Two 90-minute naps every 24 hours results in 42 hours of operating time. (See "Sleep — A Contest Prescription," by T. Scott Johnson, KC1JI, in Nov/Dec 1988 *NCJ* and "A Sleep Strategy for DX Contesting," by Randall A. Thompson, K5ZD, in Sep/Oct 1994 *NCJ* and updated at **www.contesting.com/articles/37**) The archives of the CQ-Contest reflector have numerous posts on the subject, as well.

Another popular strategy is to catnap for a few minutes right at the operating position whenever you need a bit of sleep. The trick is to wake back up before too much time goes by. A long nap in the operating chair can be uncomfortable, as well.

When should you sleep? Analysis of your hourly rate from previous contests shows when it is most productive to sleep if you don't plan to stay awake for the entire contest. For example, if your rate went to 5 per hour at 0800 UTC and only one of those contacts was a multiplier, perhaps an hour's rest would have helped you more the next day. Another good idea is to check out a rate sheet from a multi-multi station from the 3830 reflector archives and look for times of lowest activity on the various bands. Those may be good times for you to sleep.

Food and Fitness

There as many opinions about the right food for contesting as there are contest operators. In general, contesters prefer light fare during the contest that's easy to digest and keeps blood sugar levels topped off. Some operators like to "carbo-load" before the contest, just as for a bike race. Experiment with different favorites to see what keeps you nourished without making you drowsy. Eat lightly to avoid a post-meal "low."

Another consideration is the mechanics of eating while you're operating. CW and digital contests have a built-in advantage over voice as you aren't trying to eat and operate with the same apparatus! Perhaps that's why CW contesting remains popular and digital contesting is becoming more popular? Without trying to tell you what to eat, finger foods and drinkable soups are great contest meals! Another tip: Crunchy foods create a huge amount of local QRM in headphones.

What about coffee and energy drinks? Caffeine and herbal "boosters" do pick up your mental energy for a while but the fall off afterwards can be worse than not having the beverage in the first place. Many contesters try not to use any kind of stimulant until the second day of a contest when the boost is really needed. Try to go into a contest refreshed and caught up on sleep. Don't try to coffee or cola your way through.

While contesting doesn't require a lot of physical activity — just the opposite — it certainly does burn a lot of calories. Being physically fit does have a measurable effect on one's stamina and the ability to remain alert and focused. Prepare for big contest efforts with regular exercise and attention to your diet. You'll be more comfortable and able to maintain high performance levels longer.

Breaks

Would you subject yourself to a 48-hour airplane flight without breaks or the opportunity for some activity? Of course not, so why do it in the ham shack? Sitting in one position for long periods of time is not healthy. You need to get up every once in a while and stretch. A short walk is recommended but even operating from a standing position can help. Use headphones with a cord long enough to permit bending and stretching. Let the computer do the work while you limber up.

There are very few contests in which you can't take a few minutes every few hours to get a little exercise. Activity is often the perfect tonic when you're dragging at oh-dark-thirty with a slow QSO rate. To find the right times for breaks, take a look at logs from previous years and ask other contesters. Make reminders to yourself so that those breaks happen as they should.

Bathroom breaks can be managed by managing your liquid intake. Be sure to stay hydrated but avoid having a continuously full beverage glass. You'll wind up visiting the facilities way too often! Note that leaving the keyer in beacon mode while you take a pit stop is considered bad contest manners!

MULTIOPERATOR CONTESTING

Nowhere else in Amateur Radio will you find the camaraderie that exists in operating a multiop station. Shared experiences are always more enjoyable and there's no better way to share the contest experience than with a group of enthusiastic friends.

Multi-ops provide an ideal training ground for operators new to contesting, allowing the new operator to learn from contesters having years of experience. Multi-ops also allow those who have the desire and skills but not the time or energy to participate as a competitive single-op entry.

There are generally two types of multi-ops: the multi-op, single-transmitter (MS or MOST) and the multi-op multi-transmitter (MM). The multi-op, two-transmitter (M2) class is actually an offshoot of the multi-single class. It is designed for stations capable of putting two signals on the air at the same time. Each contest's multi-single rules are different and should be studied carefully before operating in the contest.

Multioperator contesting can be a lot of fun. (L-R) W2RQ, W2NO and W1GD were part of the W2GD team during the 2010 ARRL 160 Meter Contest. They operated from the facilities of radio station WYRS-FM in West Creek, New Jersey. (*K9CT photo*)

Multi-Single and Multi-Two

The multi-single class was originally conceived as a way to keep a single station on the air for the entire contest by more than one operator. It has evolved over time into a very competitive category. In many cases more than one station is used during the course of the contest — a "run station" that strives for the maximum of QSOs and a "mult station" that searches for multipliers. Strategy plays an important part in the planning and operation of the multi-single station. The key is to determine how a second station and operator can be used for maximum effectiveness.

Multi-single stations are generally limited to a certain number of band changes per hour or are required to spend a minimum amount of time on a particular band before changing bands. The multi-single participant must use those band changes strategically. For example, before a band change is made for purposes of working a multiplier, the operator manning the multiplier station should make a band map of stations to work before changing bands. The operator might even record those stations in the memories of the transceiver. At the band change, the mult station becomes the run station for a few minutes (usually at least 10 minutes). Any multipliers in the band map are worked, along with any other easy QSOs possible and some CQing on the new band. Assuming rate is lower than on the original run band, control is then returned to the hot band and the run station resumes calling CQ. This process repeats again and again on the same or other bands wherever the operators decide it is worthwhile to make the band change.

While the limitations on the multi-single stations (and multi-two) may seem somewhat restrictive, they create a class of competition for multi-op stations that are not set up with individual stations for every band. Multi-single has been a popular category over the years. Easing of the restrictions

would definitely raise the level of equipment required to be competitive. Recent winners in multi-single categories use two or three independent stations at one QTH.

Multi-two category rules are very similar to multi-single, with the addition of a second run station and a single mult station trading off band changes between the two run stations. The strategy to maximize output of a multi-two station is an interesting challenge and often requires four complete stations to really maximize the score.

Multi-Multi

The multi-multi station consists of exactly what the name implies: many operators and many transmitters with only one transmitting on any band at one time. Successful multi-multi stations often have two-station capability on each band. One chases multipliers on the band while the other one calls CQ throughout the contest. Only one transmitted signal per band at any time is allowed but that's easy to ensure with an interlock circuit or software function that prevents both transmitters from being keyed at once. It's no wonder that these stations make very high scores in the contests where the category is permitted.

These stations provide excellent training grounds for new operators as staffing a multi-multi is one of the more difficult tasks in contesting. You can frequently get "chair time" at one if you make the acquaintance of one of the regular operators. You may be calling "CQ Canada" on 160 meters during the daytime but it's worth it to gain the experience. You'll always value the opportunity to watch and hear the operators go about their business at a top multi-op.

The multi-multi is also useful to the beginning operator for learning what is possible on each band. The successful multi-multi is required to work all bands almost all the time. By doing so, one can learn about those midnight over-the-pole openings on 15 or 20, how early 40 meters opens to Asia, how 80 meters opens before sunset and stays open an hour or two after sunrise, and what contacts might be possible at those times. It's a great way to gain useful experience in every phase of contesting by operating with experienced teachers of the contest art.

PROPAGATION

When it's all said and done, the fact is that the contest starts at the given date and time and regardless of the propagation, you still have to compete. Knowing what's likely to happen will give you an edge, however. (You may want to start by reviewing the "Propagation" section of the DXing chapter in this book.)

In general, for North American stations, your antenna on 10 and 15 meters should follow the Sun. It should be east to southeast at the morning band opening, moving south by local noon, then west, southwest and northwest until after sunset. Openings to the east may last longer, so use discretion. Twenty meters will open to the west at sunrise but may be more productive to the east. The lower the sunspot activity, the more important 20 meters will be.

All three nighttime bands (160, 80 and 40) may open at sunset, generally to the east but sometimes to the southeast. The southeast opening may yield some Asian or Africans in a DX contest. Nighttime is the right time for Asia and Oceania on these bands. In the morning, the bands will be open to the west, although a southwesterly path will again yield Asian DX. At European sunrise the low bands will be open in that direction, with 160 and 80 closing before 40, which is likely to stay open much longer.

Twenty meters will often share characteristics with both the low and high bands. It is more likely to be like the high bands in periods of low sun activity and like the low bands during high sunspot activity.

Someday, you will experience a Sudden Ionospheric Disturbance (SID) from a solar flare, probably during times of high solar activity. If that happens, it will sound as though someone slowly turned the bands off. If you experience an SID, try going to a higher band and possibly beaming south. Sometimes nothing works until the band comes back but more often than not you may find that there is less absorption on the higher bands and maybe some propagation to somewhere. Take heart in the knowledge that it's just as bad for everybody else! Wait it out and don't give up.

Develop your band plans from experience, from the previous year's logs, and by listening to the bands at different times in the weeks leading up to a contest. See what regions are coming in on which band and how the band sounds. The spotting networks are invaluable for this, since you can review the spots for a week or two, learning what bands seem to be working to various areas of the world at a given time.

REMEMBER, CONTESTING IS FUN!

Of course there are many good reasons for contest participation; improving station and operator capability foremost among them. But the main reason it is so popular (and when did you ever hear as much activity on the bands as during a contest?) is that it's *fun*. Over the years, you'll find that you work a lot of the same people regularly and it's fun to say hello by giving them a contact. You'll develop new topics of conversation as you run into them on the air between contests. Meeting other contesters in person adds another dimension to contesting. It provides the opportunity to see the faces of your on-air friends and builds a special camaraderie. Try it and see!

GLOSSARY

10-minute rule — refers to a limit on the number of band changes permitted in an hour or how long a station is required to operate on a band after making a band change

3830 — a popular website and e-mail reflector for reporting scores after the contest (**lists.contesting.com/_3830**)

Alligator — a station whose signal is loud but cannot hear calling stations well

Assisted — obtaining information about other stations in the contest from other stations or the Internet (does *not* refer to physical assistance in operating), also called Unlimited

Band map — a display of call signs received from the spotting network organized by frequency

Bonus — extra points added to a score for making a specific type of QSO, for contacting specific stations or operating in a specified way

Breakdown — a table showing the QSOs and multipliers worked on each band

Busted — an incorrect spot, call sign or exchange

Cabrillo — a format standard for contest logs

Check partial — compare the logged call to calls already logged in the contest; Super Check Partial uses a database of calls known to be active

Checklog — submitted logs that are only used in the log checking process and are not listed in the results for competitive purposes

Claimed score — the score based on the logged contacts before log checking

Confirmation number — a receipt number generated by an automated log submission process

Cut numbers — letter abbreviations for Morse numerals, such as N for 9, A for 1, T for zero, and so forth

Deadline — closing date for score and log submissions for a contest

DQ — disqualified, the result of rules violations

Dupe — duplicate contact, a station that has been worked before and can't be contacted again for point credit

Exchange — the information that must be exchanged in a contest QSO

Golden log — a log in which all contact information has been copied correctly

Grid square — the grid locator as defined by the Maidenhead Locator system, can be either 4- or 6-character

Hired gun — a guest operator, usually referring to someone highly skilled

Hold — in reference to a frequency, to maintain a presence on a frequency by calling CQ

LCR — Log Checking Report, the output of the log checking process for a submitted log

Lockout — a device or software that prevents two transmitters from being keyed on the same band at the same time

MO, MS, MM, M2 — Multi-Operator; Multi-Operator Single-Transmitter; Multi-Operator Multi-Transmitter; Multi-Operator Two-Transmitter

Move —to coordinate a change to another band to contact a station for additional multiplier credit

Mult — shorthand for multiplier

Not in the log (NIL) — a QSO that cannot be cross-referenced to an entry in the log of the station with which the QSO is claimed

Off-time — required periods of non-operation during a contest

Packet — a general term now referring to the worldwide spotting networks

Penalty — points removed during the log checking process in response to errors

QSO B4 — "QSO before" meaning a duplicate contact

QSO points — the point credit for a specific QSO

Rate — the equivalent number of stations that would be worked in an hour, based on various time periods (last hour, last 10 minutes, last 10 stations, last 100 stations, and so forth)

Robot — a software program that processes logs submitted by e-mail

Rover — a mobile station that operates while in motion or from multiple locations in a contest

Run — to work stations by calling CQ; a run also means a steady stream of callers in response to CQs

S&P — search-and-pounce, the technique of tuning for stations to work instead of calling CQ

Schedule — arrange to make a contact later in the contest

Serial number — the sequential number of the contact in the contest — first contact, second contact, 199th contact, and so on

SO, SOAB, SOSB — Single Operator; Single-Operator All-Band; Single-Operator Single Band

SOA, SOU — Single-Operator Assisted, Single-Operator Unlimited (see **Assisted**)

SO2R — Single-Operator, Two Radio; a technique of listening to two radios at once in order to run on one band while tuning on a second to find multipliers and other unworked stations.

SPC or **S/P/C** — State, Province, Country, the most common three location-based types of multipliers

Spot — an announcement of a station's call and frequency via a spotting network

Sprint — a short contest, usually six hours or less

Summary sheet — an entry form provided by contest sponsors containing information about the operator and the submitted log

Sunday driver — casual operators who appear late in the contest (usually Sunday afternoon) to make a few QSOs

UBN — Unique, Busted, Not In Log; the three ways in which a QSO can be declared invalid

Unique — a call sign that was not in any other submitted log

Unlimited — see Assisted

Zones — either ITU or CQ zones, used frequently as part of contest exchanges

RESOURCES

Magazines & Newsletters

ARRL *Contest Update* —
www.arrl.org/the-arrl-contest-update
National Contest Journal — **www.ncjweb.com**
Contest columns appear regularly in *CQ* Magazine —
www.cq-amateur-radio.com
Radio-sport — **www.radio-sport.net** — an online magazine about contesting

Websites & E-mail Reflectors

ARRL Contest Branch — **www.arrl.org/contests** (part of the On The Air section of the ARRL website)
Contesting.com — **www.contesting.com** — a general site about contesting (part of the eham.net website)
Contest Wiki — **wiki.contesting.com** — general and detailed information about contesting

3830 score reporting —
lists.contesting.com/mailman/listinfo/3830
CQ-Contest reflector —
lists.contesting.com/mailman/listinfo/cq-contest
Contest University — **www.contestuniversity.com** — contest training organization
World-Wide Radio Operators Foundation — **wwrof.org** — an organization that supports contesting and contest sponsors
RTTY Contesting — **www.rttycontesting.com** — a comprehensive website on RTTY contesting with plenty of information for beginners

Online Contest Calendars

ARRL Contest Corral — **www.arrl.org/contests** (also monthly in *QST*)
SM3CER Contest Service — **www.sk3bg.se/contest**
WA7BNM Contest Calendar —
www.hornucopia.com/contestcal

HF Digital Communications

We tend to think of the HF bands in terms of voice (SSB and AM) and CW activity. With the ubiquity of the personal computer, however, digital communication has seen an increasing HF presence as well. This has been particularly true for amateurs who are forced to operate in restricted situations using such things as hidden antennas and low output power. They've discovered that a few watts with a digital mode can still take them considerable distances, even around the world.

EVOLUTION AND REVOLUTION

Radioteletype, better known as *RTTY*, was one of the first Amateur Radio digital modes. Hams began using it in the late 1940s and the technology remained essentially unchanged for more than 30 years. If you had visited an amateur RTTY station prior to about 1980, you probably would have seen a hulking mechanical teletype machine, complete with rolls of yellow paper. The teletype would be connected to the transceiver through an interface known as a *TU*, or *terminal unit*. An oscilloscope would probably have graced the layout as well. Oscilloscopes were necessary for proper tuning of the received signal. The entire RTTY conversation was printed on, and had to be read from, an endless river of paper.

The first serious change occurred when affordable microprocessor technology appeared in the late 1970s. That's when we started to see TUs that included their own self-contained keyboards and displays, making the mechanical teletype

The modern HF digital mode station centers around a desktop or laptop computer, although tablets are rapidly gaining in popularity. Here, Robert Wood, W5AJ, operated an ARRL RTTY Roundup contest from Aruba with the call sign P4ØP.

(and all that paper!) obsolete. When personal computers debuted in the early 1980s, they became perfect companions for the new TUs. The PC functioned as a "dumb terminal," displaying the received data *from* the TU and sending data *to* the TU for transmission. Some TUs of this era offered ultra-sharp receive filters that allowed hams to copy weak signals even in the midst of horrendous interference. TU models such as the HAL Communications ST-8000 were renowned for their performance. Some RTTY operators still use ST-8000s to this day.

In the late 1980s, conventional terminal units began to yield to sophisticated devices known as *multimode controllers*. As the name suggests, these compact units handle several different digital modes in one package, typically RTTY, packet, AMTOR and PACTOR. The Kantronics KAM, AEA PK-232 and MFJ-1278 are well-known examples. Like TUs, multimode controllers are standalone devices that communicate with your personal computer. When using a multimode controller, your computer is, once again, acting as a dumb terminal — all of the heavy lifting is being done by the controller and its self-contained software known as *firmware*. These controllers functioned as radio modulators/demodulators, or *modems*, converting data to modulated audio signals for transmission and also converting received signals back to data for display.

The winds of change began to stir again in the early 1990s when *sound cards* appeared as accessories for personal computers. At first, sound cards were used for little more than…well…*sound*. They made it possible for computer users to enjoy music, sound effects in their computer games and other applications. But as sound cards became more powerful, hams began to realize their potential. They discovered that with the right software a sound card could function as a modem, too.

Peter Martinez, G3PLX, exploited the potential of the sound-card-as-modem when he created an entirely new amateur digital mode known as *PSK31*. It was not only a new mode, but a new way of using sound cards. The sound card not only decoded the received signal, it created the transmitted signal too. The only piece of hardware necessary (other than the transceiver, of course!) was a simple interface that allowed the computer to switch the radio from receive to transmit, and vice versa.

In the years that followed, sound cards became more powerful and versatile. They also began showing up as sound *chips* on personal computer motherboards and inside deluxe interfaces. Hams responded by developing more new digital modes to go with them. At the time this book went to press, there were well over a dozen sound-card HF digital modes with more in their pre-release stages.

The hardware multimode controllers are still with us, but they are primarily used for modes like PACTOR that require more processing muscle and precise timing than a typical personal computer can provide on its own. All of the other Amateur Radio HF digital modes have gone the way of the sound card.

HF TRANSCEIVERS FOR DIGITAL OPERATING

As far as the radio is concerned, the requirements for HF digital are surprisingly straightforward. You don't need to run out and purchase a special radio with sophisticated features. All you need is an SSB voice transceiver. Any transceiver made within the last 20 years will work well with most HF digital modes. Even very old SSB transceivers can be pressed into service.

When considering an older radio, however, there are two things to keep in mind:

Stability — Older transceivers, especially radios that use vacuum tubes, may tend to drift in frequency. Drift is deadly to digital communications. If you must use an old rig as your HF digital transceiver, you may need to allow it to warm up for as long as 30 minutes prior to operating.

Transmit/Receive Switching Speed — One digital mode known as PACTOR requires the radio to jump from receive to transmit (and back) in milliseconds. Many older radios can achieve this, but it is hard on their switching relays.

If your radio dates from about 1990 to the present day, you'll likely be in fine shape. These rigs are stable and most include all the features you'll need for HF digital. The singular exception involves some of the inexpensive SSB transceivers designed for low-power (QRP) operating. These rigs aren't usually intended for digital applications, so their stability may be questionable. They may also not offer connections to external devices through jacks known as *ports*.

Radio Ports

Modern radios get along surprisingly well with computers and other external devices. In fact, most modern HF transceivers are designed with external devices in mind. They offer a variety of ports depending on the model in question.

Figure 8.1 — Today's transceivers usually include a multipin accessory jack for connecting audio into and out of the radio and for transmit/receive switching. This jack could be labeled ACC or DATA or DIGITAL or a similar name. Check your transceiver manual for detailed information about using this jack.

Nearly every HF rig manufactured within the past decade includes an "accessory" port of some kind. **Figure 8.1** shows a typical example. Typically these are multipin jacks (as many as 13 pins) that provide connections for audio into and out of the radio, as well as a pin that causes the radio to switch from receive to transmit whenever the pin is grounded. This is often called the *PTT* or *push to talk* line. Some manufacturers also call it the *Send* line.

These accessory ports are ideal for connecting the kinds of interface devices we use to operate HF digital. In addition to the PTT function, accessory ports provide receive audio output at *fixed* levels that never change no matter where the VOLUME knob is set. This is a highly convenient feature that you'll appreciate when operating late at night after everyone has gone to bed. You can turn the VOLUME knob to zero and still have all the receive audio you need!

Be aware that some radio manufacturers label accessory ports as *data* or *digital* ports. This causes no end of confusion because modern rigs often offer two types of connections: a true accessory port with audio and transmit/receive keying lines and another port that allows a computer to actually control the radio. The confusion occurs when hams attempt to figure out which ports they need to use.

For the purpose of getting on the air with HF digital, the only type of radio control you should care about is the ability to switch from receive to transmit and back again. That connection is available at the *accessory port*, even though the port may go by a different name.

The kind of control the transceiver manufacturers have in mind goes way beyond the act of simply switching between transmit and receive. They are talking about the computer taking over almost every function of the radio; that's a different animal entirely. Full computer control usually involves software that does many things such as displaying and changing the transceiver's frequency, raising and lowering the audio level, scanning memory frequencies and a great deal more.

Some computer control software is so elaborate that the radio itself can be placed out of sight and all control conducted at the keyboard and monitor screen. Many amateurs use this capability to control their rigs remotely over the Internet at great distances.

What? No Radio Ports?

What if your SSB transceiver doesn't have an accessory port? No problem.

You can use the microphone jack as your connection for transmit/receive switching as well as the audio input. For the audio output, you can use the external speaker or headphone jack. This isn't an ideal situation, but it works. In fact, many HF digital operators take this approach.

COMPUTERS

As this chapter was being written, the computer world was entering a state of flux.

From the early 1980s through about 2005, the desktop computer was king among ordinary consumers and Amateur Radio operators. This is a computer in a separate, stand-alone case connected to a monitor, keyboard and mouse. Inside the computer case there is a sound device of some sort, either a dedicated sound card or a set of sound-processing chips on the motherboard. The computer connects to peripheral devices through the use of serial (COM) ports.

From 2005 onward we saw two important changes. One was the fact that laptop computers became more powerful and affordable. The other was that serial ports disappeared in favor of USB ports in both laptops *and* desktop machines.

By 2010 laptops (and to a lesser degree, netbooks) began to dominate Amateur Radio stations. As hams upgraded their computers, they no longer saw the need for bulky desktop systems when sleek laptops would do quite nicely.

As this book went to press, even laptops were facing stiff competition from *tablet* computers such as the Apple iPad. In Amateur Radio stations, laptops and desktops are still the most popular computers, but this is likely to change as more ham applications are developed for tablets.

The good news is that most HF digital software does not require powerful computers. Any ordinary off-the-shelf consumer-grade computer will do the job. If you are buying new, don't overspend for a powerful computer you won't need.

If you're thinking about a small netbook, be careful to check the specifications. Some netbooks don't include audio ports and as you'll see shortly, audio ports are highly important.

In terms of operating systems, the vast majority of HF digital software is written for Microsoft *Windows*. Some of these programs were created during the *Windows XP* era, but they run well on both *Windows Vista* and *Windows 7*.

There is HF digital software available for *MacOS* as well, although not as much variety. *Linux* users will find a number of HF digital applications, too.

If you are considering a new or used computer (desktop or laptop), here are a few rule-of-thumb shopping specifications:

■ The processor clock frequency ("speed") should be 1.5 GHz or better.

■ The computer should have as much memory as possible, not just to run the ham applications smoothly, but the operating system as well.

■ Either a built-in wireless (Wi-Fi) modem or an Ethernet port. Although it isn't necessary for ham work, chances are you'll want to connect your station to the Internet from time to time. If so, you'll need a wireless modem or Ethernet port to do so.

■ A CD-ROM drive for loading new software that is only available on CD (a less common need today, but don't sell yourself short).

The Rise of the Tablets

The Apple iPad was among the first tablets out of the gate and it continues to dominate the market. If you own an iPad, or can travel to an Apple store to see one in the flesh, you'll instantly understand why. These thin, slick computers with gorgeously bright 10-inch screens are perhaps the perfect platforms for modern digital media. They can send and receive e-mail, display TV shows and movies, browse the Internet, act as e-book readers, become game platforms and do a great deal more. iPads are highly reliable and virtually immune to viruses. For hundreds of millions of people throughout the world, they are ideal go-anywhere computers.

Beyond the genius of its design, the iPad has risen to the consumer technology throne on the power of Apple's popular iTunes store, which offers more than 700,000 applications as of mid-2012. There's an *app* for just about every purpose imaginable.

Other tablet manufacturers are playing catch up at this point. Amazon's tablet is gaining ground and others such as the Samsung Galaxy are carving out their market shares.

Some developers have already released apps for HF digital, primarily for the Apple iPad. Most notable among these are the *Multimode* and *I-PSK31* apps created by Luca Facchinetti, IW2NDH (**Figure 8.2**). Both of these apps allow

Figure 8.2 — *Multimode* **by Luca Facchinetti, IW2NDH, receiving PSK31 on an Apple iPad.**

SOFTWARE

In the beginning, HF digital programs were designed for one specific mode, such as *DigiPan* for PSK31 (**www.digipan.net**) or *MMTTY* for RTTY (**hamsoft.ca/pages/mmtty.php**). While mode-specific software still exists, the trend has been strongly in favor of multimode software that can operate many different HF digital modes.

Among the most popular multimode applications are …

Windows
> *MixW* (**mixw.net**)
> *MultiPSK* (**f6cte.free.fr/index_anglais.htm**)
> *Fldigi* (**www.w1hkj.com/Fldigi.html**)

MacOS
cocoaModem
> (**www.w7ay.net/site/Applications/cocoaModem/**)
Multimode
> (**www.blackcatsystems.com/software/multimode.html**)

Linux
> *Fldigi* (**www.w1hkj.com/Fldigi.html**)

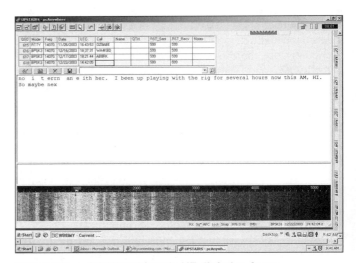

Figure 8.3 — *MixW* **multimode HF digital software.**

you to send and receive RTTY and PSK31 — two of the most popular HF digital modes. They are both available in the iTunes store.

The Importance of Sound

With few exceptions, every computer you are likely to purchase today will include a either a dedicated sound card or a sound chipset. This feature is absolutely critical for HF digital operation because most of the modes you'll enjoy depend on sound devices to act as radio *modems — mod*ulators/*demo*dulators.

The audio from your radio enters your computer via the sound device where it is converted (demodulated) to digital data for processing by your software. The results are words or images on your computer monitor. When you want to transmit, this same sound device takes the data from your software, such as the words you are typing, and converts it to shifting audio tones according to whatever mode you are using. This conversion is a form of modulation. The tones are then applied to your radio for transmission.

The simplest built-in sound devices are those found in laptops and tablets. They provide two ports to the outside world: microphone (audio input) and headphone (audio output). These are perfectly adequate for HF digital work. Desktop computers often have a similar arrangement, although the output port is usually labeled SPEAKER. A line-level input may also be included for stronger audio signals. In all cases these ports come in the form of ⅛-inch stereo jacks.

Some desktop computers offer sound cards that plug into the motherboard. These devices are more elaborate. Some sound cards can offer as many as 12 external connections.

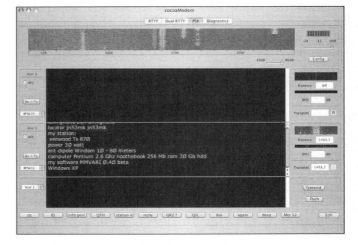

Figure 8.4 — *cocoaModem* **for** *MacOS.*

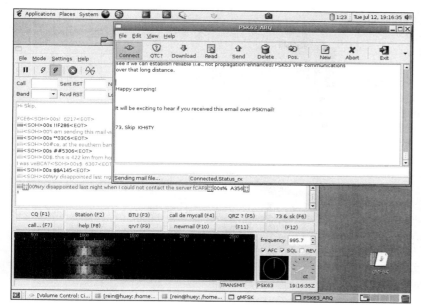

Figure 8.5 — *Fldigi* for *Linux*.

Figures **8.3** to **8.5** show examples of multimode programs in action.

THE INTERFACE

At rock bottom an interface has only one job to do: to allow the computer to toggle the radio between transmit and receive. It achieves this by using a signal from the computer to switch on a transistor (see **Figure 8.6**). This transistor conducts and effectively brings the transceiver's *PTT* (push to talk) line to ground potential or very close to it. When the PTT line is grounded, the transceiver switches to transmit. When the signal from the computer disappears, the transistor no longer conducts and the PTT line is electrically elevated above ground. The result is that the transceiver returns to the receive mode.

The signal from the computer appears at a specific pin on a serial (COM) or USB port. Your HF digital software generates the signal when you click your mouse on TRANSMIT or some other button with a similar label.

If an interface can be so straightforward,

couldn't you just build your own? Yes, you could. Many amateurs enjoy HF digital with simple interfaces like the one shown here. In addition to the switching circuit in Figure 8.1, they connect shielded audio cables between the computer and the radio to carry the transmit and receive audio signals. See **Figure 8.7**.

To Roll or Not to Roll

There are good reasons to roll your own interface, the cost savings being chief among them. On the other hand, if you purchase an interface off the shelf you'll be able to benefit from enhanced design features, depending on how much you want to pay. The short list of useful features includes:

Independent audio level controls. These are knobs on the front panel of the interface that allow you to quickly raise or lower the transmit or receive audio levels. Many amateurs prefer to manage the audio levels in this fashion compared to doing it in software.

CW keying. Full-featured interfaces handle more than just HF digital. They can also use keying signals from the computer to send Morse code with a separate connection to the transceiver's CW key jack. This allows you to send CW from your keyboard rather than by hand, a useful feature for higher speed CW exchanges during contests.

FSK keying. If you want to operate RTTY with the FSK

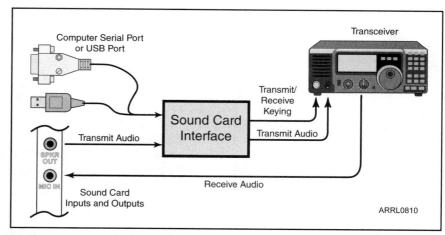

Figure 8.7 — The sound card interface installs between your computer and your HF transceiver. Its primary function is to allow your computer to switch your radio between transmit and receive, but many models perform additional functions such as providing audio isolation.

Figure 8.6 — The simplest way to key a radio using a computer is through a single-transistor circuit like this. The input connects to the serial cable coming from the computer (or from the USB/serial adapter). Either the RTS or DTR pins can be used, depending on what your software requires. The pin numbers for 25- and 9-pin plugs are shown.

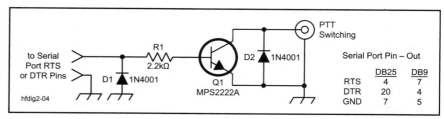

function of your transceiver, assuming your rig offers such a function, the FSK keying feature translates keying signals from your computer into the MARK/SPACE data pulses necessary for FSK RTTY.

Microphone input. If you are making HF digital connections to your radio through the microphone jack rather than the rear panel accessory port, you'll need to unplug the interface cable whenever you want to use your microphone for a voice conversation. To make operating more convenient, some interfaces allow you to keep your microphone plugged into the interface at all times, switching between your microphone or computer as necessary.

Transceiver control. Remember that a basic interface does not allow your computer to truly control your radio, except in the sense that it can switch your radio between transmit and receive. Deluxe interfaces include the extra circuitry needed to allow full computer control of your transceiver. Sometimes referred to as *CAT* (computer aided transceiver), this is a separate function that passes all the available controls from your radio to your computer. Depending on the type of transceiver you own and the software you are using, CAT allows you to change frequency, switch modes, raise and lower power levels and much more. If your transceiver has the ability to connect directly to your computer through an RS-232 serial connection, USB cable or Ethernet port, you don't need the CAT feature. The CAT function is primarily intended for radios that use transistor-transistor (TTL) signals for control. Manufacturers sell their own CAT interfaces, but they tend to be expensive. An interface with CAT functionality brings everything together in one affordable box.

Built-in sound device. Several interface designs include a built-in sound device. This is particularly handy in that it liberates the sound device in your computer for other functions. You can enjoy music on your computer, for example, without having to worry that you are meddling with the sound levels you've set up for HF digital operating. In addition, an interface with a built-in sound device greatly reduces the number of cables connecting the computer and radio. The audio signals, as well as transmit/receive keying functions, are all carried over a single USB cable; there are no connections to your computer's sound ports.

Pre-made cables. Most commercial interface manufacturers either include cables specifically wired for your radio free of charge, or offer them at an additional cost. This significantly reduces the hassle of wiring your HF digital station.

At the time of this writing, a basic off-the-shelf interface costs about $50; a multi-featured deluxe interface runs as high as $400. You'll need to shop among the manufacturers to find an interface that has the features you desire at a cost you are willing to pay. The most popular interface manufacturers include MFJ (**www.mfjenterprises.com**); microHAM (**www. microham-usa.com**); RigExpert (**www.rigexpert.com**); TigerTronics (**www.tigertronics.com**); and West Mountain Radio (**www.westmountainradio.com**). **Figure 8.8** shows some typical units from these vendors.

(A)

(B)

(C)

(D)

(E)

Figure 8.8 — A sampling of commercially available transceiver interfaces from microHAM (A), MFJ (B), RigExpert (C), TigerTronics (D) and West Mountain Radio (E). Some models provide basic connections for audio and TR switching. Others include extra features such as a built-in sound card chip set for digital modes, transceiver control or a CW keyer.

When an Interface Isn't an Interface — PACTOR

Throughout this chapter we've held fast to an overarching assumption: that the mode you will choose to operate will use software that transmits and receives through a sound device. The sound device can be inside the computer or within the interface. Either way, it is at the heart of your ability to communicate.

There is one exception to this assumption: *PACTOR.*

PACTOR is a digital mode invented by two German amateurs in 1991 and it has been evolving ever since. PACTOR is unique because it is capable of 100% error-free communication at global distances on the HF bands. This makes PACTOR the hands-down favorite when messages must get through error free. That's why PACTOR is the most widely used digital mode among those who participant on the HF side of the Winlink network. We'll discuss Winlink later in this chapter.

PACTOR works its magic by sending data in small chunks or *frames.* The receiving station analyzes the data and keeps whatever has arrived without errors. It transmits a short burst back to the originating station and tells it to repeat the frame. With luck, the next retransmission of the frame will arrive with most of the data intact, or with at least enough intact data that the receiving station can mix and match between the "new" and "old" frames to come up with a complete 100% error-free frame.

All of this back-and-forth transmitting makes a characteristic *chirp-chirp-chirp* sound on the air. It also requires a fast-switching transceiver and a lot of computational horsepower. To this date no one has written a computer program that is capable of doing PACTOR with sound devices. The PACTOR timing parameters are too strict and computer operating system timing tends to be too loose.

So, the manufacturers have packaged dedicated microprocessor circuitry into a stand-alone box. This box, often called a *controller,* has the speed and efficiency to meet the requirements for PACTOR. It can do other modes as well such as PSK31 and RTTY. Unlike a desktop or laptop computer, a controller doesn't labor under the burden of an operating system and it isn't required to fulfill a broad range of simultaneous tasks.

If you want PACTOR capability, you must purchase a controller. On the Winlink e-mail network you may be able to get away with an older PACTOR I controller that you'll find selling for a few hundred dollars, but to step up to modern PACTOR II you will most definitely need the $1000+ units manufactured by SCS Corporation on the web at **www.scs-ptc.com**.

The SCS model PTC-IIIusb is a good choice because it offers a wide range of features in a controller that plugs directly into your computer's USB port. You can purchase a set of cables to connect the PTC-IIIusb to your transceiver. In addition to PACTOR II, this controller will do PSK31, RTTY, CW, slow scan TV, packet radio and more.

Tablet Connections

With the use of tablet computers becoming more widespread, we're seeing an increasing number of amateurs putting these devices to work in their stations.

When this book went to press, the most popular tablet by a wide margin was the Apple iPad. As we discussed earlier in this chapter, there are already several iPad applications available for HF digital, specifically for RTTY and PSK31.

The main problem with using an iPad for HF digital is making the connections to the transceiver and keying the transceiver between transmit and receive. There are two ways of connecting iPads to the outside world:
- The microphone/headphone jack
- The docking port

If you purchase an Apple Camera Connection Kit and plug it into the docking port, you will suddenly have a USB connection to the iPad.

Unfortunately, this does not mean that you can plug in an HF digital USB interface. A USB interface draws more power than the iPad can provide, so the iPad will generate an error. An alternative is to use the Camera Connection Kit with a sound device designed for use with the iPad such as the Griffin iMic (**store.griffintechnology.com**).

The headphone/microphone jack is another option. This jack requires an unusual four-conductor plug. The connection diagram is shown in **Figure 8.9**. You can use this diagram along with a four-conductor plug to make your own transmit/receive audio adapter. The alternative is to purchase one premade from companies such as KV Connection at **www.kvconnection.com**. (Note that cables for iPhones will work for iPads as well.)

Now that you've solved the audio problem, what about keying the radio? The iPad provides no means whatsoever to attach any kind of keying device. The solution is to use the iPad's transmit audio to do the job. In the March 2011 issue of *QST,* Skip Teller, KH6TY, described a sound-activated digital interface that will key your radio when it receives audio from the iPad ("Digital VOX Sound Card Interface," page 34).

TigerTronics makes a device that operates on the same principle. Their SignaLink SL-1+ interface also uses a VOX keying circuit. The SL-1+ is available from TigerTronics at **www.tigertronics.com**.

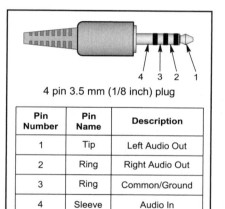

4 pin 3.5 mm (1/8 inch) plug

Pin Number	Pin Name	Description
1	Tip	Left Audio Out
2	Ring	Right Audio Out
3	Ring	Common/Ground
4	Sleeve	Audio In

QS1008-Eclec01

Figure 8.9 — A diagram of the iPad headphone/microphone plug.

Don't Overdrive Your Transceiver!

When you're setting up your rig for your first PSK31 transmission, the temptation is to adjust the output settings for "maximum smoke." This can be a serious mistake because overdriving your transceiver in PSK31 can result in a horrendous amount of splatter, which will suddenly make your PSK31 signal much wider than 31 Hz — and make you highly unpopular with operators on adjacent frequencies.

As you increase the transmit audio output from your sound card or multimode processor, watch the ALC indicator on your transceiver. The ALC is the automatic level control that governs the audio drive level. When you see your ALC display indicating that audio limiting is taking place, you are feeding too much audio to the transceiver. The goal is to achieve the desired RF output with little or no activation of the ALC.

Unfortunately, monitoring the ALC by itself is not always a sure bet. Many radios can be driven to full output without budging the ALC meter. You'd think that it would be smooth sailing from there, but a number of rigs become decidedly nonlinear when asked to provide SSB output beyond a certain level. (Sometimes this

nonlinearity can begin at the 50% output level.) We can ignore the linearity issue to a certain extent with an SSB voice signal, but not with PSK31 because the immediate result, once again, is splatter.

So how can you tell if your PSK31 signal is really clean? Unless you have the means to monitor your RF output with an oscilloscope, the only way to check your signal is to ask someone to give you an evaluation on the air. The PSK31 programs that use a waterfall audio spectrum display can easily detect "dirty" signals. The splatter appears as rows of lines extending to the right and left of your primary signal. (Overdriven PSK31 signals may also have a harsh, clicking sound.)

If you are told that you are splattering, ask the other station to observe your signal as you slowly decrease the audio level from the sound card or processor. When you reach the point where the splatter disappears, you're all set. Don't worry if you discover that you can only generate a clean signal at, say, 50 W output. With PSK31 the performance differential between 50 W and 100 W is inconsequential.

SO WHAT'S OUT THERE?

What can you do with your new HF digital station? More than you might imagine. There are more than a dozen different HF digital modes on the air today, but only a handful are used extensively. Let's concentrate on the modes you're most likely to encounter.

RTTY

Good old radioteletype (RTTY) is still holding its ground on the HF bands. In fact, it is still the most popular digital mode for contests and DXpeditions (where groups of hams travel to rare locations to operate).

As with so many aspects of Amateur Radio, it is best to begin by listening. **Table 8.1** shows where to find digital mode activity on the various HF bands. There's almost always something happening on 20 meters, so try there first. Tune between 14.070 and 14.095 MHz and listen for the long, continuous *blee-blee-blee-blee* signals of RTTY. What you are hearing are the two alternating *mark* and *space* signals that RTTY uses in its binary *Baudot* coding scheme.

Depending on your transceiver and interface, you may use *audio frequency shift keying* (*AFSK*) or *frequency shift keying* (*FSK*) to transmit RTTY. The end result sounds the same on the air.

In AFSK, the audio tones for mark and space are generated by the computer and/or interface and fed into your transceiver's microphone input. For AFSK, make sure your transceiver is set for lower sideband (LSB). That is the RTTY convention.

Your rig may have an FSK mode (sometimes labeled DATA or RTTY). Many hams prefer operating this way because

Table 8.1
Popular HF Digital Frequencies

Band (Meters)	Frequencies (MHz)
10	28.070–28.120
12	24.920–24.930
15	21.070–21.110
17	18.100–18.110
20	14.070–14.099
30	10.130–10.140
40	7.080–7.125
80	3.570–3.600
160	1.800–1.810

it allows them to use the transceiver's narrow IF filters to screen out interference. Just as on CW, with RTTY you can use 500 Hz or narrower filters to get rid of nearby signals. When you operate in FSK mode, your computer is not generating the mark and space tones. It is merely sending data pulses to the radio and the radio is creating its own mark and space signals. (This often requires a special connection to the transceiver. Consult your manual.)

Contests

A good time to observe RTTY activity is during a contest. There is at least one RTTY contest every month. See the sidebar "HF Digital Contesting" and the Contesting chapter elsewhere in this book.

With your software in the RTTY mode, tune across a

RTTY signal. Your software likely includes some kind of tuning indicator to help you line up the mark and space signals correctly so that the software can start decoding. The tuning indicator may be part of a waterfall display. It might consist of two parallel lines that line up with mark and space, or it could even be a simulated oscilloscope display. Check your software manual and experiment with any variable settings. With some experience, you will be able to correlate the sound of the RTTY signal with the visual indicator and quickly tune in a new signal.

As you tune in the signal, you should see letters marching across your screen. If you've stumbled across a contest, you may see something like this…

AA5AU 599 CT CT 010 010 DE WB8IMY K

In this instance, AA5AU is receiving a 599 signal report from WB8IMY in the state of Connecticut. This is also WB8IMY's tenth contact during the contest (that's the repeated "010"). The letter "K" means "over to you."

Most contest operators create "canned" messages, called *macros*, in their software. A macro can be set up to place your radio in the transmit mode, send a string of text, then return the radio to receive. Macros eliminate the need to type the same thing over and over, which comes in handy in a contest where you may be making hundreds of contacts.

Let's assume that you have a contest CQ stored in a macro right now. Tap the appropriate key (or click your mouse on the designated button) and your RTTY macro will do the rest…

(The radio enters the transmit mode)

CQ CONTEST DE WB8IMY WB8IMY CQ

(The radio returns to receive)

Most RTTY contest operators set up additional macros to send the exchange, ask for repeats, acknowledge the received information and so forth.

Other Activities

Of course hams still enjoy chatting on RTTY, just like they do on SSB or CW, and you may see them exchanging names, locations, antenna descriptions and other items of interest. RTTY DXing is popular too, and so you may run across "pileups" on DX stations. If the DX station is rare, the QSOs may just be rapid-fire exchange of signal reports and call signs, just like on voice or CW.

Occasionally a rare DX station will operate split — receiving above or below the transmit frequency. That makes it easier to separate signals when many are calling. As always, it's a good idea to listen for a few minutes to determine the DX station's operating style and respond accordingly.

PSK31

PSK31 is the most widely used HF digital communications mode on the HF bands today. Most PSK31 activity involves casual conversation, although there are a few PSK31 contests as well.

PSK stands for *phase shift keying*, the modulation method used to generate the signal; *31* is the bit rate. Where RTTY uses two specific frequencies to communicate the binary data, PSK31 does the same thing by creating an audio signal that shifts its phase 180° in sync with the 31.25 bit-per-second data stream. A 0 bit in the data stream generates an audio phase shift, but a 1 does not. The technique of using phase shifts (and the lack thereof) to represent binary data is known as *binary phase-shift keying*, or *BPSK*. If you apply a BPSK audio signal to an SSB transceiver, you end up with BPSK modulated RF. At this data rate the resulting PSK31 RF signal is only about 50 Hz wide, which is actually narrower than the average CW signal.

With such a narrow bandwidth, PSK31 makes the most of a very small amount of spectrum. Transmit power is highly concentrated, meaning that you don't need a lot of power to communicate over great distances. (Most PSK31 operators use less than 50 W output.) At the receiving end, the PSK31 software uses digital signal processing to detect the phase changes, even in very weak signals. The result is that PSK31 rivals or exceeds the weak-signal performance of CW.

Its terrific performance not withstanding, PSK31 will not always provide 100% copy; it is as vulnerable to interference as any digital mode. And there are times, during a geomagnetic storm for example, when ionospheric propagation will cause slight changes in the frequency of the signal you're trying to copy. (When you are trying to receive a narrow-bandwidth, phase-shifting signal, frequency stability is very important.) This effect is almost always confined to the polar regions and it shows up as very rapid flutter, which is deadly to PSK31. The good news is that these events are usually short-lived.

If you are operating your transceiver in SSB without using narrow IF or audio-frequency filtering, the bandwidth of the receive audio that you're dumping to your sound card is about 2000 to 3000 Hz. With a bandwidth of only about 50 Hz, a lot of PSK31 signals can squeeze into that spectrum. Your software acts like an audio spectrum analyzer, sweeping through the received audio from 100 to 3000 Hz and showing you the results in a waterfall display that continuously scrolls from top to bottom. What you see on your monitor are vertical lines of various colors that indicate every signal the software can detect. Bright yellow lines represent strong signals while blue lines indicate weaker signals.

Most of the PSK31 signals on 20 meters are clustered around 14.070 MHz. You'll also find PSK31 activity on 3.580, 7.070 and 21.070 MHz. PSK31 signals have a distinctive sound unlike any digital mode you've heard on the ham bands. You won't find PSK31 by listening for the *deedle-deedle* of a RTTY signal, and PSK31 doesn't "chirp" like the TOR modes. PSK31 signals *warble*.

Start by putting your radio in the USB (upper sideband) mode and parking it on or near a PSK31 frequency (tune until you see a number of lines in the waterfall). Do not touch your rig's VFO again. Just boot up your software and get ready to have fun.

It is not at all uncommon to see several strong signals (the audible ones) interspersed with wispy blue ghosts of very weak "silent" signals. Click on a few of these ghosts and you may be rewarded with text (not error free, but good enough to understand what is being discussed).

As you decode PSK31 signals, the results will be a conversation on your monitor…

Yes, John, I'm seeing perfect text on my screen, but I can

barely hear your signal. PSK31 is amazing! KF6I DE WB8IMY K

I know what you mean, Steve. You are also weak on my end, but 100% copy. WB8IMY DE KF6I K

HF Digital Contesting

Some hams shun contesting because they assume they don't have the time or hardware necessary to win — and they are probably right. But winning is not the objective for most contesters. You enter a contest to do the best you can, to push yourself and your station to whatever limits you wish. The satisfaction at the end of a contest comes from the knowledge that you were part of the glorious frenzy, and that you gave it your best shot!

Contesting also has a practical benefit. If you're an award chaser, you can work many desirable stations during an active contest. During the ARRL RTTY Roundup, for example, some hams pay special attention to looking for "new ones" to add to their Digital DXCC award totals. Jump into the North American RTTY QSO Party and you stand a good chance of earning most or all of your Worked All States (WAS) award in a single weekend.

RTTY contesting has exploded in popularity, and every month brings one or more contests to try — too many to list here! Check Contest Corral in *QST* or **www.arrl.org/contest-calendar** to see what events are coming up.

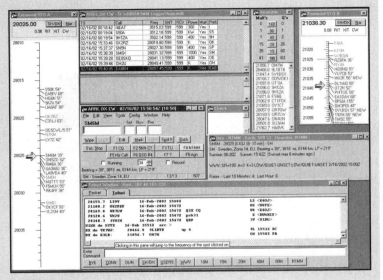

N1MM Logger.

Contest Software

No one says you have to use software to keep track of your contest contacts, but it certainly makes life easier! One of the fundamental elements of any contest program is the ability to check for duplicate contacts or dupes. Working the same station that you just worked an hour ago is not only embarrassing, it is a waste of time.

The better contest programs feature immediate dupe checking. When you enter the call sign in the logging window, the software instantly checks your log and warns you if the contact qualifies as a dupe.

The more sophisticated programs "know" the rules of the popular digital contests and they can quickly determine how a contact counts under the rules of the contest in question. Some contests allow more points for contacts with stations in other countries or on other continents.

A good software package will also help you track multipliers. It will display a list of multipliers you've worked, or show the ones you still need to find. Some contests allow you to work stations for multiplier credit only once, regardless of the band. Other contests will allow you to count multipliers worked once per band.

One of the most widely used contest software packages in the HF digital world is *Writelog* for *Windows*, which you'll find at **www.writelog.com**. *Writelog* has a built-in RTTY module or you can use it with the free *MMTTY* RTTY application, which is available at **hamsoft.ca/pages/mmtty. php**.

Another digital contest favorite is the free *N1MM Logger* at **n1mm.hamdocs.com/tiki-index.php**. *N1MM* by itself does not have RTTY capability, but you can add this functionality by installing *MMTTY*.

For more information about RTTY contesting and contest operating in general, see the Contesting chapter elsewhere in this book.

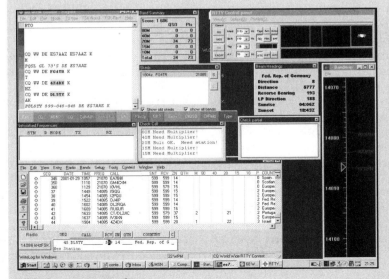

Writelog **contest software.**

If you find a station calling CQ and you want to reply, don't worry about tuning your radio. The software will use your sound card to generate the PSK31 transmit signal at exactly the same audio frequency as the received signal. When applied to your radio, this audio signal will create an RF signal that is exactly where it needs to be.

Some PSK31 programs and processor software offer type-ahead buffers, which allow you to compose your response "off line" while you are reading the incoming text from the other station. Just type what you wish to send, then press the keyboard key or click on the software "button" to transmit. Some software includes memories for storing CQ messages, name, location and other common QSO elements.

MFSK16

An MFSK signal consists of 16 tones, sent one at a time at 15.625 baud, and they are spaced only 15.625 Hz apart. Each tone represents four binary bits of data. With a bandwidth of 316 Hz, the signal easily fits through a narrow CW filter. MFSK16 has a distinctive musical sound that some compare to an old-fashioned carnival calliope.

MFSK16 can be tricky to tune. You must place the cursor at exactly the right spot on the signal pattern in the waterfall display. It takes some skill and patience to tune MFSK, but the results are worth the effort. MFSK offers excellent weak-signal performance and is a conversational mode like PSK31. Listen for the "music" of MFSK just above the PSK31 frequencies.

Hellschreiber

Are the Hellschreiber modes really HF digital? Or, are they a hybrid of the analog and digital worlds? Check out **Figure 8.10**.

Some argue that the Hellschreiber modes are more closely related to facsimile since they display text on your computer screen in the form of images (not unlike the product of a fax machine). On the other hand, the elements of the Hellschreiber "image text" are transmitted using a strictly defined digital format rather than the various analog signals of true HF fax or SSTV.

The Hellschreiber concept itself is quite old, developed in the 1920s by Rudolf Hell. Hellschreiber was, in fact, the first successful direct printing text transmission system. The German Army used Hellschreiber for field communications in World War II, and the mode was in use for commercial landline service until about 1980.

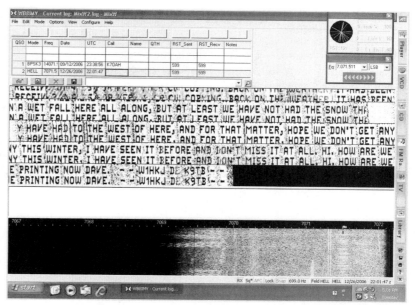

Figure 8.10 — Hellschreiber signals are displayed in repeating lines that look like an old-fashioned dot-matrix printer.

As personal computers became ubiquitous tools in ham shacks throughout the world, interest in Hellschreiber as an HF mode increased. By the end of the 20th century amateurs had developed several sophisticated pieces of Hellschreiber software and had also expanded and improved the Hellschreiber system itself.

Like PSK31, the Hellschreiber modes are intended for live conversations. Most of the activity is found on 20 meters, typically between 14.076 and 14.080 MHz. As with other conversational modes, you simply type and send your text. The main difference involves what is actually seen on the receiving end.

Feld-Hell is the most popular Hellschreiber mode among HF digital experimenters. It has its roots in the original Hellschreiber format, adapted slightly for ham use. Each character of a Feld-Hell transmission is communicated as a series of dots, with the result looking a bit like the output from a dot-matrix printer. A key-down state is used to indicate the black area of text, and the key up state is used to indicate blank or white spaces. One hundred and fifty characters are transmitted every minute. Each character takes 400 ms to complete. Because there are 49 pixels per character, each pixel is 8.163 ms long.

Most multimode software packages offer Hellschreiber. You won't find many Hell signals on the air, but conversing in this mode is a unique experience. Listen for odd "scratchy" signals just above the PSK31 frequencies.

PACTOR

Unlike the sound card modes we've discussed so far, PACTOR is a burst mode. That is, it sends and receives data in segments or bursts rather than in a continuous stream. When a burst of data arrives, the receiving station quickly checks for errors caused by noise, interference or fading. If the data is corrupted, the receiving station transmits a brief signal known as a NAK (nonackowledgment) and the data burst is repeated. If the data arrives intact, or if the receiving station has enough information to "repair" any errors, an ACK (acknowledgment) is sent and the next block of data is on the way. This system of rapid-fire data bursts, ACKs and NAKs guarantees a 100% error-free information exchange between stations.

PACTOR and Winlink 2000

More than 50 HF digital stations worldwide have formed a remarkably efficient Internet information exchange network, including e-mail, binary file transfer and global graphic WX reporting. Running Winlink 2000 software and using PACTOR, PACTOR II or PACTOR III protocols, these facilities transfer information between HF stations and the Internet. They also share information among themselves using Internet forwarding.

The Need for Speed

When you're operating the burst modes such as PACTOR and Clover, your success will be largely measured by how fast your transceiver can switch from transmit to receive.

For example, a PACTOR station transmits a 960-ms long data block, then waits up to 170 ms for a 120-ms ACK or NAK signal from the receiving station. If the ACK or NAK fails to arrive before this 170-ms window closes, the data block will be repeated. PACTOR's patience is not endless though. If the ACKs or NAKs still fail to arrive after a certain number of repeated data blocks, your processor will declare the link "broken."

With this critical timing in mind, it's important to understand that the time it takes for your SSB transceiver to switch from transmit to receive is deducted from the 170-ms window. This has a substantial effect on how far you can communicate with PACTOR.

Let's say that your rig is a bit on the slow side. It switches from transmit to receive at a lazy 90 ms. Deduct 90 from 170 and you'll see that your window has suddenly shrunk to 80 ms.

Now deduct the delays at the receiving station. Let's be generous and say that his rig can switch within 40 ms. Now your window has collapsed to 40 ms. A radio signal can travel approximately 3700 miles — roundtrip — in 40 ms. This means that the maximum range of your PACTOR station would be roughly 4000 miles.

It is best to shop for an SSB transceiver that has the fastest transmit/receive turnaround. *QST* Product Reviews often publish this information in their data tables. Look for it and let it guide you to the best choice. When in doubt, the fewer milliseconds, the better!

The network evolved in the 1990s from the original AMTOR-based *APLink* system, authored by Vic Poor, W5SMM. *APLink* was a network of stations that relayed messages to and from each other and the VHF packet network. As PCs became more powerful, and as PACTOR and Clover superseded AMTOR, a new software system was needed. That need brought about the debut of Winlink, again authored by Vic Poor, W5SMM, with additions from Peter Schultz, TY1PS. Winlink itself evolved with substantial enhancements courtesy of Hans Kessler, N8PGR. To bring the Internet into the picture Winlink stations needed an e-mail "agent" to interface with cyberspace. To meet that requirement Steve Waterman, K4CJX enlisted the help of Jim Jennings, W5EUT and Rick Muething, KN6KB, to add *NetLink*.

Early in 2000 the system took the next evolutionary leap, becoming a full-featured Internet-to-HF gateway system known as Winlink 2000 or "WL2K" (see **www.winlink.org**). Jim Corenman, KE6RK, concurrently developed software called *AirMail* to act as the end-user portion of Winlink 2000. Winlink 2000 is a network of participating stations (PMBOs); all connected to a central server (CMBO), which is the "hub" for Internet connectivity to Internet e-mail and position reporting. Currently *RMS Express* is the preferred Winlink 2000 radio e-mail client. It is in active development by the Winlink Development Team and is well-supported.

Thanks to these advancements, an HF digital operator at sea, for example, can now connect to a Winlink 2000 participating network station using *RMS Express*, and exchange Internet e-mail with non-ham friends and family. He can also exchange messages with other amateurs by using the Winlink 2000 network stations as a traditional global "mailbox" operation.

Most Winlink 2000 participating stations scan a variety of HF digital frequencies on a regular basis, listening on each frequency for about two seconds. By scanning through frequencies on several bands, the Winlink 2000 stations can be accessed on whichever band is available to you at the time.

Using *RMS Express*, Winlink 2000 features include…

■ Text-based e-mail with binary attachments such as DOC, RTF, XLS, JPG, TIF, GIF, BMP or other files.

■ Position inquiries accessible from both the Internet graphically via APRS and YotReps, e-mail, or radio to track the mobile user.

■ Graphic and text-based weather downloads from a list of over 400 weather products, covering the entire globe.

■ Pickup and delivery of e-mail regardless of the participating station accessed.

■ End-user control of which services and file sizes are transmitted from the participating stations, including the ability for each user to redirect incoming e-mail messages to an alternate e-mail address.

■ The ability to use the Internet via Telnet instead of a radio transmission.

■ The ability to use any web browser to pick up or deliver mail over Winlink 2000.

■ The inclusion of a propagation program in *RMS Express*

to predict the best band for connection to any Winlink 2000 participating station.

Hardware and Software Requirements

In addition to your HF SSB transceiver, you'll need a multimode processor that is capable of communicating in binary mode with either PACTOR I, PACTOR II or PACTOR III. At the time this book was published, only the SCS PTC series of multimode communications processors mentioned earlier in this chapter met this requirement. See **Figure 8.11**.

Figure 8.11 — The PTC-IIIusb is one of several multimode communication processors from SCS that offers PACTOR II or III.

Accessing a Winlink 2000 Station

Information about operating procedures may be found at **www.winlink.org** or within the *RMS Express* help files. *RMS Express* can operate your radio if you set it up properly. Just choose a station, pick a frequency and push SEND. All information transfer is automatic and would be set up prior to the actual transmission just like any other e-mail agent. A continually updated list of stations and a catalog containing weather as well as other helpful information may be automatically maintained through *RMS Express*.

Remember that Winlink 2000 stations usually scan through several frequencies. If you can't seem to connect, the Winlink 2000 station may already be busy with another user, or propagation conditions may not be favorable on the frequency you've chosen. Either try again later or use the built-in propagation feature to connect on another band.

Sending E-mail to and from the Internet

From the Internet side of Winlink 2000, friends and family can send e-mail to you just as they would send e-mail to anyone else on the Net. In fact, the idea of Winlink 2000 is to make HF e-mail exchanges look essentially the same as regular Internet e-mail from the user's point of view. Internet users simply address their messages to **<your call sign>@winlink.org**. For example, a message addressed to **wb8imy@winlink.org** will be available when WB8IMY checks into *any* Winlink 2000 station.

Through the *RMS Express* software the ham user can address messages to non-hams, or to other hams, for that matter, by using the same format used in any other e-mail program.

Although Winlink 2000 supports file attachments, remember that the radio link is *very* slow (especially compared to the Internet). Sending an attachment of more than 40 kbytes is usually not a good idea. Text, RTF, DOC, XLS, JPG, BMP, GIF, WMO, GREB and TIF files are permitted as long as they are small enough to comply with the particular user-set limit. Where possible, Winlink 2000 compresses files. For example, a 400 kbyte BMP file may be compressed to under 15 kbytes. However, this is an exception rather than the rule. Also, the transmission protocol provides additional compression of approximately 35%. Speed depends on the PACTOR protocol used. PACTOR II is approximately four to six times faster than PACTOR I. Some stations are now using PACTOR III, which is even faster.

JT65 AND JT65-HF

By now amateurs are used to the sounds most digital modes create. They've learned to recognize the constant warbling tones of PSK31, the rhythmic pulses of PACTOR, the "scratchy" rumble of Hellschreiber or the multi-tone music of RTTY, MFSK16 and others.

But JT65 is unique. It marches, as Thoreau said, to the beat of a different drummer. If you've never heard it before it will stop you cold. As you tune across a JT65 signal you'll hear tones of varying pitch that "play" slowly, like someone lazily pecking on an electronic keyboard.

Cryptic and strange as the tones may be, you might be surprised to learn that they carry call signs, signal reports and other bits of information. Even more surprising is the fact that information can be extracted from a JT65 signal even when it is extremely weak.

The "JT" in JT65

JT65 debuted as part of the *WSJT* software suite created by Dr Joe Taylor, K1JT. As a Nobel Prize winning scientist

who studies pulsars and other distant astronomical objects, Joe has a keen interest in weak signals. Joe's software exploits the power of modern desktop and laptop computers to separate weak signals from noise and decode the information they contain. With just a sound card or sound chipset and a transceiver interface, *WSJT* makes it possible for hams with modest stations to enjoy VHF meteor scatter communication and even moonbounce, where signals are literally bounced off the surface of the Moon and returned to Earth. *WSJT* is available for free downloading at **physics.princeton.edu/pulsar/K1JT/**.

In the beginning, JT65 was embraced by some members of the moonbounce community and it was an instant success. Thanks to JT65, amateurs with single long-boom Yagi antennas and 150 W of RF output can experience the thrill of communicating over the longest "long path" of all.

But it wasn't long before someone wondered what would happen if JT65 was used on the HF bands. Digital communication on HF isn't nearly as challenging as getting a signal to the Moon and back, so it stood to reason that there would be plenty of "performance margin" to provide fascinating results. To no one's surprise, this turned out to be true. Using a variant of JT65 known as JT65A, even a few watts of JT65 modulated RF to a wire dipole antenna resulted in transcontinental and even global communication.

So What is JT65?

The short and simplified answer to this question is that JT65 is a weak-signal digital mode that uses one-minute transmit/receive sequences, meaning that you transmit within a one-minute window and then listen for one minute. Transmission actually begins 1 second after the start of a UTC minute and stops precisely 47.7 seconds later. There is a 1270.5 Hz synchronizing tone and 64 other tones. This combination gives JT65 its unusual musical quality.

Time synchronization is critical to JT65. If you are running *Windows 7* or *Vista*, you can synchronize your computer time with Internet time servers. Just explore the DATE AND TIME menu under *Window's* Control Panel. *Windows XP* users may want to investigate free software such as *Dimension4* (**www.thinkman.com/dimension4/**) to keep accurate time automatically.

JT65 is not a "conversational" mode like, say, PSK31. Instead, the idea is to exchange only the basic information required for a valid contact: call signs and signal reports. *JT65-HF* measures the actual received signal strength and incorporates it into the exchange. When you receive a report during a *JT65-HF* exchange, you'll know exactly how strong your signal is (in dB) at the other end.

JT65 contacts count for many awards such as Worked All States (WAS) or the DX Century Club (DXCC). Aside from the fun of award chasing, it is amazing to see who you can contact with JT65 while using miniscule amounts of power. Some JT65 enthusiasts are using output levels in the

milliwatt range. In fact, 50 W is considered "high power" in the JT65 world.

Dedicated JT65 Software

JT65 is one of several modes in the *WSJT* package. However, Joe Large, W6CQZ, thought more amateurs might try JT65 on HF if it was available in software specifically designed to make it easier to enjoy contacts. The result was his *JT65-HF* application for *Windows* and it soon proved Joe's hunch correct. Since Joe's software made its debut, JT65 activity on the HF bands has increased substantially. *JT65-HF* software is available free at Joe's Sourceforge page at **sourceforge.net/projects/jt65-hf/** and also on the ARRL website at the *Get On the Air with HF Digital* page at **www.arrl.org/hf-digital**. The remainder of this chapter describes JT65 operation with *JT65-HF*.

The JT65-HF Main Screen

Let's take a look at the *JT65-HF* main screen, section by section, starting at the top. See **Figure 8.12**.

The waterfall display dominates most of the top portion of the *JT65-HF* main screen. Whenever *JT65-HF* is running, it sweeps through your receive audio spectrum from 0 to 2000 Hz. Every signal it detects appears in this window.

You'll notice that the waterfall is divided into two halves to the right and left of the center "zero" point. The display markers are positive to the right of the zero (0 to 1000) and negative to the left of the zero (0 to –1000). Along the top of the waterfall you'll see a red bracket. If you click your mouse cursor within the waterfall the red bracket will move to the position you just clicked. The bracket represents your 200 Hz transmit/receive window.

JT65-HF can operate in simplex (transmitting and receiving on the same frequency) and split (transmitting and receiving on different frequencies). Most of your contacts will be simplex, but it is worthwhile to know that *JT65-HF* has split-frequency capability. Two brackets appear when operating split — red for the transmit frequency and green for the receive frequency.

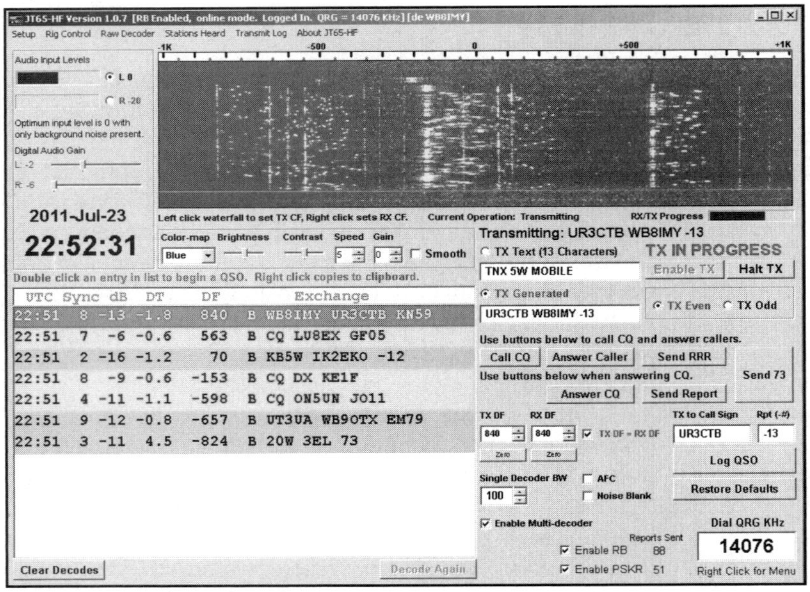

On the left side of the waterfall, you have the right and left channel audio input controls. When the band is quiet (when there are no signals), you should adjust the right and left channel controls to achieve 0 dB on both channels. Too much or too little audio makes it difficult to decode signals.

Below the waterfall you'll see controls for color, brightness, contrast, speed and gain. You're safe leaving all these at their default settings. There is little need to change them unless you're having difficulty viewing the waterfall or unless you are running *JT65-HF* on a slow computer.

Moving to the lower right section we have a number of check boxes and buttons. These may seem confusing but their functions will become more apparent when we make our first contacts.

MESSAGE TO TX is the text you are sending

Figure 8.12 — The *JT65-HF* software by Joe Large, W6CQZ.

to the other station. You can send text manually in the TX TEXT window, but you are limited to 13 characters. Immediately below this window you see the red-labeled TX GENERATED window. This window is for transmitted text that *JT65-HF* generates automatically, either when you click on one of the buttons below, or when you click on a line in the decoding window. Again, the function of this window will become clear as we step through your first contact.

To the right of the message windows are buttons to enable or halt transmission. Below these buttons is the section that allows you to choose whether you wish to transmit on even or odd minutes. With JT65 you transmit and receive in turns — during one minute you transmit and during another minute you receive. Therefore, one minute will be an odd-numbered minute (such as 2105 UTC) and the next minute will be an even-numbered minute (such as 2102 UTC).

In most instances *JT65-HF* will make the choice for you. However, when calling CQ you get to choose when you will begin transmitting — on an even or odd minute. You definitely don't need to worry about even and odd minutes when you are answering someone else's call. That station has already selected which minute (even or odd) he will use. When you respond, *JT65-HF* will automatically choose the opposite minute.

Below the text-generating buttons you'll find several other interesting sections. The TX DF and RX DF sections are for split-frequency applications. For the vast majority of your JT65 contacts you will work simplex, so you want to leave the TX DF = RX DF box checked. An exception to the rule is when you are calling CQ, which we'll address later.

Below the TX DF and RX DF sections you'll find the controls for SINGLE DECODER BW (Bandwidth) and MULTI DECODER SPACING. This is another set of controls you'll rarely have a reason to change from their default values. Normally you'd never disable the multiple-signal decoder unless you are using a particularly slow computer. The default of 100 Hz for single bandwidth is usually adequate.

Put a checkmark in the AFC (automatic frequency control) box so that *JT65-HF* can compensate for stations that may be drifting a bit. If you live in an area with frequent storms or other sources of noise, put a checkmark in the NOISE BLANK box as well.

ENABLE MULTI-DECODER does exactly that. When enabled the decoder will attempt to find and decode all possible JT65 signals within the 2 kHz passband. Unless you are using a slow computer that has difficulty processing so much information at once, always leave this box checked.

To the right you'll find the LOG QSO button. When you click this button *JT65-HF* will save your contact information (who you worked, when, etc) to the file *jt65hf_log.adi* in the *JT65-HF* directory in a standard ADIF format that you can import into your computer logging software.

Finally, at the bottom of the lower right portion of the *JT65-HF* window you'll find two checkboxes labeled ENABLE RB and ENABLE PSKR, along with a sizeable window labeled DIAL QRG KHZ. If you are using transceiver-control software to read the transceiver frequency, the frequency will appear in this window. If you're not, you can right click your mouse cursor in this window and select from the list of common JT65 frequencies.

Why would you bother showing your operating frequency in the QRG window? The answer is that if you've checked the ENABLE RB and ENABLE PSKR windows *JT65-HF* will automatically access your home Internet connection and share your data (the stations you've heard and how strong they were) with W6CQZ's reverse beacon (RB) website at **jt65.w6cqz.org/receptions.php** and with the PSKReporter (PSKR) website at **pskreporter.info/pskmap.html** — if you've enabled this feature in the station setup screen. The information is extremely helpful to your fellow amateurs who study propagation, experiment with new antennas and so on. To make the information useable, however, they need to know your listening frequency; that's what the QRG window is all about.

Watch the Action

As is the case so often in Amateur Radio, when trying a new operating mode the best practice is to spend plenty of time listening *first*.

Start by looking at the list of JT65 frequencies in **Table 8.2**. Select a frequency and place your transceiver in the USB mode. Tune to that frequency and start the *JT65-HF* software. If there are stations transmitting, you'll see them in the waterfall display right away. You may notice that their signal traces seem to curve somewhat before settling into a regular pattern. That's a symptom of *JT65-HF* running its sample correction routine on your sound device. Depending on what sort of sound device you are using, a couple of minutes may pass before you are able to begin decoding transmissions.

When everyone stops transmitting at about the 48-second mark, use the opportunity to quickly adjust the audio gain controls to achieve 0 dB on both channels.

As the next minute begins, you should hear or see other stations starting their transmissions. Just sit back and watch. You'll notice that each transmission is comprised of a line — possibly a broken line — with several dots appearing to the

---

Table 8.2
Common JT65 Frequencies
(All frequencies assume a transceiver display in USB mode.)
   1838 kHz
   3576 kHz
   7076 kHz (European stations often use 7039 kHz)
14076 kHz
10139 kHz
18102 kHz
21076 kHz
24920 kHz
28076 kHz

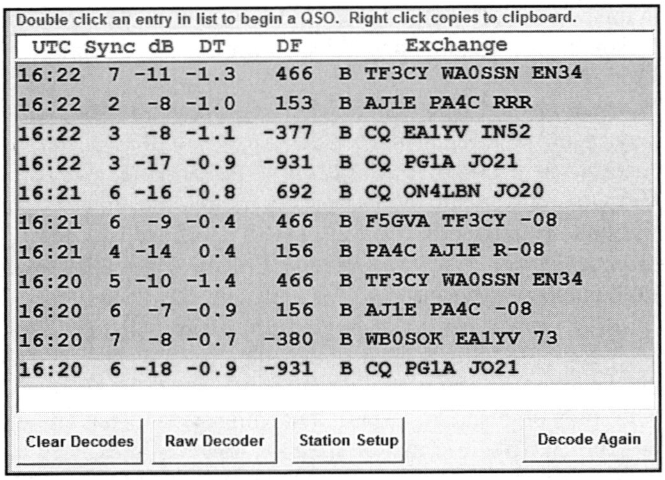

UTC	Sync	dB	DT	DF	Exchange
16:22	7	-11	-1.3	466	B TF3CY WA0SSN EN34
16:22	2	-8	-1.0	153	B AJ1E PA4C RRR
16:22	3	-8	-1.1	-377	B CQ EA1YV IN52
16:22	3	-17	-0.9	-931	B CQ PG1A JO21
16:21	6	-16	-0.8	692	B CQ ON4LBN JO20
16:21	6	-9	-0.4	466	B F5GVA TF3CY -08
16:21	4	-14	0.4	156	B PA4C AJ1E R-08
16:20	5	-10	-1.4	466	B TF3CY WA0SSN EN34
16:20	6	-7	-0.9	156	B AJ1E PA4C -08
16:20	7	-8	-0.7	-380	B WB0SOK EA1YV 73
16:20	6	-18	-0.9	-931	B CQ PG1A JO21

Clear Decodes	Raw Decoder	Station Setup	Decode Again

Figure 8.13 — The *JT65-HF* signal decoding window (see text).

immediate right. The line represents the synchronizing tone and the dots are all the remaining tones.

When the clock reaches the 48 second point, everyone should stop transmitting automatically. Within the next few seconds you should see text appear in the window at the lower left.

Some of the text may be highlighted in green. These are stations calling CQ. You'll see other text shaded in gray. When you're involved in a conversation, the transmissions intended for you are highlighted in red.

Look at the sample decoding screen in **Figure 8.13.** First, let's decipher the headings along the top of the window, beginning at the far left.

UTC: The time the signal was decoded in UTC.

Sync: This is a measurement of the strength of the synchronizing tone. The higher the number, the better the sync signal.

dB: The strength of the JT65 signal in decibels. The lower the number, the stronger the signal. Zero dB is the strongest possible.

DT: How much the decoded station's time deviated from your time, measured in seconds or fractions of seconds. Ideally the decoded stations should be within 2 seconds of your computer's time, preferably less than 1 second.

DF: How far the signal frequency deviates, in hertz, above or below the zero center point of the waterfall display. A negative number is a signal to the left of zero; a positive number is a signal to the right of zero.

Exchange: The text the transmitting station actually sent. If you see two call signs, the transmitting station is the *second* call sign.

Just to the left of the exchange text you'll see either a B or a K. This is a reference to the kind of error correction algorithm that *JT65-HF* used to validate the text. B stands for *BM*, a simple Reed Solomon algorithm. K means *KVASD*, a much more complex algorithm. One way to think about this is to imagine that a K means that *JT65-HF* had to work particularly hard to make sense of the signal. If so, this station may present a challenge if you attempt to complete a contact.

As you observe the exchanges you'll probably see a pattern emerging. JT65 exchanges usually, though not always, follow a strict sequence. It goes like this, starting at 2102 UTC …

2102 CQ WB8IMY FN31
WB8IMY has begun sending CQ on an even minute from grid square FN31.
2103 WB8IMY N1NAS EN72
N1NAS replies and tells WB8IMY that he is located in grid square EN72.
2104 N1NAS WB8IMY -11
WB8IMY replies with a signal report of –11 dB.
2105 WB8IMY N1NAS R-15
N1NAS acknowledges the signal report from WB8IMY with an "R" followed by a signal report (–15).
2106 N1NAS WB8IMY RRR
WB8IMY sends "RRR," which means "Roger, roger, roger." Everything has been received and the exchange is complete.
2107 WB8IMY N1NAS 73
N1NAS sends 73 — best wishes.
2108 N1NAS WB8IMY 73
WB8IMY sends his 73 as well. The contact has ended.

Instead of sending 73, you'll often see stations sending bits of "free hand" text instead. They are doing this by typing the text into the TX TEXT window. You may see something like 40W LOOP ANT, which is shorthand for "I'm running 40 W to a loop antenna."

Chapter 9

Image Communications

As Amateur Radio operators, we communicate via radio. That's what our hobby is about. A natural extension to radio communication is television or image communication. Sound interesting? That's what this chapter is all about.

Thousands of Amateur Radio operators in the USA have ventured beyond voice, CW or digital text-based modes and regularly transmit and receive still pictures or full motion video on the ham bands. In the first part of this chapter, we will concentrate on fast scan amateur television (FSATV), usually just called ATV. This section was originally prepared for previous editions by Art Towslee, WA8RMC. It has been extensively revised and updated for this edition by Tom O'Hara, W6ORG. Later in the chapter we will explore slow scan television (SSTV).

Nick Klos, AC6Y, worked with local amateurs to develop an airborne ATV station that hams could use to assist the Corona, California, police department during emergencies. The complete portable system includes a 70 cm ATV transceiver, ID generator, LCD television, 2 meter/70 cm FM transceiver and antenna duplexer. A 12 V, 18 Ah battery provides power.

AMATEUR TELEVISION (ATV) OVERVIEW

Are you interested in public service communications? You can assist with public safety by transmitting video of local events such as parades, marathons, various disaster drills, and so forth back to aid stations and operation centers. Maybe you'd like to share home videos with fellow ATVers or transmit the local ham club meeting with live color video and sound. You can record meetings and events and transmit them later for those who could not attend in person.

In general, ATV is like the television that broadcasters have been transmitting for over 50 years. However, much simpler equipment is used. At first you may think that ATV is overly complex and expensive, but it is not the case on both counts. Yes, the video waveform itself is rather complex, but it is easy and not too expensive to transmit and receive mainly because of commercially available home entertainment, video security and amateur TV equipment.

For ATV, you may already own two of the three main components in a basic station — the camera and receiver. The required camera can be the same camcorder that you use to record your family and vacation memories or it can be an inexpensive security camera. The audio and video (AV) cable from the camera is plugged directly into the ATV transmitter.

Off the air photos show transmission of the monthly San Bernardino Microwave Society meeting over local ATV repeaters. At the right, Marty Woll, N6VI, gives a report on the progress of the band plan updates to the club.

ATV History

ATV generally appeals to hams more interested in the technical portion of the hobby. Therefore, many have little concern with contests but lean toward building, modifying and working on equipment. Initially, if you didn't build it, you weren't successful in ATV because there was very little affordable and readily available commercial equipment. Today that's changed dramatically so more and more non-technical people are entering this fascinating side of Amateur Radio and learning to be quite technical as they progress.

Back in the 1950s, very few people experimented with amateur television. Those who did tended to be TV broadcast engineers who had the knowledge and equipment to get started.

In the '60s there was very little commercial equipment available. Most of the experienced ATVers were busy converting the transmitter portion of taxicab UHF radios and trying to squeeze those extra few milliwatts out of a 2C39 or 5894 tube. They got, if they were lucky, a few watts of RF. Feed lines were lossy, so if a watt was delivered to the antenna, that was good.

On the receiving side, the situation was even more difficult. The only way to use commercially available stuff was to modify (retune) a UHF tube-type tuner so that it would cover 439 MHz. Bell Telephone had a special low-noise tube known as the 416B that could be used for a receiving preamp if one of these could be found. If located, you then had to find a machinist willing to fabricate a socket and housing for the circuitry.

Transmitters and receivers were difficult enough but the real stumbling block was the camera. Black and white vidicon cameras were available but generally not on the surplus market. The cheapest way to generate video was with a photo multiplier tube using a TV raster as the scanning device (another story for another day). This method only produced still pictures.

The '70s introduced widespread use of those tiny solid-state devices called transistors and a new era of experimentation began. Many types of low-noise devices became available, but not necessarily affordable for all. Numerous ATV articles appeared in ham magazines for both transmitting and receiving equipment. Black and white vidicon cameras were now becoming more available.

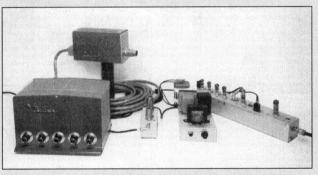

Laird Campbell, W1CUT (SK), described this 70 cm ATV transmitter in November 1962 *QST.* Typical of early ATV stations, it uses a combination of homebrew and commercial equipment. Getting a UHF amateur television station up and running in this era was quite an achievement!

The '80s and early '90s were transitional, as more and more modifiable commercial units became available, as well as some gear designed specifically for the ham market. When this happened, more hams got involved because it no longer required an engineer to make things work.

Today, individual transistors of earlier times are reduced dramatically in size, combined into entire circuits on a single integrated circuit (IC) and packaged into complete radios. Even more dramatic is the cost reduction. A complete radio circuit is cheaper now than a single transistor was in the '70s. As a result, low-cost, high-efficiency circuitry for ATV without modification is available to everyone. A wealth of inexpensive consumer camcorders and other AV equipment is now available at hamfests.

Twenty years ago, no one even dreamed this could happen. So what's next? Have we approached the limit? No, we're still on a nearly vertical learning curve with many more exciting things yet to come. Total digital processes are now emerging, so get involved and join the excitement of the adventures of amateur television.
— *WA8RMC*

Receiving your first ATV picture can be as easy as connecting your broadcast TV set to a rooftop 70 cm amateur band antenna (more on this later). The antenna should use the polarization (vertical or horizontal) common in your area.

You'll find most ATV activity on the 70 cm (420-450 MHz) band, but 33 cm (910-920 MHz), 23 cm (1250-1280 MHz) and 13 cm (2410-2450 MHz) are also used. Check the *ARRL Repeater Directory* to see if there is a local ATV repeater in your area and contact the owner or sponsoring group to find the most used frequencies, antenna polarization and information on ATV nets or other regular activity.

Before transmitting, it is good practice to find out the local band plan and which frequencies are used in your area for ATV. Analog AM ATV channels are about 6 MHz wide, so basically there is only room for two 70 cm ATV frequencies

to be used because of potential interference to and from amateurs using other modes and to avoid ATV signal overlap into the adjacent channel or outside the band edge.

Nets are a great source of regular ATV activity. To keep the net interesting, one week's net might be to show and tell a project, vacation video or just has everyone wearing a funny hat. See **Figure 9.1**.

Setting up an ATV contact often involves calling "CQ ATV" on the local 2 meter FM voice ATV calling and talk-back frequency — typically 144.340 or 146.430 MHz simplex. "Talk back" means that during the ATV contact, the stations use 2 meter voice to allow the receiving stations to talk back at the same time as the 70 cm ATV transmitting station talks on the sound subcarrier which is heard from the TV speaker. It's much like talking on the telephone.

Figure 9.1 — To keep it interesting, some ATV net nights have themes such as "show a project," "the kids" or just "something crazy." Here Mark Fischer. W6MAF, shows his talking fish. Many repeaters stream their ATV net video and audio over the British Amateur Television Club (BATC) website — see **www.batc.tv**.

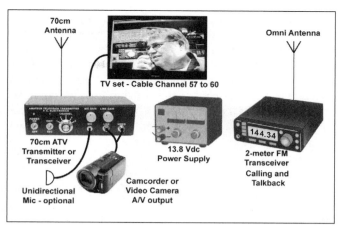

Figure 9.2 — Here is the block diagram of a basic 70 cm ATV station. Any television with an analog cable tuner can be the receiver. The ATV transmitter provides TR switching to shift the antenna between it and the receiver. A 2 meter transceiver is commonly used to make initial contact and also for talking back to the ATV transmitting station. Audio either from the camera mic or an external directional mic is transmitted with the video.

THE ATV STATION

Receivers

The frequency of cable channels 57 to 61 are actually within the 420-450 MHz (70 cm) ham band so the TV receiver is able to tune them directly. Analog cable channel tuners will be required in new digital TVs for some time per FCC §15.118(b), but here is a great way to get some use from your old analog-only TV. You can use it for ATV, especially if it does not go to blue screen or shut off if no signal is present as some of the newer sets do.

Cable Channel 57 is 421.25 MHz and is popular for ATV repeater outputs. Cable Channel 60 (439.25 MHz) is often used for ATV repeater inputs and for simplex DX. Due to technical band plan considerations for sharing with other modes, cable Channel 61 (445.25 MHz) is not used because all local band plans use this part of the band for FM and digital voice repeaters. Usually 434.0 MHz is used rather than 433.25 MHz, which is cable Channel 59, to keep the sound subcarrier out of the satellite subband. In most areas, 426.25 MHz is used instead of cable Channel 58 (427.25 MHz) which keeps the sound subcarrier out of the weak signal subband. It is not a problem to receive these off-set signals given that analog cable TV channels are 6 MHz wide and the TV sets automatic frequency control (AFC) can lock on to ATV stations that are up to 1 MHz off the exact cable video carrier frequency.

Downconverters

An ATV downconverter that mixes the 70 cm ham band down to TV Channel 3 can also be used between the antenna and TV. Older TV sets that do not have cable tuners need a downconverter for ATV because the old broadcast UHF TV channels from 14 up are not the same as cable TV channels and do not cover the 70 cm ham band. ATV transceivers actually don't have a receiver in them, but instead have a downconverter. The TV is the actual receiver that does most of the system amplification, filtering, detection and processing of the video you see on its screen.

Downconverters can tune the exact ATV frequency and generally have a lower noise preamp stage for better sensitivity than the average TV. Downconverters are also used for analog ATV on the 33 and 23 cm ham bands and mix down to TV Channel 3 or 8 respectively.

Antennas

Most stations use a 70 cm beam antenna rather than an omnidirectional antenna to receive ATV. The beam has gain to help with received signal levels and directivity to minimize multipath ghosting in the picture. But rather than rotating the 70 cm beam searching for activity on the air, it is more efficient to monitor a 2 meter ATV calling and talk-back frequency with a 2 meter omnidirectional antenna. If you can work someone on 2 meter FM voice with an omni antenna, it is a good indication that you have a chance to see them on 70 cm ATV using a 70 cm beam.

Once 2 meter contact is made, 70 cm beams can be aligned roughly toward each other, the ATV transmitter turned on and then the beam headings adjusted for least snow in the received picture. Running full duplex audio is also a real interactive advantage with this image mode for moving the camera or zooming in on objects in the picture being discussed or asking immediate questions.

If you have a 70 cm antenna on the roof already, it is worth connecting it to the TV and giving it a try. However, if ATV stations in your area use the opposite antenna polarization, you can expect about 20 dB less signal. Ideally, ATV should be cross polarized to nearby users of other modes to reduce potential interference. But in many areas the polarization — horizontal for weak signal CW and SSB and vertical for FM voice repeaters — was determined by the earliest users and what they already had up on the tower.

Antennas designed for ATV are broader in bandwidth than ones used for FM voice repeaters, satellite and weak signal CW or SSB. Depending on how your existing antenna was designed, it may not have the same gain across the band or at the ATV frequency. Still, the signal might be strong enough to see that first picture so give it a try with whatever antenna you already have. Later, especially if you want to transmit ATV, you can add an antenna for the correct polarization and frequency. Some hams like to use circular polarization or cross polarized antennas to enable working all modes with one antenna if tower space is limited. Low loss coax, N connectors and attention to weatherproofing all connections are a must on the 70 cm band and higher frequencies.

ATV DX

For some hams the thrill of making far-away contacts drives them to make station improvements and ATVers are no exception. See the ATV DX records at **www.hamtv.com/atvdxrecord.html** for an idea of what distances are possible.

DXers looking for ATV stations hundreds of miles away during periods of temperature inversion skip that typically occurs in the early summer months will put up large horizontally polarized arrays as high as possible and optimized for 439.25 MHz, the prime ATV DX frequency.

An antenna-mounted preamp will cancel the loss in a long run of coax feed line for best receive sensitivity. Hardline or other low-loss coax is used to ensure that as much of the transmitted signal as possible reaches the antenna.

The 2 meter simplex ATV DX coordination frequency of 144.34 MHz is monitored for DX openings. Some operators listen with an FM or SSB voice receiver to the 439.25 MHz video carrier frequency for sync buzz from far away stations. The noise floor can be more than 20 dB lower with an FM or SSB voice receiver because of its narrower bandwidth, and so the sync buzz will be heard well before video signals are strong enough to be copied.

Instead of QSL cards to commemorate a DX ATV contact, the receiving station will take a photograph of the TV screen and then email it to the transmitting station (**Figure 9.3**). A contact is deemed valid if the call letters can be seen in the snow.

Transmitters

Now let's look at transmitting. Amplitude modulated analog 70 cm is the most popular for ATV as mentioned earlier because most people already have two of the three basic components. Also, the lower the frequency, the farther the signal goes given the same transmit power, transmit and

Figure 9.3 — During a summer opening W8ZCF in Cincinnati Ohio received this picture from W8URI 133 miles away in Mt Gilead, Ohio, on 439.25 MHz.

Figure 9.4 — A 5 W 70 cm transmitter and optional companion downconverter is a good plug and play combination for public service events or the home station. (photo courtesy of *PC Electronics*)

receive antenna gains and coax loss factors.

Multimode UHF transceivers rarely include ATV because the signal is composed of a complex amplitude modulated carrier with a 4.5 MHz FM sound subcarrier (see the sidebar, "ATV Signal Characteristics"). The modulator in the transmitter must be capable of wide bandwidth and good linearity over the bandwidth to preserve high resolution and color video. Therefore most all ATV transmitters are standalone units designed specifically for this mode, such as the one shown in **Figure 9.4**.

ATV transmitters accept the standard composite video signal (1 V peak-to-peak into 75 Ω) and line level audio from camcorders, cameras and other video devices with AV outputs. An RCA phono jack color coded yellow is common for home video components, while audio jacks are color coded red and/or white. Basically, any consumer video device you have been using that is plugged into a TV, home theater or VCR AV input can also be plugged into an ATV transmitter.

In addition, many ATV transmitters also have a low level mic input that is handy for using a separate unidirectional low-impedance dynamic mic. The directional mic is useful to avoid a feedback loop with the 2 meter radio speaker, cut down on extraneous noise, or to do voice-over commenting when transmitting a recording.

In addition to adjusting the audio gain control or the distance from the mic that you are probably used to with voice modes, ATVers quickly find that they must be concerned with focus and lighting of the scene. In the shack, you don't

ATV Signal Characteristics

Most ATV is analog AM double sideband (DSB), with the widest component being the sound subcarrier out ±4.5 MHz. As can be seen in the accompanying figure, the video power density is down more than 30 dB at frequencies greater than 1 MHz from the carrier — more than 90% of the spectrum power is in the first 1 MHz on both sides of the carrier.

To fit within a 6 MHz wide channel, analog television broadcast stations used an approach called vestigial sideband (VSB). VSB involves suppression, but not elimination, of the lower sideband so that it occupies less than 1 MHz. In addition, instead of combining a 4.5 MHz subcarrier to produce sound, broadcast stations used a second sound transmitter offset above the video carrier by 4.5 MHz so that the sound signal does not appear in the lower sideband.

DSB and VSB are both compatible with analog cable TV tuners, but the lower sound and color subcarriers are rejected in the TV set IF filter as unnecessary. In the case of VSB, less than 5% of the lower sideband energy is attenuated. The other significant energy frequencies are the sound (set in the ATV transmitter at 15 dB below the peak sync) and the color at 3.58 MHz (greater than 22 dB down).

If the band is full and the lower sideband color and sound subcarrier frequencies need to be used by a dedicated link or repeater, a VSB filter in the antenna line can attenuate them another 20 to 30 dB, or the opposite antenna polarization can be used for more efficient packing of the spectrum.

Since most amateur linear amplifiers reinsert the lower sideband to within 10 dB of DSB, a VSB filter in

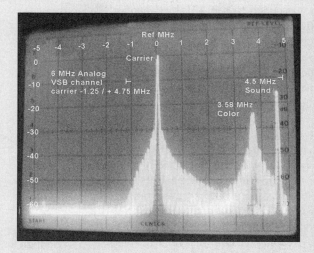

Spectral display of a color analog AM VSB ATV signal. Spectrum power density varies with picture content, but typically 90% of the sideband power is within the first 1 MHz.

the antenna line is the only cost-effective way to reduce the unnecessary lower sideband subcarrier energy if more than 1 W is used. In the more populated areas, 2-m calling or coordination frequencies are often used to work out operating time shifts or other techniques to accommodate all users sharing or overlapping the same segment of the band. — *W6ORG*

---

want the bags under your eyes to appear larger than they are! Placing a light behind the camera helps to minimize the shadows you might get from only having an overhead room light.

ATV transmitters are available at various RF power output levels from 50 mW to 20 W PEP. An alternative is to use a cable TV modulator that typically has an RF output between 0.1 and 13 mW. For higher power, both types of transmitters would add linear amplifiers designed for class A or AB operation and wide band amplitude modulation.

On the 70 cm band, for a basic home station running 5 W PEP and 5 element beams at both ends, you can expect snow-free video over a line-of-sight path of up to 25 miles. That may be enough to work a local ATV repeater. To double the distance for the same picture quality or raise one P unit at the same distance, you will need to raise the effective radiated power (ERP) by 6 dB. (On ATV, signal reports are given in P units — P0 is barely recognizable, while P5 is snow-free. See the section on Signal Reports later in this chapter.) **Figure 9.5** shows possible line-of-sight distances for various transmitter levels in the 70 cm band.

Antenna gain and placement for a line-of-sight path are the keys to reliable ATV communications. The antenna system should be your first improvement project, and it will help both transmitting and receiving. Snow-free line-of-sight distance can be predicted when transmitter power, antenna gains and feed-line loss are known, but if there are obstructions in the path the signal may suffer some attenuation. Check the path on 2 meter FM voice to find a magic spot on the roof or mast. If you are still not getting a snow-free picture, you can try a bigger antenna, lower loss coax, or as a final option, add a linear amplifier.

AM Cable Modulators

Analog AM cable modulators are currently low in price and can be used without modification if your local band plan allows for activity on the exact frequency of 427.25 MHz (channel 58) or 439.25 MHz (channel 60). Cable modulator output power is specified in dB above 1 millivolt (dBmV) into 75 Ω. They typically range in power output from 40 to 60 dBmV (0.1 to 13 mW into 50 Ω).

Most cable modulators contain a surface acoustic wave (SAW) upper vestigial sideband (VSB) filter. (See the sidebar, "ATV Signal Characteristics" for more information on VSB.) Upper VSB filters start rolling off the 6 MHz passband at –1.25 MHz and +4.75 MHz from the video carrier frequency. It is not recommended to use 421.25 (Channel 57) without a VSB filter in the antenna line to attenuate the lower sideband signal outside the amateur band limits. If an amplifier is added, the lower sideband level will rise due to the intermodulation distortion generated in the amplifier.

Cable modulators have a 75 Ω output, but the small mismatch to a 50-Ω input linear amplifier is negligible. Care must be taken to drive an amplifier strictly within its linear range which is often half its Amateur Radio maximum output power rating. The specified 1-dB gain compression level is a good maximum peak envelope power point.

Keeping the amplifier in its linear range is necessary to keep the video signal sync tip from compressing. Many ATV transmitters have a "sync stretcher" or "blanking pedestal" adjustment to compensate for a linear amplifier's gain compression at higher output levels. Sync stretchers allow driving linear amplifiers to higher output levels, but cable modulators don't have this feature.

Cable modulators operating at lower frequencies can also be connected to a transverter that converts 2 meter signals to a higher frequency band. For instance, cable Channel 19 is 151.25 MHz and would output on 439.25 MHz with a 144-to-432-MHz transverter. The crystal in the transverter may have to be changed so the signal from the cable modulator ends up exactly on your local ATV frequency, or the transverter input may have to be retuned.

Digital ATV

Digital cable modulators are still quite high in price, but are coming down if you want to try your hand at digital ATV (D-ATV) transmission. This mode requires even more attention to lightly driving true linear amplifiers and preventing sideband growth and intermodulation distortion. D-ATV is still largely an experimental activity among Amateur Radio operators due to its current cost and complexity to transmit. However, some amateurs are using D-ATV successfully as seen in **Figure 9.6**.

Unlike analog TV, where the picture is snowy but visible if signals are weak, digital TV is all or nothing. Above a signal-to-noise ratio of around 15 dB you get a perfect picture, but below that you get nothing. This is known as the *cliff effect* and occurs around the same signal level as a P1 or P2 AM or FM analog ATV picture. Also with D-ATV you do have to get used to a little time delay when talking back on 2 meters.

Digital TV (DTV) Standards

There are three basic digital video broadcast (DVB) standards in use. A brief description of each follows. More technical information may found in the Image Communications

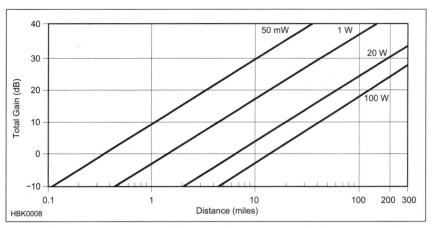

Figure 9.5 — This graph shows the possible line-of-sight distances for P5 (snow free) video reception for various analog AM ATV transmitter levels in the 70 cm band. Power levels shown are in PEP. The Total Gain is calculated by adding the antenna gain (dBd) for both the receive and transmit antennas and then subtracting the feed line loss (in dB) at both ends. For other bands: 33 cm, subtract 6 dB; 23 cm, subtract 9 dB; and 13 cm, subtract 15 dB. For FM ATV (4 MHz deviation, 5.5 MHz sound), add 12 dB. For ATSC 8-VSB digital TV, the sudden loss of picture "cliff effect" distance is found by adding 26 dB. If the noise figure of the first stage in the downconverter is greater than 2 dB, subtract for each dB over 2.

Figure 9.6 — Crisp, clear digital ATV through the ATCO WR8ATV repeater.

chapter on the *The ARRL Handbook* CD-ROM.

DVB-T was developed for terrestrial digital television communication and is used by US broadcast television stations for digital and HDTV. Known best as ATSC (Advanced Television Systems Committee) with 8VSB *modulation* (8 quadrant Vestigial Sideband), it is designed to overcome the effects of multipath reflections that cause "ghosts" in analog TV reception. DVB-T employs a very complex signal and a high data rate. This is fine for over-the-air broadcast television to homes, but is impractical for mobile or portable ham use as it does not respond well to antenna movement.

DVB-C was developed for cable DTV using *quadrature amplitude modulation* (QAM). A cable does not have the distortion and multipath effects and needs a much simpler digital modulation. QAM 64 D-ATV is being experimented with in the US because it can be received by most digital televisions directly. That makes it easier for ATVers to try out this mode, although it is more susceptible to multipath distortion than DVB-S.

The DVB-S standard was developed for satellite digital television transmission using *quadrature phase shift keying* (QPSK) modulation, which is a type of FM modulation. DVB-S is also the standard of choice for many amateur digital TV enthusiasts. It offers very good performance without taking up more bandwidth than an analog TV signal. Free To Air satellite receivers are used for DVB-S operation and can be found on the Internet. They should not be confused with equipment for subscription satellite TV services such as DirecTV.

A group of Dutch hams pioneered an innovative DVB-S system using an MPEG-2 encoder and a DVB-S I/Q board. This system has since been widely adopted in the D-ATV community.

D-ATV is still largely an experimental activity among Amateur Radio operators. You'll find more information online in the D-ATV Yahoo Group at **groups.yahoo.com/group/ DigitalATV**.

ATV Accessories

Whether you are using an analog or digital cable modulator plus linear amplifier or a standalone ATV transmitter module, you will need to add a transmit/receive (TR) antenna relay with enough isolation (40 dB typically) to put no more than 1 mW into the TV or downconverter antenna input. Manufactured ATV transceivers and some transmitters have antenna TR relays built-in, and they also switch off the dc power to the downconverter in transmit.

When using just a TV set to receive, it is difficult to switch off the TV power when going to transmit, so be prepared to turn down the volume before flipping the transmit switch. Don't be surprised that your picture looks a mess in transmit — your transmitted signal is going to overload the TV past its automatic gain control (AGC) limit.

Receiving your own transmitted signal on a TV in the shack is most often distorted from the overload and multipath signals. A diode detector in the antenna line with a 75 Ω line driver set to 1 V p-p and connected to a video monitor or the AV input of another TV will show your true transmitted picture.

LICENSING, LIMITS, REPEATERS, IDENTIFYING

ATV can be transmitted by any ham with a Technician license or higher on any ham band 420 MHz and above. Some regional limitations exist for frequency and power levels in parts of the United States, so check the *ARRL Repeater Directory* and FCC §97.303 or local sources before operating. Activity concentrates on different frequencies in different parts of the USA. However, most ATV activity can be found in the 420-440 MHz portion of the 70 cm band. Once you become involved with the people using the ATV repeater or 2 meter ATV coordination and talk back frequency, you'll find that help with equipment selection, troubleshooting and all-around technical information will be plentiful.

ATV Repeaters

ATV repeaters usually transmit on 421.25 or 426.25 MHz (cable Channel 57 or 58) and receive on 434.0 or 439.25 MHz (cable Channel 59 or 60) and have VSB filters in the antenna lines. An in-band ATV repeater needs at least 12 MHz separation and special duplexers and VSB filters to prevent the 6 MHz wide channels from desensing the repeater receiver. A few ATV repeaters transmit on 439 MHz and receive on 426 or 427 MHz.

The nature of the AM ATV signal is that the sideband power, except for the 4.5 MHz sound subcarrier at –15 dBc, drops off by more than 30 dB at ±1 MHz each side of the video carrier. While other narrower bandwidth modes operating within the 6 MHz channel may not experience any interference from the ATV signal, the ATV receiver will see the interference from other signals in the channel.

Areas with many active FM voice repeaters below 444 MHz have opted to use 434.0 upper or 439.25 MHz

Richard Logan, WB3EPX, is an active ATV operator. His station is designed with space limitations in mind.

lower VSB for their ATV repeater to avoid this interference possibility. Most ATV stations transmit both sidebands which makes them compatible with repeaters receiving either VSB. Upper VSB is standard, the same as cable TV.

Some areas elected to go crossband with the repeater input or output on a higher band so as to free up one of the two possible 70 cm ATV channels for simplex. Crossband repeat also makes it easier to link adjacent ATV repeaters. You can receive your own transmitted video with just the right amount of antenna separation or the addition of high-pass or low-pass filters when working through a crossband repeater.

Repeater antenna polarization may be horizontal or vertical depending on the repeater owner's preference, but being cross polarized to your neighbors using other modes will give the least probability of interference in the picture. There are cost and other technical factors that must be considered also for choosing the antenna polarization at commercial repeater sites.

Some ATV repeaters mix the 2 meter calling and talkback audio on with the received sound subcarrier. A tower-mounted camera ("tower cam") with ID that can be remotely panned and tilted using DTMF tones on the 2 meter or sound subcarrier audio can monitor approaching weather systems or ice build ups on antennas at the repeater communications site. A number of ATV repeaters are connected via the Internet and have streaming video of their outputs.

STATION IDENTIFICATION

Identifying on ATV has the same requirements of any other mode — you must transmit your call sign after 10 minutes of continuous operation and at the end of a transmission. On ATV, you can do that by speaking on the sound subcarrier or making your call sign plainly visible in the picture. Some operators use a QSL card. Others use something as simple as a felt-tip pen scribble on a piece of paper, while others use an automatic video overlay board.

Signal Reports

When you watch an ATVer's picture, you want to tell the sender how well it is being received. You could say, "Your picture is 20% snow." But that terminology is vague and wordy. The only exceptions are "I can't see it at all," or "You're perfectly snow-free," which we all understand. It's analogous to the digital 1s or 0s indicating on or off, but it's the shades of gray that become a bit more arbitrary. To solve this problem, the P system was developed for AM ATV signal

reception. It goes like this: P stands for picture level and is divided into six levels from P0 to P5. For a visual representation of what the AM signal for each P-unit level looks like, see **Figure 9.7**.

A signal received as P0 is recognizable as to its existence only. No detail is discernible and usually only sync bars can be seen in the snow. Since the minimum recognizable signal change is about 3 dB, 6 dB steps are easily recognized and they represent a convenient increment. The numbers continue in 6 dB steps from P0 to P5. P5 is a snow-free signal and is 30 dB stronger than P0. Beyond that, ATVers tend to say "P5 plus," or "broadcast quality."

P-unit reporting is universal across the USA and in other countries as well. This system is accurate only for AM because of the near-linear levels. P-unit reporting of FM signals can be used as long as it's understood that it will not be 6 dB per P unit because of the nonlinear nature of the receiver limiter and detection system.

UHF TO MICROWAVES

While most ATV activity is on the 70 cm band, the higher bands can be fun to experiment with and offer some advantages. Full duplex video can expedite communications with each end transmitting on a different band at the same time.

For example, hams support the Angeles Crest 100 Mile Endurance Run. Hams at a remote, hard-to-get-to mountain aid station transmit on 70 cm to the next aid station 6 miles distant, and the other station transmits back at the same time on 23 cm. This allows medical personnel to make much better runner assessments and treatment suggestions than if they communicated by voice alone. It also lets a runner's crew and friends see and talk to him or her and to find out what assistance or support might be needed later.

The higher bands are often used for point-to-point links between ATV repeaters; for alternate inputs, outputs or modulation types; for short links to an emergency communications van; for simultaneous multiple camera operations; or any time 70 cm gets too active.

Technical Considerations

Generally, all the transmission factors become more significant as the frequency goes up from UHF through microwaves. Path loss increases 6 dB as the frequency doubles, primarily because antenna area decreases for the same gain.

To make up for it, higher gain antennas are used. With higher gain comes narrower beamwidth and that means more attention to aligning the antennas for best signal.

Beam antennas made for ATV are most often broadened bandwidth versions of those made for weak signal work at a dB or so sacrifice in gain for the same boom length. On 70 cm, a home station looking for the most gain would select an antenna like the one shown in **Figure 9.8** and tuned for the ATV transmit frequency. Of course available room on the tower or mast is a limiting factor. On higher bands, the antennas are physically smaller and easier to fit.

Loop Yagi antennas are broad band and are popular on the 900 and 1200 MHz bands. "BBQ grill" dishes used on 2.4 GHz have a lot of gain for their 2 × 3 foot size. There are many different antenna types and characteristics to choose from depending on your application and antennas are always a subject of much discussion on the air.

Coaxial cable attenuation increases with frequency and distance, so larger low-loss coax cable or hardline are used for the higher bands or for longer runs. Check *The ARRL Antenna Book* or manufacturer's data for cable attenuation per 100 feet on the intended band before you buy. Belden 9913, Times LMR-400 and Andrew CNT-400 are low-loss versions of RG-8 size (0.405 inch diameter) coax. With N

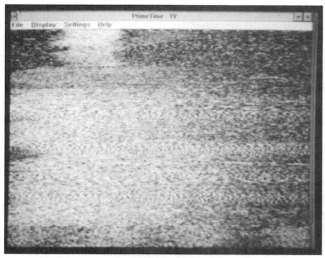

P0 — Picture is barely recognizable. Only sync bars can be seen.

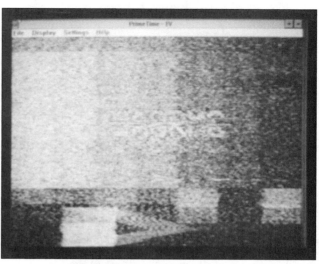

P1 — 6 dB > P0. Picture is recognizable, but extremely snowy.

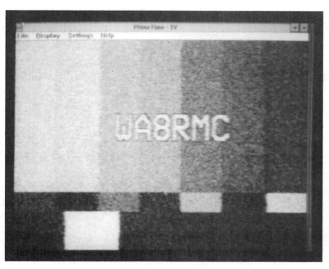

P2 — 12 dB > P0. Picture is easily recognizable, but lacks detail and still is quite snowy.

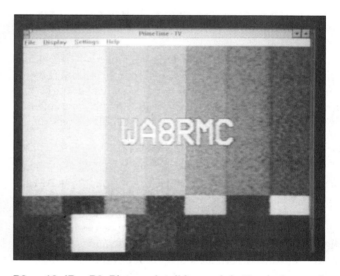

P3 — 18 dB > P0. Picture detail is much better, but snow is still visible

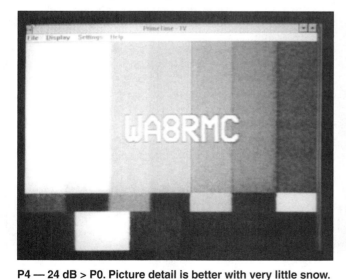

P4 — 24 dB > P0. Picture detail is better with very little snow.

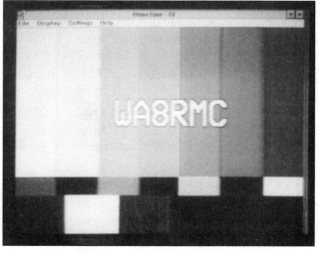

P5 — 30 dB > P0. Picture is snow free.

Figure 9.7 — The P-level signal reporting system used

Figure 9.8 — W8SJV's antenna arrays. Sandwiched between his HF beam (below) and his 2-meter Yagi (above) is a 21-element 15-dBd Yagi on a 14-foot boom. John uses this for his ATV work, and has reported excellent results.

connectors they have less than 3 dB loss per 100 feet on 70 cm. This size coax is considered a minimum for home ATV stations.

Low-noise antenna-mounted preamps can cancel the coax loss, but a remote preamp adds complications. The preamp must be powered, and it must be switched out of line with RF relays in sequence to transmit with the same antenna. Some commercially available preamps handle this nicely.

FM ATV Operation

Experimentally, using the US standard, FM ATV gives increasingly better picture-to-noise (snow) ratios than AM analog ATV at receiver input signals greater than 5 µV. Because of the wider noise bandwidth and FM threshold effect, AM analog video can be seen in the noise well before FM ATV or digital ATV. For DX work, it has been shown that AM signals are recognizable in the snow at up to four times (12 dB) greater distance than FM or DTV signals, with all other factors equal. Above the FM threshold, however, FM rapidly overtakes AM. FM snow-free pictures occur above 50 µV, or four times farther away than with AM signals. The crossover point is near the signal level where sound and color begin to appear for all three systems. **Figure 9.9** compares analog AM, FM and digital ATV across a wide range of signal strengths.

Occupied bandwidth is almost 19 MHz using the narrow FM ATV standard of 4 MHz deviation and 5.5 MHz sound subcarrier.

Figure 9.9 — Three approaches to ATV receiving. This chart compares AM, FM and digital ATV as seen on a TV receiver and monitor. Signal levels are into the same downconverter with sufficient gain to be at the noise floor. The FM receiver bandwidth is 17 MHz, using the US standard. The straight vertical line for DTV around –93 dBm illustrates the cliff effect described in the text.

Therefore, FM ATV is only used in the bands above 902 MHz and not on 70 cm where interference with the many voice repeaters, satellite and weak signal stations would make it impractical. You will find some areas that run AM ATV on the 33 or 23 cm bands if they favor having more channels available in the band versus just one or two FM ATV channels. Consult your local band plan.

FM ATV requires using a complete receiver with an AV output connected to a monitor or re-modulated AM to Channel 3 and a TV set. There a few manufactured AM or FM ATV transmitters and receivers in the USA but most of the imported gear is FM. Hams have modified low-cost, license-free FCC Part 15 wireless video transmitters and receivers for use on the 900 MHz, 2.4 GHz and 5.6 GHz ham bands and then added amplifiers.

Care must be taken that the selected FM center frequency is at least 8 MHz inside the band edges. Half of the 2.4 GHz Part 15 band is outside of the ham band and some of the imports are potentially not compliant for amateur use because they have channels way outside the bands. Check the channel switch often to make sure it has not been accidently changed and is set for inside the ham band.

Most of these Part 15 wireless AV systems do not have pre-emphasis and de-emphasis networks in their modulators. These networks would need to be added in the video lines if used in your area and you want the better FM signal-to-noise advantage.

Many amateurs have used old C band satellite TV receivers that tune 950-1450 MHz — covering the 23 cm band. Some even tune down to the amateur 33 cm band directly. Since they were designed to work with an antenna-mounted low-noise block downconverter (LNB), most C band receivers require a preamp to bring the system gain high enough to reach the noise floor.

De-emphasis is built in to these receivers as well as dc

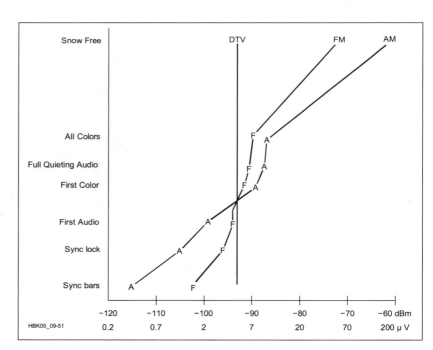

power on the antenna coax for the satellite LNB. You will need to disable the dc before connecting to your antenna unless you want to use it for your preamp. These receivers are designed for satellite TV which has the wider 11 MHz deviation and a bandwidth of 27 MHz. The video gain control inside the receiver needs to be found and turned up for the

1 V p-p video output. On the 3.3 GHz band and above, these C band satellite receivers are used directly with antenna-mounted low noise downconverters or LNBs.

There is some ATV activity on the 10 GHz band. Gunnplexers are easily modulated with video on the Varicap input for 10.4 GHz ATV.

ATV APPLICATIONS AND ACTIVITIES

Here's where it gets fun. After the station is built and a number of contacts have been made, the imagination starts to roam. "What else can I get involved in?" After all it's great talking with and seeing the ATVers but sometimes that's not enough. Many other activities could use ATV involvement — but they sometimes just don't know it! That helps form groups and then clubs dedicated to helping other activities. After all, it's a hobby so it's supposed to be fun. Get involved and make it just that.

Emergency Communications and Public Service Events

ATV can add remote eyes and ears to an emergency operation center (EOC) to more efficiently allocate and use resources. It can provide an early warning at parades and races with a view of the event back to event operations or aid stations. At public service events you can establish a video link up to a mile line-of-sight using 5-element beams and a 50-mW ATV transmitter. A 5-element 70 cm beam is less than 3 feet long and easy to transport. **Figures 9.10** and **9.11** show a portable ATV station used to provide communications at public service events.

Transmitting at races and parades on city streets, you can expect many reflections from buildings, street light and traffic signal posts, cars and other metal objects. If a reflected signal arrives with not much attenuation at the receive site, its amplitude and phase with some delay will mix with the direct signal — resulting in ghosting or sync tearing. Using beams will not only give gain in the desired direct path, but also, compared to an omni antenna, reduce the power to and

from the sides and rear of the antennas toward the RF reflecting objects.

Tripod speaker stands with two or three 5-foot mast sections make a good portable antenna setup and allow you to easily move them around for best signal strength (see **Figure 9.12**). Having the antennas 10 to 15 feet above the ground can reduce blockage to the line-of-sight path when people or vehicles pass between the two antennas (this could make the picture jump). A 2 meter voice link using handhelds is a good way for the receiving station to give the transmitting station instructions for fine-tuning antenna placement. The 2 meter link can also be used to communicate where to point the camera during the event.

If running pedestrian portable ATV, you can clip an antenna to a cap or hard-hat to keep it as high as possible. It is always best to check the locations or do a trial run a few weeks before the event to map out the best antenna locations and desired camera angles. The required battery life or availability of ac line power for the length of the event should be determined ahead of time also.

Emergency communications and public service operations tend to have long transmit times unless multiple camera sites are used. You have to remember to identify every 10 minutes, and it's a good idea to use that as a reminder to also check that the transmitter is properly ventilated and the temperature has not risen to the "too hot to touch" level. Sun angles are an important consideration for transmitter heat dissipation, camera and TV placement, and they should be checked in advance during the hours of the event. As with photographs, having the sun at your back will give the best picture contrast and least shadowing. Similarly, the TV screen can be washed out if facing the sun. The TV receiver is best placed in the shade if possible without compromising the viewing ability of

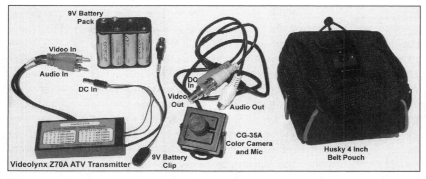

Figure 9.10 — Here's a portable ATV pouch system that's easy to deploy for public service or emergency events requiring video over short distances. The equipment is powered by eight AA-size NiMH batteries that are good for about an hour of continuous operation. Using seven AA-size alkaline batteries will extend that to almost 2 hours. (A ½-20, 1¾ inch round-head screw with a nut on the end is used to jumper the eighth battery slot if alkaline cells are used so as not to exceed the maximum voltage to the transmitter.)

Figure 9.11 — Here's the ATV pouch system ready for use. A hose clamp is used to fasten a small color camera to the antenna mast and offers a convenient place to hang the ATV transmitter pouch. This makes a nice quick and easy set up for fixed portable operation at public service events.

Figure 9.12 — The portable ATV transmitter sends live video to the finish area from a critical traffic intersection during a 10K run.

Figure 9.13 — Engineering students at the Temple University ARC (K3TU) built this radio-controlled Earthbound version of a Mars Rover to put their knowledge to use in solving a practical design problem. Equipped with GPS, sensors and telemetry, the Rover includes a camera and 70 cm ATV transmitter so the operator can see where the Rover is headed.

those using the information from the video. Brightness and contrast levels are going to be different in the field than they are in the home. Familiarize yourself with how to make these adjustments using the manual controls as well as the remote before the event.

Radio Controlled Vehicles

ATV transmitters can be carried by radio controlled (RC) vehicles including airplanes, helicopters, cars and boats. The ATV transmitter can be part of a more complex package, as shown in **Figure 9.13**.

Radio controlled airplanes with a camera and ATV transmitter aboard can give you a pilot's eye view. A 50 mW on 70 cm transmitter with a ground plane antenna works well for about a half mile around a flying field. Modified 900 MHz and 2.4 GHz license-free wireless AV transmitters with the cases stripped off to minimize size and weight can also be used for short range RC video in aircraft, cars and boats.

The RC control transmitter must not be in the same band as the ATV transmitter so that the ATV signal does not overload the RC receiver in the vehicle. Antenna, transmitter placement and possibly high and low pass filters can keep the ATV transmitter from overloading and capturing the RC control receiver. It is a good idea to test for positive control at the farthest distance on the ground before flying.

Balloons

High altitude balloon launches are popular. Hams fill up a 6-foot (or larger) weather balloon with helium, hang a foam box below it. The box can carry a video camera, 1 W transmitter and battery with an omnidirectional antenna hung below it (**Figure 9.14**). Some add a GPS receiver with video overlay to put the location, altitude and direction on the

video. The payload might also include a 2 meter transmitter with APRS to track the location on a map over the Internet — **www.aprs.fi**. These balloons can reach heights beyond 100,000 feet (19 miles) and usually send back spectacular pictures of Earth's curvature and near outer space. See **Figure 9.15**. Also, at that altitude the reception distance extends beyond 500 miles, so it provides an exciting show for many viewers.

Weather Spotting

Are you interested in being a weather spotter? You know, they are the people who chase tornadoes to give the local weather service details about the incoming storm. Well, chasing severe weather is not what many consider fun, but ATVers and ham members of SKYWARN frequently provide video and audio to assist the spotters. Here is an activity that a local ATV amateur repeater group can get involved with. For example, the ATV group in central Ohio (ATCO) provides this service by retransmitting local TV station radar on the ATV repeater upon command to assist the weather spotters with up-to-date video of an incoming storm. When not in service, any ATVer can bring up the radar signal on command to check on weather conditions.

Computer Graphics

Like to play with computer graphics or Power Point presentations? The same DVI, mini-DVI or VGA-to-AV adapters that are used to connect your computer to a video projector or

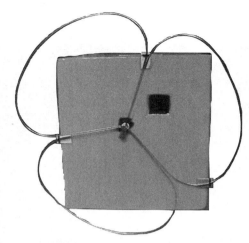

Figure 9.14 — N8UDK mounted an Old Antenna Lab 70-cm Little Wheel horizontal omni antenna to the bottom of his high-altitude balloon ATV payload. The camera is mounted inside the insulated foam package and looks out through the square cutout.

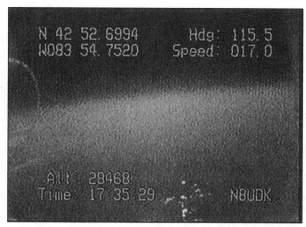

Figure 9.15 — An ATV camera view from a balloon at 93,399 ft shows the blackness of space, the curvature of the earth and hazy clouds below. Note that the standard NMEA altitude data output from GPS receivers is in meters.

video monitor can be plugged into the ATV transmitter and shown to other hams. Have a contest on net night for the one that comes up with the best computer generated call ID. Show the pictures stored in your computer of the family, vacations or ATV DX. Cable TV tuners that plug into the computers USB port enable watching and even recording ATV or screen grabbing a photo to play back later. A laptop with a cable TV USB dongle makes a nice portable ATV receiver for viewing or documenting emergency communications, public service events, RC, rockets and balloon launches.

Summary

With the information presented here, some help from local ATVers, and ideas gathered from other sources including the Internet, you will be well on the road toward a successful ATV station. It's a lot of fun and you'll amaze your friends with your capability.

Special thanks to the many folks who helped with needed information and assistance in the preparation of this material.

Where to Get More Information

1) **The Internet**. This is a wonderful resource of activity, because many ATV clubs and special applications groups post activity details on their Internet homepages. Area activity, as well as frequencies used, provides details of where and when to look for signals. Some of the most active and useful Web sites are:

Columbus, Ohio ATCO Group: **www.atco.tv**
Amateur Television Network: **atn-tv.org**
Baltimore, Maryland BRATS Group: **bratsatv.org**
Detroit, Michigan DATS Group: **www.detroitatvrepeater.com**
Amateur Television Directory: **atv-tv.org**
WB8ELK Balloons: **fly.hiwaay.net/~bbrown/**
ATV at a trail race: **www.foothillflyers.org/hamtvac100.html**

2) **Hamfests**. Check *QST* magazine or visit **www.arrl. org/hamfests-and-conventions-calendar** for a list of hamfests or ham conventions in your area. Most of the larger

hamfests post signs about ATV activity and have ATV forums.

3) *ARRL Repeater Directory*. Check this annual reference for ATV repeater listings.

4) **Local ham store**. Ask about ATV activity in the area. Most ATVers are well known in these places so a list of individual hams involved in ATV can be compiled. Contact these individuals. Most active ATVers are willing to help newcomers and frequently invite potential ATVers to their ham shack to see firsthand what it is all about.

5) **ATV equipment dealers**. Many are willing to share information about where their equipment is sold. If you are interested in a given manufacturer's equipment, ask about it and find out who owns that item in your area. Most will help you. A few of the larger original equipment ATV dealers that have been in business for a number of years are:

PC Electronics — Transmitters, downconverters, antennas, cameras, app notes: **www.hamtv.com**
Downeast Microwave — Transverters, amplifiers, preamps: **www.downeastmicrowave.com**
Directive Systems — High gain antennas: **www.directivesystems.com**
Old Antenna Lab — Wheel omni and beam antennas: **www.hamtv.com/oal.html**
M2 — Wide variety of antennas: **www.m2inc.com**
MFJ — Transmitters, preamps, Mirage amplifiers: **www.mfj.com**
KH6HTV Video — Digital and analog transmitters: **kh6htv.com**
Videolynx — Transmitter modules: **www.hamtv.com/videolynx.html**
ATV Research — cable TV modulators and cameras: **www.atvresearch.com**

6) **Ham Magazines**. Check *QST* and other ham magazines for ATV related articles and advertising. *ATVQ magazine* is dedicated solely to amateur television. Check **atvquarterly.com** for details. *The ARRL Handbook* ATV section also contains good reference information.

SLOW-SCAN TELEVISION (SSTV)

The previous sections discussed fast-scan amateur television, used to send wide-bandwidth full-motion video in the 420 MHz and higher bands. In contrast, slow-scan television (SSTV) is a method of sending still images in a narrow bandwidth and is widely used on the HF bands, although SSTV is sent via FM repeaters and amateur satellites too. This section is based on material prepared by Dave Jones, KB4YZ, for *The ARRL Handbook*.

Images are our most powerful communication tool. They can make us understand and remember better than of our other senses. SSTV allows us to add images to our verbal communications via Amateur Radio. **Figure 9.16** shows a sample SSTV image.

Working with the SSTV can provide much more than just swapping pictures. It provides a practical way to learn about radio propagation, computers and computer graphics. As with any activity, the more involved you become, the more knowledgeable you become about all the intricacies.

SSTV is also a great way to get others involved in Amateur Radio or enhance other activities. Consider adding SSTV capability to your emergency communications, public service, Field Day or Jamboree on the Air station.

SSTV Basics

Traditional SSTV is an analog mode, but in recent years several digital SSTV systems have been developed. All make use of standard Amateur Radio transceivers — no special radio gear or antennas required. SSTV transmissions require only the bandwidth of SSB voice, and they are allowed on

Figure 9.16 — Color SSTV image received from International Space Station in Martin 1 mode on 145.800 MHz FM.

any frequencies in the HF and higher bands where SSB voice is permitted. SSTV does not produce full motion video or streaming video. **Figure 9.17** shows a typical SSTV station.

Computers and Sound Cards

A computer with sound card is required to use most of the software popular for SSTV. Software for the *Windows* operating system is the most popular, but other choices are

SSTV History

SSTV originally involved the transmission of a visual image from a live video source. Images were black-and-white. Specific audio tones represented black, white and shades of gray, and other audio tones were used for control signals. The receiving station converted the tones back into an image for display on a picture tube. It took 8 second to send a picture, and everything fit in the same bandwidth used for SSB transmissions.

Copthorne Macdonald, WA2BCW, now VY2CM, developed the first SSTV system. In 1958, MacDonald used a surplus long-persistence phosphor radar monitor to display SSTV images. The images were created using a vidicon camera or a flying-spot scanner. One frame of video had 120 lines and was sent at a rate of 15 lines per second (that's where the 8 seconds fits in). Three frames were sent back-to-back to maintain an image on the monitor. For many years, home-built systems were the only way to participate in SSTV. These were bulky, expensive and complex.

Robot Research produced SSTV equipment throughout the 1970s and 1980s. Their Robot 1200C scan converter, introduced in 1984, represented a giant leap forward for SSTV — all the SSTV functions were performed within a single box. (A *scan converter* is a device that converts signals from one TV standard to another. In this

case, it converted SSTV signals to and from devices intended for fast scan television.) With updates and modifications, many 1200Cs are still in use today.

DOS-based PCs became a popular component for SSTV systems in the early 1990s. These hybrid systems were part hardware and part software. Most systems had an external box that processed the audio and performed the analog-to-digital conversion. One example is the Tasco Electronics TSC-70 Telereader color scan converter that was used on the MIR space station to send pictures from space. Kenwood introduced Visual Communicator VC-H1, a portable SSTV unit that included a built-in camera and LCD monitor. Other scan converters were made, but none are produced any more.

The personal computer with sound card has become the hardware of choice to send and receive images, replacing specialized devices. Today's powerful PCs and SSTV software are the heart of a modern SSTV station. The PC processes the incoming and outgoing SSTV audio using the sound card, while the software manages the acquisition, storage, selection and editing of the SSTV pictures. If you have a PC in your ham station, adding software and an interface (to connect the computer sound card to the transceiver) is all that it takes to get started in this fascinating mode.

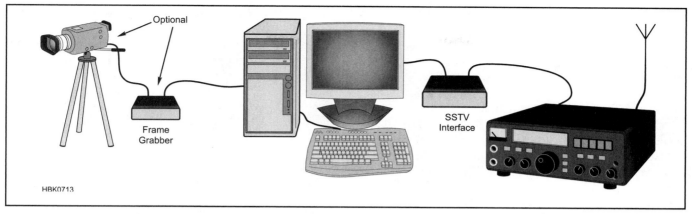

Figure 9.17 — Modern stations need only a sound card equipped PC and simple interface to send and receive SSTV.

available. Hardware and software setup is similar to that described for sound card modes in the chapter on **HF Digital Communications**; refer to that chapter for additional information. Most sound cards will work, but sample rate accuracy is important for some SSTV modes (more on this later).

Within *Windows*, the MASTER VOLUME and WAVE controls set the levels for the transmitted SSTV audio. All other mixer inputs should be muted. Equalizer and special effects should not be used. *Windows* sounds should be disabled to prevent them from going out along with the transmitted SSTV audio. The RECORDING control is used to select the input for receiving the SSTV audio. Adjust LINE IN or MICROPHONE as needed for the proper level. MIC BOOST should not be used.

Transceiver Interface

Interfacing the transceiver to the PC sound card can be as simple as connecting a couple of audio patch cables. Sound cards generally have stereo miniature phone jacks, so use matching plugs when making these connections. Only one audio channel is required or desired — the left channel. This is the tip connection on the plug. Use shielded cable with the shield connected to the sleeve (ground) on the plug. Ground loop problems may be avoided by using an audio isolation transformer.

The connection for receiving SSTV audio from the transceiver may be made anywhere that received audio is available. The best choice is one that provides a fixed-level AF output. This will ensure that sound card levels will not have to be adjusted each time the volume on the transceiver is adjusted. You can use a headphone or speaker output if that's all that is available. If the received output level is enough for the LINE IN input on the sound card, use it, otherwise use the MICROPHONE input. If the level is too high for LINE IN, an attenuator may be required.

Use the LINE OUT connection on the sound card for the transmitted SSTV audio output. The cable for transmitted SSTV audio should go to the transceiver's AFSK connection. If the transceiver does not have a jack for this, then the microphone jack must be used — requiring a more elaborate interface. TR keying can be provided using the transceiver's

VOX. Other methods for activating transmit include manual switching, a serial port circuit, an external VOX circuit and or a computer-control command.

Commercially made sound card interfaces are available. Most of the sound card interfaces for the digital modes are suitable for SSTV. The microphone will be used regularly between SSTV transmissions, so consider its use along with the ease of operation when setting up for SSTV.

A useful resource is the sound card interface web page by Ernie Mills, WM2U, at **www.qsl.net/wm2u/interface.html**.

Transceiver Requirements

An SSB voice transceiver with a stable VFO is necessary for proper SSTV operation. The VFO should be calibrated and adjusted to be within 35 Hz of the dial frequency (more on this later). The transceiver's audio bandwidth should not be constrained so as to infringe on the audio spectrum used by SSTV. Optional filters should be turned off unless they can be set to 3 kHz or wider. SSTV software has its own DSP signal processing tools, so they are not needed in the transceiver. Most of the other transceiver settings should turned be off, including transmit or receive audio equalization, noise blanker or noise reduction, compression or speech processing, and passband tuning or IF shift.

Adjust your transmitter output for proper operation with the microphone first, according to instructions in your manual. Then adjust the sound card output for desired drive level. For SSB operation, receiving stations should see about the same S-meter reading for the SSTV signal as for voice. Properly adjusted levels and clean audio quality will improve the reception of the transmitted signal as well as reduce interference on adjacent frequencies. The SSTV signal is 100% duty cycle. If your transceiver is not designed for extended full-power operation, reduce the power output using the *Windows* VOLUME CONTROL.

SSTV may be transmitted using AM, FM or SSB. Use the same mode as you would use for voice operation on a given frequency. On HF, use the same sideband normally used for voice on that band. SSTV activity can be found on HF, VHF, UHF, repeaters, satellites, VoIP on the Internet and almost anywhere a voice signal can get through.

SSTV Operating Practices

Analog SSTV images are, in a sense, broadcast. They arrive as-is and do not require the recipient to establish a two-way connection. Most SSTV operation takes place on or near specific frequencies. Common analog SSTV frequencies include 3.845, 3.857 and 7.171 MHz in LSB and 14.227, 14.230, 21.340 and 28.680 MHz in USB. Establish a contact by voice first before sending SSTV. If no signals can be heard, on voice ask if there is anyone sending. It may be that someone is sending but you cannot hear them. If there is no response, then try sending a "CQ picture." Note that on popular frequencies, weak signals can often be heard. In this case, wait for traffic to finish before sending SSTV even if you got no response to your voice inquiry.

Receiving SSTV pictures is automatic as long as your software supports the mode used for transmission (more on SSTV modes in later sections). Once a picture is received, it will be displayed and may be saved.

When selecting images to send, consider appropriateness, picture quality and interest to the recipient. Choose an SSTV mode that suitable for the image to be sent, band conditions, signal strengths and the recipient's receive capability. Announce the SSTV mode prior to sending. Avoid sending a CW ID unless required by regulations. Describe the picture only after it is confirmed that it was properly received.

To send SSTV, use your software to select and load a picture to send. It will be displayed in a transmit screen. Next, select the SSTV transmission mode. Click the transmit button, and your transceiver will go into transmit and send the SSTV audio. When the SSTV transmission is over, the transceiver returns to receive. Be sure to send the full frame or the next picture sent may not be received properly because it may not start scanning from the top.

Source for Images

The Internet is a popular source for images. With the unlimited number of images available, it is surprising how often the same Internet pictures keep popping up on SSTV. Use a little imagination and come up with something original.

A digital camera is one of the best ways to create an original picture of your own. The subject matter could be almost anything that you might have available. Pictures of the shack, equipment and operator are always welcomed. A live camera or web cam can provide an almost instant snapshot. Please keep your shirt on and comb your hair!

For those who like to discuss technical details, diagrams and schematics might be your ammunition. A flatbed scanner is ideal for importing diagrams, schematics and photographs. Screen shots of what is on the computer monitor can be saved simply by hitting the PRINT SCREEN key on the keyboard. Use the Paste function in *Windows* to transfer the image to your SSTV or image editing software.

Any image editing program can be used to make your own CQ picture, test pattern, video QSL card or 73 picture. Include your own personal drawings. Make your images colorful with lots of contrast to make them really stand out. You can also transmit pictures of your home, areas of local interest, other hobbies, projects, maps, cartoons and funny pictures.

It is common to have call sign, location and perhaps a short description as text on the pictures. If two calls are placed on an image, it is understood that the sender's call is placed last. Signal reports may also be included. Once the images are saved, they provide a convenient confirmation of contact.

Analog SSTV

With slow scan, the fastest frame rate is 8 seconds so full motion video is not possible. SSTV signal characteristics are discussed in detail in the Image Communications chapter on *The ARRL Handbook* CD-ROM.

Two popular modes for sending and receiving color SSTV pictures are called Martin and Scottie (named after their developers). Within each family are several different modes (Martin 1, Martin 2 and so forth). The various modes have different resolutions and scan rates.

Information about the size or resolution for each mode is generally available in the SSTV software. Better quality images will result when the source image is sized and cropped to the same dimensions used by the mode with which it is transmitted. Slower scan rates can provide better quality; those are the modes that take longer to send for the same resolution.

Each mode has a vertical interval signaling (VIS) code that identifies the mode being sent. When these codes are received, it readies the system to receive in the proper SSTV mode. For VIS detection to work, the receiver must be tuned within 70 Hz of the transmitted frequency. Two stations tuned exactly on the SSTV frequency but with VFO errors of +35 Hz and −35 Hz could successfully pass the VIS codes. As mentioned previously, each transceiver must have the VFO and display calibrated within 35 Hz to ensure VIS code detection with the transceiver set to the SSTV frequency.

Received images are displayed in near real time as they are decoded. Almost any SSTV signal that is heard can produce an image, but it is rare to receive an image that is perfect. Changes in propagation or transceiver settings will become apparent as the image continues to scan down the screen. Noise will damage the lines received just as it occurs. Interference from other signals will distort the image or perhaps cause reception to stop. Signal fading may cause the image to appear grainy. Multipath will distort the vertical edges. Selective fading may cause patches of noise or loss of certain colors.

Images that are received with staggered edges are the result of an interruption of the sound card timing. Check with other operators to see if they also received the image with staggered edges. If not, then it may be your computer that has the problem and not the sending station. Some possible solutions are to close other programs, disable antivirus software and reboot the computer.

Under good conditions, images may come in "closed circuit." This means that the quality appears nearly as good as a photograph. SSTV has a reporting system similar to the RST

(A)   (B)

Figure 9.18 — If the sound card clock is inaccurate, analog SSTV images may appear slanted (A). The same image is shown at B after calibrating the clock.

reporting system used on CW. For analog SSTV it is RSV — readability, signal strength and video. Video uses a scale of 1 to 5, so a report of 595 would be the same as closed circuit.

Analog SSTV Software

A variety of software programs are available for SSTV (see **Table 9.1**). Some multimode programs include SSTV and digital modes, while others are dedicated to SSTV. One very popular SSTV package is the *Windows* program *MMSSTV* by Mako Mori, JE3HHT. For more information or to download a copy, visit **hamsoft.co/pages/mmsstv.php**. Other SSTV software has similar features.

Sound card sample rate accuracy is important for some modes. Analog SSTV is one of them: pictures will appear *slanted* if the clock is off. See **Figure 9.18**. The *MMSSTV* Help file includes detailed information on several ways to do a quick and easy calibration (see the Slant Corrections section). The best method is the one that uses a time standard such as WWV. (Before performing this calibration procedure, you must have the sound card interface connected so *MMSSTV* can detect received audio.) After performing the clock calibration, chances are, the timing will also be correct for transmit. If not, *MMSSTV* provides a means for making a separate adjustment for transmit.

The *MMSSTV* Yahoo group is a valuable resource: **groups.yahoo.com/group/MM-SSTV**.

Digital SSTV

Several forms of digital SSTV have been developed, but the modulation method most widely used for digital SSTV as of 2012 is derived from the shortwave broadcast system Digital Radio Mondiale (DRM). *HamDRM* by Francesco Lanza, HB9TLK, is a variation of DRM that fits in a 2.5 kHz bandwidth and is used in various programs.

The DRM digital SSTV signal occupies the bandwidth

Table 9.1

SSTV Software

Windows
Analog SSTV
ChromaPIX — **barberdsp.com/cpix/chroma.htm**
MMSSTV — **hamsoft.ca/pages/mmsstv.php**
Mscan— **mscan.com/?page_id=2**
ROY1 — **roy1.com/download_ita.htm**
SSTV32— **webpages.charter.net/jamie_5**
W95SSTV— **barberdsp.com/w95sstv/w95sstv.htm**

Multimode
JVComm32 — **jvcomm.de/index_e.html**
MixW — **mixw.net**
MultiPSK — **f6cte.free.fr/index_anglais.htm**

Digital SSTV
DIGTRX — **www.digtrx.com**
EasyPal — **vk4aes.com**
WinDRM — **n1su.com/windrm**

MacOS
MultiMode — **www.blackcatsystems.com/software/ multimode.html**
MultiScan — **web.me.com/kd6cji/MacSSTV**

Linux
MMSSTV — **hamsoft.ca/pages/mmsstv.php**
QSSTV — **users.telenet.be/on4qz**

For links to additional software and notes on setup and operation, see **www.qsl.net/kb4yz**

---

between 350 and 2750 Hz. Digital SSTV using DRM is not a weak signal mode like the narrow bandwidth data modes such as PSK31. An S9 or better signal with little or no noise may be required before the software is able to achieve a sync lock and receive data.

Digital SSTV Setup

A popular DRM digital SSTV program is *EasyPal* by Erik Sundstrup, VK4AES (**www.vk4aes.com**). Digital SSTV uses the same type of PC and sound card setup described in the SSTV Basics section, but a more capable computer is required. For *EasyPal*, a 2 GHz or faster PC running *Windows XP* or newer operating system is required. As soon as the *EasyPal* software is installed, it is ready to receive pictures.

Unlike analog SSTV, the software detects and compensates automatically for clock timing differences so sound card calibration is not required. Software will also automatically adjust ±100 Hz for mistuned frequency.

With DRM SSTV the call sign is sent continuously. This may allow others to identify the transmitting station and perhaps turn an antenna in the right direction for better reception. Many sub modes are available, with various transmission speeds and levels of robustness. The sub mode is automatically detected and receiving starts automatically. Decoding is done on the fly, so there is no waiting for the computer to finish processing before the image appears.

Power output may appear low as measured by a conventional wattmeter. The actual signal strength as seen by others should be about the same as the SSB voice signal. Avoid capacitors in the audio lines as they may interfere with the phase of the digital signal.

DRM audio levels are low, so there may be problems getting the signal to trigger a VOX circuit. Set the transceiver for full RF output. Then adjust the sound card VOLUME CONTROL output until the transmitter shows little or no ALC indication. With an FM transmitter, keep the output level low to avoid overdeviation.

Operating Digital SSTV

Before jumping into digital SSTV, try analog SSTV first. Copy some pictures to see if the sound card setup works. The level adjustments for analog SSTV are not as critical as those for DRM.

Common DRM SSTV frequencies include 3.847, 7.173, 7.228 MHz in LSB and 14.233 MHz in USB. Tune your VFO to the whole number in kHz (for example, 14,233.0). If a sending station is far off frequency, use the pilot carriers as seen in the software spectrum display as a guide. Adjusting the VFO while receiving an image is not advised as it will delay synchronization.

The signal-to-noise ratio (SNR) as displayed in the software is a measure of the received signal quality. The higher the SNR the better — decoding will be more reliable. Under very good band conditions this number may exceed 18. In that case, a higher speed mode may work. Because of the way the software measures the SNR, the peak value displayed for SNR may require 20-30 seconds of reception. Adjustments made on either end may change the SNR. Sub modes with less data per segment take longer to send, but they are more robust and allow for copy even if the SNR is low.

Getting the Whole Picture

Noise and fading may prevent 100% copy of all the segments. Any missing segments may be filled in later. Your software can send a *bad segment report* (*BSR*) that lists all the missing segments for a file that has only been partly received. In response, the other station can send a *FIX* that should complete the file transfer. If not, the BSR and FIX process may be repeated.

Digital SSTV is very interactive and may involve several stations on frequency sharing images. FIX transmissions intended for another station may provide some of your missing segments — or even all of them. A third party that copied the original transmission may also send a FIX or resend the image. Incremental file repair is possible even after several other transmissions are received. The more stations on frequency, the better the chance that one of them is in a position to help out with a FIX.

EasyPal has a feature to provide a higher level of error correction so that 100% copy of all the segments is not necessary to receive the complete file. The transmitted file is encoded with redundant data so that the original file may be recreated even though not all the segments were received. The receiving station must also be running *EasyPal*.

Encoded files have interleaved redundancy using Reed-Solomon (RS) error correction. Four different levels of RS encoding may be selected before the file is sent. Very Light Encode (RS1) is the lowest level. Transmission time for a file using RS1 will be increased by 13%. When receiving a file encoded with RS1, only 90% of the segments must be received before the file can be decoded and a picture displayed. This may happen even before the transmission is complete. Receiving RS encoded files is automatic, there is no need to select it for receive. Decoding of the file received with RS encoding will occur automatically. The use of RS encoding on the HF bands can reduce the need for BSRs and FIXs and has been found to make the file transfer process more efficient. Encoding may not be necessary on noise-free channels such as VHF FM.

Figure 9.19 — *EasyPal* DRM digital SSTV software is used to exchange high quality, color images. Several levels of error correction and various transmission speeds are available.

Propagation only becomes a factor as it may take longer for the data to get through during poor conditions. The images received will be identical to the ones sent because the data in the files will also be identical. Replays will always be an exact copy. Multipath propagation does not disrupt DRM transmissions unless it is severe or results in selective fading.

Figure 9.19 shows an *EasyPal* screen following successful reception of an image.

Image Size

Pictures of any size or resolution may be sent over digital SSTV. The sending station must pay careful attention to file size, though, or the transmission time may become excessively long. Compressing image files is necessary to get the transmit time down to a reasonable amount. Most images will be converted into JPEG 2000 (JP2), a lossy compression method that shows fewer artifacts. A slider varies the JP2 compression level, and a compromise must be made between image quality and file size. The smaller the file, the more visible the artifacts, but the faster it is sent.

Small image files may be sent without using compression. Some file types such as animated GIF files cannot be compressed, so they must be sent "as is."

A "busy picture" is one that shows lots of detail across most of the image area. This type of picture can be challenging to compress into a file size small enough to send yet still maintains acceptable quality. Reducing the resolution by resizing and creating a much smaller image is the solution. Just about any busy picture can be resized down to 320 × 240 pixels, converted into JP2, and still look good when displayed on the receiving end.

About 2 minutes transmission time is the acceptable limit for the patience of most SSTV operators. A typical DRM digital SSTV transmission will take about 105 seconds for a file 23 KB in size, RS1 encoded and requiring 209 segments.

Sending Digital SSTV Images

The ideal DRM signal will have a flat response across the 350 to 2750 Hz spectrum. The transceiver should be allowed to pass all frequencies within this bandwidth. In order to maintain the proper phase relationships with all the subcarriers, the signal must be kept linear. Avoid overdriving the transmitter and keep the ALC at the low end of the range. Eliminate hum and other stray signals in the audio.

The process of transmitting an image starts with selecting an image and resizing or compressing it if needed, as described in the previous section. Within *EasyPal*, when the transmit button is clicked, the image file will be RS encoded if that option is selected. Then the resulting file will be broken down into segments and sent using DRM.

In receiving DRM, the audio is decoded and segments that pass the error check will have their data stored in memory. When enough of the segments are successfully received, the RS file is decoded and the JPEG 2000 image file is created. The content of this file should be identical to the JPEG 2000 image file transmitted.

It can be quite gratifying to receive your first digital SSTV picture. A lot has to go just right, and there is little room for errors. Propagation and interference always play havoc. There is no substitute for a low noise location and good antenna when it comes to extracting the image from the ether. Be patient and when the right signal comes by you will see the all the lights turn green and the segment counter will keep climbing. You won't believe the quality of the pictures!

Help for all aspects of digital SSTV is available on Yahoo Groups DIGSSTV: **groups.yahoo.com/group/digsstv**.

Amateur Satellites

Hams were present at the dawn of the Space Age, creating the first amateur satellite in 1961, and we've been active on the "final frontier" ever since. Even so, satellite-active hams compose a relatively small segment of our hobby, primarily because of an unfortunate fiction that has been circulating for many years — the myth that operating through amateur satellites is difficult and expensive.

As with any other facet of Amateur Radio, satellite hamming is as expensive as you allow it to become. If you want to equip your home with a satellite communication station that would make a NASA engineer blush, it will be expensive. If you

Sean Kutzko, KX9X, (foreground) and Mike Corey, KI1U, listen to an amateur satellite pass.

want to simply communicate with a few low-Earth-orbiting birds using less-than-state-of-the-art gear, a satellite station is no more expensive than a typical HF or VHF setup.

What about difficulty? Prior to 1982, hams calculated satellite orbits using an arcane manual method that many people found unfathomable. In truth, the manual method taught you a great deal about orbital mechanics, but it was viewed by some as being too difficult. Today computers do all of the calculations for you and display the results in easy-to-understand formats (more about this later). Satellite equipment also has become much easier for the average ham to use.

SATELLITE ORBITS AND TRACKING

If you've ever been to a major sports event, you may remember the vendors who strolled throughout the stadium, hawking colorful "program" booklets that contained the complete rosters of each team, player statistics, photographs and more. You could hear them shouting over the public address system, "Get your program! You can't tell who the players are without a program!" Strange as it may sound, the sports program has a parallel in the satellite world.

When this chapter was written, there were no amateur satellites traveling in *geostationary* orbits. The speed of a satellite in geostationary orbit matches the speed of the Earth's rotation at the equator. As a result, it remains fixed at a single point in the sky 24 hours a day. There is never any doubt about where the satellite is located. You simply aim your antenna at the bird and communicate. Home satellite TV systems are

good examples of this concept. Their rooftop parabolic dish antennas never move — they don't need to. Their target is always in the same place.

Amateur satellites — often known as *OSCARs*, Orbiting Satellites Carrying Amateur Radio — usually travel in orbits close to the Earth, or in oblong, elliptical orbits that take them far into space (beyond where geostationary birds reside) before bringing them back toward Earth for a close, slingshot pass. The speeds of these satellites do not match the speed of the Earth's rotation, so they do not remain at fixed points in the sky. Instead, amateur satellites rise above the horizon, soar to a certain altitude (elevation) and then set below the horizon once again. Depending on the nature of the orbit, a satellite may be above the horizon for hours or for only a few minutes. The satellite may appear several times each day, but each pass will be at a different maximum elevation and will follow a different track across the heavens. To add to the confusion, a satellite may not appear at the same times each day, although it will follow predictable arrival patterns when plotted over days or weeks.

To enjoy an Amateur Radio satellite you need to know where it is, when it will arrive and how it will move across the sky. In other words, to identify these "players," you do indeed need a "program." You need a basic understanding of satellite orbits and a *program* in a different sense of the word: a computer program that will take the information about a satellite's orbit and turn it into accurate predictions of when it will appear.

Types of Orbits

Most active amateur satellites are in various types of *Low Earth Orbits* (LEOs), although there are satellites planned for future launch that will travel in the elliptical *High Earth Orbits* (HEOs) mentioned previously. Let's take a brief look at several of the most common orbits.

An *inclined* orbit is one that is inclined with respect to the Earth's equator. See **Figure 10.1**. A satellite that is inclined 90° would be orbiting from pole to pole; smaller inclination angles mean that the satellite is spending more time at lower latitudes. The International Space Station, for example, travels in an orbit that is inclined about 50° to the equator. Satellites that move in these orbits frequently fall into the Earth's shadow (eclipse), so they must rely on battery systems to provide power when the solar panels are not illuminated. Depending on the inclination angle, some locations on the Earth will never have good access because the satellites will rarely rise above their local horizons.

A *sun-synchronous* orbit takes the satellite over the north and south poles. See **Figure 10.2**. There are two advantages

to a sun-synchronous orbit: (1) the satellite is available at approximately the same time of day, every day and (2) everyone, no matter where they are, will enjoy at least one high-altitude pass per day.

A *dawn-to-dusk* orbit is a variation on the sun-synchronous model except that the satellite spends most of its time in sunlight and relatively little time in eclipse. See **Figure 10.3**.

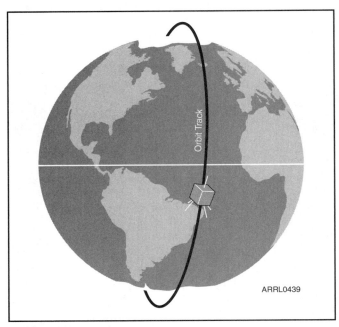

Figure 10.2 — A *sun-synchronous* orbit takes the satellite over the north and south poles. A satellite in this orbit allows every station in the world to enjoy at least one high-elevation pass per day.

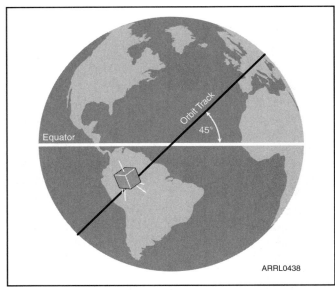

Figure 10.1 — An *inclined* orbit is one that is inclined with respect to the Earth's equator. In this example, the satellite's orbit is inclined at 45° to the Equator.

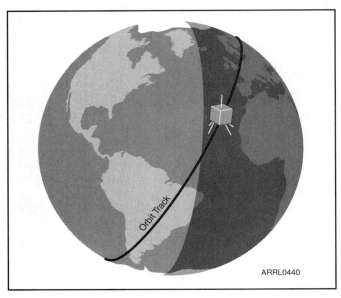

Figure 10.3 — A *dawn-to-dusk* orbit is a variation on the sun-synchronous model except that the satellite spends most of its time in sunlight and relatively little time in eclipse.

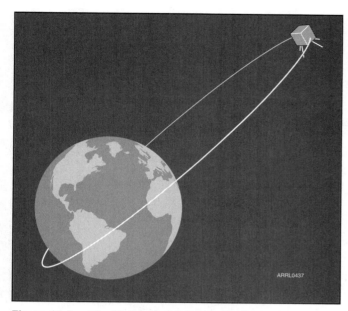

Figure 10.4 — The Molniya orbit is an elliptical orbit that carries the satellite far into space at its greatest distance from Earth (apogee). To observers on the ground, the satellite at apogee appears to hover for hours at a time before it plunges earthward and (often) sweeps within 1000 km at its closest approach (perigee).

The *Molniya* High Earth Orbit (**Figure 10.4**) was pioneered by the former Soviet Union. It is an elliptical orbit that carries the satellite far into space at its greatest distance from Earth (apogee). To observers on the ground, the satellite at apogee appears to hover for hours at a time before it plunges earthward and sweeps to (sometimes) within 1000 km

or so of the Earth at its closest approach (perigee). One great advantage of the Molniya orbit is that the satellite is capable of "seeing" an entire hemisphere of the planet while at apogee. Hams can use a Molniya satellite to enjoy long, leisurely conversations spanning thousands of kilometers here on Earth. When this book was being written, there were no active Molniya hamsats in orbit.

Satellite Footprints

Speaking of how much of our planet a satellite sees, it is important to understand the concept of the satellite's *footprint*. A satellite footprint can be loosely defined as the area on the Earth's surface that is "illuminated" by the satellite's antenna systems at any given time. Another way to think of a footprint is to regard it as the zone within which stations can communicate with each other through the satellite.

Unless the satellite in question is geostationary, footprints are constantly moving. Their sizes can vary considerably, depending on the altitude of the satellite. The footprint of the low-orbiting International Space Station is about 600 km in diameter. In contrast, the higher orbiting OSCAR 52 has a footprint that is nearly 1500 km across. See the example of a satellite footprint in **Figure 10.5**. The amount of time you have available to communicate depends on how long your station remains within the footprint. This time can be measured in minutes, or in the case of a satellite in a Molniya orbit, hours.

Understanding Your Place in the World

Before you can track an amateur satellite and communicate with it, you must first determine your own location with reasonable accuracy and understand your orientation to the expected path of the satellite.

Determining your location on the globe in terms of latitude and longitude coordinates is much easier today than it used be. If you own a Global Positioning System (GPS) receiver, you can use it to determine your coordinates almost instantly. You simply take the receiver outdoors (or hold it up to a window), wait for it to obtain enough signals to determine your position, and then write down the resulting latitude and longitude coordinates.

If you don't own a GPS receiver, the Internet is your next best option. There are a number of mapping websites where you can enter your street address and see a map that includes your latitude and longitude.

How precise do you need to be? If you plan on using movable directional "beam" antennas for your satellite station, the more precision the better. These antennas create focused radiation patterns, so you want to be sure they are pointing in the proper direction. Your satellite tracking software will determine this direction for you, but its ability to give you accurate aiming information is highly dependent on it "knowing" where you are located in the first place.

On the other hand, if you are using omnidirectional antennas that create broad radiation patterns, or directional antennas that don't move, the need for precision is less critical. In fact, the latitude and longitude of the nearest city will

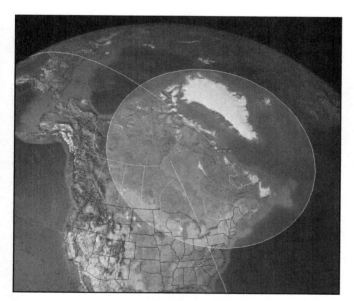

Figure 10.5 — This image shows the circular footprint of OSCAR 52 as depicted by *NOVA* satellite-tracking software. The footprint indicates the area of the Earth that is visible to the satellite at any given time.

suffice. You can get this information from the US Geological Survey website at **www.usgs.gov**. Look for the link to the Geographic Names Information System.

Azimuth and Elevation

Once the tracking software knows your approximate position, it can predict a satellite's path across your local sky. The software will indicate the satellite's predicted position in terms of its *azimuth* and *elevation* relative to your station.

Azimuth describes the satellite's position in degrees referenced to true north. See **Figure 10.6** and imagine your station in the center of a giant compass circle that is divided in degree increments from 0 to 360. North is 0° (it is also 360°), east is 90°, south is 180° and west is 270°. If your tracking software indicates that you need to point your antenna to an azimuth of 135° to intercept the satellite, for example, you're going to point the antenna southeast.

Let's take a look at a more detailed example. Once again, your station in **Figure 10.7** is in the center of the compass circle. According to your satellite tracking program, the International Space Station (ISS) is scheduled to rise above your local horizon at precisely 03:57:30 UTC. The program may describe the satellite's azimuth path like this:

Time	Azimuth (degrees)
03:57	307
03:58	350
03:59	0
04:00	11
04:01	20
04:02	30

When you plot these azimuth points on the circle, you can quickly see the horizontal path the satellite is going to take. The bird is going to rise in your northwestern sky and quickly move toward the east, finally dipping below your northeast horizon at about 30°. If you have rotating antennas, you can see that they'll need to be pointing northwest at the beginning of the satellite's pass. As the satellite moves across the sky, your antennas will need to track around the circle from 307°, to 0° and so on until they are pointing at 30° azimuth when the satellite finally disappears.

Let's add another dimension to our satellite track — *elevation*. Elevation is simply the angle, in degrees, between your station and the satellite, referenced to the Earth's surface. See **Figure 10.8**. The elevation angle begins at 0° with the satellite at the horizon and increases to 90° when the satellite is directly overhead. Elevation is every bit as critical as azimuth if you are using directional antennas. Not only do your antennas need to be pointed at the satellite as it appears to move in the horizontal plane, they must also tilt up and down to track the satellite as it moves in the vertical plane. Many amateur satellite stations use devices known as *az/el* (azimuth/elevation) *rotators* to move their directional antennas in both planes as the satellite streaks across the sky.

Even if you are not using movable antennas, knowing a satellite's elevation track is important for another reason. Unless you live in a flat location, chances are you do not have

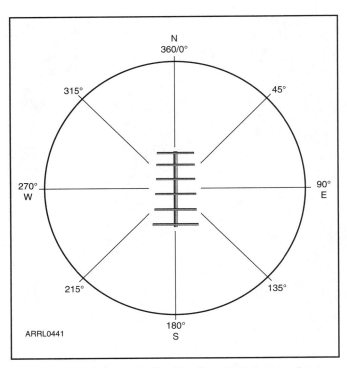

Figure 10.6 — Azimuth is the direction, in degrees referenced to true north, that an antenna must be pointed to receive a satellite signal. Imagine your station in the center of a giant compass circle that is divided in degree increments from 0 to 360. North is 0° (actually, it is also 360°), east is 90°, south is 180° and west is 270°.

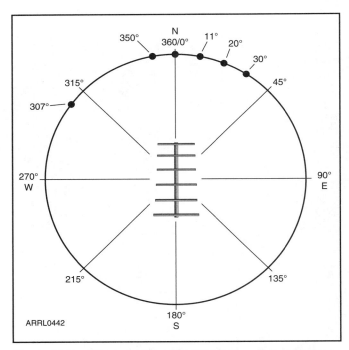

Figure 10.7 — The azimuth path of the International Space Station for our hypothetical pass.

a clear view to the horizon in every direction. Perhaps there are serious RF obstacles such as mountains, hills or buildings blocking the way. If you are trying to receive a microwave signal from a satellite, the RF absorption properties of trees can present serious obstacles, too. The elevations of these objects represent your true *radio horizons* in whichever direction they may lie. If you have a ridge to the north with a maximum elevation of 30° above the horizon as viewed from your station, your northern radio horizon *begins* at 30° elevation. You can't communicate with a satellite in your northern sky until it rises above 30°, so you'll have to take that fact into account when you view the information provided by your satellite tracking software. Your software may tell you that the AOS (acquisition of signal) time is 0200 UTC as the satellite rises in the north, but you won't be able to receive the bird until it reaches 30°, which may be a few minutes later.

Usually — and particularly for satellites in low Earth orbits — as the satellite's elevation angle increases, its distance from you decreases. This is a good thing since the closer the satellite, the stronger the radio signal. With that idea in mind, the higher the elevation of a satellite pass, the better, right? Well…yes and no. Remember that satellites are moving at high speeds relative to your position. As they move closer to you (move higher in elevation), the *Doppler Effect* increasingly comes into play.

The Doppler Effect

The Doppler Effect, named after scientist Christian Doppler (1803-1853), is the apparent change in frequency of sound or electromagnetic waves, varying with the relative velocity of the source and the observer. See **Figure 10.9**. Thanks to the Doppler Effect, as a satellite moves toward your location, its signal will *increase* in frequency; as it moves away from you, its signal will *decrease* in frequency.

When considering the Doppler Effect, it is important to realize that the satellite's transmit frequency is *not* changing. What is changing is the frequency of its signal *at your station*. You probably experience the Doppler Effect almost every day. When a fire truck approaches at high speed on a nearby freeway, you hear its siren blaring at a higher pitch,

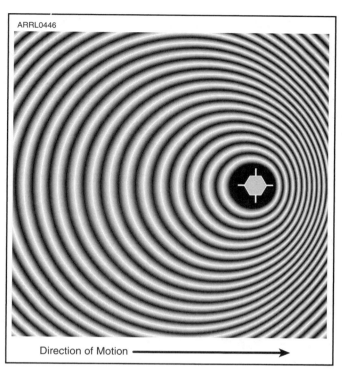

Figure 10.9 — It is sometimes helpful to think of the Doppler Effect as being caused by radio waves "crowding up" as a satellite moves toward your location. As a result, its signal will appear to *increase* in frequency as it moves toward you; as it moves away from you, its signal will *decrease* in frequency.

shifting downward as the truck passes and speeds off into the distance. The same thing happens with satellites, but unlike an earthbound fire truck that is moving at 60 MPH, the satellite is screaming by at thousands of miles per hour. The proportional difference between your speed and the speed of the satellite is enormous — high enough to shift the received frequency of a radio wave!

On a practical level, a high-elevation satellite pass can be problematic because the frequency shift caused by the Doppler Effect can be considerable. The effect also increases the higher you move in frequency. It can be quite a juggling act to adjust your receiver while trying to carry on a conversation.

Azimuth and Elevation Combined

Let's combine azimuth and elevation for a truly realistic satellite track, using our previous example of the International Space Station. We'll add the station's downlink frequency so we can see the Doppler Effect in action.

Time	Azimuth (degrees)	Elevation (degrees)	Frequency (MHz)
03:57	307	0	145.804
03:58	350	10	145.803
03:59	0	18	145.800
04:00	11	9	145.798
04:01	20	5	145.797
04:02	30	0	145.795

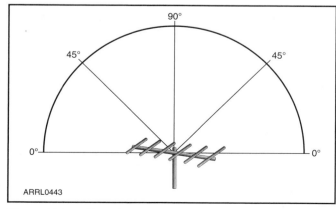

Figure 10.8 — Elevation is simply the angle, in degrees, between your station and the satellite, referenced to the Earth's surface.

In this example, the International Space Station rises to an elevation of 18° at 03:59 UTC before sinking back down to the horizon at 04:02 UTC. This is considered a low-elevation pass. If you have objects in your northern sky that rise above 18° elevation, you won't be able to communicate with the space station during this pass. The space station is transmitting at 145.800 MHz, but you'll notice that the frequency change caused by the Doppler Effect is minimal because the distance and relative velocity between you and the space station doesn't change dramatically.

Now we'll modify our example, making it a high-elevation pass.

Time	Azimuth (degrees)	Elevation (degrees)	Frequency (MHz)
03:57	307	0	145.810
03:58	350	10	145.808
03:59	0	25	145.806
04:00	11	40	145.804
04:01	20	65	145.802
04:02	30	80	145.800
04:03	36	60	145.798
04:04	41	45	145.796

Time	Azimuth (degrees)	Elevation (degrees)	Frequency (MHz)
04:05	50	29	145.794
04:06	55	15	145.792
04:07	59	0	145.790

There are several interesting things to note in this example. Did you notice that this high-elevation pass (topping out at 80° at 04:02 UTC) had a longer overall duration than the previous low-elevation pass? The low-elevation pass lasted only 5 minutes; this pass was a full 10 minutes in length. Obviously, when an object is tracking to a high elevation in the sky (almost directly overhead in this example), it is in the sky for a longer period.

Did you also notice what the Doppler Effect did to the downlink signal frequency at your station? Because the distance and relative velocity between you and the space station changed substantially during the pass, the Doppler Effect was very much in play. The result was a receive frequency that began at 145.810 MHz, shifted down to 145.800 MHz at maximum elevation, and then continued downward until it reached 145.790 MHz as the station slipped below the horizon. That's a 20 kHz frequency shift throughout the pass!

SATELLITE TRACKING SOFTWARE

You'll find satellite software programs written for *Windows*, *Mac* and *Linux* operating systems. Several popular applications are listed in **Table 10.1**. When computers were first employed to track amateur satellites, they provided only the most basic, essential information: when the satellite will be available (AOS, acquisition of signal), how high the satellite will rise in the sky and when the satellite is due to set below your horizon (LOS, loss of signal). Today we tend to ask a great deal more of our tracking programs. Modern applications still provide the basic information, but they usually offer many more features such as:

■ The spacecraft's operating schedule, including which transponders and beacons are on.

■ Predicted frequency offset (Doppler shift) on the link frequencies.

■ The orientation of the spacecraft's antennas with respect to your ground station and the distance between your ground station and the satellite.

■ Which regions of the Earth have access to the spacecraft; that is, who's in QSO range?

■ Whether the satellite is in sunlight or being eclipsed by the Earth. Some spacecraft only operate when in sunlight.

■ When the next opportunity to cover a selected terrestrial path (mutual window) will occur.

■ Changing data can often be updated at various intervals such as once per minute…or even once per second.

A number of applications do even more. Some will control antenna rotators, automatically keeping directional antennas aimed at the target satellite. Other applications will also control the radio to automatically compensate for frequency changes caused by Doppler shifting. **Figures 10.10** to **10.12** show some examples.

Adding additional spacecraft to the scenario suggests more questions. Which satellites are currently in range?

Table 10.1
A Sampling of Satellite Tracking Software

Name	Source	Operating System	Radio Control?	Antenna Control?
Nova	www.arrl.org/shop	Windows	No	Yes
SatPC32	www.amsat.org (store)	Windows	Yes	Yes
SatScape	www.satscape.info/home/	Windows	Yes	Yes
MacDoppler	www.dogparksoftware.com/MacDoppler.html	Mac OS	Yes	Yes
Predict	www.qsl.net/kd2bd/predict.html	Linux	No	Yes
WinOrbit	www.sat-net.com/winorbit/	Windows	No	No

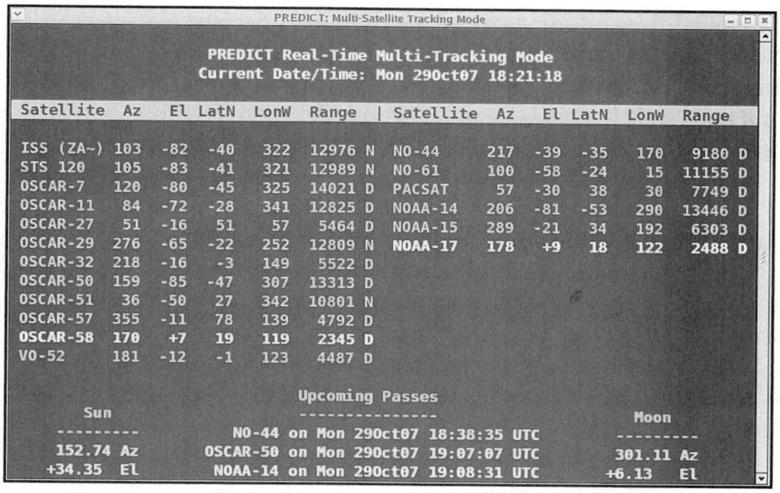

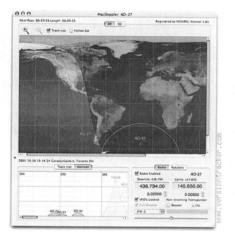

```
┌─────────────────────────────────────────────────────────────┐
│              PREDICT: Multi-Satellite Tracking Mode      _□ x │
├─────────────────────────────────────────────────────────────┤
│             PREDICT Real-Time Multi-Tracking Mode             │
│             Current Date/Time: Mon 29Oct07 18:21:18           │
│                                                               │
│ Satellite  Az    El LatN  LonW  Range │ Satellite  Az    El LatN  LonW  Range │
│                                                               │
│ ISS (ZA~)  103  -82  -40   322  12976 N  NO-44      217  -39  -35   170   9180 D │
│ STS 120    105  -83  -41   321  12989 N  NO-61      100  -58  -24    15  11155 D │
│ OSCAR-7    120  -80  -45   325  14021 D  PACSAT      57  -30   38    30   7749 D │
│ OSCAR-11    84  -72  -28   341  12825 D  NOAA-14    206  -81  -53   290  13446 D │
│ OSCAR-27    51  -16   51    57   5464 D  NOAA-15    289  -21   34   192   6303 D │
│ OSCAR-29   276  -65  -22   252  12809 N  NOAA-17    178   +9   18   122   2488 D │
│ OSCAR-32   218  -16   -3   149   5522 D                        │
│ OSCAR-50   159  -85  -47   307  13313 D                        │
│ OSCAR-51    36  -50   27   342  10801 N                        │
│ OSCAR-57   355  -11   78   139   4792 D                        │
│ OSCAR-58   170   +7   19   119   2345 D                        │
│ VO-52      181  -12   -1   123   4487 D                        │
│                                                               │
│         Sun                    Upcoming Passes           Moon │
│      ---------                 ---------------        -------- │
│                     NO-44 on Mon 29Oct07 18:38:35 UTC         │
│      152.74 Az    OSCAR-50 on Mon 29Oct07 19:07:07 UTC  301.11 Az │
│      +34.35 El     NOAA-14 on Mon 29Oct07 19:08:31 UTC  +6.13 El │
└─────────────────────────────────────────────────────────────┘
```

Figure 10.10 — *Predict* **is satellite tracking software for** *Linux.*

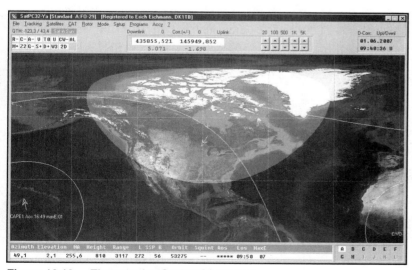

Figure 10.11 — If you own a Mac, you can track amateur satellites with *MacDoppler.*

Figure 10.12 — The popular *Sat32PC* **software.**

How long each will be accessible? Will any new spacecraft be coming into range in the near future? Obviously there is a great deal of information of potential interest. Programmers developing tracking software often find that the real challenge is not solving the underlying physics problems, but deciding what information to include and how to present it in a useful format. This is especially true since users have different interests, levels of expertise and needs. Some prefer to see the information in a graphical format, such as a map showing real-time positions for all satellites of interest. Others may prefer tabular data such as a listing of the times a particular spacecraft will be in range over the next several days.

There are also several Internet sites where you can do your tracking online. This eliminates all the hassles associated with acquiring and installing software. The currently available online tracking sites are not as powerful or flexible as the software you can install on your PC, however. One interesting site of this type is maintained by AMSAT-NA and you'll find it at **www.amsat.org/amsat-new/tools/**.

Getting Started With Software

There are so many different types of satellite software, and they change so frequently, it would be foolhardy to attempt to give you detailed operational descriptions in any book. The book would be obsolete a month after it came off the press!

Even so, there are a number of aspects of satellite-tracking software that rarely change. For example, we spent some time discussing how to determine your location with sufficient accuracy to be useful for satellite tracking. The next step is to get that information into your chosen program.

Most programs will ask you to enter your station location as part of the initial setup process. Some applications use the term "observer" to mean "station location," but the terms are synonymous for the sake of our discussion. Sophisticated programs will go as far as to provide you with a list of cities that you can select to quickly enter your location. Other programs will ask you to enter your latitude and longitude coordinates manually.

When entering latitude, longitude and other angles, make sure you know whether the computer expects degree-minute or decimal-degree notation. Following the notation used by the on-screen prompt usually works. Also make sure you understand the units and sign conventions being used. For example, are longitudes may be specified in negative number for locations west of Greenwich (0° longitude). Latitudes in the southern hemisphere may also require a minus sign. Fractional parts of a degree will have very little effect on tracking data so in most cases you can just ignore it.

Dates can also cause considerable trouble. Does the day or month appear first? Can November be abbreviated Nov or must you enter 11? The number is almost always required. Must you write 2010 or will 10 suffice? Should the parts be separated by colons, dashes or slashes? The list goes on and on. Once again, the prompt is your most important clue. For example, if the prompt reads "Enter date (DD:MM:YY)" and you want to enter February 9, 2010, follow the format of the prompt as precisely as possible and type 09:02:10.

When entering numbers, commas should never be used. For example, if a semi-major axis of 20,243.51 km must be entered, type 20243.51 with the comma and units omitted. It takes a little time to get used to the quirks of each software package, but you'll soon find yourself responding automatically.

Once you have your coordinates entered, you're still not quite done. The software now "knows" its location, but it doesn't know the locations of the satellites you wish to track. The only way the software can calculate the positions of satellites is if it has a recent set of *orbital elements*.

Orbital Elements

Orbital elements are a set of six numbers that completely describe the orbit of a satellite at a specific time. Although scientists may occasionally use different groups of six quantities, radio amateurs nearly always use the six known as Keplerian Orbital Elements, or simply *Keps*. (Kepler, you may recall, discovered some interesting things about planetary motion back in the 17th century!)

These orbital elements are derived from very precise observations of each satellite's orbital motion. Using precision radar and highly sensitive optical observation techniques, the North American Aerospace Defense Command (NORAD) keeps a very accurate catalog of almost everything in Earth orbit. Periodically, they issue the unclassified portions of this information to the National Aeronautics and Space Administration (NASA) for release to the general public. The information is listed by individual catalog number of each satellite and contains numeric data that describes, in a mathematical way, how NORAD observed the satellite moving around the Earth at a very precise location in space at a very precise moment in the past.

Without getting into the complex details of orbital mechanics (or Kepler's laws!) suffice it to say that your software simply uses the orbital element information NASA publishes that describes where a particular satellite was "then" to solve the orbital math and make a prediction (either graphically or in tabular format) of where that satellite ought to be "now." The "now" part of the prediction is based on the local time and station location information you've also been asked to load into your software.

Orbital elements are frequently distributed with additional numerical data (which may or may not be used by a software tracking program) and are commonly available in two forms, as shown in **Table 10.2** — NASA Two-Line Elements, such as the ones shown for OSCAR 27, and AMSAT Verbose Elements, such as those shown for OSCAR 52.

Let's use the easier-to-understand AMSAT format to break down the meaning, line by line.

The first two entries identify the spacecraft. The first line is an informal *satellite Name*. The second entry, *Catalog Number*, is a formal ID assigned by NASA.

The next entry, *Epoch Time*, specifies the time the orbital elements were computed. The number consists of two parts, the part to the left of the decimal point that describes the year and day, and the part to the right of the decimal point that describes the (very precise) time of day. For example, 96325.465598 refers to 1996, day 325, time of day .465598.

The next entry, *Element Set*, is a reference used to identify the source of the information. For example, 199 indicates element set number 199 issued by AMSAT. This information is optional.

The next six entries are the six key orbital elements.

Inclination describes the orientation of the satellite's orbital plane with respect to the equatorial plane of the Earth.

RAAN, Right Ascension of Ascending Node, specifies the orientation of the satellite's orbital plane with respect to fixed stars.

Eccentricity refers to the shape of the orbital ellipse. You may recall our earlier discussion of elliptical Molniya orbits. These orbits are highly eccentric. The value of the eccentricity element also yields some rough information as to the shape of the orbit the satellite is following. The closer this number is to "0", the more circular the orbit of the satellite tends to be. Conversely, an eccentricity value approaching "1", indicates the satellite is following a more elliptically shaped (possibly a Molniya) orbital path.

Table 10.2
Orbital Elements

NASA Two-Line Elements for OSCAR 27
AO-27
1 22825U 93061C 08024.00479406 -.00000064 00000-0 -86594-5 0 8811
2 22825 098.3635 349.6253 0008378 336.4256 023.6532 14.29228459747030

AMSAT Verbose Elements for OSCAR 52
Satellite: AO-52
Catalog Number: 28375
Epoch Time: 08024.16334624
Element Set: 14
Inclination: 098.0868 deg
RA of Node: 056.7785 deg
Eccentricity: 0.0083024
Arg of Perigee: 232.8417 deg
Mean Anomaly: 126.5166 deg
Mean Motion: 14.40594707 rev/day
Decay Rate: 7.0e-08 rev/day^2
Epoch Rev: 18752
Checksum: 310

For example, many Molniya orbit satellites have eccentricities in the 0.6 to 0.7 range.

Argument of Perigee describes where the perigee of the satellite is located in the satellite orbital plane. Recall that a satellite's perigee is its closest approach to the Earth. When the argument of perigee is between 180 and 360° the perigee will be over the Southern Hemisphere. Apogee — a satellite's most distant point from the Earth — will therefore occur above the Northern Hemisphere.

Mean Anomaly locates the satellite in the orbital plane at the epoch. All programs use the astronomical convention for mean anomaly (MA) units. The mean anomaly is 0 at perigee and 180 at apogee. Values between 0 and 180 indicate that the satellite is headed up toward apogee. Values between 180 and 360 indicate that the satellite is headed down toward perigee.

Mean Motion specifies the number of revolutions the satellite makes each day. This element indirectly provides information about the size of the elliptical orbit.

Decay Rate is a parameter used in sophisticated tracking models to take into account how the frictional drag produced by the Earth's atmosphere affects a satellite's orbit. It may also be referred to as rate of change of mean motion, first derivative of mean motion, or drag factor. Although decay rate is an important parameter in scientific studies of the Earth's atmosphere and when observing satellites that are about to reenter, it has very little effect on day-to-day tracking of most Amateur Radio satellites. If your program asks for drag factor, enter the number provided. If the element set does not contain this information, enter zero — you shouldn't discern any difference in predictions. You usually have a choice of entering this number using either decimal form or scientific notation. For example, the number –0.00000039 (decimal form) can be entered as –3.9e–7 (scientific notation). The e–7 stands for 10 to the minus seventh power (or 10 exponent –7). In practical terms e–7 just means move the decimal in the preceding number 7 places to the left. If this is totally confusing, just remember that in most situations entering zero will work fine.

Epoch Revolution is just another term for the expression "Orbit Number" that we discussed earlier. The number provided here does not affect tracking data, so don't worry if different element sets provide different numbers for the same day and time.

The *Checksum* is a number constructed by the data transmitting station and used by the receiving station to check for certain types of transmission errors in data files. It does not bear any relationship to a satellite's orbit.

In the "old days" of satellite-tracking software you had to enter the orbital elements by hand. This was a tedious and risky process. If you entered an element number incorrectly, you would generate wildly inaccurate predictions.

Today, thankfully, most satellite-tracking programs have greatly streamlined the process. One method of entering orbital elements is to grab the latest set from the AMSAT-NA website at **www.amsat.org** (look under "Keps" in the main menu). You can download the element set as a text file and then tell your satellite-tracking program to read the file and create the database. Another excellent site is **CelesTrak** at **celestrak.com**. Your program will probably be able to read either the AMSAT or NASA formats.

If you're fortunate to own sophisticated tracking software such as *Nova*, and you have access to the Internet, the program will reach into cyberspace, download and process its Keps automatically. All it takes is a single click of your mouse button. Some programs can even be configured to download the latest Keps on a regular basis without any prompting from you.

SATELLITE OPERATING

Satellite operating is unlike any other Amateur Radio activity. It is more than a matter of sitting down before your radio and making a contact. As you've learned in previous chapters, you have to know when the satellite is available, what path it will take from horizon to horizon, what uplink/downlink bands are in use and how you will deal with the Doppler Effect. All this amounts to a high-tech juggling act as you attempt to communicate with a spacecraft hurtling through the vacuum of space at many thousands of miles per hour.

But the challenge of satellite operating is part of the enjoyment. If it was as easy as making a contact on your

---

Table 10.3
Satellite Uplink/Downlink Mode Designators

Satellite Band Designations	Common Operating Modes (Uplink/Downlink)
10 meters (29 MHz): H	V/H (2 meters/10 meters)
2 meters (145 MHz): V	H/V (10 meters/2 meters)
70 cm (435 MHz): U	U/V (70 cm/2 meters)
23 cm (1260 MHz): L	V/U (2 meters/70 cm)
13 cm (2.4 GHz): S	U/S (70 cm/13 cm)
5 cm (5.6 GHz): C	U/L (70 cm/23 cm)
3 cm (10 GHz): X	L/S (23 cm/13 cm)
	L/X (23 cm/3 cm)
	C/X (5 cm/3 cm)

local FM repeater, it wouldn't be nearly as fun. Even veteran operators will tell you that there is nothing like the thrill of making contact through a satellite. Even in our highly technical age, the sheer wonder of what you're doing never fails to inspire.

Several satellites with Amateur Radio uplinks and downlinks reach orbit every year. Some are research satellites that use amateur frequencies to relay telemetry data to Earth. Others are full-fledged ham satellites that sport uplink/downlink transponders. The transponders are labeled according to their uplinks and downlinks. See the list in **Table 10.3**. For instance, a Mode U/V transponder has an uplink on the 70 cm band (U) and a downlink on the 2 meter band (V).

Even under the best circumstances satellites are temporary things. Active satellites become inactive. Spacecraft in low orbit eventually re-enter our atmosphere. Satellites in higher orbits succumb to the hostile environment of space and become silent. It is impossible for a printed book to remain up to date with the status of the Amateur Radio satellite. With that in mind, your best source for current satellite information is the AMSAT website at **www.amsat.org**. In particular, check the Satellite Status page at **www.amsat. org/amsat-new/satellites/status.php**. A list of the Amateur Radio satellites most active when this book went to press appears in **Table 10.4**.

Single-Channel "Repeater" Satellites

The single-channel repeater satellites are among the easiest birds to work, not just from an equipment standpoint, but also from an operational perspective.

You can make contacts through these low-Earth orbiting satellites with little more than a dual-band (2 meter/ 70 cm) FM mobile transceiver and an omnidirectional antenna — even a dual-band mobile whip will do. You can use a dual-band handheld radio as well, but don't expect success with its compact flexible antenna. Instead, you'll need something more substantial such as a dual-band Yagi. **Figure 10.13** shows an example.

Unfortunately, the popularity of FM repeater satellites is a handicap. Many stations attempt to use them, but only one station at a time can be repeated. Thanks to the "capture effect" inherent in FM receiver design, the strongest station at any given moment is the station that is demodulated and repeated. If several stations are received at nearly the same signal level, the result on the output is an unintelligible squeal.

When an FM repeater satellite is experiencing heavy use you'll hear stations in the clear, separated by screeches and sentence fragments. They tend to be congested during weekend passes when hams have more opportunities to take to the airwaves. Unless you have plenty of uplink power on 2 meters (50 W or more) and a directional antenna, your best bet is to try FM repeater satellites during less popular times. Passes during weekday mornings are significantly less crowded. Weekday evening passes offer another worthwhile opportunity, although they can be crowded as well.

Because of the wide FM signal bandwidth (about 5 kHz), it is relatively easy to compensate for Doppler frequency shifting. There is no need to monitor your own downlink signal, which makes it possible to use ordinary dual-band FM transceivers that do not have full-duplex capability. In fact, you can exploit the *memory channels* in your radio to make Doppler compensation as simple as pushing a button.

Nearly all modern dual-band transceivers allow you to program memory channels for split-band operation, but

Table 10.4
Active Amateur Radio Satellites

Satellite	Uplink (MHz)	Downlink (MHz)	Mode
AMSAT-OSCAR 7	—	29.502	Beacon
	—	145.975	Beacon
	—	435.100	Beacon
	145.850 - 145.950	29.400 - 29.500	SSB/CW, non-inverting
	432.125 - 432.175	145.975 - 145.925	SSB/CW, inverting
AMSAT-OSCAR 27	145.850	436.795	FM repeater
International Space Station	144.490	145.800	Crew contact, FM (Rgn 2/3)
	145.200	145.800	Crew contact, FM (Rgn 1)
	145.990	145.800	Packet BBS
	145.825	145.825	APRS digipeater
	—	144.490	SSTV downlink
	437.800	145.800	FM repeater
Saudi-OSCAR 50	145.850	436.795	FM Repeater, 67 Hz CTCSS
VUSAT-OSCAR 52	—	145.860	CW Beacon
	—	145.936	Carrier Beacon
	435.220 - 435.280	145.870 - 145.930	SSB/CW, inverting

Figure 10.13 — Jerry Clement, VE6AB, using a hand-held transceiver and a tiny antenna to make contact through an FM repeater satellite.

consult the manual on how to go about doing it. For each channel you will need to program an uplink transmit frequency on 2 meters and a corresponding downlink receive frequency on 70 cm. Note that some FM repeater satellites may use CTCSS tones to control access, just like earthbound repeaters. If so, you'll need to program the correct CTCSS tone in each memory slot as well.

When the satellite pops above the horizon (acquisition of signal, AOS), select memory channel 1. Three minutes later, switch to memory channel 2 as the Doppler Effect begins to influence the uplink and downlink signals. You don't have to keep an eye on your watch. You'll know it is time to switch when the downlink signals become distorted and noisy. As the satellite reaches its maximum elevation (zenith), switch to channel 3. A minute later, select channel 4 and remain there until nearly the end of the pass (loss of signal, LOS) when you switch to channel 5. Note how memory channels are programmed to increment the uplink frequency *upward* throughout the pass while the downlink frequency ratchets *downward*. This guarantees Doppler compensation on your uplink signal for the satellite's receiver as well as on the downlink for your receiver.

Many transceivers allow you to substitute alphanumeric "tags" for the displayed memory channel frequencies. If your radio offers this feature, you can use it to label each memory in a distinctive manner. That way, you won't forget which memory to choose as the satellite is streaking overhead.

Here are some general FM repeater satellite operating tips…

■ **If you hear nothing on the downlink frequency, do not transmit.** It is quite possible that the satellite can hear *you* at times when you cannot hear *it*. By transmitting "in the blind," you'll cause unnecessary interference to everyone else. You can hear an FM repeater satellite coming into range by turning off your squelch and listening as the noise suddenly "quiets" and voices emerge.

■ **Do not call "CQ."** Operate the satellite as you would an FM repeater. Simply state your call sign and wait for a response, or answer someone else who has transmitted their call sign. A longwinded "CQ CQ CQ CQ…" merely ties up the satellite (and makes you very unpopular).

■ **Keep it short and don't hog the satellite.** If you establish contact, good for you! Just keep the conversation as short as possible. Always remember that passes last only 10 or 15 minutes and there are many other hams waiting for their chance. Avoid lengthy discussions of weather, antennas and so on. Of course, you may be lucky and find that the satellite is nearly empty. If that's the case, go ahead and chat but make sure you leave gaps between your transmissions in case someone else wants to make contact.

■ **If there is a conversation in progress, don't interfere.** Wait until it is complete before you begin throwing in your call sign.

A typical FM repeater satellite exchange might sound like this:

"WJ1B"
"WJ1B this is N9ATQ."
"N9ATQ this is WJ1B in Cheshire, Connecticut. Fox Nancy 31. Name is Harold."
"Good morning! I'm in Quincy, Illinois. Echo Nancy 40. Name is Craig. You're putting an excellent signal into the satellite."
"That's great. I'm just running 10 watts in my car."
"Sounds perfect to me, Harold. Hope to catch you on again. 73! N9ATQ clear."
"73, Craig. WJ1B clear."

Notice how short the conversation is. Did you also notice the cryptic references to "Fox Nancy 31" and "Echo Nancy 40?" Those are *grid square* designations and they require a bit of explanation.

Know Thy Grid

Grid square designators amount to a shorthand description of a station's general location. In the previous example, "Fox Nancy 31" translates to FN31, an imaginary rectangle centered on the state of Connecticut.

These rectangles measure 1° latitude by 2° longitude and are the vital components of the *Maidenhead Locator System,* but hams simply refer to them as *grid squares*. Each grid square is labeled with a two-letter/two-number code (such as FN24). This handy designator uniquely identifies the grid square and your approximate location in latitude and longitude; no two have the same identifying code. Grid square designations can become even more precise by adding two additional letters (such as FN24kp), but hams rarely use the six-character versions.

Hams exchange grid square designators because they are critical for operating awards, which are certificates or plaques that you receive for various achievements. Nearly all VHF operating awards involve the exchange of grid square designators. The more unique grid squares you contact and verify (either with paper QSL cards or electronic receipts), the more awards you qualify for. Some grid squares have few, if any, hams living within their boundaries, so contacts with stations in these "rare grids" are highly prized.

As a satellite operator, you already know your approximate latitude and longitude, so you can use this information to determine your grid square. Just go to the ARRL website at **www.arrl.org/grid-locater** for more information and resources.

Linear Transponder Satellites

Single-channel satellites are attractive because of the minimal ground station equipment required to work them. Their major shortcoming, however, is their inability to support more than one conversation at a time. As a single-channel satellite operator, you're under constant pressure to make short-duration contacts so that others can use the bird.

In contrast, linear transponder satellites relay an entire range of frequencies at once, not just a single channel. A linear transponder can, as a result, support many simultaneous conversations. There can still be interference issues, but once you've established contact you can chat for as long as you wish — or at least as long as the satellite is available to you. For low-Earth orbiting satellites, conversations can span 10 or 15 minutes. If the satellite in question is a high-Earth orbiter (HEO), conversations can last for *hours*.

Linear transponders are either *inverting* or *non-inverting*. An inverting transponder relays a mirror image of the uplink passband. This means that a *lower* sideband signal on the uplink becomes an *upper* sideband signal on the downlink. At the same time, a signal at the *high end* of the uplink passband will appear at the *low end* of the downlink passband. A non-inverting transponder relays the uplink signals exactly as they appear in the passband — sidebands remain unchanged and the relative position of an uplink signal in the downlink passband remains the same.

For engineering design reasons, most linear transponders are of the inverting variety. This presents a challenge when you're on the air. As you're *increasing* your uplink frequency, for example, you have to remember that your downlink frequency is *decreasing* — "heading the other way," as it were. Fortunately, a number of transceivers designed for satellite use have *reverse VFO tracking* among their features. This locks the uplink and downlink VFOs in a reverse arrangement. If you tweak the uplink VFO to increase your signal frequency by, say, 5 kHz, the downlink (receive) VFO will automatically shift downward by the same amount.

Finding Yourself...and Others

Full duplex operation is strongly recommended for linear transponder satellites. Because of the relatively narrow bandwidths of SSB and CW signals, the Doppler Effect will be more pronounced. You need to be able to hear your own signal while you are transmitting so that you can make frequent adjustments to the downlink receiver to maintain the tone (CW) or voice clarity (SSB).

It is possible to use a computer to estimate Doppler frequency shifts and apply receiver correction automatically (assuming your radio is under computer control). This is high-tech guesswork at best, though. The better, more accurate, solution is to slip on a pair of headphones and correct for Doppler by listening to your own downlink signal. (Headphones are necessary to help you avoid creating feedback through the satellite.)

Before you attempt your first conversation on a linear transponder satellite, it's best to gain some practice at receiving your own signal during a pass. For this example, let's use VUSAT-OSCAR 52, a popular bird with an inverting linear transponder (see **Figure 10.14**). Let's also assume that you are operating SSB. If you pick 435.230 MHz, for instance, as your uplink frequency, you might expect to hear yourself somewhere in the vicinity of 145.920 MHz. For SSB, the convention is to transmit lower sideband on the uplink, which inverts to upper sideband on the downlink.

If you are using separate transmitters and receivers, set your transmitter for 435.230 MHz LSB and leave it there. If you are using a multiband satellite-capable transceiver with a VFO tracking feature, "unlock" (disable) the tracking and set the transmitter VFO for 435.230 MHz LSB.

As OSCAR 52 climbs above the horizon, start sweeping your receive VFO through the 2 meter downlink passband, listening for signals as you go. (Another technique is to listen for a satellite's beacon, if available.) As soon as you hear activity, tune your receiver to 145.920 MHz. If the frequency is clear, begin transmitting your call sign and perhaps the word "testing." As you speak, tune your downlink receiver back and forth from 145.920 to about 145.930 MHz. It may take a couple of minutes, but with luck you'll soon hear your own voice rising out of the noise. When you do, tune it in quickly until your voice sounds normal. Congratulations! You've just

Figure 10.14 — A view of OSCAR 52 just prior to launch. It is the small, dark cube below and to the right of the large commercial satellite above.

heard your own signal being relayed by a spacecraft!

This is a good time to experiment. Stop tuning your receiver and note how Doppler Effect changes the sound of your voice. Practice retuning to keep your voice sounding normal. If you are using a satellite transceiver, try locking the uplink and downlink VFOs and observe how the reverse tracking affects your signal.

Calling CQ

Once you've become comfortable with finding your own signal, try calling CQ. Tune your uplink transmitter and downlink receiver to the frequencies of your choice. (If your radio has a VFO tracking feature, make sure it is unlocked.) When the satellite comes into range, start calling CQ as you listen for your voice on the downlink. Once you hear it, tweak your receiver as necessary to keep your voice sounding normal.

Don't be surprised if you suddenly hear a string of CW beeps. That's good news — it's the sound of someone who has heard your CQ and is quickly adjusting their uplink transmitter while sending a continuous series of Morse "dits" with a CW keyer. They are trying to hear their own signal and bring it to approximately the same frequency as your own. Alternatively, you may hear an off-frequency, high-pitched voice that suddenly "swoops" into your CQ. Once again, that is another station that has heard you and is preparing to answer.

Once the conversation is underway, all you have to do is adjust your uplink frequency to keep your voice, and the voice of the other operator, sounding normal. If your conversational companion is operating properly, he is doing the same thing.

Answering a CQ

A duplex transceiver with a VFO tracking feature comes in handy when you're answering someone else's CQ. Once you've set the uplink and downlink VFOs, activate the tracking function to keep them locked together. Now all you have to do is tune through the downlink passband with the receive VFO while the uplink (transmit) VFO follows you automatically. If you discover someone calling CQ, tune him

in and then unlock the tracking. With your uplink VFO now operating independently, begin answering the other station as you gently adjust the *uplink* VFO to bring your signal on frequency. Once your frequency matches his (when your voice or CW tone sounds normal on the downlink), enjoy the conversation and compensate for Doppler by adjusting the uplink VFO.

If you are using separate rigs for the uplink and downlink, you'll need to tune in the station calling CQ, then make a quick estimate of the correct corresponding uplink frequency. Begin answering and adjust your uplink radio until your signal matches his on the downlink.

How Much Power is Enough?

The issue of uplink power and linear transponders has always been controversial. Obviously, you want to use enough power to generate a listenable signal on the downlink. For low-Earth orbiting satellites, that may amount to only 30 or 50 W, depending on the type of antenna you are using. For the high-Earth orbiters, uplink power levels of 100 to 150 W are common.

Unfortunately, there is a "more-is-better" obsession among some amateurs. A listenable downlink signal is not sufficient — they want a *loud* signal. Some of these operators, for example, are working the low-Earth orbiters by using directional antennas *and* 100 W of output power or more. The result can be an effective radiated power level in excess of *1 kW!*

The net effect of such a powerful signal on a linear transponder is to swamp its receiver. All signals weaker than the high-power station will be dramatically reduced in strength on the downlink; some may disappear altogether. This is because the satellite is dedicating the lion's share of its output to relaying the loud uplink signal while starving everyone else.

To be a good neighbor on a linear transponder satellite, the rule of thumb is to use only the uplink power necessary to keep your signal about as strong as everyone else's. If the satellite has a telemetry beacon, another technique is to use the beacon as the standard for downlink signal strength. In other words, your downlink signal should never be louder than the beacon.

Legally, Safely, Appropriately – The FCC Rules and You

Legally — Safely — Appropriately. These are the three hallmarks that allow each radio amateur to fully enjoy his or her on-the-air experience.

It is the responsibility of each amateur to operate his or her station within the rules governing the Amateur Radio Service (legally). The second responsibility is to take precautions to ensure that their activity doesn't pose harm to themselves or others (safely). And finally, each amateur is charged with making sure that on-the-air activities are in keeping with the operating standards set by the rules, as well as those standards that have developed within the amateur community over time (appropriately).

This chapter is intended to answer most of the common questions posed by active hams and to guide you to other resources for more information about the rules and regulations. To get the most from this material, you'll need a current copy of the FCC rules and regulations. They are available from several sources in booklet form (**Figure 11.1**), or you can look on the ARRL website at **www.arrl.org/part-97-amateur-radio**.

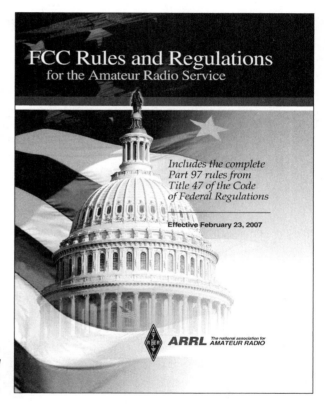

Figure 11.1 — A current copy of the FCC rules is a must for every station. One excellent resource is *FCC Rules and Regulations for the Amateur Radio Service*, published by the ARRL and available online at www.arrl.org/shop.

THE AMATEUR RADIO SPECTRUM

The electromagnetic spectrum is a limited resource. Every kilohertz of the radio spectrum represents precious turf that is blood sport to those who lay claim to it. Fortunately, the spectrum is a resource that cannot be depleted — if misused, it can be restored to normal as soon as the misuse stops. Every minute of every hour of every day, we have a fresh chance to use the spectrum intelligently.

Although the radio spectrum has been used in a certain way in the past, changes are possible. Needs of the various radio services evolve with technological innovation and growth. There can be changes in the frequency bands allocated to the amateur service, and there can be changes in how we use those bands.

Amateur Radio is richly endowed with a wide range of bands starting at 1.8 MHz and extending above 300 GHz. Thus, we enjoy a veritable smorgasbord of bands with propagation "delicacies" of every type. To our benefit, radio propagation determines how far a signal can travel. Specific frequencies may be reused numerous times around the globe.

WHERE DO THE RULES COME FROM?

International Regulation of the Spectrum

Amateur Radio frequency band allocations don't just happen. Band allocation proposals must first crawl through a maze of national agencies and the International Telecommunication Union (ITU) with more adroitness than a computer-controlled mouse. Simultaneously, the proposals affecting Amateur Radio have to run the gauntlet of competing interests of other spectrum users.

Treaties and Agreements

To bring some order to international relationships of all sorts, nations sign treaties and agreements. Otherwise (with respect to international communications) chaos, anarchy and bedlam would vie for supremacy over the radio spectrum. Pessimists think we already have some of that, but they haven't any idea how bad it could be without international treaties and agreements.

International Telecommunication Union

The origins of the ITU trace back to the invention of the telegraph in the 19th century. To establish an international telegraph network, it was necessary to reach agreement on uniform message handling and technical compatibility. Bordering European countries worked out some bilateral agreements. This eventually led to creation of the ITU at Paris in 1865 by the first International Telegraph Convention, which yielded agreement on basic telegraph regulations.

Plenipotentiary Conferences

The ITU has Plenipotentiary Conferences every four years. A "Plenipotentiary" is a conference that is fully empowered to do business. The conferences determine general policies, review the work of the Union and revise the Convention if necessary. The conferences also elect the Members of the Union to serve on the ITU Council, and elect the Secretary-General, Deputy Secretary-General, the Directors of the Bureaus and members of the Radio Regulations Board.

World Radiocommunication Conferences

ITU World Radiocommunication Conferences (WRCs) are held every few years with agendas agreed at the previous WRC and confirmed by the ITU Council. Various issues related to Amateur Radio may come up at these conferences. For example, amateur frequency allocations may be made or modified. Some examples are the creation of the 30, 17 and 12 meter bands in 1979; the worldwide amateur allocation of 7000 to 7200 kHz in 2003; or our new secondary allocation at 472 to 479 kHz in 2012. In addition, changes made to the primary allocations of another service may affect the secondary status of Amateur Radio allocations. **Figure 11.2** shows just a portion of the main meeting room at the WRC-12.

Inter-American Telecommunication Commission (CITEL)

CITEL is the regional telecommunication organization for the Americas. It is a permanent commission under the Organization of American States (OAS), with a secretariat in Washington, DC. The CITEL Assembly meets every four years, while its committees meet one or more times yearly. ARRL and IARU Region 2 are active participants in Permanent Consultative Committee no. 3 (PCC. III — Radiocommunications).

Telecommunications Regulation within the United States

Practically from the day you started studying for your first Amateur Radio license, you encountered two terms that brought home the significance of the responsibilities that accompany an Amateur Radio license. Those two terms are FCC and Part 97.

FCC of course refers to the Federal Communications Commission, the agency of the US government responsible for making and enforcing the rules for the Amateur Radio Service. This five-person commission is charged with writing the rules that govern the licensing process for the various radio services in the US — commercial and private. The FCC oversees services as diverse as broadcast television and radio; communications services, such as wireless technologies; and wired

Figure 11.2 — World Radiocommunication Conferences (WRCs), conducted by the ITU, are held every few years to amend the international Radio Regulations. At the 2012 conference, after years of preparatory work, we were successful in achieving a new secondary allocation of 472 to 479 kHz. (*N3AO photo*)

services, such as cable television and telephone carriers. The FCC is charged with determining the standards for obtaining a federal license for the various services, as well as determining the privileges and technical standards that must be adhered to by each licensee.

Assisting the Commissioners in this task are hundreds of employees. These experts help develop the standards and criteria for licensing and for operating under a Commission license. They also handle enforcement issues when rules are violated.

Code of Federal Regulations

The rules for all US telecommunications are found in *Code of Federal Regulations (CFR)*. The 50 "titles" of the CFR contain the laws and regulations of the United States. Those laws and regulations dealing with telecommunications are found in Title 47 of the CFR.

Title 47 is further divided into three general subsections, each including additional sections known as "Parts." The three main subsections include the rules and responsibilities for the three units of the federal government that are responsible for some area of national telecommunication policy. The first subsection, which includes Parts 0 through 199 are the rules for the Federal Communications Commission. The remaining two subsections are the regulations for the Office of Science and Technology Policy and National Security Council (under direction of the White House), and for the National Telecommunications and Information Administration (NTIA), under the Department of Commerce.

The functions relating to assignment of frequencies to radio stations belonging to, and operated by, the United States Government are assigned to the Assistant Secretary of Commerce for Communications and Information (Administrator, NTIA). Among other things, NTIA:

1) Coordinates telecommunications activities of the Executive Branch;

2) Develops plans, policies and programs relating to international telecommunications issues;

3) Coordinates preparations for US participation in international telecommunications conferences and negotiations;

4) Develops, in coordination with the FCC, a long-range plan for improved management of all electromagnetic spectrum resources, including jointly determining the National Table of Frequency Allocations; and

5) Conducts telecommunications research and development.

Obviously, the FCC and the NTIA work closely together on many issues relating to radio spectrum. Amateur Radio shares on a secondary basis many of the UHF and higher frequency bands with a variety of government agencies. As long as we remain good sharing partners, these agencies can be powerful advocates for protecting Amateur Radio frequencies from other users. It is important to remember that on bands where Amateur Radio is designated as secondary, Amateur Radio in essence operates as a "guest" on those bands, and have specific obligations not to cause harmful interference to the radio service designated as primary on that band.

For the most part, the rules for the Amateur Radio Service are contained in CFR Title 47, Part 97. That's why the term "Part 97" is used when referring to the rules for Amateur Radio. It is important to note that sections of Title 47 other than Part 97 do impact the Amateur Radio Service in some way. For example, Part 2 contains specific information on geographic areas where amateur operations are restricted, such as power limitations around certain US military sites. Part 15 contains standards for unlicensed low-power devices that could cause potential interference to amateur bands. The best resource to view the current versions of these related parts is online at **ecfr.gpoaccess.gov**. This is the official online version of the CFR, maintained by the National Archives.

Why We Are Here

The five basic principles for the Amateur Radio Service are clearly established at the very beginning of the rules:

§97.1 Basis and purpose.

The rules and regulations in this part are designed to provide an amateur radio service having a fundamental purpose as expressed in the following principles:

(a) Recognition and enhancement of the value of the amateur service to the public as a voluntary noncommercial communication service, particularly with respect to providing emergency communications.

(b) Continuation and extension of the amateur's proven ability to contribute to the advancement of the radio art.

(c) Encouragement and improvement of the amateur service through rules which provide for advancing skills in both the communication and technical phases of the art.

(d) Expansion of the existing reservoir within the amateur radio service of trained operators, technicians, and electronics experts.

(e) Continuation and extension of the amateur's unique ability to enhance international goodwill.

Though often referred to as a hobby, Amateur Radio crosses many boundaries. The licensees of the amateur service play important supporting roles in public service and emergency communications as well as the development of new and innovative technological advancements. They function as trained communicators available to assist others, but they also participate to enjoy camaraderie and fun with the new friends they meet on the airwaves. Some amateurs seek new operating challenges or pursue hands-on opportunities to learn new things about radio or electronics. The rules recognize that amateurs have distinct talents that they make available to serve their communities.

While Amateur Radio does play a role in emergency communications, it is important to note that the FCC does not designate the amateur services as public service or first-responder radio services. Rather, Amateur Radio's role is to support existing emergency and disaster communication services when appropriate. All aspects of Amateur Radio — rag chewing, experimentation, DXing, contesting, traffic handling, emergency communications, community service and other areas — emanate from the basic purposes found in §97.1.

OVERVIEW OF THE PART 97 SUBPARTS

Part 97 is divided into six distinct subparts, A through F. Each subpart deals with rules and content in specific areas. Taken together, the subparts comprise the knowledge each licensee needs in order to legally, safely and appropriately operate on the air. Let's start with a brief overview of the parts and then jump into the details of each one.

Subpart A deals with the broad *general provisions* of what an individual is required to do when operating. It also includes specific definitions (§97.3) of various terminology used through the rules. Subpart A covers license grants, call signs and general requirements for becoming a Commission licensee. It also includes certain requirements and protections regarding your station location and antennas.

Subpart B discusses *station operation standards*. These include the responsibilities of the licensee and the control operator of any amateur station. Subpart B details permitted and prohibited transmissions, proper station identification, third party and international communications, and restricted operations.

Amateur stations are allowed special types of operations, and these are covered in **Subpart C**. Included in this portion of the rules are the regulations that govern how some of the most popular methods of amateur communications are carried out. At some point, almost every amateur will be involved with one or more of these *special operations*.

They include basic repeater operation or message forwarding systems, as well as more "exotic" operations such as satellite communications or remote control of amateur stations.

The *technical standards* of how we operate are found in **Subpart D**. Each amateur is responsible for the technical quality of their transmissions and for making sure that signals are transmitted only on frequencies authorized by their license. The frequency allocations, signal emission types and standards and power limitations for each US license class can be found here.

As one of the basic purposes of the amateur service, each licensee has a role to play in *supporting and providing emergency communications*. The guidelines for this, found in **Subpart E**, are the reason many of today's licensees got involved.

Unlike some other radio services authorized by the FCC, each person seeking to become an amateur operator must pass one or more written examinations. **Subpart F** delineates the *qualifying examination systems* through which individuals may obtain and upgrade their operating privileges.

Don't be confused or overwhelmed by the scope or magnitude of Part 97. Though some areas may be a bit complex or difficult to understand, the six subparts work together to provide the basic framework for each amateur to operate legally, safely and appropriately.

SUBPART A — GENERAL PROVISIONS

Your Amateur Radio License

Your journey into Amateur Radio begins with a single important piece of paper — your license. This grant from the FCC is actually two licenses in one — your station license and your operator license. This document is your authorization to transmit on the amateur bands and it conveys your operating privileges.

An individual who becomes a Commission licensee is granted one — and only one — operator/station license. To qualify, you must pass one or more written examinations administered by a team of Volunteer Examiners (VEs) who conduct exams under the auspices of an accredited Volunteer Examiner Coordinator (VEC). **Table 11.1** gives an overview, and exam requirements are covered in more detail later in this chapter.

Anyone, except for a representative of a foreign government, is eligible to hold a US amateur license. You must have a valid US mailing address. Remember that it is your responsibility to keep your mailing address current with the FCC. Failure to do so can result in the suspension or revocation of your license [§97.23].

Your station license designates your call sign — a prized possession for most hams. When you receive your initial

license, you will be assigned a call sign from the Sequential Call Sign Assignment System. Many amateurs choose to participate in the Vanity Call Sign program [§97.19], which allows licensees to pick their own call sign following the guidelines for their license class. More on call signs in a bit.

Keep in mind that a station license — your call sign — is only an identifier. A station license does not convey any operator privileges. All operating privileges come to you through the license class you have earned through your examinations.

The FCC maintains all licensee information in a central database known as the ULS, the Universal Licensing System. As soon as your information appears in the ULS, you are considered licensed and may operate using your assigned call and privileges. When you are issued your license, or when you renew (if you have renewed since December 3, 2001), you are also issued a Federal Registration Number (FRN). Any modification, renewal or upgrade of a license must include the licensee's FRN, which in most cases for newer licenses is printed on the license itself. You can also find your FRN using the FCC ULS online search at **wireless2.fcc.gov/UlsApp/UlsSearch/searchLicense.jsp** or ARRL's call sign lookup, available at **www.arrl.org**.

Table 11.1
Currently Issued Amateur Operator Licenses†

Class	Written Examination	Privileges
Technician	Technician-level theory and regulations. (Element 2)*	All amateur privileges above 50.0 MHz. Some CW privileges on 80, 40, 15, 10 meters. Some SSB and data privileges on 10 meters.
General	Technician and General theory and regulations. (Elements 2 and 3)	All amateur privileges except those reserved for Advanced and Amateur Extra.
Amateur Extra	Technician and General theory, plus Extra-class theory (Elements 2, 3 and 4)	All amateur privileges.

†A licensed radio amateur must pass only those elements that were not already passed successfully during the examination for the amateur license currently held. For example, the General exam includes Elements 2 and 3, but a Technician licensee would not have to re-take Element 2. Novice and Advanced licenses are no longer being issued but may be renewed. No Morse code test is required for any license.
*If you hold an expired Technician license issued before March 21, 1987, you can obtain credit for Element 3. You must be able to prove to a VE team that your Technician license was issued before March 21, 1987 to claim this credit.

License Renewals and Updates

The FCC prefers that you renew your license or make modifications (update information such as your address) on-line using ULS. It's still possible to conduct business with the Commission "the old fashioned way" — by filing paper forms — but you should know the following:

1) ARRL members may use NCVEC Form 605 for everything except requests for new vanity call signs. This is not an FCC form, but it is accepted by the FCC if it is processed by an accredited VEC. You can download a copy from **www. arrl.org/fcc-forms**. The ARRL VEC processes renewals or modifications via NCVEC Form 605 as a free membership service. Amateurs may also deal directly with the FCC using the FCC online filing system at **wireless.fcc.gov/uls/index. htm?job=home**.

2) ARRL members using the NCVEC Form 605 should send it to the ARRL VEC, 225 Main St, Newington, CT 06111. Do not send NCVEC Form 605 to the FCC; it won't be accepted. Amateurs using the FCC Form 605 must send it to the FCC, 1270 Fairfield Rd, Gettysburg, PA 17325. There is no fee for renewing your amateur license at this time, unless your call sign was issued under the Vanity Call Sign Program.

3) The FCC will not process renewal applications received more than 90 days prior to the license expiration date.

4) It's a good idea to make a copy of your renewal application as proof of filing before your expiration date. If your application is processed before the expiration date, you may continue to operate until your new license arrives. Otherwise, you may not operate until your renewal is processed.

5) If your license has already expired, it is still possible to renew since there is a two-year grace period. If it has been expired for more than two calendar years, you will have to take the current license test(s) to regain your amateur privileges.

6) You are required to keep your mailing address up to date. The FCC may cancel or suspend a license if mail is returned as undeliverable.

For more information, see **www.arrl.org/licensing-education-training**. You can also contact the VEC staff or Regulatory Information Branch at ARRL HQ for information on ULS and keeping your license current.

Call Sign Structure

The International Telecommunication Union (ITU) is an international organization that, among other things, sets the standards for the prefixes and formation of call signs in the various radio services worldwide. According to the ITU Radio Regulations, an amateur call sign must start with one or two letters as a prefix, although sometimes the first or second character might be a number (as in 8P for Barbados). The prefix is followed by a number indicating a call sign district (or "call area"), and then a suffix of not more than three letters. You can find the current allocated prefixes for each country online at **www.arrl.org/country-lists-prefixes**.

Every US Amateur Radio station call sign is a combination

Table 11.2
FCC-Allocated Prefixes for Areas Outside the Continental US

Prefix	Location
AH1, KH1, NH1, WH1	Baker, Howland Is.
AH2, KH2, NH2, WH2	Guam
AH3, KH3, NH3, WH3	Johnston Is.
AH4, KH4, NH4, WH4	Midway Is.
AH5K, KH5K, NH5K, WH5K	Kingman Reef
AH5, KH5, NH5, WH5 (except K suffix)	Palmyra, Jarvis Is.
AH6,7 KH6,7 NH6,7 WH6,7	Hawaii
AH7, KH7, NH7, WH7	Kure Is.
AH8, KH8, NH8, WH8	American Samoa
AH9, KH9, NH9, WH9	Wake Is.
AHØ, KHØ, NHØ, WHØ	Northern Mariana Is.
ALØ-9, KLØ-9, NLØ-9, WLØ-9	Alaska
KP1, NP1, WP1	Navassa Is.
KP2, NP2, WP2	Virgin Is.
KP3,4 NP3,4 WP3,4	Puerto Rico
KP5, NP5, WP5	Desecheo

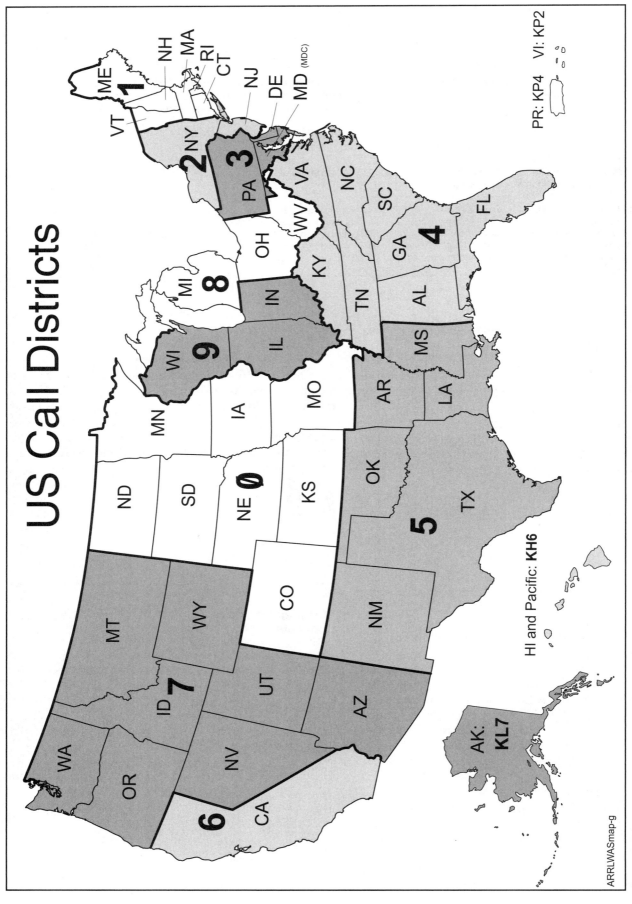

US Call Districts

PR: KP4   VI: KP2

HI and Pacific: **KH6**

AK: **KL7**

ARRLWASmap-g

Figure 11.3 —The 10 US Call Districts established by the FCC. In most cases, the number in a US amateur call sign indicates where that operator first issued that call sign. Alaska is part of the seventh call district, but has its own set of prefixes: AL7, KL7, NL7 and WL7. Hawaii is part of the sixth call district but also has its own set of prefixes: AH6, KH6, NH6 and WH6. Puerto Rico uses the prefixes KP3, KP4, NP3, NP4, WP3 and WP4, while the US Virgin Islands stations are KP2, NP2 or WP2.

of a 1 or 2-letter prefix, a number and a 1, 2 or 3-letter suffix. The first letter of every US Amateur Radio call sign will always be K, N or W, or from the AA-AL double letter block. Some examples: KA9XYZ, NN1N, WB2OSQ, KN4AQ, AB6ZZ, W3ABC. Certain prefixes are reserved for stations that are under FCC jurisdiction but located outside the continental US. Common examples are KP2 for the US Virgin Islands or KH6 for Hawaii. See **Table 11.2** for details.

The mailing address that you use when obtaining your initial sequential call sign determines the number used. The 10 call sign districts for the continental US are illustrated in **Figure 11.3**. So the call sign W1AW indicates a US station (from the prefix W). The call sign was initially assigned to that station while it was located in the first US call area (indicated by the number 1). The letters AW comprise the assigned suffix, completing the identification of that station.

Vanity Call Signs

Under the Vanity Call Sign Program, individual amateurs and club stations may select a distinctive call sign to replace the one assigned by the sequential system. There are many reasons for doing so. Some operators want shorter call signs, or call signs that are easy to say or send. A popular choice is a suffix with the initials of your name. Others may want to recapture a former call sign or that of a departed friend or family member. Some operators just grow tired of their current call sign and want to try something new.

Although there was a period in the 1970s when Amateur Extra licensees could select "1 × 2" call signs (N2CQ, K8MR and so forth), the current Vanity Call Sign Program is much broader. Beginning in 1996 amateurs could select any available call sign valid for their license class for a fee. The exact amount is subject to change each year, but it has always been reasonable considering that the term is 10 years. In addition to paying the fee when the Vanity Call Sign is originally issued, note that you must pay whatever fee is in effect at your scheduled license renewal. The number in a vanity call sign does not have to indicate the call area in which you reside.

Changing Locations

Over time, you may move to another state and find that the number in your call sign no longer matches the district of your current residence. Not a problem. You have the option of keeping your call sign even though you have changed districts, and many amateurs choose to do just that. At one time you were required to turn in your old call sign for a new one that matched your current district, but the FCC dropped this rule in the 1970s.

It's routine to hear stations on the air using call signs that do not correspond to their locations. You are not required by Part 97 to identify your station as portable or mobile, fixed or temporary, but it is certainly allowed and sometimes helps listeners understand your location. For example, N1ND operating in North Carolina might send N1ND/4 on 6 meters to help others point their beams in the right direction.

You will occasionally hear a station identify as "marine mobile" or "maritime mobile" This simply indicates that the station is being operated from on board a boat or ship in international waters. Finally you may hear a station identify as "aeronautical mobile" indicating operation from on board an airplane. While these are legal IDs, remember that operation onboard a ship or airplane must be approved by the captain of the vessel or pilot of the plane.

Antennas and Support Structures

A growing concern for many hams is the placement and location of Amateur Radio antennas and supporting structures (typically towers), such as the antenna system shown in **Figure 11.4**. Amateurs understand that the effectiveness of their stations and communications ability centers on the type and quality of their antennas. Not everyone views antennas the same way, and amateurs occasionally are drawn into disputes with the neighbors and town officials over the height and placement of antennas and support structures.

In the 1980s, the FCC recognized that amateurs sometimes need assistance in dealing with local governments and zoning boards to pursue the privileges granted by their FCC license. From this was born a powerful tool — known as

Figure 11.4 — Getting permission from local government to put up antennas and antenna supports can be a problem in some areas. FCC's PRB-1 grants limited pre-emption of local zoning regulations and requires reasonable accommodation of amateur antennas. Assistance is available from ARRL Volunteer Consulting Engineers or Volunteer Counsels. For more information, see www.arrl.org/regulatory-advocacy.

PRB-1 — that grants amateurs a limited federal preemption of local zoning ordinances and regulations. The purpose is to protect amateurs from outright prohibitions or unreasonable restrictions placed on antenna support structures.

PRB-1 has been incorporated into §97.15(b) and states: "Except as otherwise provided herein, a station antenna structure may be erected at heights and dimensions sufficient to accommodate amateur service communications. [State and local regulation of a station antenna structure must not preclude amateur service communications. Rather, it must reasonably accommodate such communications and must constitute the minimum practicable regulation to accomplish the state or local authority's legitimate purpose. See PRB-1, 101 FCC 2d 952 (1985) for details.]"

In addition to being part of the FCC rules, as of May 2012 a total of 28 states have incorporated PRB-1 protections into state law as well. You can find complete information on PRB-1 and links to the specific pieces of state legislation adopting PRB-1 at **www.arrl.org/prb-1** and links to the specific pieces of state legislation adopting PRB-1 at **www.arrl.org/state-1**.

There are two things to remember as far as PRB-1 goes. First, PRB-1 does not give amateurs *carte blanche* to do what they wish in regard to antennas and support structures. PRB-1 requires local authorities to work with the amateurs to satisfy communications needs with the minimum amount of regulation needed to meet the legitimate needs of the local authority. Local regulators may not reject *all* amateur antennas, but they don't have to allow a structure of a certain size, either.

The second important item to remember is that at this time PRB-1 applies only to regulation by local government officials. Many amateurs face similar (and sometimes more stringent) restrictions when dealing with what are known as CC&Rs — covenants, conditions and restrictions. Sometimes called simply "deed restrictions," CC&Rs are restrictions that are placed on property and deed, usually by the builder of a housing development or by a homeowner's association.

CC&Rs typically include limitations or guidelines for property appearance and use and may require approval of things such as site plan, building design and colors, placement of fences, landscaping and so on. Of concern to amateurs, CC&Rs often limit or prohibit outdoor antennas or supports. You should make it a point to find out about CC&Rs before entering into a real estate contract. They run with the property and you will have to abide by them once you're the owner.

The FCC has ruled that PRB-1 does not apply to CC&R situations. CC&Rs are private contacts, not public law or policy implemented by state or local government. For a good overview of the differences between PRB-1 issues and CC&R issues, see "What Should I Do Now?" from the May 2007 issue of *QST* and available online at **www.arrl.org/files/file/hender.pdf**.

SUBPART B — STATION OPERATION STANDARDS

When teaching license classes or speaking about my passion, I often say that your license is only the *second* most important piece of paper you receive in Amateur Radio. Of course you must have a license to get on the air, but I believe that your first QSL card (a written confirmation from another station that you have completed a two-way contact with them) is *the* most important "document" you receive.

Why do I believe that? Your first QSL card shows that you not only learned what you needed to pass the license exam, but also put that knowledge to use, got on the air and actively participated. Getting on the air is the point of the exercise, right? To do this successfully, Subpart B — Station Operation Standards — is critical to your pursuing Amateur Radio legally, safely and appropriately.

Thou Shall and Thou Shall Not...

Front and center in Subpart B, §97.101(a) may well be the most important rule of all because it lays out the overriding responsibility of each amateur licensee: "In all respects not specifically covered by FCC Rules each amateur station must be operated in accordance with good engineering and good amateur practice."

This simple sentence underscores the responsibility of each operator to use good judgment and common sense when pursuing his or her interests. It means each licensee must continue to learn how stations interact properly, cooperate with fellow amateurs and treat each operator on the air with respect.

In many ways Subpart B is a laundry list of "do's and don'ts" that enable hundreds of thousands of amateurs on the air to share our limited bandwidth. Take the time to familiarize yourself with Subpart B. By following the letter and spirit of these rules, you can maximize your enjoyment while reducing potential problems or complaints on the air. A considerate operator will apply the rules and standards found in this section to his or her daily operation.

Sharing Our Spectrum

One of the most common hassles we experience on the air is crowded conditions. For example, trying to find a clear frequency on 20 meter SSB on a busy weekend morning can be a challenge. Effective spectrum use requires the cooperation of each and every operator. That's equally true during years of low solar activity when poor high-band propagation drives everyone to the low bands, or during years of high solar activity when the bands are filled with hams coming out of the woodwork to enjoy the great conditions. Remember we all share these frequencies: No one individual or group is assigned a frequency for exclusive use [§97.101(b)].

Over the years, to promote the orderly sharing of frequencies, some "gentleman's agreements" have emerged. Known as *voluntary band plans*, these are not hard and fast FCC rules, but rather guidelines for what type of amateur activity should take place in various parts of the spectrum. For example, a station trying to work the popular PSK31 digital mode would want to operate around frequencies where that mode is generally found. Remember "good amateur practice?" Band plans are a good example.

Band plans vary from region to region, especially on the VHF and higher bands. It's worth taking the time to learn about and follow band plans for the activities, modes and bands that interest you. When everyone works cooperatively and follows the guidelines, it allows each of us to better enjoy the time we spend on the air. Current ARRL Band Plans are at **www.arrl.org/band-plan-1**. The "Considerate Operators Frequency Guide" shown in **Table 11.3** is a great quick reference to keep handy in your station.

One of the most overlooked areas of good amateur practice is found in §97.313(a): "An amateur station must use the minimum transmitter power necessary to carry out the desired communications." Follow this important rule and you'll

---

Table 11.3
The Considerate Operator's Frequency Guide

The following frequencies are generally recognized for certain modes or activities (all frequencies are in MHz) during normal conditions. These are not regulations and occasionally a high level of activity, such as during a period of emergency response, DXpedition or contest, may result in stations operating outside these frequency ranges.

Nothing in the rules recognizes a net's, group's or any individual's special privilege to any specific frequency. Section 97.101(b) of the Rules states that "Each station licensee and each control operator must cooperate in selecting transmitting channels and in making the most effective use of the amateur service frequencies. No frequency will be assigned for the exclusive use of any station." No one "owns" a frequency.

It's good practice — and plain old common sense — for any operator, regardless of mode, to check to see if the frequency is in use prior to engaging operation. If you are there first, other operators should make an effort to protect you from interference to the extent possible, given that 100% interference-free operation is an unrealistic expectation in today's congested bands.

Frequencies	Modes/Activities	Frequencies	Modes/Activities
1.800-2.000	CW	18.100-18.105	RTTY/Data
1.800-1.810	Digital modes	18.105-18.110	Automatically controlled data stations
1.810	QRP CW calling frequency	18.110	IBP/NCDXF beacons
1.843-2.000	SSB, SSTV and other wideband modes		
1.910	SSB QRP	21.060	QRP CW calling frequency
1.995-2.000	Experimental	21.070-21.110	RTTY/Data
1.999-2.000	Beacons	21.090-21.100	Automatically controlled data stations
		21.150	IBP/NCDXF beacons
3.500-3.510	CW DX window	21.340	SSTV
3.560	QRP CW calling frequency	21.385	QRP SSB calling frequency
3.570-3.600	RTTY/Data		
3.585-3.600	Automatically controlled data stations	24.920-24.925	RTTY/Data
3.590	RTTY/Data DX	24.925-24.930	Automatically controlled data stations
3.790-3.800	DX window	24.930	IBP/NCDXF beacons
3.845	SSTV		
3.885	AM calling frequency	28.060	QRP CW calling frequency
3.985	QRP SSB calling frequency	28.070-28.120	RTTY/Data
		28.120-28.189	Automatically controlled data stations
7.030	QRP CW calling frequency	28.190-28.225	Beacons
7.040	RTTY/Data DX	28.200	IBP/NCDXF beacons
7.070-7.125	RTTY/Data	28.385	QRP SSB calling frequency
7.100-7.105	Automatically controlled data stations	28.680	SSTV
7.171	SSTV	29.000-29.200	AM
7.285	QRP SSB calling frequency	29.300-29.510	Satellite downlinks
7.290	AM calling frequency	29.520-29.580	Repeater inputs
		29.600	FM simplex
10.106	QRP CW calling frequency	29.620-29.680	Repeater outputs
10.130-10.140	RTTY/Data		
10.140-10.150	Automatically controlled data stations		

ARRL band plans for 6 meters and higher frequency bands are shown in *The ARRL Repeater Directory* and on **www.arrl.org/band-plan-1**.

Frequencies	Modes/Activities
14.060	QRP CW calling frequency
14.070-14.095	RTTY/Data
14.095-14.0995	Automatically controlled data stations
14.100	IBP/NCDXF beacons
14.1005-14.112	Automatically controlled data stations
14.230	SSTV
14.285	QRP SSB calling frequency
14.286	AM calling frequency

be able to conduct your QSO while reducing interference to others on crowded bands.

Many amateurs have an interest in emergency communications and public service. It is one of the core principles of Amateur Radio previously mentioned. It is the responsibility of each licensee to give priority to stations handling emergency communications [§97.101(c)]. Good amateur practice in this area suggests that, in an emergency, you should not transmit unless you can be of direct assistance. While we all wish to be helpful, sometimes the best help in an emergency is to listen, rather than transmit.

Interference

A combination of FCC-mandated and voluntary restrictions are intended to keep us out of one another's way help, but these cannot completely eliminate interference between amateur stations — nor should we expect them to.

Let's put interference into perspective. Note that we're referring only to interference from one amateur station to another (often called QRM), not interference to consumer electronic devices or to non-amateur intruders into exclusive ham bands.

Except when it concerns emergency communications, amateur-to-amateur interference is not, in and of itself, illegal. Each amateur station has an equal right to operate; just because you've used the same frequency every evening for the past decade doesn't mean you have any more legal right to it than the person who received their license in the mail five minutes ago. The rules specifically prohibit willful or malicious interference [§97.101(d)].

What's malicious interference? Here's an example. If two hams, or groups of hams, find themselves on the same frequency pursuing mutually exclusive objectives, that's happenstance, not malicious interference. On the other hand, if one moves to another frequency and the other follows for the purpose of continuing to cause interference to the first, the second has crossed the line. If he does it enough, he'll put his license in jeopardy. Of course, what sometimes happens is that they'll all sit on one frequency and argue about who has more right to be there. All it accomplishes is to keep the frequency from being used by anyone for anything worthwhile.

Radio amateurs have the right to pursue legitimate objectives within the privileges conveyed by their licenses, but they also have the obligation to minimize the inconvenience and loss of enjoyment hams cause to others. If there's a tiny segment of a band used for international communication, it's not too much to ask that local rag chews take place elsewhere. If establishing a beacon in the middle of a densely populated area is going to cause interference to nearby weak-signal enthusiasts, an amateur can find another place to put it. And surely, in such cases amateurs don't need the FCC to tell us what growing up in a civilized society should already have taught us to do.

Control Operator Responsibility

Under all circumstances it is the station licensee (or trustee for a club station) who is ultimately responsible for the correct and proper station operation. If the station licensee has designated a control operator, the rules consider both to be equally responsible for the correct operation [§97.103(a)]. This means that the control operator must make certain that the station is being operated properly at all times [§97.105(a)]. If you, as the licensee or control operator, are in doubt as to whether the station is being operated according to the rules and good amateur practice, it is your responsibility to immediately cease the transmissions. Don't transmit again until you are certain the station can resume legal, safe and appropriate operation.

Reciprocal Operating Within the US

Under many circumstances it is legal for licensed amateurs from foreign countries to get on the air while visiting the US. To do so, several criteria must be in order.

1) There must be a current reciprocal operating agreement between the US and their home country. This agreement must be either through a multilateral treaty such as CEPT or IARP (see below) or a direct bilateral agreement between the US and their home country.

2) The foreign licensee must not hold a US amateur license and call sign. If they do, they must operate under the terms of the US license and are not eligible to operate under a reciprocal license agreement.

3) The visitor must not be a US citizen. US citizens must hold a US license to operate within the US and may not operate in the US under any type of reciprocal agreement.

The operating privileges that a visiting amateur may use while in the US depend on several factors. Visitors operating in the US under the European Conference of Postal and Telecommunications Administrations (CEPT) agreement, or under CITEL's International Amateur Radio Permit (IARP) Class 1 agreement, enjoy the full privileges of the Amateur Extra license [§97.301(a)(b)]. Holders of an IARP license other than Class 1 are entitled to VHF and up privileges [§97.301(a)].

Visitors from Canada are entitled to whatever operating privileges they hold at home, but they may not exceed the privileges of the Amateur Extra license [§97.107(a)]. This means that where their Canadian privileges differ from the US allocations (different limits on the phone operating frequencies, for example) they must stay within the privileges for US Amateur Extra licensees.

A visiting amateur who is not from Canada, or is from a country that is not party to CEPT or IARP, may operate if there is an existing bilateral agreement between the US and their home country. They may operate up to the limit of their own privileges back home, again not exceeding Amateur Extra operating privileges. For example, while they may have privileges to operate SSB on the frequency of 7.075 MHz at home, when operating in the US they may only operate CW or digital modes on that frequency since SSB operation is not permitted for a US Amateur Extra licensee on 7.075 MHz.

A visiting amateur from a country with which the US does not hold a reciprocal agreement of any sort may not operate. There is no citizenship requirement for obtaining a US amateur license, though, so any visitor may take the US license exams and then operate with a US call sign. They must provide a permanent US mailing address.

If you are operating in the US under a reciprocal agreement, you would identify your station using the letter W, followed by the number of the US call sign district in which you are operating, the procedural slant bar (/) and then your call sign issued by your home country. For example, a French licensee with the call sign F5ABC operating in the US state of Florida would identify as W4/F5ABC.

Reciprocal Operating By US Licensees Visiting Other Countries

US licensed amateurs benefit from reciprocal operating agreements when they travel outside the US. As a party to the CEPT agreement, US amateurs visiting most European countries and other countries that are signatories to the CEPT treaty have relatively easy reciprocal operating privileges. In most cases, all you need is to take your US amateur license and a copy of the CEPT agreement (which can be downloaded from **www.arrl.org/cept**) and you are set to operate. You simply use the appropriate prefix designator before your FCC-issued call sign (for example, DL/N1ND during a visit to Germany).

CITEL's IARP certificate is the basic document necessary for operating in eight Latin/South American countries. IARP does not necessarily grant you instant operating privileges, but it does facilitate the ease of licensing in the countries where it is accepted. To apply for an IARP, download the application from **www.arrl.org/iarp** and submit it, along with the processing fee indicated in the instructions, to the ARRL VEC, 225 Main St, Newington CT 06111. Please allow 2-3 weeks for processing and return mail. Expedited processing is available. Contact the ARRL VEC for more information.

For non-CEPT countries, it is usually necessary for you to make some kind of direct notification or application to the licensing authority in the country you are visiting before you can begin operating. Do not assume that you can simply begin operating even if there is a reciprocal agreement in place. With the cooperation of Veke Komppa, OH2MCN, the ARRL works to maintain a detailed list of requirements for visiting each country in the world. Details are available at **www.qsl.net/oh2mcn/license.htm**.

If you're planning a trip, it's always a good idea to review the material and start the process early. Visit **www.arrl.org/reciprocal-permit** for the most up-to-date information on reciprocal licensing. Do a little advance planning and you'll be ready for a DXpedition such as the one shown in **Figure 11.5**.

Authorized Transmissions

Normal communications via Amateur Radio are two-way in nature and according to §97.111(a) include:

1) Transmissions necessary to exchange messages with other stations in the amateur service, except those in any country whose administration has notified the ITU that it objects to such communications. The FCC will issue public notices of current arrangements for international communications;

2) Transmissions necessary to meet essential commu-

Figure 11.5 — Part of planning for a DXpedition is making sure you have the appropriate permission to operate. Reciprocal operating agreements and multilateral treaties like CEPT and IARP make it easier for hams to pack up portable stations and get on the air from other countries. *(VE3LYC photo)*

nication needs and to facilitate relief actions;

3) Transmissions necessary to exchange messages with a station in another FCC-regulated service while providing emergency communications;

4) Transmissions necessary to exchange messages with a United States government station, necessary to providing communications in RACES; and

5) Transmissions necessary to exchange messages with a station in a service not regulated by the FCC, but authorized by the FCC to communicate with amateur stations. An amateur station may exchange messages with a participating United States military station during an Armed Forces Day Communications Test.

Practically speaking, you may contact stations in the US and around the world that are authorized to conduct communications with stations in the amateur service. Your conversations should be confined to comments of technical or a personal nature when talking to amateurs outside the US [§97.117]. While you may communicate in languages other than English, you are required to identify your station in English if using voice modes. If using CW or digital communications, it is permissible to send your station identification in that mode [§97.119(a)].

Amateurs may engage in a few types of short duration, one-way transmissions spelled out in §97.111(b):

1) Brief transmissions necessary to make adjustments to the station;

2) Brief transmissions necessary to establishing two-way communications with other stations;

3) Telecommand;

4) Transmissions necessary to providing emergency communications;

5) Transmissions necessary to assisting persons learning,

or improving proficiency in, the international Morse code;

6) Transmissions necessary to disseminate information bulletins; and

7) Transmissions of telemetry.

Prohibited Communications

While a wide range of communications are legal for Amateur Radio operations, there are also some specific prohibitions. Many of the misunderstandings and disputes among Amateur Radio operators stem from these areas. Although most prohibitions are clear and simple, a few rely on each amateur to decide how to employ good amateur practice. One of the hallmarks of the amateur service is the commitment of the licensees to "self-police" our frequencies. A little thought about what we are about to transmit usually keeps us in line.

Certain types of communication are strictly forbidden. These are found in §97.113. For starters, you are never allowed to use the amateur service for your own personal business communication. This is defined in §97.113(a)(3) as "Communications in which the station licensee or control operator has a pecuniary interest, including communications on behalf of an employer." The rules do allow on-air swap nets where you can notify other hams of station equipment and accessories for sale — as long as you don't engage in that activity on a regular basis. (The rules don't define "regular basis" so here's a situation where individual amateurs must apply common sense and good amateur practice.)

One of the most frequently asked questions in relation to business communication rules is "Can I, as a paid employee of an emergency response service (such as a hospital, fire department or emergency dispatch office) be 'on the clock' while communicating via Amateur Radio during an emergency?" The FCC amended their rules in 2010 and the rules now allow paid employees who are Amateur Radio operators to operate while "on the clock" during drills and tests for no more than one hour per week and no longer than twice a calendar year for a period not to exceed 72 hours. [§97.113(a)(3)(i)].

Another frequently posed question relates to the use of a repeater autopatch to conduct business. The FCC view is that it is permissible to use the autopatch to do such routine tasks as order a pizza or call your doctor's office to tell them you are running late for an appointment. Remember, though, that a repeater owner or trustee may set more stringent standards for the use of their repeater and autopatch than required by the FCC. A good rule of thumb is "if in doubt — don't."

Amateurs provide communications free of charge and may not accept compensation for their services [§97.113(a)(2)]. Occasionally hams ask if they may accept T-shirts, hats and the like from organizers of events where hams provide public service communications. The answer is, you cannot be paid directly (money or goods) or indirectly (publicity, advertising and so on) for your service. If the organizers supply you with T-shirts, hats or other incidental items to identify you while providing your services, that's not considered material compensation. Such items may be accepted, provided the communications would have been provided whether you had received the incidental item or not. This can be one of those "gray areas," so, if in doubt, don't.

Certain transmissions are always prohibited [§97.113(a)(4)]. You may never intentionally transmit music or obscene or indecent words or language on the amateur frequencies. You must not use the amateur frequencies in connection with any criminal activity. You may not transmit information via Amateur Radio in a code or cipher that obscures or hides the meaning of the transmission. False or deceptive messages or station identification are also prohibited. These prohibitions are clear and precise, and the FCC seriously enforces them.

Communications, on a regular basis, that could reasonably be furnished using another radio service are also prohibited [§97.113(a)(5)]. For example, you might help out your local firefighters during an emergency, but they need to rely on authorized public safety frequencies and radios for their day-to-day operations.

Broadcasting

Can you broadcast traffic reports and similar information on the local repeater? The answer is a resounding *no*! Part 97.113(b) is clear: Broadcasting is not permitted on the amateur bands. The FCC defines broadcasting as "transmissions intended for reception by the general public, either direct or relayed" [§97.3(a)(10)]. You may think it is helpful as a public service to relay or retransmit traffic reports or newscasts on the local repeater, but Amateur Radio transmissions are not intended to be transmitted to and received by the general public. Even allowed one-way amateur transmissions, such as code practice or HF propagation bulletins, are intended for an audience of licensed Amateur Radio operators, not the general public.

Along these lines, you are not allowed to retransmit commercial AM or FM radio broadcasts or television audio or video. The two allowed specific retransmissions are weather bulletins transmitted by US government stations (such severe weather alerts from the various NOAA weather radio stations) and, with permission, NASA manned space communications. In both cases, remember that you may not conduct such transmissions on a routine basis.

Amateur Radio's reputation for providing accurate information means that amateur transmissions are occasionally used as a source of information by local television and radio stations. Broadcasters are aware of SKYWARN and other emergency activities and will occasionally use information from Amateur Radio communications to help with news programming. There is a fine line between what is acceptable and what is not in this area.

In an emergency, Amateur Radio can be used to directly provide news information if several conditions are met:

1) The information must be directly related to the event;

2) It must involve the immediate safety of life or property; and

3) No other means of communications is available at the time of the event.

The general rule is that Amateur Radio is not to be used for newsgathering for production purposes by the media

[§97.113(b)]. This is an important protection intended to stop encroachment by commercial news media who may see Amateur Radio as an inexpensive alternative to other communications systems.

Remember as well that the FCC rules provide some flexibility to allow the amateur community to meet its basic purpose of providing emergency communications. In a disaster or emergency, it is your responsibility as a licensed amateur to provide whatever assistance you can with emergency communications.

What can be done when providing emergency communications always is a topic for debate. It is important to understand that the FCC rules do not say "in an emergency anybody can do anything on Amateur Radio." The amateur always needs to assess the situation and make an informed decision about what is or is not an appropriate communication based on the facts. There are three criteria necessary to

make the decision on whether the communications in question are appropriate:

1) There must be an immediate threat to life or property.
2) No other communications are available at the time.
3) It's not done on a regular basis.

Amateur Radio needs to be the only communications available and there needs to be an immediate threat directly affecting life and property before taking the "anything goes" attitude. While the use of Amateur Radio may be convenient, that isn't one of the criteria set down in the rules. We understand the desire to be helpful; however, the decision on what is appropriate Amateur Radio communications in emergency situations will come down to those three criteria. [§97.403]

This doesn't mean you can't provide emergency communications. However, it does place the issue of appropriate communication using Amateur Radio at the forefront of the discussion.

Table 11.4
Third-Party Traffic Agreements List

Occasionally, DX stations may ask you to pass a message to a friend or relative in the United States. This is permitted as long as the US has signed an official third-party traffic agreement with that particular country, or the third party is a licensed amateur. The traffic must be noncommercial and of a personal, unimportant nature. During an emergency, the US State Department will often work out a special temporary agreement with the country involved. But in normal times, never handle traffic without first making sure it is legally permitted. US amateurs may handle third-party traffic with the following countries:

C5	The Gambia	TI	Costa Rica
CE	Chile	T9	Bosnia-Herzegovina
CO	Cuba	V2	Antigua and Barbuda
CP	Bolivia	V3	Belize
CX	Uruguay	V4	St Kitts and Nevis
D6	Federal Islamic Rep. of the Comoros	V6	Federated States of Micronesia
DU	Philippines	V7	Marshall Islands
EL	Liberia	VE	Canada
GB	United Kingdom	VK	Australia
HC	Ecuador	VP6	Pitcairn Island*
HH	Haiti	XE	Mexico
HI	Dominican Republic	YN	Nicaragua
HK	Colombia	YS	El Salvador
HP	Panama	YV	Venezuela
HR	Honduras	ZP	Paraguay
J3	Grenada	ZS	South Africa
J6	St Lucia	3DA	Swaziland
J7	Dominica	4U1ITU	ITU — Geneva
J8	St Vincent and the Grenadines	4U1VIC	VIC — Vienna
JY	Jordan	4X	Israel
LU	Argentina	6Y	Jamaica
OA	Peru	8R	Guyana
PY	Brazil	9G	Ghana
TA	Turkey	9L	Sierra Leone
TG	Guatemala	9Y	Trinidad and Tobago

Notes:

*Since 1970, there has been an informal agreement between the United Kingdom and the US, permitting Pitcairn and US amateurs to exchange messages concerning medical emergencies, urgent need for equipment or supplies, and private or personal matters of island residents.

Region 2 of the International Amateur Radio Union (IARU) has recommended that international traffic on the 20 and 15 meter bands be conducted on 14.100-14.150, 14.250-14.350, 21.150 -21.200 and 21.300-21.450 MHz. The IARU is the alliance of Amateur Radio societies from around the world; Region 2 comprises member-societies in North, South and Central America and the Caribbean.

At the end of an exchange of third-party traffic with a station located in a foreign country, an FCC-licensed amateur must transmit the call sign of the foreign station as well as his own call sign.

Current as of March 2012; see **www.arrl.org/third-party-operating-agreements** for the latest information.

Third Party Communications

In many cases it is permissible for a licensed amateur to provide communications on behalf of someone other than the control operator or station licensee. This is known as *third party communications* and is defined in §97.3(a)(46) as "A message from the control operator (first party) of an amateur station to another amateur station control operator (second party) on behalf of another person (third party)."

Third party communications usually fall into one of three main types:

1) *Third party messages* — written messages generally sent via traffic nets or Amateur Radio message-handling services (packet or radio e-mail);

2) *Telephone interconnection* — autopatch or phone patch communications;

3) *Direct participation* — where the third party actively participates in transmitting the message.

FCC licensed amateurs may conduct third party traffic if specific conditions are met [§97.115]. A US amateur station may transmit third-party communications to another amateur station in the US. Third party traffic is permitted with stations in foreign countries for the purpose of emergency or disaster relief communications. For routine (non-emergency) third party communications, though, there must be an agreement between the US and the government of the country where the other amateur station is located. A current list of countries with which the US has third party agreements is found in **Table 11.4**.

The control operator must always be present at the control point when third party communications are being conducted, and the control op must continuously monitor and supervise the transmissions. Third party communications may not be conducted on behalf of anyone whose US license has been revoked; is currently suspended; or has been surrendered in lieu of revocation, suspension or monetary forfeiture. Nor may third party communications be conducted on behalf of anyone subject to a cease-and-desist order relating to Amateur Radio operations [§97.115(b)(2)]. Also, no station may transmit third party communications while under automatic control unless that station is using RTTY or data emissions [§97.115(c)].

Station Identification

There is a simple reason why stations must transmit their call sign — so people will know who they are talking to. In addition, unidentified transmissions are prohibited. The rules are straightforward in this area. Part 97.119(a) states: "Each amateur station, except a space station or telecommand station, must transmit its assigned call sign on its transmitting channel at the end of each communication, and at least every 10 minutes during a communication, for the purpose of clearly making the source of the transmissions from the station known to those receiving the transmissions. No station may transmit unidentified communications or signals, or transmit as the station call sign, any call sign not authorized to the station."

You will hear a wide range of comments and opinions and variations on this simple rule. But under FCC rules you are required to give your call sign every 10 minutes during active communications and at the end of the contact you are finishing. You are not *required* to give your call sign at the start of a contact. (Common sense suggests that during routine operation you would probably want to send your call sign at the start of the contact so that the other station knows who is talking to them.) You do not have to ID your station in a roundtable discussion every 10 minutes if you haven't transmitted since the last time you identified.

A few additional rules apply to station identification requirements:

1) You should transmit your station ID using the mode in which you are communicating.

2) When conducting an international third party contact, you must give both the call sign of the station with which you are communicating and your own call sign.

3) If you are transmitting the station ID of an automatically controlled station using CW, the speed may not exceed 20 WPM.

4) If you have upgraded your license recently, you must sign the correct temporary designator, such as "temporary AG" (General class) or "temporary AE" (Extra class) until your upgrade is processed by the FCC and appears in the ULS database.

SUBPART C — SPECIAL OPERATIONS

As your experience grows and as your interests change, you may want to become involved in more specialized activities. These are not different "modes" of operation — they are different "uses" for Amateur Radio stations. When you are talking on or controlling a local repeater, sending or receiving messages through a message forwarding system such as radio e-mail or packet, or communicating through one of the Amateur Radio satellites, you are participating in a special operation, and special rules apply to your activities.

Auxiliary Stations

Amateur Radio stations are sometimes set up and controlled remotely via an RF link. A station involved in this type of activity is defined under §97.3(a)(7) as an *auxiliary station*. Auxiliary stations are often set to perform such tasks as controlling or linking repeaters or performing station control tasks, such as changing operating parameters of a remote base station. The stations that these auxiliary stations control, as well as the auxiliary stations themselves, become what the FCC refers to as a "system of cooperating stations."

Auxiliary stations have some specific operating guidelines that enable them to carry out their function while holding to the principle of effective use of our Amateur Radio spectrum. They may operate only on frequencies in the 2 meter band or higher, with the exception of these specific segments: 144.0-144.5, 145.8-146.0, 219-220, 222.00-222.15,

431-433 and 435-438 MHz [§97.201(b)]. Auxiliary stations may be automatically controlled and may transmit one-way communication [§97.201(d)(e)]. Holders of a Technician or higher license may be an auxiliary station or serve as control operator for such a system [§97.201(a)]. Finally, in cases where there is interference between two auxiliary stations, both are equally responsible to resolve the issue, unless one of the stations has been coordinated by a frequency coordinating body. In that case, the non-coordinated auxiliary station has primary responsibility to resolve the issue [§97.201(c)].

Remote Operation and Links

In today's time of deed and antenna restrictions, many amateurs find it convenient or even necessary to employ a *remote base station* (**Figure 11.6**). While not defined in Part 97, a remote base uses a form of auxiliary operation to both control and use the station. As such, they must follow the rules for auxiliary operation as well as those for remote control of a station. Remote control is defined in §97.3(a)(38) as "The use of a control operator who indirectly manipulates the operating adjustments in the station through a control link to achieve compliance with the FCC Rules."

Remote bases are not the same as repeaters. In a remote base system, the user is part of the system, whereas in a repeater system, a user is not part of the system. This means that the person transmitting on a remote base must be a control operator of the system, or working directly under the supervision of a control operator. This is different from a repeater where individual users do not have to be able to control the operation of the repeater itself.

With the advent of the modern multiband VHF/UHF radios, it has become common for individuals to use those radios for "crossband repeating." Most often, operation as a crossband repeater is actually operation as a remote base, and as such must meet the remote base rules.

Until the rules changed in December 2006, auxiliary stations were required to operate on frequencies above 222.15 MHz. It is now legal to operate an auxiliary station on the 2 meter band with the exception of 144.0-144.5 MHz and 145.8-146.0 MHz. This makes it easier to legally operate these multiband radios as remote bases. They must still have some sort of system for a control link (remember, all stations must be controlled by some legal mechanism). They must also have some sort of timer or means of shutting down the system after three minutes should the control link fail [§97.213]. But with auxiliary stations allowed on 2 meters, the user's ID over both sides of the link serves to legally ID the remote station when operating as a crossband repeater.

It is also common to link repeaters to one another or to an Internet connection (such as IRLP, EchoLink or simply a computer gateway). This linking of radios constitutes a system of cooperating stations and involves the concepts of remote bases and auxiliary stations. The auxiliary station rules apply. One of the big concerns to keep in mind when participating in interconnection to the Internet is to ensure that there is no access to Amateur Radio via the Internet by a non-amateur without an appropriate control operator. As with all amateur

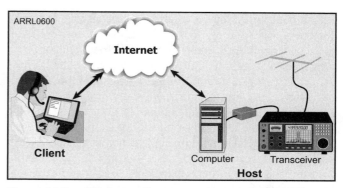

Figure 11.6 — Modern software, computer-controlled radios and the Internet make remote operation easier than ever, but you need to follow the rules. Be sure to review the requirements in Subpart C for details on auxiliary and remote base operation.

communications, the Part 97 rules for station identification, interference and other normal operating issues apply.

Of concern when Internet-linking is involved is "Who can operate the station?" If you use the Internet to link to a radio transmitter in another country, what rules apply? If you are activating a link that is generating RF, the FCC considers you the control operator. So you need to make sure you have operating privileges where the transmitter is located. Think of the Internet as a long microphone cord. The issue is "where is the RF being transmitted?" A US amateur connecting via the Internet to a station in China would not be eligible to transmit because the US does not have a reciprocal operating agreement with China. A US Extra class licensee connecting via an Internet link to an HF station in Switzerland would be able to operate, because the US has reciprocity with the Swiss through the CEPT agreement.

Repeater Stations

Almost every ham uses repeaters at one time or another. A repeater is defined in §97.3(a)(39) as "An amateur station that simultaneously retransmits the transmission of another amateur station on a different channel or channels." Any station owned by a Technician or higher licensee may operate as a repeater on 6 meters and up, and General or higher licensees may also operate as a repeater on 10 meters. Repeater operation is not allowed in these segments of those bands: 28.0-29.5, 50.0-51.0, 144.0-144.5, 145.5-146.0, 222.0-222.15, 431.0-433.0 and 435.0-438.0 MHz [§97.205(b)].

By their nature, repeaters tend to be placed in locations that are not easily accessible, such as mountaintops or tall buildings. This means they are frequently controlled remotely. Remote control can be achieved through several means. A dedicated wireline or non-published telephone line is permissible. If the repeater also has an autopatch interface to the telephone line, there must be an additional control link. That's needed because it would not be possible to terminate operation of the repeater via the telephone line if the problem was being caused by the failure of that line. You may also use a radio control link through an auxiliary station as a means of remote control for the repeater station. It is also permissible for a repeater to be under automatic control [§97.205(d)]. It is important to remember that regardless of the type of control, the licensee is *always* responsible for the proper operation of the repeater.

One of the most common repeater problems involves repeater users who transmit communications that violate the rules — obscene material or music, for example. While the rules state that the control operator is not accountable when such actions occur [§97.205(g)], it is still their responsibility to ensure that the repeater is being operated under the rules. In such cases the control operator should shut down the repeater until the problem is resolved. If necessary to ensure proper operation of the repeater, it is permissible for the repeater owner to limit its use to only certain stations [§97.205(e)]. A repeater is not a "public utility." No licensee has the automatic right to use a specific repeater. Repeater owners may always make rules for use of their equipment that are more stringent than those imposed by Part 97. Failure to abide by those additional rules can lead to the revocation of your privilege to use that specific repeater.

You won't have to spend much time on the VHF and UHF bands to realize that they are crowded. To deal with this congestion, a series of frequency coordinating groups have developed to try and manage the repeater spectrum. From §97.3(A)(22): A frequency coordinator is "An entity, recognized in a local or regional area by amateur operators whose stations are eligible to be auxiliary or repeater stations, that recommends transmit/receive channels and associated operating and technical parameters for such stations in order to avoid or minimize potential interference."

These coordinating groups work on local or regional policies to maximize the efficient use of the available spectrum as well as minimize interference issues or problems. The National Frequency Coordinator's Council (NFCC) certifies most frequency coordinating groups. Each group develops procedures for a designated territory and maintains an accurate database of coordinated repeaters within that area.

When repeater owners experience harmful interference, coordinators assist in resolving the problems. If an interference issue involves a coordinated and uncoordinated repeater, §97.205(c) states that the primary responsibility for resolving the issue rests with the uncoordinated repeater.

Message Forwarding Systems

Improvements in technology mean changes in our ability to communicate with new methods. As with any operating method — new or old — we need to ensure that we adhere to the rules. Part 97.3(a)(31) defines a message forwarding system as "A group of amateur stations participating in a voluntary, cooperative, interactive arrangement where communications are sent from the control operator of an originating station to the control operator of one or more destination stations by one or more forwarding stations." These systems now operate on HF, VHF and UHF and often a message may pass among several frequency bands as it makes its way to the recipient.

The licensee of the originating station of a message is always primarily accountable for any message content that violates FCC rules [§97.219(b)]. But the responsibility does not stop there. The first forwarding station must make sure that the originator of a message is authorized to send messages over the system and must take responsibility for any messages it retransmits into a system. In essence it has the responsibility to act as a "filter" to protect other stations down the line [§97.219(d)(1),(2)]. However subsequent forwarding stations also have the responsibility to terminate any message they are aware of that is in violation of the rules, even though they are not responsible for it reaching them [§97.219(3)].

Remember that Part 97 rules apply at all times. The rules regarding third-party traffic, business communications, obscene and indecent materials, and so forth apply to messages sent via message forwarding systems just as they do to "real time" amateur communications.

An unattended HF digital station may be automatically controlled while transmitting RTTY or data emissions, but these stations are restricted to specific frequencies. There are no restrictions at 6 meters and above. On HF, only these segments are allowed: 28.120-28.189, 24.925-24.930, 21.090-21.100, 18.105-18.110, 14.0950-14.0995, 14.1005-14.112, 10.140-10.150, 7.100-7.105 and 3.585-3.600 MHz [§97.221(b)].

Automatic control is authorized only if the station is responding to an interrogation from a station under local or remote control. In addition, no transmission from an automatically controlled system may occupy a bandwidth of more than 500 Hz [§97.221(c)(1),(2)].

SUBPART D — TECHNICAL STANDARDS

Many amateurs find this subpart of the rules to be the most confusing — or least interesting. It's an important section because here you will find the specifics rules that determine the frequencies, transmitter power and emission types you may use. This subpart also governs the quality of the signals you are allowed to transmit.

License Classes

Currently there are three levels of Amateur Radio license issued in the US — Technician, General and Amateur Extra. Each level of license requires you to pass an examination administered by a team of at least three Volunteer Examiners (VEs) working under the direction of an FCC-certified Volunteer Examiner Coordinator (VEC).

The Technician license requires that you correctly answer a minimum of 26 questions on a 35-question written test. To earn the General license, you pass the Technician exam and then an additional 35-question General exam (again with 26 correct answers minimum). The Amateur Extra license requires that you pass the Technician and General examinations, as well as a 50-question Amateur Extra exam (with at least 37 correct answers).

The written exam questions cover rules and regulations, radio and electronic theory, antennas, safety, operating techniques and other amateur practices. The FCC no longer requires candidates to pass a Morse code examination for any amateur license.

There are two additional US license classes — Novice and Advanced. No new Novice or Advanced licenses have been issued since April 15, 2000. Current Novice and

---

Table 11.5
The Electromagnetic Spectrum with Amateur Service Frequency Bands by ITU Region

Wave-length	Frequency	Nomen-clature	Metric Band	Amateur Radio Bands by ITU Region		
				Region 1	Region 2	Region 3
1 mm	300 GHz	EHF Milli-metric	1 mm	241-250	241-250	241-250
			2 mm	142-149	142-149	142-149
		M i c	2.5 mm	119.98-120.02	119.98-120.02	119.98-120.02
			4 mm	75.5-81	75.5-81	75.5-81
			6 mm	47-47.2	47-47.2	47-47.2
1 cm	30 GHz	r o SHF Centi-metric	1.2 cm	24-24.25	24-24.25	24-24.25
		w	3 cm	10-10.5	10-10.5	10-10.5
		a	5 cm	5.65-5.85	5.65-5.925	5.65-5.85
			9 cm		3.3-3.5	3.3-3.5
10 cm	3 GHz	v e UHF Deci-metric	13 cm	2.3-2.45	2.3-2.45	2.3-2.45
		s	23 cm	1240-1300	1240-1300	1240-1300
			33 cm		902-928	
			70 cm	430-440	430-440	430-440
1	300 MHz	VHF Metric	1.25 m		222-225	
			2 m	144-148	144-148	144-148
			6 m		50-54	50-54
10	30 MHz	HF Deca-metric	10 m	28-29.7	28-29.7	28-29.7
			12 m	24.89-24.99	24.89-24.99	24.89-24.99
			15 m	21-21.45	21-21.45	21-21.45
			17 m	18.068-18.168	18.068-18.168	18.068-18.168
			20 m	14-14.350	14-14.350	14-14.350
			30 m	10.0-10.150	10.1-10.150	10.1-10.150
			40 m	7-7.1	7-7.3	7-7.1
			80 m	3.5-3.8	3.5-4	3.5-3.9
100	3 MHz	MF Hectometric	160 m	1.81-1.85	1.8-2	1.8-2
1000	300 kHz	LF Kilometric				
10,000	30 kHz	VLF Myriametric				
100,000	3 kHz					

Note: This table should be used only for a general overview of where Amateur Service and Amateur-Satellite Service frequencies by ITU Region fall within the radio spectrum. They do not necessarily agree with FCC allocations; for example, the 70 cm band is 420-450 MHz in the United States.

Advanced licensees may continue to renew at expiration and use frequencies, modes and power levels for that license as allowed in the rules.

Frequency Bands

Bands of frequencies are allocated to the amateur service from 1800 kHz (73 kHz in the UK) to over 300 GHz. **Table 11.5** gives an overview of the radio spectrum and shows the amateur service bands allocated in the International Telecommunication Union (ITU) Radio Regulations.

Development of band plans is an ongoing process. It requires planners to research, invite and digest comment from amateurs, arrive at a mix that will serve the diverse needs of the amateur community, and adopt a formal band plan. This is a process that can take a year or more on the national level and a similar period in the International Amateur Radio Union (IARU). Nevertheless, new communication modes or changes in the popularity of existing ones can make a band plan updated just a few years ago look obsolete.

Such revolutionary change has taken place in the past decade with the popularity of new digital modes. Changes of this magnitude cause the new users to scramble for frequencies and some of the existing mode users to draw their wagons in a circle. The national societies (such as ARRL), their staffs and committees, and the IARU have the job of sorting out the contention for various frequencies and preparing new band plans. Fortunately, we have not exhausted all possible ways of improving our management of the spectrum so that all Amateur Radio interests can be accommodated.

Here are some band-by-band highlights:

The 160 Meter Band

The 160 meter band, 1800-2000 kHz, provides some excellent DX opportunities in addition to local operations. The basic problem with allocations in this band has been competition with the Radiolocation Service. New pressures are possible as a result of planned expansion of the medium-frequency broadcast band in the 1605-1705 kHz range.

The 80 Meter Band

While US amateurs enjoy the use of 3500-4000 kHz, not all countries allocate such a wide range of frequencies to the 75/80 meter band. There are fixed, mobile and broadcast operations, particularly in the upper part of the band.

The 60 Meter Band

The FCC has granted amateur secondary access on upper sideband (USB), CW or RTTY emissions (emission designators 2K80J3E, 2K80J2D, and 60H0J2B, respectively) to five discrete 2.8-kHz wide channels at the frequencies shown in **Table 11.6**:

While the center channel is the allocated frequency, on USB, amateurs must set their transceivers to the amateur tuning frequency. This is very important. General, Advanced and Amateur Extra licensees may operate on these channels with no more than 100 W PEP ERP (effective radiated power). In this case, ERP is calculated by multiplying transmitter power

Table 11.6
60 Meter Frequencies

Channel Center	Amateur Tuning Frequency
5332 kHz	5330.5 kHz
5348 kHz	5346.5 kHz
5358.5 kHz	5357.0 kHz
5373 kHz	5371.5 kHz
5405 kHz	5403.5 kHz

by antenna gain relative to a dipole. That means 100 W to a dipole is the maximum allowed, but if you use an antenna with more gain than a dipole you must reduce transmitter power accordingly. If you use an antenna other than a dipole, you must include information about its gain characteristics in your station log [§97.303(s)].

The 40 Meter Band

In 2009, the 7100-7200 kHz segment became amateur exclusive, eliminating a longstanding problem with interference from international broadcast stations. International broadcasting is still allowed from 7200-7300 kHz, but the amateur exclusive status is the 7100-7200 kHz segment has alleviated much of the crowding.

The 30 Meter Band

The 30 meter band, 10100-10150 kHz, is excellent for CW and digital modes. The only problem is that US amateurs must not cause harmful interference to the fixed operations outside the US. This restricts transmitter power output to 200 W and is one reason for not having contests on this band.

The 20 Meter Band

The workhorse of DX is undoubtedly the 20 meter band, 14000-14350 kHz. It offers excellent propagation to all parts of the world throughout the sunspot cycle and is virtually clean of interference from other services.

The 17 Meter Band

The 18068-18168 kHz band was awarded to amateurs on an exclusive basis, worldwide, at WARC-79. It was made available for amateur use in the US in January 1989. It shares propagation characteristics with 15 and 20 meters.

The 15 and 12 Meter Bands

The 21000-21450 and 24890-24990 kHz bands are excellent for DX during the high part of the sunspot cycle. They also offer some openings throughout the rest of the sunspot cycle.

The 10 Meter Band

Spanning 28000-29700 kHz, this is an exclusive amateur band worldwide. Its popularity rises and falls with sunspot numbers and propagation.

The VHF and Higher Bands

The 6 meter band is not universal, but the trend seems to be toward allocating it to amateurs as TV broadcasting vacates the 50-54 MHz band. It is also excellent for amateur exploitation of meteor-scatter communications using various modes including digital.

Two meters is heavily used throughout the world for CW, EME (moonbounce), SSB, FM and packet radio. The US allocation is 144-148 MHz. Satellites occupy the 145.8-146 MHz segment.

US amateurs have a primary allocation at 222-225 MHz, which is largely used for repeaters. The Commission has allocated 219-220 MHz to the Amateur Radio Service on a secondary basis, only for stations participating in fixed, point-to-point digital messaging systems. There are special provisions to protect domestic waterways telephone systems using that band.

The 70 cm band is prime UHF spectrum. The 430-440 MHz band is virtually worldwide, whereas the 420-430 MHz and 440-450 MHz bands are not. Frequencies around 432 MHz are used for weak-signal work, including EME, and the 435-438 MHz band is for amateur satellites. The 70-cm band is the lowest frequency band that can be used for fast-scan television and spread spectrum emissions.

The 33 cm band (902-928 MHz) is widely shared with other services, including Location and Monitoring Service (LMS), which is primary, and ISM (industrial, scientific and medical) equipment applications. A number of low-power devices including spread spectrum local area networks operate in this band under Part 15 of the FCC's Rules.

The 1240-1300 MHz band is used by Amateur Radio operators for essentially all modes, including FM, ATV and packet. By regulation, the 1260-1270 MHz segment may be used only in the Earth-to-space direction when communicating with amateur satellites.

Amateur Radio is primary at 2390-2417 MHz. While the amateur service has a secondary allocation in the 2300-2450 MHz band in the international tables, in the United States the allocation is 2390-2400 MHz and 2390-2417 MHz primary, and 2300-2310, and 2417-2450 secondary. Most of the weak-signal work in the US takes place around 2304 MHz, while much of the satellite activity is in the 2400-2402 MHz segment.

The remaining microwave and millimeter bands are the territory of amateur experimenters. It is important that the amateur service and the amateur satellite service use these bands, and contribute to the state of the art in order to retain them. There is growing interest on the part of the telecommunications industry and the space science community to fully exploit the 20-95 GHz spectrum.

It is important to remember that we share frequency allocations on many of our bands above 420 MHz. For example, while we have a frequency allocation between 420 and 450 MHz, we are only the secondary user (with the Radiolocation Service designated as primary). In any case where an amateur station as a secondary user causes harmful interference to the primary user (regardless of band), it is the sole responsibility of the amateur station to mitigate or eliminate that interference.

Certification and Standards for External RF Power Amplifiers

Certain types of Amateur Radio equipment are required

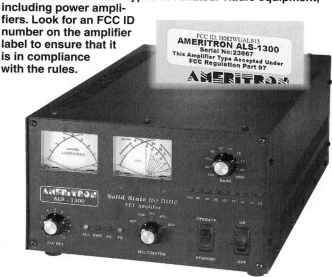

Figure 11.7 — Subpart D is the Technical Standards section. This subpart includes rules governing FCC Certification of certain types of Amateur Radio equipment, including power amplifiers. Look for an FCC ID number on the amplifier label to ensure that it is in compliance with the rules.

to have FCC Certification (formerly known as type-acceptance). Primarily this is done to combat the modification of Amateur Radio gear for illegal use on frequencies in and around the Citizens Band (CB) Service frequencies (commonly referred to as 11 meters). New RF power amplifiers such as the one shown in **Figure 11.7** are required to exhibit no amplification between 26 and 28 MHz, and they may not be designed to allow easy modification to do so [§97.317(a)(3) and (b)].

Frequency Allocations and Emission Types

Part 97.301 lays out the specific frequency allocations for each type of amateur license, and §97.305 delineates the types of emissions that are permissible on each portion of each band. The chart in **Figure 11.8** summarizes this information.

Emission Standards

In keeping with the principle of good amateur practice, it is important that the signals transmitted by an amateur station be "clean." But it is for more than on-the-air aesthetics — good signal quality reduces interference and problems on the bands, which in turn makes our operating time more enjoyable and easier.

The rules are clear about signal quality. No station should occupy more bandwidth than is necessary for the type of communication being conducted [§97.307(a)]. Your modulated signal must not exceed the band segments authorized for your license [§97.307(b)]. Spurious emissions must be reduced as much as possible and corrected if they are causing harmful interference [§97.307(c)]. The remaining paragraphs of 97.307 deal with specifications for various modes.

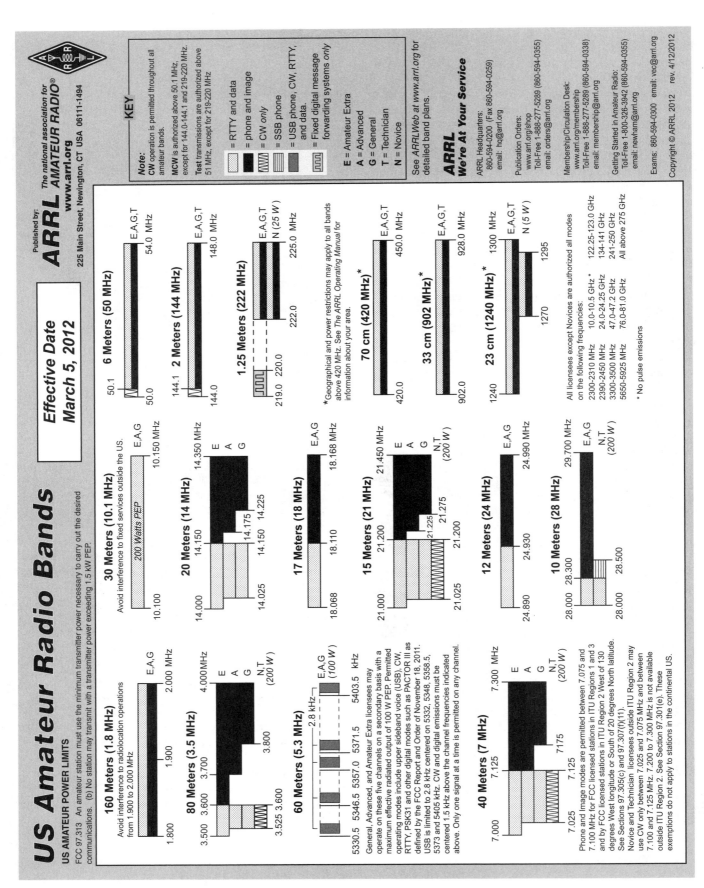

Figure 11.8 — US amateur operating privileges.

SUBPART E — PROVIDING EMERGENCY COMMUNICATIONS

Providing emergency communications is one of the basic purposes of the Amateur Radio service. Because of its importance, Part 97 devotes a small but significant Subpart to special rules for use during emergencies. Amateurs routinely provide communications in the aftermath of natural disasters such as the tornado shown in **Figure 11.9**.

Emergency communication means "essential communication needs in connection with the immediate safety of human life and immediate protection of property when normal communication systems are not available" [§97.403(b)]. This rule section in essence states when life or property are at risk, nothing in the Part 97 rules prevents the licensee from using Amateur Radio to try to obtain the help or relief needed. Part 97.405 goes further when it states that a station in distress should use *any means at its disposal* to "attract attention, make known its condition and location, and obtain assistance." As FCC officials have stated, "In a real emergency — do what is necessary."

This isn't a responsibility to be taken lightly nor is it a *carte blanche* approval to do anything you may want to do. The FCC records are full of enforcement actions involving stations that "cried wolf" or made false claims. The trust that the FCC places in the amateur community gives us a lot of latitude during emergencies, but it is a trust that each licensee must responsibly bear. Keep in mind that a real emergency needs to exist — avoid the claim that what was done was done "because it was an emergency" or "it might have helped just in case" simply as a means to justify the rules to be skirted.

Often when participating in an emergency (or when practicing for them through drills, nets or public service events) you may use self-assigned "tactical" call signs (such as "Shelter 1") during your communications. While these are not prohibited by Part 97, remember that you are still required to give your FCC-assigned call sign at least every 10 minutes during the contact and at the end of your communications.

Figure 11.9 — Emergency communications is important enough that it warrants its own section, Subpart E. Amateur Radio volunteers may be found at operations centers or out in the field. Here, Mickey Gillespie, KJ4KZT, sends in a damage report following devastating tornado events in Alabama. (*Roger Smith photo*)

SUBPART F — QUALIFYING EXAMINATION SYSTEMS

As discussed previously, the FCC delegates most of the Amateur Radio examination process to the amateur community itself, through the Volunteer Examiner (VE) program. The FCC maintains the standards for what classes of license are available in the US [§97.501] and what is necessary to pass the various examinations [§97.503]. The actual content, preparation and administration of exams are determined by Volunteer Examiner Coordinators (VECs).

The individual VECs are responsible for training and certifying qualified Amateur Radio operators to serve as Volunteer Examiners (**Figure 11.10**). They are also responsible for implementing the FCC guidelines for administration of exams and filing the results of those exams electronically with the FCC.

The individual VECs across the US work jointly through the National Conference of Volunteer Examiner Coordinators (NCVEC). The NCVEC is responsible, through its Question Pool Committee, to maintain a common question pool for each license class [§97.523].

SUMMARY

The wide variety of Amateur Radio bands, modes and activities available to you can be overwhelming at times. At every step you have to ensure that you are operating your station legally, safely and appropriately — no small task! While the regulations can seem daunting, the answers to most rules and regulations questions and issues can be determined from a good review of Part 97.

Figure 11.10 — Volunteer Examiner (VE) teams make it possible for you to take license exams. Whether you're going for your first license or an upgrade, you can find the nearest exam session on the ARRL website at www.arrl.org/licensing-education-training.

This chapter was not intended to provide an exhaustive discussion of every rule and regulation. Rather, it's intended to answer the most commonly asked questions. Each amateur is encouraged to have a copy of the current rules handy.

Remote Station Control Over the Internet

Twenty-first century hams face new challenges when it comes to finding places to operate. We're increasingly plagued by antenna restrictions, interference issues and other roadblocks that make it nearly impossible to enjoy Amateur Radio in our homes.

If it isn't possible to establish a ham station where you live, the next best alternative is to set it up somewhere else and operate by remote control. This is not a new concept. Hams have been building remotely controlled stations for decades.

From the earliest days, amateurs have experimented with wired remote control over relatively short distances. In the beginning, these stations were controlled by elaborate systems using small electric motors and relays to manipulate transmitters and receivers. In more recent times, the favored approach was wireless RF control, primarily on UHF frequencies as required under FCC Rules at that time (the FCC has since expanded RF remote control to the 2 meter band).

RF remote control remains a viable option for some, but it is technically and legally complicated. For the RF link to function properly, you must have transceivers at both ends of the path, along with all the necessary hardware to pass the commands (and audio) to and from the radios. The FCC requires that the control link transceivers automatically identify themselves at least every 10 minutes, which also requires dedicated circuitry to make this possible (Morse code identifiers at the very least).

Of course, the strongest objection to an RF link is the fact that it is limited in terms of usable distance. At VHF or UHF there is a practical limit to how far the linked radios can be from each other and still enjoy reliable signals. The greater the distance, the more power and antenna gain is needed at both ends. Someone who already lives under severe antenna restrictions isn't going to be able to erect, say, a long-boom UHF Yagi antenna to communicate with a distant remote station. Fortunately, the relentless march of technology has provided a much easier solution for remote control — *the Internet*.

Thanks to the Internet, hams now have the ability to remotely operate any station at any distance — without the complications and limitations of RF linking. The Internet is the perfect medium for passing large amounts of data between distant locations. For our purposes the data amounts to telemetry information, audio and even video when necessary.

HOW IT WORKS — THE BIG PICTURE

Let's say that you own a well-equipped home station and you'd like to share your good fortune with some of your friends. Or, perhaps you are a ham living under onerous restrictions and you'd like to establish a remote station so that you can finally get on the air. In either case, a remote-controlled solution is definitely available. All it takes is a monetary investment (depending on how much hardware you already own) along with careful planning and a reasonable amount of perseverance.

See the illustration in **Figure 12.1**. The station you wish to control is known as the *host*. It's a host because it "hosts" all the gear necessary to transmit and receive RF signals, as well as a computer to act as the middleman between the Internet and the station hardware.

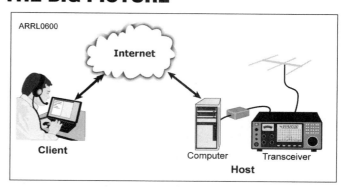

Figure 12.1 — A simplified diagram illustrating Internet remote control of a distant Amateure Radio station.

What is the FCC's Position on Internet Remote Control?

If you've shopped for FM mobile transceivers, no doubt you've seen models that offer the ability to separate the front panel (or control head) from the rest of the radio. This is a terrific convenience feature. It allows you to put most of the radio out of sight in the trunk of your car, or perhaps under a seat, while only the lightweight front panel remains in the open. The front panel is much easier to mount than a full-sized transceiver, yet it puts all the control functions and displays at your fingertips while it communicates with the rest of the radio through a slender cable.

The reason I bring this up is because it offers the perfect analogy of how the Federal Communications Commission regards Internet remote control of an Amateur Radio station. To put it simply, the host is the radio in the trunk, the client is the front panel hanging off the dashboard and the Internet is the interconnecting cable.

As far as the FCC is concerned, the Internet is just a very long cable. In this situation, the FCC's concern is limited to the issue of who controls the host station and how they identify themselves on the air. It doesn't matter where the operator is located — across the street or on the opposite side of the world.

According to FCC Rules, the client is the *control operator*, the person responsible for the proper operation of the host station. The control operator is *not* the person whose call sign is on the license at the host location. In fact, no one needs to be present at the host location *so long as the client is able to maintain control.* The concept of "control" in this sense also requires that the client have the ability to shut down an unattended host transceiver should something go awry.

Since the client is the control operator, the client can only operate the host station within the privileges of his or her license. For instance, the call sign of the host station may belong to someone licensed as an Amateur Extra, but if the client holds a Technician license he or she can only operate the host station on frequencies and modes granted to Technicians.

When it comes to call signs, the client is free to use his or her call sign or the call sign of the host station (if the host station licensee grants permission). In practice, clients usually identify in a specific way to avoid confusion. They will say something like, "This is WB8IMY operating through N6ATQ in Escondido, California."

If we start talking about Internet remote control that extends across international borders, the legal aspects become more complicated.

■ A foreign amateur can access and operate an US-based Internet remote control station only if he or she is a citizen of a country that has entered into a multilateral operating agreement with the United States or a citizen of a country that shares a bilateral reciprocal operating agreement with the US. The latest list of participating countries is available on the ARRL website at **www.arrl. org/bilateral-reciprocal-agreements**.

When operating in this fashion, the individual at the client station must identify using "W" and the number of the FCC call letter district in which the host station is based, followed by a slash and his or her non-US call sign, for example W3/G1ABC.

■ An American amateur can access and operate a foreign-based Internet remote control station only if the host station is in a country that allows remote station control under its regulations. Ask the owner of the host station to check with the authorities and make sure such operating is legal. If remote operation is allowed, the American amateur must use the call sign prefix of the country where the host station is located, followed by his or her call sign. For example, if the host station is in Austria, I would need to identify as OE/WB8IMY.

If the remote station is the host, that makes the remote operators "guests," right? Well . . . no. In geek-speak, remote users are known as *clients*.

At the risk of being overly simplistic, this is the shopping list for a typical host station:
- A transceiver with a computer interface
- A computer
- Host software
- An Internet connection

A client station typically includes:
- A computer
- A microphone/headset for voice operation and perhaps a CW key
- Client software
- An Internet connection

Host Transceivers and Interfaces

The host transceiver can be almost anything — HF, VHF or whatever. The only requirement is that it has the ability to communicate with a computer and share its transmit/receive keying and audio lines.

Fortunately, this capability is found in just about every transceiver manufactured within the last 10 years. Some transceivers offer direct computer interfacing through various ports. Once the transceiver and computer are communicating with each other, the computer can poll (query) the rig and obtain information such as the current frequency and band, IF filter selections, RF gain settings and much more. At the same time, the computer can send commands to the transceiver. It can tell the radio to switch to a new frequency or mode, increase or decrease output power and so on.

The transceiver control interface usually doesn't transport audio signals. Those are often handled separately, typically through a *sound card interface* with cables going between the computer and the transceiver. You will also find devices on the market that combine transceiver control and sound card interfacing in a single package.

The Host Computer

The host computer doesn't have to be anything special or expensive. You're not asking it to store large files or display elaborate graphics. All it needs to do is communicate with the transceiver and the Internet, and run the host software. Technically speaking, the host computer doesn't even need a display monitor. No one at the host station will be looking at it, unless someone needs to access the computer to perform maintenance.

Most amateurs (about 95% at the time of this writing) run computers equipped with various flavors of the *Windows* operating system. Consequently, most host software is written for *Windows*. Be that as it may, you can just as easily use a *Mac OS* or *Linux* computer at the host station.

Whichever operating system you choose, a host computer can be remarkably affordable. If you really want to shave costs, you can probably pick up a used desktop PC for a couple of hundred dollars that will do the job nicely. On the other hand, prices of new computers in recent years have been plunging like proverbial stones. When this book went to press, for example, it was possible to purchase a brand-new, fully loaded desktop computer running *Windows 7* for less than $500.

Internet Access

The success of your remote station will depend greatly on the type of Internet access you have available at the host and client ends of the path. There are several flavors of Internet access, each with their own advantages and disadvantages.

Dial-Up

Generally speaking, dial-up Internet service, using a conventional telephone line and modem, is the least attractive option for remote station control. Dial-up connections are the slowest and least reliable of the bunch. If you have a clean telephone line and a good-quality, so-called "56k" V.90 modem, the top speed you can achieve is 53,000 bits per second downstream (*from* the Internet), and 33,600 bps upstream (*to* the Internet). In the US, the FCC limits the downstream dial-up speed to 53,000, and the protocol itself limits the upstream speed to 33,600.

This is not to say that it is flatly impossible to use a dial-up connection for remote station control, but it can be extremely frustrating. Dial-up access for either a host or client should be the choice of last resort.

Cable

Many cable TV companies offer Internet service through the cable system itself, using a *cable modem* installed in each household. This piggybacks two-way digital traffic on special RF channels. In general, cable modem Internet service is an excellent choice. Upstream speeds are usually 128 kbps or better and downstream speeds are almost always at least 1.5 Mbps, often much more depending on how much you are willing to pay. The main disadvantage is that the service can slow down if many of your neighbors are using it at the same time, since the last-mile bandwidth is being shared among many subscribers. It also requires, of course, that you be a customer of your cable TV company, and thus might not be cost-effective if you receive TV service some other way.

Digital Subscriber Line (DSL)

This is a form of high-speed Internet that rides over the existing telephone wiring between your home and the phone company's switching center, or to a device known as a Remote Terminal. Since digital signals can share the line simultaneously with analog signals, you can enjoy DSL service without having to install a second telephone line. With special filters installed on each analog telephone, family members can chat to their heart's content, oblivious to the fact that Internet data is flowing at the same time. A special DSL modem acts as the interface to the computer.

Like cable Internet, DSL is also an excellent choice for remote station operating. Although its top speeds are generally less than comparable cable Internet service, the bandwidth is fixed since it isn't being shared with neighbors. So, its actual speed may be higher than cable at many times of the day.

Fiber Optic

Rather than sending information as electrical signals on copper cables, some Internet providers rely on pulses of laser light surging through bundles of glass fiber (hence the name *fiber optic*). You may hear this type of service referred to as *FTTP* — Fiber To The Premises. Verizon Corporation calls their fiber optic system *FiOS* and some are starting to use this term to apply to any form of fiber optic Internet.

If you're lucky enough to live in a neighborhood that offers this kind of service, give it strong consideration. Fiber optic features very high-speed Internet access, along with telephone and television service, all riding on the same fiber. It is blazingly fast and likely to become the wave of the home Internet future. But the fiber optic rollout has been slow and is confined primarily to major urban areas. It will be years before fiber optic becomes as commonplace as DSL or cable.

Satellite

Several companies offer Internet service via satellite. For many rural consumers, this is the only option for broadband access. Satellite broadband commonly takes the form of modems that receive and transmit to satellites in geosynchronous orbit, which means that these spacecraft effectively hover over the United States 24 hours a day. The downside of satellite access is the distance. Since you are swapping data with a satellite 22,000 miles away, you are looking at a 44,000 mile path between the host station, the satellite and the satellite's ground station (and, hence, the Internet). This distance is sufficient to cause a slight delay, known in the computer world as *latency*. It isn't likely to have much impact on voice operations, but CW might be problematic.

Satellite communication with typical Ku-band systems is also affected by heavy rain or snow. As satellite TV viewers will tell you, loss of signal during heavy precipitation is a common occurrence. If you live in an area blessed with harsh winters, you may also face the problem of ice or snow build-up on the antenna itself. Ice can accumulate to the point where the signal isn't strong enough to reach the detection threshold of the receiver. Fortunately, small dish covers are available for the satellite TV market along with dish heaters and vibrators to keep them clear of ice and snow.

Since Broadband over Power lines (BPL) failed to deliver on its promise of providing Internet service to rural areas, satellite-delivered Internet has become increasingly popular and prices have fallen to more affordable levels.

Terrestrial Wireless

Wireless has become a catch-all label for any sort of Internet access delivered by ground-based radio systems. Wireless can mean the type of wireless access that you may have as part of your home network, or what you may encounter in a coffee shop, hotel or airport. This sort of wireless access is generally referred to as Wireless Fidelity, or simply *WiFi*.

Wireless can also mean Internet access delivered by cellular telephone companies. So-called *smartphones* such as the popular Apple iPhone communicate with the Internet this way. There are also adaptors available for laptop and desktop computers that will allow them to access the Internet through the cell phone data systems. Data rates are typically on the order of 750 kbps, although newer 4th generation networks are capable of much higher speeds. Cost is an issue with this type of access, since data plans cost extra and if you exceed the monthly limit you'll pay hefty surcharges. That said, remote station control doesn't usually require the transfer of large amounts of data.

Finally, the cutting edge of high-speed wireless is being offered through a technology known as Worldwide Interoperability for Microwave Access, better known as *WiMAX*. WiMAX roll out has been slow to date, and there are several competing systems, so it is not a common means of Internet access, at least so far. Like a cable Internet connection, satellite and terrestrial wireless services are typically shared services. A lot of users or one or two users passing a lot of data through the system are likely to cause slowdowns, or in extreme cases, momentary lost connections.

How Does Remote Operating Impact Contesting and Awards?

Every contest and award program has its own rules. Take care to read them carefully before you consider using a remotely controlled station as part of your contesting or paper-chasing strategy. Concerning ARRL awards and contests…

■ **The DX Century Club (DXCC):** Remote-control contacts are valid, so long as the host and client are located within the same DXCC entity. For instance, if you live in New York and use a host station in New Mexico to make DX contacts, those contacts are eligible for DXCC credit since both the client and host are within the United States. However, you can't claim DXCC credit for contacts you might make while using a host located in, say, Australia. And credit can only be claimed for the call sign you are using on the air — either the host's or your own.

■ **Worked All States (WAS):** Contacts via remote control are valid, but the host and client must not be separated by more than 50 miles.

■ **VHF/UHF Century Club (VUCC):** Remote-control contacts are valid, but host and client must be within the same grid square.

Those hams who happen to contact remote stations for award credit must understand that the contact counts *only in terms of where the host station is located, not the client operator.* For example, let's say that a client in western North Dakota is operating a remote station 30 miles away and just over the state line in Montana, but is identifying on the air as being in North Dakota. If a ham is hunting the Worked All States award and desperately needs North Dakota, he or she will be disappointed to learn that working this station counts for credit for contact with Montana since that's where the host transceiver is actually located. This is why clients should frequently identify their host station locations when operating remotely.

When it comes to ARRL contests, remote operating is permitted in all ARRL competitions, but all elements (transmitter, receiver, etc) of the host station must be located within a 500-meter diameter circle.

NETWORKS BIG AND SMALL

In the computer world, a network is a system of interconnected computers that share information. In computerspeak, however, we can subdivide the word "network" in several ways. The most common are *LAN* and *WAN*.

LAN is an acronym for Local Area Network. This is a network that exists in a specific area, such as a home or business. If you've set up a computer network in your house, you have created a LAN. In fact, your remote controlled station will be part of a LAN, which is why we're devoting some ink to this discussion.

Once we step outside the confines of our homes or businesses and start interacting with the wider world, we've entered the WAN — Wide Area Network. A WAN is a vast network that is comprised of countless LANs. It may span cities, states, nations and continents to form a global web of interconnected computers. That sounds an awful lot like the Internet, doesn't it? Well, yes, the Internet is indeed a WAN. It's the mother of all WANs!

What's Your Network Address?

Every computer on a network has an address. So do many devices that have internal microprocessors. These so-called *network-aware devices* may include everything from printers to personal digital music players. To understand how data is moved across a network and shared with all these devices — including your host station — it helps to get a handle on the subject of network addresses.

One way to imagine the Internet is to consider an urban neighborhood with many houses. Think of your own house, in fact. If someone wants to send you a postal letter, they might address it like this:

Bob Johnson
12 Vista Ave
Omaha, NE 68046

This is known as a *hierarchical address*. Working upward from the bottom line (and disregarding the ZIP code for the sake of our discussion), a letter processor who sorts by state might look at the envelope and say, "I'll toss this one into the bin that is going to Nebraska."

Once the letter arrives at a sorting facility in Nebraska, a person (or more likely a robot these days) will look at the left-hand side of the bottom line and say, "This one goes to Omaha."

Finally, a sorter in Omaha glances at the middle line and gives the letter to a postal delivery person whose route includes Vista Avenue. In other words, the address begins at a very wide point — the entire country, in our example — and narrows to a very specific house.

Internet Protocol addresses, better known as *IP addresses*, work in much the same way. An IP address is a set of numbers used to locate and identify a device on a network, working from a wide area down to a very specific location. The device using the address can be a computer, a server, a router or even an Amateur Radio transceiver (assuming it is equipped with a network connection). The addresses are unique within the network. That is, two devices can never have the same IP address. If that happens, the data packets won't know where to go and you'll have a nasty condition called an IP conflict.

Examples of IP addresses are: 192.168.66.5 or 127.0.0.1

The second example above is the default IP address assigned to any standalone machine. So, if your machine is not connected to any network, its address is 127.0.0.1. This is also called the *localhost* address.

Chances are, you aren't even aware of your home Internet IP address. If you'd like to see it, go to a website that displays IP addresses such as **www.whatismyip.com**.

Just like a website, the network that supports your host station needs to have a consistent IP address, one that everyone can remember — one that never changes. The problem is that many IP addresses are *dynamic*, which is another way of saying that they are subject to change without notice. The software technology at the core of this issue is known as *DHCP* (dynamic host configuration protocol).

Internet service providers (ISPs) use DHCP because it solves the dilemma of having too many users and not enough IP addresses. In a nutshell, when a DHCP-configured computer or other network device connects to a network, it immediately sends a query that asks, in so many words, "What's my address?" The DHCP server manages a pool of IP addresses and it responds by assigning an IP address, a *lease* (the length of time the assignment is valid), and other IP configuration parameters. Once the address is established, the computer or device is ready to communicate.

In contrast, a *static* address is just what the term implies. It is an address that the DHCP server assigns and maintains permanently; it never changes.

For the great majority of Internet users, the issue of static and dynamic IP addresses is irrelevant. As long as they can access the Internet, they could care less about addressing. Most are not even aware than IP addresses exist.

But if you are setting up a remote station, you care very much! If the IP address changes daily, your clients will never be able to connect. Imagine trying to deliver a package to a house whose address is different every day and you can appreciate the problem. There are two solutions to this conundrum:
1. Buy a static address. Most ISPs will be happy to establish a static IP address for you — for an additional monthly charge, of course. Rates vary, but you can expect a static address to tack between $20 and $30 onto your monthly bill. Some ISPs may require you to pay for "Business class" service to get a static IP address. Sometimes a side benefit of paying for the Business class service is that the upload speed may be faster than a normal home-type connection.
2. Use an address translation service such as Dynip (**www. dynip.com**). For an annual fee (typically about $30), these services track your ever-changing dynamic IP address and automatically route traffic to you. The way it works is rather simple. The service assigns a domain name to you such as W1ABC.Dynip.com. At the same time, you install a small program in your computer. This program constantly looks at your IP address. Should your address suddenly change, the program instantly passes this information back to the translation service. If someone attempts to connect to your computer at W1ABC.dynip.com, the service will automatically re-route the connection to your current IP address.

Firewalls, Routers and Security

In the early days of the Internet, computers could usually exchange information freely, simply by knowing each other's host name (or Internet address). No one worried very much about security. But as the Internet expanded and found its way into almost every home, the *cybercriminals* weren't far behind.

When you open your station for access via the Internet,

you're facing the possibility of infection or invasion. The good news is that there are a number of steps you can take to greatly reduce your risk to the point where it is well within the range of what most reasonable people consider to be acceptable.

■ **Install an effective anti-virus program**. The best way to avoid viruses that arrive in e-mail or through web browsers is by installing anti-virus software. The more sophisticated anti-virus programs will scan your e-mail and all other areas of your computer system for threats and will remove whatever they find. The programs also update themselves on a regular basis to stay one step ahead of the criminals.

If you purchase a new computer, chances are it will come with a trial version of anti-virus software already installed. When the trial period ends, buy the software if you are happy with it. It's an investment you won't regret.

Some readers might add that using a computer with a *Mac OS* or *Linux* operating system is a protective measure since most viruses target *Windows* PCs. This is indeed true, but there is nothing magical about *Mac OS* or *Linux* that makes them invulnerable to viruses. The people who create viruses and unleash them on the world are seeking the greatest bang for their antisocial buck. Therefore, they want to see their creations infect the largest number of computers possible. Since roughly 95% of the computers in use today are running a version of the *Windows* operating system, that makes *Windows* systems the prime targets.

■ **Activate or install a firewall**. A firewall is a software application that blocks unauthorized access to your computer's ports. If you are using a *Windows XP*, *Vista* or *Windows 7* computer, you'll discover that it has a software firewall already incorporated. Advanced security suites such as those offered by McAfee and many others also include software firewalls. Regardless of who is providing the firewall, *turn it on*. It is one of your best defenses.

The only problem with activating a firewall, however, is the fact that it will effectively close most of your computer's ports and you'll need to spend some time telling the firewall software to re-open them so that your remote-control software can communicate with the outside world.

■ **Use a dedicated computer**. A "dedicated" computer is one that functions solely as the host for your remote-controlled station. Nothing beyond the necessary hosting software exists on its hard drive. No financial records, no personal information, nothing you can't afford to lose.

Used computers are extremely inexpensive these days. Unless your host station is working with some hefty applications such as software defined radio, a bargain-basement computer is perfectly adequate. Such a computer still needs a working firewall and anti-virus software, but should the worst-case scenario come to pass, your loss will be minimal.

■ **Use a *router***. A router is, as the name implies, a piece of hardware that "routes" data in a network. These inexpensive devices have become standard equipment in home networks throughout the country. Some cable and DSL modems have routers built in.

A router allows you to create your own LAN and share your Internet connection with several different users under one roof. Routers translate the main IP address and automatically distribute data by assigning individual IP addresses to each computer or device. This makes it very difficult for a hacker to identify and access the individual machines. Routers also have their own sets of ports, which they will block unless you tell them otherwise

■ **Secure your router**. Most routers use User ID and password protection to restrict access to their inner workings. As you'll see later, you will need to use this access to modify your router settings and make them compatible with remote access. The routers often ship with the User ID set to ADMIN and the password set to PASSWORD. You'd be astonished at how many people never change these. Hackers are counting on the strong probability that you won't change yours, either. Change the user ID and password, and then keep a record in a safe place.

STATION HARDWARE REQUIREMENTS

There are a few considerations to keep in mind when designing your remote station. Transceiver audio and control signals for radios and accessories will need to travel the Internet, and so there are some special requirements to look for.

Wiring for Remote Sound

Just about every computer manufactured within the last several years includes sound capability, either through a stand-alone *sound card* or an embedded sound *chipset*. The ability to get audio to and from the host transceiver and the Internet is critical to any remotely controlled station.

In a typical laptop computer, you'll find the sound device making itself evident through jacks labeled MIC and PHONES, or something similar (or perhaps just microphone and headphone symbols). At the risk of stating the obvious,

MIC is the audio (microphone) input and PHONES is the audio (headphones) *output*.

In a desktop computer you'll find similarly labeled jacks, although the desktop will likely opt to switch the output label from PHONES to SPEAKERS. It may also include a LINE IN jack for higher-level audio input.

Receive Audio

If the host transceiver offers fixed-level audio output at an accessory jack, this is the best source for receive audio. You won't have to worry about someone at the host location accidentally nudging the transceiver VOLUME control up or down. The audio signal to the sound device remains the same regardless of where the VOLUME control is set.

Most transceivers provide such an output, although they may label it differently. In many instances it is one pin among several in a rear-panel jack. In addition to the receive-audio output, this same jack may carry connections for transmit/receive switching and other functions. As always, when in doubt, consult the manual.

If your radio doesn't have a fixed-level audio output, you'll need to use the external speaker or headphone jack. The problem with using this source is that someone can inadvertently change the output level.

Transmit Audio

Just as receive audio goes *to* the sound device, transmit audio comes *from* the same device. When it comes to transmit audio, the most straightforward approach is to treat the sound device *output* as you would a microphone. That is, wire it directly into the microphone jack of the transceiver.

The alternative is to send the transmit audio to the transceiver's accessory jack — if it includes a transmit audio input (not all do). The problem with doing so, however, is that you may bypass the transceiver's speech processing circuitry. Not everyone uses speech processing, so perhaps this isn't particularly important to you.

External Sound Devices

The latest trend in sound devices for Amateur Radio has been to create external interfacing units that contain their own built-in audio chipsets. In addition to processing audio, these all-in-one devices also provide transmit/receive switching, which we'll discuss next. They are gaining in popularity because they are extremely easy to install and use. These handy units have their own independent audio controls so you don't have to worry about setting the correct levels or the prospect of those levels changing when you least expect it.

Transmit/Receive Switching

Among the many tasks your host computer will handle, one of the most important is transmit/receive switching. If you think of the Internet as a very long microphone cord, the host computer is effectively functioning as the client's push-to-talk (PTT) switch.

Every host software application provides a means to key the transceiver, usually through the computer's serial (COM) or USB ports. The most common way to make the switching connection between the computer and the radio is through a *sound card interface*. These devices appeared in the Amateur Radio market as sound card digital modes began to flourish and they've become standard equipment in stations throughout the world. Sound card interfaces are available in many different configurations from small and inexpensive to elaborate and pricey.

A typical sound card interface executes its switching function by grounding the transceiver keying line at the rear-panel accessory jack, or the PTT line at the microphone jack. This places the rig into the transmit mode.

This is a straightforward function, so you don't need an expensive sound card interface to get the job done. Of course, the more upscale the sound card interface, the more features it offers. Some models include built-in isolation for

Figure 12.2 — The Tigertronics SignaLink is typical of the devices known as "sound card interfaces." It allows your computer to switch your transceiver between receive and transmit. It also provides isolation for the audio lines.

the transmit audio line, the receive audio line or both. Others offer front-panel audio gain controls (no more *Windows* audio mixer screens). Check the advertising pages of *QST* and you'll find these products being sold by manufacturers such as MFJ Enterprises, West Mountain Radio, microHAM, Tigertronics (**Figure 12.2**) and many others.

If you'd prefer to roll your own, you can do that as well. See **Figure 12.3**. This simple keying interface will ground the PTT or other transmit line whenever a logic high appears on the designated COM port pin. If your computer doesn't have serial ports (they are fading fast these days!), you can also use a serial-to-USB converter. **Figure 12.4** shows a typical sound card interface connection between a computer and a transceiver.

It's important to mention that you may be able to use the VOX (voice-operated switching) function in your transceiver to automatically switch from transmit to receive when the radio senses the transmit audio from your sound card. This approach completely removes the need for a TR switching circuit, COM port and so on. The weakness of this technique is that it will cause your radio to transmit when it senses *any* audio from your computer — including miscellaneous beeps, music, and other sounds. Just remember to turn off Windows Sounds by accessing the Audio group under Control Panel.

If you're setting up a multimode host station, you'll be happy to know that a number of sound interfaces support not just voice or digital operation, but also CW with separate CW keying lines. Several also support frequency shift keying (FSK) for use with RTTY.

CAT Interfacing

Controlling a transceiver means mean more than just transmit/receive switching. This is about establishing a digital conversation between the computer and the radio, allowing the computer to send commands to the radio and the radio to communicate its information to the computer (and, ultimately, back to the client). Such an exchange is possible because modern transceivers contain microprocessor computers of their own. All we're really doing is setting up an interface link so that the host computer can exchange information with the computer in the radio.

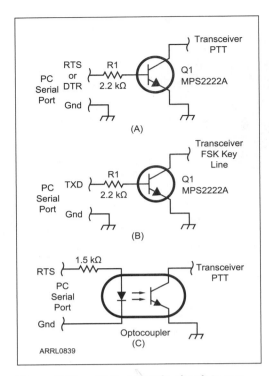

Figure 12.3 — At A, a simple circuit to use the computer COM port to key your transceiver PTT, and at B, a similar circuit for FSK keying. Q1 is a general purpose NPN transistor (MPS2222A, 2N3904 or equiv). At C, an optocoupler can be used to provide more isolation between radio and computer. On a DB9 serial port connector: RTS, pin 7; DTR, pin 4; TxD, pin 3; GND, pin 5.

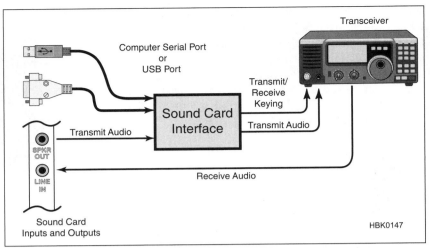

Figure 12.4 — A typical interface connection between a computer and a transceiver. Note that the transmit audio connects to the radio through the interface, and transmit/receive keying is provided by the computer serial port. Newer sound card interfaces are often designed to work with computer USB ports.

You may hear this type of transceiver/computer interfacing referred to as CAT — *computer aided transceiver*. CAT is a term originally established by Yaesu to refer to the control protocol used with its transceivers. ICOM employs a transceiver communication format that they refer to as *CI-V*. CAT, however, has grown to become a generic label for external transceiver control, regardless of the brand in question.

The amount of digital communication that takes place over a CAT link can vary from one radio to another. Some transceivers provide access to channel memories only. This is typical of mobile and handheld rigs. Other transceivers provide a wealth of information to the outside world and allow access to almost every function imaginable.

Transceivers communicate with computers in various ways and there is no established standard. The short list includes…

■ **RS-232 (including IF-232 and FIF-232)**: This is classic serial data communication with some variations — the same kind you'll find in many computers and other devices. It usually shows up as a 9-pin (DB9) socket on the transceiver's back panel. RS-232 is among the easiest approaches to CAT because all you need is an ordinary serial cable between the radio and the PC. Unfortunately, RS-232 ports are not common features in Amateur Radio transceivers.

■ **TTL**: Otherwise known as *Transistor-Transistor Logic*, TTL was earliest form of transceiver/computer communication and it is still common today. The problem with TTL is that it is incompatible with serial communication. So, to get a computer to talk to a radio with a TTL port you need a level converter interface. You'll occasionally see these called "CAT interfaces." If you purchase these interfaces from the transceiver manufacturers, they will be somewhat expensive. The economical alternative is to buy a third-party converter, or a deluxe sound device that includes a TTL converter.

The connection between the TTL interface and the computer is usually made through a standard serial cable. However, if your computer lacks a serial port, you will need to use a serial-to-USB converter.

■ **USB**: Transceiver manufacturers have been rather slow to get aboard the USB bandwagon, but a few have done so in their higher-end radios. If you are lucky enough to own one of these rigs, connecting the radio to the computer is as easy as plugging in a USB cable.

■ **Ethernet**: At the time this book went to press, only a couple of Amateur Radio transceivers offered Ethernet ports. One example is the Ten-Tec Omni VII HF transceiver.

Ethernet is the communication standard used in computer networks (the official name is IEEE 802.3). If you have access to the Internet through cable or DSL, the modems connect to your computer through Ethernet ports. If you have a router in your home network, it makes its hard wire connections through Ethernet ports as well. Any device with an Ethernet port is *network aware*, which means that it is assigned its own IP address on the network just like any other computer and can be accessed (and controlled) in the same way. As you might imagine, a network-aware transceiver with an Ethernet port is ideal for remote station control.

Controlling the Antenna System

The type of antenna control you require depends, of course, on the type of antenna system you've installed at your host station. If the host station operates on only one band with a single antenna, you don't need to worry about controlling the antenna system at all. This is also true if your host station uses a multiband antenna such as a trap dipole that performs well on several bands and requires no external band switching circuitry.

On the other hand, if your host station is connected to a proverbial antenna farm, the possibilities become quite a bit more interesting!

For example, you can give your clients access to a rotatable antenna and allow them to aim it in any direction they desire. There are a number of third-party devices that will connect between the antenna rotator controller and the host computer. These devices allow the computer to send commands to the rotator and communicate the antenna position back to the client operator. They typically connect between the rotator control box and the computer through a printer (LPT) port or a serial (COM) port at the computer. Some units install within the rotator control box itself. For example, the Rotor-EZ unit from Idiom Press (**www.idiompress.com/rotor-ez.html**) is an add-on for CD45, Ham-II, Ham-III, Ham IV and TailTwister rotator controllers and it includes an RS-232 option for remote control. See **Figure 12.5**. The controller sold by EA4TX at **www.ea4tx.com/products/ars-rotators.htm** provides computer control for a wide variety of rotator models. You may even discover that the rotator manufacturer sells a computer interface as an accessory item.

All the interfaces in the world will not do much good if your host/client software doesn't support remote rotator control. Not all do, so research the available software carefully. Some applications do not control the rotator directly, but instead launch a separate program to do so. For example, there is N8LP's free *LP-Rotor* software for *Windows* that's designed to be used with the Hy-Gain DCU-1 or Rotor-EZ interfaces for Hy-Gain rotators. You'll find it at **www.telepostinc.com/ LP-Rotor-Html/**.

If you have more than one antenna at your disposal, you'll be pleased to learn that antenna *switching* is straightforward and need not involve the computer at all. There are a number of electronic antenna switches on the market. Some are designed for use indoors at the station console, while others are intended for outdoor installation. What many of these have in common is the ability to connect to a transceiver's *band data* output.

Many modern transceivers provide a band data port on the rear panel where certain signal voltages appear according to which band has been selected. This is the *band data*. For instance, a pin may have 6 V dc applied to it when the transceiver is placed on the 17 meter band, but 8 V dc when it is switched to 15 meters. An electronic antenna switch can use this information to switch from one antenna to another automatically as a transceiver changes bands.

Note that on some transceivers you won't find a port labeled "band data" so you'll need to check the manual. Some rigs provide the band information at the port used to connect control lines for linear amplifiers or automatic antenna tuners. Others supply this information on one of the accessory jack pins.

Figure 12.5 — The Rotor-EZ unit from Idiom Press shown inside an antenna rotator controller.

Automatic band switching is the best choice for obvious reasons. In this way, antenna switching is transparent to the client operator and is one less piece of information that has to be communicated over the Internet link. But if the transceiver you are using does not offer a band data port, you can still connect many brands of electronic antenna switches directly to the computer. Here again, however, your host software must have the ability to switch antennas via the COM or LPT ports.

Amplifiers

Is it possible to add a high-power amplifier to a host station transceiver? The answer is … *maybe*. Tuning an amplifier via Internet remote control is a dicey proposition at best, so if you must use an amplifier you need one that is (1) dedicated to a single band and antenna so it never needs tuning, or (2) will switch bands and tune itself automatically.

Modern high-power solid-state amplifiers offer automatic band selection and various models provide 500 W to 1500 W output. These amps are designed to be as worry free and easy to operate as possible. The instant the radio transmits, the amplifier senses the RF frequency and selects the correct band. This is ideal for remote operating since the client isn't even aware that the amplifier has switched bands.

Not many remote-controlled stations use amplifiers. Cost is a factor, but so is the added complexity and the greater tendency of an amplifier to invoke Murphy's Law. (If something can fail, it will fail, and always in the worst way.) For example, adding an amplifier increases the RF level in the host environment; computers are notorious for behaving badly when high RF levels are present.

This is not to say that you cannot or should not use RF power amplifiers in your host station. Just be prepared to deal with possible RF-induced glitches. Having a copy of the *ARRL RFI Book* at hand is probably a good idea.

FAILSAFES

If you are careful in planning and assembling your remote-control station, you have an excellent chance of enjoying years of trouble-free operation. However, there is an ancient Russian proverb worth remembering: "When we speak of the future, the devil laughs."

Failure is always lurking in the details. We may sincerely believe that we've anticipated and solved every possible problem that could occur, but inevitably we'll be proven wrong. The devil almost always gets his due, one way or the other.

So if failure is unavoidable in a remote-control environment, you need to have mechanisms in place to mitigate the damage. According to the Federal Communications Commission, we need to have the means to shut down the radio if things go haywire. To quote the FCC Rules…

§97.213(b) Provisions are incorporated to limit transmission by the station to a period of no more than 3 minutes in the event of malfunction in the control link.

Imagine a scenario in which a client operator is transmitting at the very moment a power surge occurs at the host station. The host computer suddenly freezes and becomes unresponsive to commands. The transceiver continues transmitting and the client is helpless to shut it down. The licensee of the host station is out enjoying dinner with the family and blissfully unaware of what is happening at home. The family won't return for hours and there is no one else available to pull the plug!

This is the nightmare that fills many a host station owner with dread. Not only would the station be operating illegally after the three-minute mark, the transceiver and other components are likely to be damaged after what could be hours of continuous transmission. Taking this to the extreme, it is even conceivable that a device could self-destruct in such a fashion that it ignites a fire.

Your first line of defense might be the transceiver itself. A number of transceivers have a feature known as *Auto Power Off*, or something with a similar label. It allows you to specify a transmit time limit. If the operator exceeds the time limit, the radio automatically shuts down, or at least stops transmitting. If your host transceiver offers this feature, set the limit to three minutes.

Some readers may object to what seems like such a short time span, but three minutes is more than adequate for normal conversation. If you don't believe it, start talking and time yourself. You'll discover that you can say a great deal in just three minutes.

Others may point out that the three-minute rule only applies if the control link malfunctions. This is true, but how does the host computer determine that the control link has indeed malfunctioned? Yes, it is possible to create software that can detect a control link failure, but what if the computer itself fails, as in our nightmare scenario?

The FCC has made it clear that remotely-controled stations must have a means to shut down the transmitter that is *independent of the control link itself*. This makes perfect sense. It would be foolhardy to design a remote-control station that relied exclusively on its own control link to stop a runaway transceiver. There must be an alternative.

Perhaps the easiest solution is to establish an alternate control line via telephone. This would consist of a DTMF (*TouchTone*) decoder/controller permanently attached to a telephone line at the host station. Ideally, the telephone line would be separate from lines used for voice access or DSL. It would have its own number and would be strictly dedicated to serving as your failsafe link. Should the worst come to pass, the client (or any other trusted individual) could place a call to the dedicated number and punch in a code to turn off the transceiver.

DTMF controllers are fairly common. For example, there is the Velleman remote-control kit available from Circuit

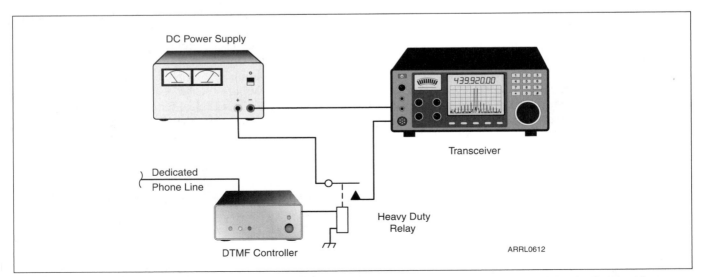

Figure 12.6 — A DTMF controller attached to a dedicated telephone line can serve as your master failsafe. If something goes seriously wrong, you can call the private number, activate the DTMF control and interrupt dc power to the transceiver.

Specialists (**www.circuitspecialists.com/k6501.html**), or the industrial-grade Viking RAD-1 (**www.vikingelectronics. com**). Ramsey Electronics offers their own DTMF remote-control kit as well (**www.ramseyelectronics.com**). Be careful to check the specifications when shopping for a DTMF controller. Some units are quite sophisticated; they'll answer the incoming call, request password entry and even provide a status report. Other units offer only basic features and some require a separate answering machine to seize the telephone line in response to a call.

The most direct way to terminate transmission is to have the controller break the power line to the transceiver. See Figure 12.6. To do this, however, you'll need a high-current relay in the power supply line; the tiny relays in the controllers won't tolerate the current.

Installing a failsafe system is a bit like buying insurance. With luck, you never need it, but you're awfully glad to have it when you do. One side benefit to adding a phone line and DTMF remote control is that it could be used to restart the control computer and radio. Computers can be finicky things and the ability to remotely power it off and then back on again can solve a bunch of problems easily. Otherwise, a run to the remote site might be needed to reset a frozen PC in the middle of the night.

SOFTWARE CHOICES

One of the most efficient ways to accomplish Internet remote control is to exchange the least amount of data possible between the host and client. At minimum, the client software needs to communicate commands to the host, such as changing frequencies or switching from receive to transmit. At the same time, the host must send brief bursts of information about the state of the radio (and the rest of the station) to the client. By keeping these exchanges brief and the required throughput low, it is possible to do remote station control using slower Internet connections.

A less efficient, but more flexible option is to essentially allow the client to take over the host computer and operate as if seated in front of it. The downside of this approach is that it is much more demanding of your Internet resources. High-speed connections at both ends of the pipe are necessary.

Of course, regardless of how the client is controlling the host, there is also the issue of transmit and receive audio. Depending on the software you choose, this may be handled by separate VoIP software (such as *Skype* **www.Skype.com**) running in tandem with your station control application. See **Figures 12.7** to **12.9**.

Skype is often recommended because it is free, popular and easy to use. You'll need to install *Skype* on the host computer and set up an account for the host. Also, you will need to configure *Skype* to use the transmit and receive audio devices in your computer. For instance, if you have your receive audio going to the LINE INPUT of your computer's sound device, you'll want to configure *Skype* to get its microphone audio from that source. This is the audio *Skype* will pass over the Internet to the client. If you are using an external sound device such as a USB interface like the RigBlaster Advantage or Tigertronics Signalink, be careful to look for the correct device name when configuring *Skype*. Instead of "Tigertronics Interface" in the *Skype* menu, you're likely to see it labeled "USB Codec" or something similar.

Make sure to configure the host *Skype* to automatically answer incoming calls. This is important since there won't be a human at the host site to pick up the client call for you!

Every client computer must also have *Skype* installed and each will need its own *Skype* account. Again, however, *Skype* is free so this is not a problem.

Figure 12.7 — In *Skype*, starting or accepting a call is as easy as a single mouse click.

Each client will also need to send a request to the host to be added to the host's contact list. Yes, you'll need a person at the host to accept the request, but this step only needs to be done once. The name of the host will appear on the client's *Skype* contact list once the request is accepted. To call the host, all the client operator has to do is select the host from the list.

Low Throughput Control

One of the most popular software packages for remote transceiver control over slower "low throughput" connections is *TRX-Manager*, a Windows application by Laurent LaBourie, F6DEX. See **Figure 12.10**. *TRX-Manager* creates a user interface that is an approximation of the transceiver model you've selected (it supports a large number of

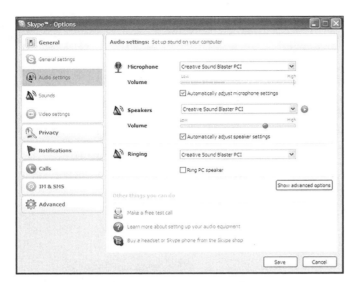

Figure 12.8 — Look closely at this *Skype* setup screen and you'll see that the box labeled "Automatically adjust microphone settings" has been checked. For our application, particularly at the host station, this box should not be checked. We don't want *Skype* to automatically adjust the audio level from the radio (the "microphone audio"). This will cause *Skype* to mute weaker signals that clients will want to hear.

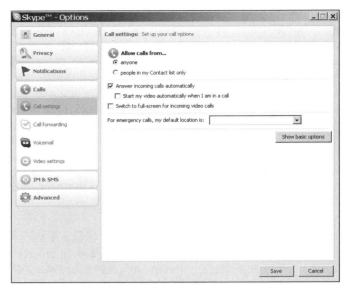

Figure 12.9 — You'll want *Skype* at the host location to answer calls automatically. You'll find this setting under TOOLS, then OPTIONS, then CALLS. Click on the SHOW ADVANCED OPTIONS button. Make sure the box labeled "Answer incoming calls automatically" is checked.

transceivers). *TRX-Manager* is also capable of controlling antenna switches and rotators.

There are no host or client versions of *TRX-Manager*; the same software must be running at both locations. *TRX-Manager* is distributed in the US and Canada by Personal Database Applications at **www.hosenose.com/ TRX-Manager/**.

High Throughput Control with Virtual Network Computing

Virtual Network Computing (VNC) is a fancy term for "remote control." It is a method of making the desktop of one computer visible — and controllable — on another computer over the Internet.

One advantage of VNC is operational simplicity. Other than a VoIP application such as *Skype* to carry the audio (yes, you still need that), the client computer only needs a copy of the VNC program. At the host computer, all that's needed is another copy of the VNC software and a program that can control the radio and any other attached devices such as antenna switches or rotators. That program could be *DXLab Commander* (**Figure 12.11**), a free application for *Windows* that you'll find at **www.dxlabsuite.com/commander**. There are a number of alternatives. If it can run on the host computer, it can be controlled by VNC.

Another advantage of VNC is that it is often *platform independent*, which is just another way of saying that the host and client computers don't necessarily have to be running the same operating systems. A client with a Mac computer, for example, can use VNC to remotely access a *Windows* computer.

There are two principal *disadvantages* to using VNC for remote station control. If the host or client computers are

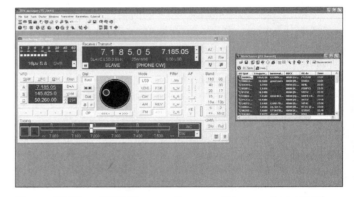

Figure 12.10 — *TRX-Manager* is a popular remote control application that supports a number of different radios and also offers antenna switching and rotator control.

using asymmetrical Internet access with a relatively slow upload speed (less than 650 kbps), latency can become a problem. The client operator may experience, for example, a delay of a second or two between clicking the mouse cursor on a button to select an antenna and the time that the display is updated to show that switching actually has taken place. If the host desktop display is busy, say with a continuously scrolling waterfall showing PSK31 signals, this effect can be particularly pronounced.

The other issue involves security. With VNC the client operator has complete access to the host computer. Unless the control operator configures the host computer to deny access to certain areas, this could be a sensitive issue. Fortunately, most VNC applications provide ways to limit how much of the host machine the client can access. And as we discussed earlier, this is also a strong argument for using a dedicated computer at the host location, a computer that doesn't contain sensitive information.

Of course, with VNC there is still the problem of firewalls and routers. You'll need to configure both to allow the VNC applications to communicate. The VNC documentation usually specifies which ports you need to open and some applications such as the *LogMeIn* software use Virtual Private Networking to keep port hassles to a minimum. Remember that you must have VNC software at the remote (client) and host locations. The client VNC only operates when the client needs it, but the host VNC must run continuously, forever standing by for a connection.

A quick web search will show that there are many VNC applications available. Some are free, some are not. The features they offer vary widely. Popular VNC packages include *TightVNC* (**www.tightvnc.com**), Symantec's *PCAnywhere* (**us.norton.com/symantec-pcanywhere**) and *RealVNC* (**www.realvnc.com**), just to name a few. There are also VNC style services that use third-party computers and Virtual Private Networking to implement remote control, such as GoToMyPC and LogMeIn (**secure.logmein.com**).

It is even possible to perform VNC control over cellular or WiFi networks from your Apple iPhone, iPod Touch or other smartphone with applications such as *Mocha* (**www.mochasoft.dk/iphone_vnc.htm**). *Mocha* is not VNC

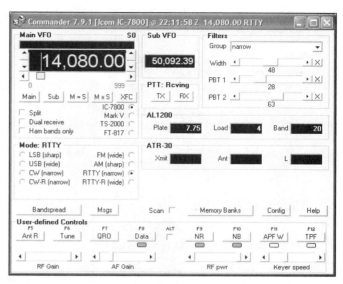

Figure 12.11 —The *DXLab Commander* program by Dave Bernstein, AA6YQ, at www.dxlabsuite.com/commander/.

software by itself; it is a client application. You still need a VNC host application from *RealVNC* or another provider to run on the host computer. You will also need *Skype* running at both ends to carry the audio.

STATION CONFIGURATIONS

Remote-control systems can be as simple or complex as you desire. It really boils down to how much time and money you wish to spend. Note that each configuration also includes the telephone-based emergency shutdown system we discussed earlier.

#1 — The Simple Station

The station shown in **Figure 12.12** gives the client access to voice operation on a single band. A single band, single mode setup is relatively easy to implement because you don't need to use antenna tuners or switches. Although the client is limited to transmitting on one band, nothing prevents listening on several bands, even though the antenna may be less than optimal on a given frequency.

#2 — Multiband with a Single Antenna

In **Figure 12.13** we've gone from a single to a multiband antenna. To keep it simple, however, it is critical that the antenna not require the use of a tuner to operate on its individual bands. In this example we're using a multiband trap dipole that provides a low SWR on every band.

It is worth mentioning that some remotely tuned antennas such as the SteppIR models provide control units that can operate automatically by tapping into a transceiver's band data output or the host computer's serial port. These antennas can adjust themselves automatically when the client switches bands, or the client may be able to initiate the adjustments himself.

Another possibility is a single antenna with an RF-sensing antenna tuner that automatically seeks the lowest SWR for a given band whenever the client keys the transceiver.

#3 — Multiple Bands and Multiple Antennas

Remote switching between multiple antennas is not that difficult. There are antenna switches available that connect to computer serial ports for remote control (**Figure 12.14**), and some provide their own control programs. Others will connect to so-called *band decoders* that select the proper antenna whenever the transceiver changes bands. You'll even encounter switches that will connect directly to a transceiver's band-data output.

See the advertising pages of *QST* magazine for remote-control antenna switches manufactured by MFJ Enterprises, DX Engineering (**www.dxengineering.com**) and Array Solutions (**www.arraysolutions.com**), among others

#4 — Adding an Antenna Rotator

In **Figure 12.15** we have two antennas at the host station, one of which uses a rotator. As we discussed, many antenna rotators can be controlled remotely, often through third-party devices that connect between the rotator control hardware and the computer. Some remote station control applications such as *TRX-Manager* have the built-in ability to talk to these devices. The trick is to communicate the antenna direction back to the client operator. Remote control by VNC comes in handy in this application since the client can simply bring up

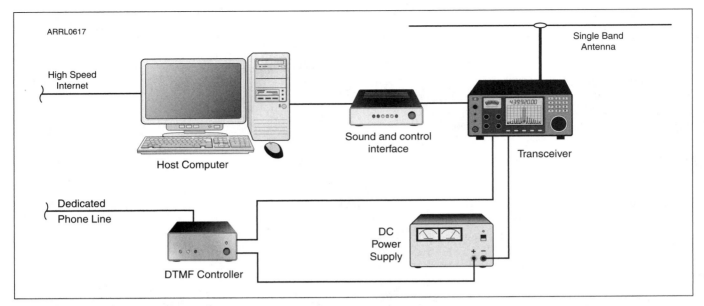

Figure 12.12 — Here is an example of the simplest remote-control approach possible. The single transceiver is interfaced to the host computer. It is also attached to a single-band antenna (no antenna switches or tuners necessary). Notice that this example includes the DTMF failsafe shutdown system we discussed. Its purpose is to give you an alternate means of shutting down the transceiver . . . just in case.

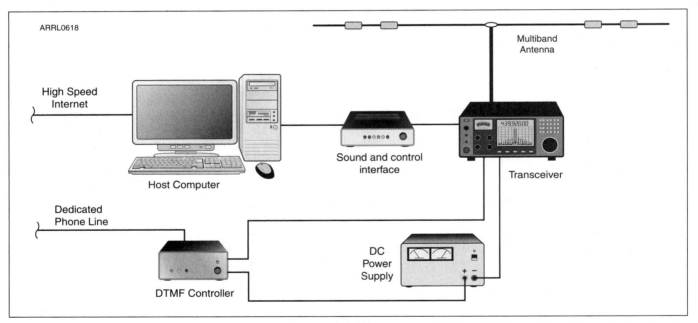

Figure 12.13 — With this host configuration we've added a multiband antenna. This could be a multiband trap dipole of any other type of antenna that switches bands automatically (perhaps through an RF-sensing remote antenna tuner). Simplicity remains the key attribute. The host computer controls the transceiver through a CAT interface and sends/receives audio and does transmit/receive switching through the same interface. Alternatively, the host computer may communicate with the radio through separate CAT and audio/switching interfaces.

the rotator control software directly and adjust the position of the antenna.

#5 — Remote CW

Yes, CW by Internet remote control is possible, but success varies. The easiest way is to use VNC and allow the client operator to bring up a piece of host software — either a CW/digital multimode program such as *Fldigi* (**www.w1hkj.com/Fldigi.html**), or dedicated CW terminal such as *CWType* (**www.dxsoft.com/en/products/cwtype/**). The client would simply type the text and the software would translate it to Morse code and key the radio accordingly. The CW receive audio would go back to the client via the VoIP link (**Figure 12.16**).

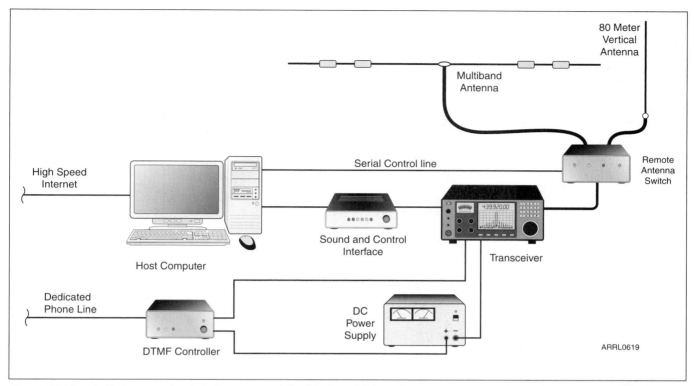

Figure 12.14 — Let's turn our host station up a notch with the addition of an antenna switch. Notice that the switch is connected directly to the host computer. It is assumed that the computer will be running a host application that supports antenna switching (most likely through one of the computer COM ports), or the computer may be running a separate antenna switching application. The antenna switch itself can be located indoors or outdoors.

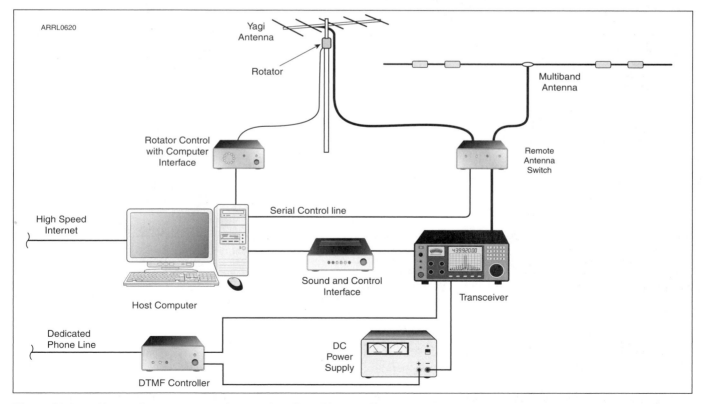

Figure 12.15 — Now we've gone to maximum client flexibility by offering an antenna rotator. If you only have one antenna, the antenna switch is obviously unnecessary. However, you will need a device to interface the rotator controller to the computer. Also, the host application must support rotator control (along with the means of passing the antenna position information back to the client), or you'll have to run a separate application to talk to the rotator control interface.

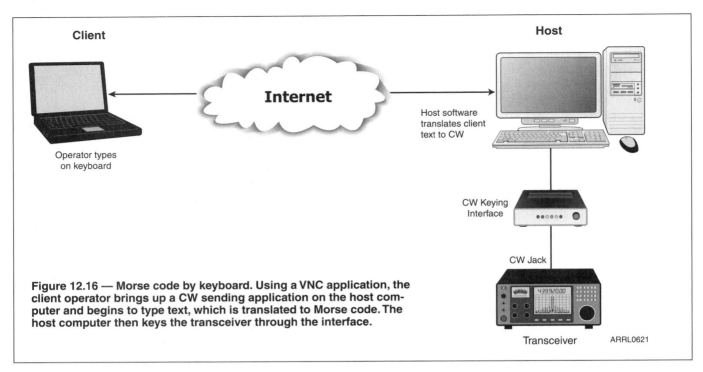

Figure 12.16 — Morse code by keyboard. Using a VNC application, the client operator brings up a CW sending application on the host computer and begins to type text, which is translated to Morse code. The host computer then keys the transceiver through the interface.

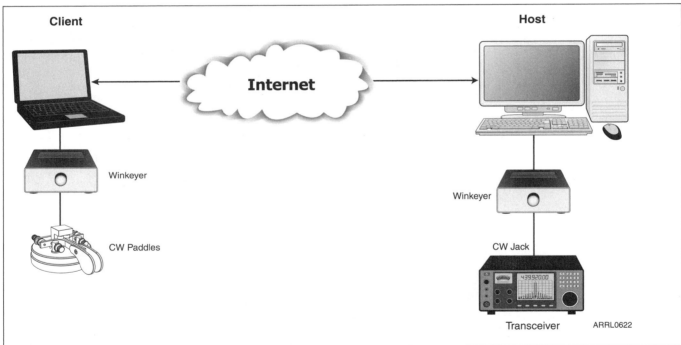

Figure 12.17 — "Real" CW by remote control. Both the client and host computers are running *WinKeyer Remote Control*. The client operator works a set of CW paddles attached to a K1EL WinKeyer, which is itself attached to the client computer. The on/off keying is translated to data and transferred to the host computer and, finally, to the host WinKeyer that keys the radio.

CW purists may balk at this idea. It is really little more than digital keyboarding, not far removed from operating RTTY or PSK31. K1EL offers an alternative that brings real CW keying back into the picture. The solution is a bit of software called *WinKeyer Remote Control* that allows two K1EL WinKeyer CW keyers to transfer their on/off keying outputs to each other — one at the host and one at the client — over

the Internet (**Figure 12.17**). The software is free and available for download at **k1el.tripod.com/WKremote.html**.

#6 — No Host Computer Required!

In early 2010, Mikael Styrefors, SM2O, developed a device known as the RRC-1258MkII, better known as the RemoteRig. This is a completely self-contained turnkey solution for remote control of several types of ICOM, Kenwood, Yaesu and Elecraft transceivers. RemoteRig is actually sold as a package of two devices: one placed at the host transceiver and the other at the client location. This unit handles not only the command and control functions, but also the audio stream. Therefore, a computer at the host location is unnecessary unless you need it to control other items such as antenna rotators. The disadvantage, on the other hand, is that every client would need to have an RRC-1258. If you're putting together a remote station that is intended for a single client, this isn't an issue, but it would be problematic for multiple users.

Operating Awards

Awards hunting is a significant part of the life support system of Amateur Radio operating. It's a major motivating force behind many of the contacts that occur on the bands day after day. It takes skillful operating to qualify, and the reward of having a beautiful certificate or plaque on your ham shack wall commemorating your achievement is very gratifying. If you've been on the air for a while, you can probably get a good start by pulling out your shoebox of QSLs on a cold, winter afternoon to see what gems you already have on hand.

Aside from expanding your Amateur Radio-related knowledge, chasing awards is also a fascinating way to learn about the geography, history or political structure of another country, or perhaps even your own. This chapter provides information on awards sponsored by ARRL plus some other awards that may be of interest to you.

Hams enjoy exchanging QSL cards and collecting them to count for various awards. Whether you're chasing DX countries, US states, grid locators, call sign prefixes or counties, the QSL card is the foundation upon which most awards are based. In recent years, hams have gravitated toward ARRL's electronic Logbook of The World to help bolster DXCC and WAS totals, but everyone loves to receive a colorful QSL card in the mail from a "rare one."

AWARD BASICS

There are some basic considerations to keep in mind when applying for awards. Always carefully read the rules, so that your application complies fully. Use the standard award application if possible. Make sure your application is neat and legible, and that it indicates clearly what you are applying for. Official rules and application materials are available directly from the organization sponsoring the particular award. You can often find the needed information and forms on the web. If you need to get something by postal mail, always include an SASE (self-addressed, stamped envelope) or, in the case of international awards, a self-addressed envelope with IRCs (International Reply Coupons, available from your local Post Office) when making such requests. Sufficient return postage should also be included when directing awards-related correspondence to Awards Managers. Many (if not most) are volunteers. Above all, be patient!

If QSL cards are required with your application, send them the safest possible way and always include sufficient return postage for their return the same way. It is vital that you check your cards carefully before mailing them. Make sure each card contains your call sign and other substantiating information (band, mode, and so on). Never send cards that are altered or have information crossed out and marked over, even if such modifications are made by the amateur filling out the card. Altered cards, even if such alterations are made in "good faith," are not acceptable for awards. If you are unsure about a particular card, don't submit it. Secure a replacement.

None of the above is meant to diminish your enthusiasm for awards hunting. These are just helpful hints to make things even more fun for all concerned. Chasing awards is a robust facet of hamming that makes each and every QSO a key element in your present or future Amateur Radio success.

ARRL AWARDS

To make Amateur Radio QSOs more enjoyable and to add challenge, the League sponsors awards for operating achievement, some of which are the most popular awards in ham radio. Except for the Code Proficiency awards, US applicants must be League members to apply. It is advisable to always check the current fee schedule. Complete information and current fees for all of the ARRL awards described here may be found online at **www.arrl.org/awards**.

First Contact Award

This handsome certificate commemorates that special first on-the-air contact. To give a new ham this special recognition, visit **www.arrl.org/first-contact** and fill in the contact details (call signs, date, time, band, mode and so on). Submit the information online and ARRL will send you a certificate completed with the contact information that you provided. There's a place for you to sign and date when presenting the award.

Code Proficiency Certificate

You don't have to be a ham to earn this one. But you do have to copy one of the W1AW qualifying runs. (The current W1AW operating schedule is printed periodically in *QST* and listed on **www.arrl.org/w1aw**.) Twice a month, five minutes worth of text is transmitted at the following speeds: 10-15-20-25-30-35 WPM. For a real challenge, W1AW transmits 40 WPM four times a year.

To qualify at any speed, just copy one minute solid. Your copy can be written, printed or typed. Underline the minute you believe you copied perfectly and send this text to ARRL HQ along with your name, call (if licensed) and complete mailing address, along with the appropriate fee. Your copy is checked directly against the official W1AW transmission copy, and you'll be advised promptly if you've passed or failed. If the news is good, you'll soon receive either your initial certificate or an appropriate endorsement sticker. Check **www.arrl.org/code-proficiency-certificate** for the current fee schedule.

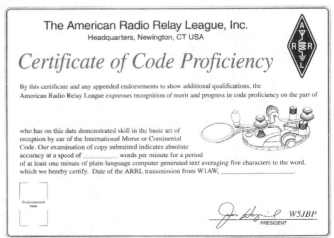

Worked All States (WAS)

The Worked All States (WAS) award is available to all amateurs worldwide who submit proof of having contacted each of the 50 United States. The WAS program includes 10 different awards for working all states on various bands and modes, as well as endorsement stickers for working various kinds of stations.

To earn the basic WAS award, establish two-way communication on the amateur bands with each state. There is no minimum signal report required. Any or all modes and amateur bands (except 60 meters) may be used for general WAS. The District of Columbia may be counted for Maryland.

Contacts must all be made from the same location, or from locations no two of which are more than 50 miles apart. Club station applicants must include the club name and call sign of the club station (or trustee).

Contacts may be made over any period of years. Contacts must be confirmed in writing, preferably in the form of QSL cards. Original confirmations must be submitted (no photocopies). Confirmations must show your call and indicate that two-way communication was established. Specialty awards and endorsements must be shown as two-way (2×) on that band and/or mode. Contacts made with Alaska must be dated January 3, 1959 or later, and with Hawaii dated August 21, 1959 or after.

ARRL's online Logbook of the World (LoTW) also supports the WAS program. If you are an LoTW participant, you can upload your logs and track your progress on various WAS awards and endorsements. When you have gathered the LoTW confirmations needed for an award, you can even apply online. Details on LoTW are given later in this chapter.

Specialty awards (numbered separately) are available for OSCAR Satellite, SSTV, 432 MHz, 222 MHz, 144 MHz, 50 MHz and 160 meters. The Digital award, issued for working any digital mode (PSK31, AMTOR, PACTOR, RTTY, G-TOR and so forth) is also available. The Digital and Phone awards are dated but not numbered, except RTTY.

Endorsement stickers for the basic mixed mode/band award and any of the specialty awards are available for CW,

Novice, QRP, Packet, EME and any single band. The Novice endorsement is available for the applicant who has worked all states as a Novice licensee. QRP is defined as 5 W output as used by the applicant (the station you work does not need to be running QRP as well), and is affirmed by signature of the applicant on the application.

Contacts made through "repeater" devices or any other power relay method cannot be used for WAS confirmation. (A separate WAS is available for OSCAR satellite contacts.) All stations contacted must be "land stations." Contact with ships (anchored or otherwise) and aircraft cannot be counted. The only exception is permanently docked exhibition ships, such as the Queen Mary and other historic ships. Those are considered land based in the state where they are docked.

All US applicants must be ARRL members to participate in the WAS program. DX stations are exempt from this requirement.

HQ reserves the right to "spot call" for inspection of cards (at ARRL expense) of applications verified by an HF Awards Manager. The purpose of this is not to question the integrity of any individual, but rather to ensure the overall integrity of the program. More difficult-to-be-attained specialty awards (222 MHz WAS, for example) are more likely to be so called. Failure of the applicant to respond to such a spot check will result in non-issuance of the WAS certificate.

Disqualification: False statements on the WAS application or submission of forged or altered cards may result in disqualification. ARRL does not attempt to determine who has altered a submitted card; therefore do not submit any marked-over cards. The decision of the ARRL Awards Committee in such cases is final.

Application Procedure (please follow carefully): Confirmations (QSLs) and application form may be submitted to an approved ARRL Special Services Club HF Awards Manager for checking. If you can have your application verified locally, you need not submit your cards to HQ. If you cannot have your application verified locally, send your application, cards, and required fees to HQ, as indicated on the application form. You can search for the nearest ARRL HF Awards Manager (Card Checker) by following the link from **www.arrl.org/was**.

Forms and the latest rules for WAS are available online at **www.arrl.org/was**. Be sure that when cards are presented for verification (either locally or to HQ) they are sorted alphabetically by state, as listed on the back of application form.

All QSL cards sent to HQ must be accompanied by sufficient postage for their safe return, and the required fee (see **www.arrl.org/was**). A WAS pin is available along with the certificate.

Five-Band WAS (5BWAS)

This award is designed to foster more uniform activity throughout the bands, encourage the development of better antennas and generally offer a challenge to both newcomers and veterans. The basic WAS rules apply, including cards being checked in the field by HF Awards Managers. In addition, 5BWAS carries a start date of January 1, 1970, and contacts

Worked All States Award

WAS

The American Radio Relay League
recognizes

has submitted confirmation of having conducted two way communication
with amateur stations in each of the states constituting the
United States of America.

ARRL The national association for
AMATEUR RADIO

President

Worked All States Award

President, ARRL

before that do not count. Unlike WAS, 5BWAS is a one-time-only award; no band/mode endorsements are available. Contacts made on 1.8, 5, 10, 18 and 24 MHz are not valid for 5BWAS. Forms and the latest rules for WAS are available online at **www.arrl.org/was**.

All QSL cards sent to HQ must be accompanied by sufficient postage for their safe return, and the required fee (see **www.arrl.org/was**). A special 5BWAS pin and 5BWAS plaque are also available.

Triple Play WAS

The Triple Play WAS (Worked All States) Award (**www.arrl.org/triple-play**) is available to all amateurs worldwide who use Logbook of The World (LoTW) to confirm QSOs with each of the 50 states on voice, CW and digital modes. All contacts *must* be confirmed in Logbook of The World — no QSL cards or other means of confirmation are eligible for this award.

Contacts must be made after 0000Z on January 1, 2009, to be considered for this award. LoTW automatically uses this criterion. There are no endorsements for the Triple Play WAS Award.

The Triple Play WAS Award is a serial-numbered award starting with #1, as determined by the time stamp of the electronic application submitted via LoTW. Awards issued are tracked and presented on the ARRL website.

Rules for Triple Play are similar to the other WAS awards. Two-way communications must be established on amateur bands with each state on each mode. There is no minimum signal report required. Any or all bands (except 60 meters) may be used for the Triple Play WAS. The District of Columbia may be counted for Maryland. Contacts must be made from the same location, or from locations no two of which are more than 50 miles apart. Club station applicants must include the club name and call sign of the club station (or trustee).

Contacts made through "repeater" devices or any other power relay method cannot be used for WAS confirmation. A separate WAS is available for Satellite contacts. All

stations contacted must be "land stations." Contact with ships, anchored or otherwise, and aircraft, cannot be counted. EXCEPTION: Permanently docked exhibition ships, such as the Queen Mary and other historic ships will be considered land based.

A US applicant must be an ARRL member to participate in the WAS program. DX stations are exempt from this requirement.

Attempts to falsify data, logs, or other application operations may be grounds for disqualification. The decision of the ARRL Awards Committee in such cases is final.

Application instructions and fees for Triple Play WAS may be found on the LoTW website. In addition to a handsome certificate, plaques are available.

Worked All Continents (WAC)

In recognition of international two-way Amateur Radio communication, the International Amateur Radio Union (IARU) issues Worked All Continents (WAC) certificates to Amateur Radio stations around the world. WAC is issued for working and confirming two-way contacts with all six continents (North America, South America, Oceania, Asia, Europe and Africa) on a variety of bands and modes. The ARRL DXCC List includes a continent designation for each DXCC country.

To apply for WAC, US amateurs must have current ARRL membership. All other applicants must be members

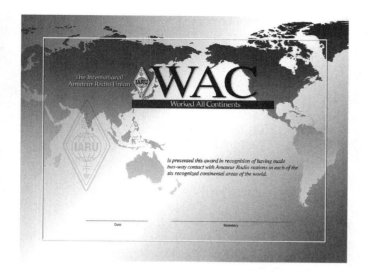

of their national Amateur Radio Society affiliated with IARU and must apply through their Society only.

The following WAC certificates are available: Basic Certificate (mixed mode); CW Certificate; Phone Certificate; Image Certificate; Digital Certificate; Satellite Certificate.

The following WAC endorsements are available: QRP endorsement (5 W output or less); 1.8 MHz endorsement; 3.5 MHz endorsement; 50 MHz endorsement; 144 MHz endorsement; 430 MHz endorsement; 1270 MHz endorsement; any higher-band endorsement.

5 Band WAC: For the primary 5 Band WAC certificate, you must work six continents on each of these five bands: 10, 15, 20, 40 and 80 meters. Upon completion of these bands, endorsements are available for remaining amateur bands. A 6 Band WAC endorsement is available.

All contacts must be made from the same country or separate territory within the same continental area of the world. All QSL cards (no photocopies) must show the mode and/or band for any endorsement applied for.

Current rules and forms are available online at **www.iaru.org/wac/**. For amateurs in the US or countries without IARU representation, applications and QSL cards may be sent to the ARRL Awards Manager, 225 Main St, Newington, CT 06111. After verification, the cards will be returned, and the award sent soon afterward. Sufficient return postage for the cards is required.

For amateurs in the United States, QSL cards can also be approved by an official ARRL DXCC Card Checker (see **www.arrl.org/dxcc-card-checker-search**). QSOs listed in an applicant's DXCC award account in the DXCC computer system may also be used for confirmation. In this case, on the application form applicants MUST fill in details of the QSOs they want to use for WAC confirmation in the space provided.

QSO confirmations in ARRLs Logbook of The World (LoTW) system cannot be used for WAC confirmation.

Check **www.iaru.org/wac/** for the latest information about WAC and for the current fee schedule.

A-1 Operator Club (A-1 Op)

Only the best operators can qualify for membership in the A-1 Operator's Club. Members must demonstrate superior competence and performance in the many facets of Amateur Radio operation: CW, phone, procedures, copying ability, judgment and courtesy. You must be recommended for the certification independently by two amateurs who already are A-1 Ops. This honor is unsolicited; it is earned through the continuous observance of the very highest operating standards. For more information, see **www.arrl.org/a-1-op**.

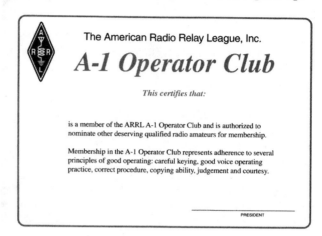

Extra Class Certificate Program

Reminiscent of the *original* FCC Amateur Radio Extra Class License Certificate (no longer available), this beautiful certificate allows the Amateur Extra licensee to display evidence of his achievement. The Amateur Extra Class Radio Operator certificate indicates the name and call sign of the operator as well as the date he or she achieved this top grade. Send your name (exactly as you wish it to appear) and address and the date you were issued your Amateur Extra license (the year is close enough) to the Awards Branch at ARRL HQ. Check **www.arrl.org/extra-class-program** for current processing fees for this certificate.

VHF/UHF Century Club Award

The VHF/UHF Century Club (VUCC) is awarded for contacts on 50 MHz and above with stations located in Maidenhead 2° × 1° grid locators. Grid locators are designated by a combination of two letters and two numbers (for example, W1AW is in FN31 in central Connecticut). More information on grid locators can be found in the VHF/UHF Operating chapter or online at **www.arrl.org/grid-squares**. The *ARRL Amateur Radio Map of North America*, *The ARRL World Grid Locator Atlas* and the *ARRL Grid Locator for North America* are available from **www.arrl.org/shop** and show grid locators in the US.

The VUCC certificate and endorsements are available to amateurs worldwide. ARRL membership is required for US hams, possessions and Puerto Rico. The minimum number of grid locators needed to qualify for a certificate is as follows: 50 MHz, 144 MHz and Satellite — 100 credits; 222 MHz and 432 MHz — 50 credits; 902 MHz and 1296 MHz — 25 credits; 2.3 GHz — 10 credits; 3.4 GHz, 5.7 GHz, 10 GHz, 24 GHz, 47 GHz, 75 GHz, 119 GHz, 142 GHz, 241 GHz and Laser (300 GHz) — 5 credits.

Endorsements are available for additional contacts at these levels: 50 MHz, 144 MHz and Satellite — 25; 222 MHz and 432 MHz — 10 credits; 902 MHz and above 5 credits

Contacts must be dated January 1, 1983, and later to count. Separate bands count for separate awards. Repeater and/or crossband contacts are not permitted except for Satellite awards. Contacts with aeronautical mobile stations do not count, but maritime mobiles are okay.

For VUCC awards on 50 through 1296 MHz and Satellite, all contacts must be made from locations no more than 200 km apart. For SHF awards, contacts must be made from a single location, defined as within a 300 meter diameter circle.

Application procedure (please follow carefully): Confirmations (QSLs) and application forms must be submitted to an approved VHF Awards Manager (Card Checker) for certification. You can download the most current rules and forms, as well as search for the nearest ARRL VHF Awards Manager, by following the links from **www.arrl.org/vucc**. If a VHF Awards Manager is not available, cards may be checked by an ARRL DXCC Card Checker (see **www.arrl.org/dxcc-card-checker-search**). Foreign VUCC applications should be checked by the Awards Manager for their IARU Member Society in their respective country. Do not send cards to HQ, unless asked to do so.

For the convenience of the Awards Manager in checking cards, applicants may indicate in pencil (pencil *only*) the grid locator on the address side of the cards that do not clearly indicate the grid locator. The applicant affirms that he/she has accurately determined the proper location from the address information given on the card by signing the affirmation statement on the application. Cards must be sorted alphabetically by field and then numerically from 00 to 99 within that field. (For example, DM03, DM04, EN42, FN20, FM29 and so on.)

Where it is necessary to mail cards for certification, sufficient postage for proper return of all cards and paperwork, in addition to appropriate fees, must be included along with a separate self-addressed mailing label. An SASE is not necessary when a certificate will be issued, since a special mailing tube is used. ARRL accepts no responsibility for cards handled by mail to and from VHF Awards Managers and will not honor any claims.

Enclosed with the initial VUCC certificate from HQ will be a computer printout of the original list of grid locators for which the applicant has received credit. When applying for endorsements, the applicant will indicate in RED on the right hand side of the page those new grid locators for which credit is sought, and submit cards for certification to an Awards Manager. A new updated computer printout will be returned with appropriate endorsement sticker(s). Thus, a current list of grid locators worked is always in the hands of the VUCC award holder, available to the VHF Awards Manager during certification, and a permanent historical record always maintained at HQ.

VUCC awards are supported by Logbook of The World (LoTW). Instructions for setting up a VUCC account in LoTW and applying for awards may be found at **www.arrl.org/vucc**.

Fred Fish Memorial Award (FFMA)

The Fred Fish Memorial Award was created in honor of Fred Fish, W5FF (SK), who is the first amateur to have worked and confirmed all 488 Maidenhead grid squares in the 48 contiguous United States on 6 meters. The award will be given to any amateur who can duplicate W5FF's accomplishment. This award also encourages operation on the VHF bands from rare grid squares (known as Grid DXpeditions) to help activate all 488 grids.

The rules of FFMA closely follow the VUCC rules. Complete rules, application forms and resources such as a list of all required grid squares and a survey of rare grids may be found at **www.arrl.org/ffma**.

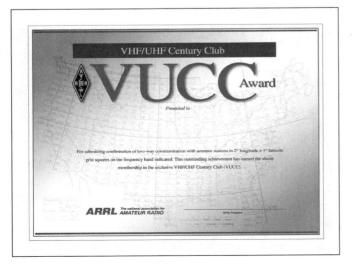

DX Century Club (DXCC)

DXCC is the premier operating award in Amateur Radio. The DXCC certificate is available to League members in the US and possessions, and Puerto Rico, and all amateurs in the rest of the world. There are several DXCC awards available and fall roughly into four categories:

Mixed bands and modes: Mixed

Mode specific: Phone, CW, Digital, Satellite

Band specific: All contacts on 160, 80, 40, 30, 20, 17, 15, 12, 10, 6 or 2 meters and 70 cm.

The basic award level is 100 DXCC entities. Endorsements are available in specific increments beyond the 100 entity level. The DXCC Honor Roll is awarded to those participants who are closing in on working all current entities, and the #1 Honor Roll plaque is available when you work them all.

The complete DXCC rules are quite lengthy. You can download the most current rules and forms, as well as search for the nearest DXCC Card Checker following the links from **www.arrl.org/dxcc**.

The DXCC Challenge

The DXCC Challenge Award is given for working and confirming at least 1000 DXCC Entities on any amateur bands, 1.8 through 54 MHz (except 60 meters). The Challenge award is in the form of a plaque, which can be endorsed in increments of 500. Entities for each band are totaled to give the Challenge standing. Deleted entities do not count for this award. All contacts must be made after November 15, 1945. QSOs for the 160, 80, 40, 30, 20, 17, 15, 12, 10 and 6 meter bands qualify for this award. Contacts on bands with fewer than 100 confirmed entities are acceptable for credit for this award. Check **www.arrl.org/dxcc** for fees and more information.

The DeSoto Cup is presented to the DXCC Challenge leader as of the 31st of December each year. The DeSoto Cup is named for Clinton B. DeSoto, whose definitive article in October 1935 *QST* forms the basis of the DXCC award. Only one cup will be awarded to any single individual. A medal

will be presented to the winner in subsequent years. Medals will also be awarded to the second and third place winners each year.

5BDXCC

For those who enjoy the thrill of the hunt on more than one band, the Five-Band DXCC (5BDXCC) award is a formidable accomplishment. This award encourages more uniform DX activity throughout the amateur bands, encourages the development of more versatile antenna systems and equipment, provides a challenge for DXers, and enhances amateur-band occupancy.

The 5BDXCC certificate is issued after the applicant submits QSLs representing two-way contact with 100 different DXCC countries on each of the 80, 40, 20, 15 and 10 meter Amateur Radio bands. 5BDXCC is endorsable for additional bands: 160, 30, 17, 12, 6 and 2 meters. In addition to the 5BDXCC certificate, a 5BDXCC plaque is available at an extra charge.

ARRL DXCC List Criteria

The ARRL DXCC List is the result of progressive changes in DXing since 1945. Each entity on the ARRL DXCC List contains some definable political or geographical distinctiveness. While the general policy for qualifying entities for the ARRL DXCC List has remained the same, there has been considerable change in the specific details of criteria which are used to test entities for their qualifications. See the DXCC rules at **www.arrl.org/dxcc/** for the most current information.

QRP DXCC

In recognition of the popularity of QRP (low power) operating, the ARRL offers the QRP DX Century Club, or QRP DXCC. The award is available to amateurs who have contacted at least 100 DXCC entities (see the list at **www.arrl.org/dxcc/**) using 5 W output or less, and standard DXCC rules apply. Contacts may have been made at any time since November 15, 1945, and no QSLs are required.

The QRP DXCC is a one-time award and is non-endorsable. Certificates will be dated, but not numbered. This award is separate and distinct from the traditional DXCC award program. Credits are not assigned to other DXCC awards.

The award is available to amateurs worldwide, and you do not have to be an ARRL member to qualify. To apply for the QRP DXCC, just send a list of your contacts including call signs, countries/entities and contact dates. Do not send QSLs. The list must also carry a signed statement from you

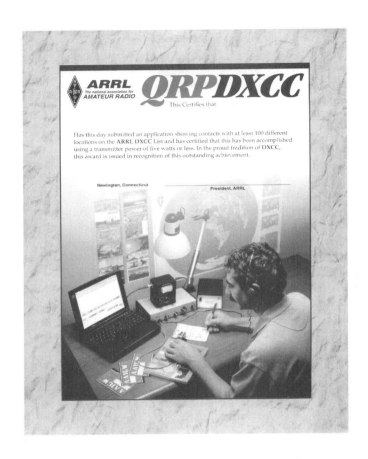

that all of the contacts were made with 5 W RF output (as measured at the antenna system input) or less.

More information, forms and the current application fee may be found at **www.arrl.org/qrp-dxcc**. Along with your contact list, include the application fee. Make sure to indicate your mailing address and your name as you want it to appear on the certificate. Mail everything to: QRP DXCC, ARRL, 225 Main St, Newington, CT 06111.

RSGB ISLANDS ON THE AIR — IOTA

The IOTA Program was created by Geoff Watts, a leading British shortwave listener, in the mid-1960s. When it was taken over by the RSGB in 1985 it had already become, for some, a favorite award. Its popularity grows each year and it is highly regarded among amateurs worldwide. The information given here is just a summary of the program. Full information, rules and forms may be found at **www.rsgbiota.org**.

The IOTA Program consists of 21 separate certificates. They may be claimed by any licensed radio amateur eligible under the General Rules, who can produce evidence of having made two-way communication, since November 15, 1945, with the required number of Amateur Radio stations located on the islands both worldwide and regional. Part of the fun of IOTA is that it is an evolving

program with new islands being activated for the first time.

The basic award is for working stations located on 100 islands/groups. There are higher achievement awards for working 200, 300, 400, 500, 600, 700, 800, 900 and 1000 islands/groups. In addition there are seven continental awards (including Antarctica) and three regional awards — Arctic Islands, British Isles and West Indies — for contacting a specified number of islands/groups listed in each area. The IOTA World Diploma is available for working 50% of the numbered groups in each of the seven continents. A Plaque of Excellence is available for confirmed contacts with at least 750 islands/groups. Shields are available for every 25 further islands/groups. The IOTA 1000 Islands Trophy is available for contacting 1000 IOTA groups.

Mini plates are available for additional IOTA groups in increments of 25.

Applicants must register and create an account on the IOTA website at **www.rsgbiota.org**. Electronic applications are strongly encouraged and award credits may be tracked online. The rules require that QSL cards be submitted to nominated IOTA checkpoints for checking. These checkpoints are listed on the IOTA website and in the *RSGB IOTA Directory and Yearbook*.

RSGB IOTA Directory

The official source of IOTA information is the

RSGB IOTA Directory. This publication lists thousands of islands, grouped by continent and indexed by prefix, details the award rules, and provides application forms and a wealth of information and advice for the island enthusiast. The colorful new IOTA certificates are also shown. The latest *RSGB IOTA Directory* is an essential purchase for those interested in island-chasing. Copies are available from the ARRL at **www.arrl.org/shop**.

CQ MAGAZINE AWARDS

Worked All Zones (WAZ)

The *CQ* WAZ Award will be issued to any licensed amateur station presenting proper QSL cards as proof of contact with the 40 zones of the world as defined in the award rules. QSL cards may be checked by any authorized *CQ* checkpoint or sent directly to the WAZ Award Manager, Floyd Gerald, N5FG, 17 Green Hollow Rd, Wiggins, MS 39577, e-mail **n5fg@cq-amateur-radio.com**. Many of the major DX clubs in the United States and Canada and most national Amateur Radio societies abroad are authorized *CQ* checkpoints. Check the *CQ* website, **www.cq-amateur-radio.com**, for the current rules, zone lists, forms, checkpoints, processing fees and payment information. Paper copies of zone maps, rules and application forms are available from the WAZ Award Manager or CQ Communications, 25 Newbridge Rd, Hicksville, NY 11801. Send a business-size (4 × 9-inch), self-addressed envelope with two units of First-Class postage or $2 (US stations), or a self-addressed envelope and 3 IRCs (non-US stations).

The official *CQ* WAZ Zone Map and the printed zone list will be used to determine the zone in which a station

is located. Confirmation must be accompanied by a list of claimed zones, using *CQ* Form 1479, showing the call letters of the station contacted within each zone. Form 1479 should also clearly show the applicant's name, call letters and complete mailing address, as well as the award being applied for (such as Mixed, SSB, single band, and so forth).

All contacts must be made with licensed, land-based, amateur stations operating in authorized amateur bands, 160-10 meters. Any legal type of emission may be used, providing communication was established after November 15, 1945.

All contacts submitted by the applicant must be made from within the same country. It is recommended that each QSL clearly show the station's zone number. When the applicant submits cards for multiple call signs, evidence should be provided to show that he or she also held those call letters. Any altered or forged confirmations will result in permanent disqualification of the applicant. Decisions of the *CQ* DX Awards Advisory Committee on any matter pertaining to the administration of this award will be final.

All applications should be sent to the WAZ Award Manager after the QSL cards have been checked by an authorized *CQ* checkpoint.

WAZ By Mode and Band

In addition to the basic Mixed Mode award, certificates are available for these modes: AM, SSB, CW. RTTY, SSTV and Digital (any digital mode except RTTY). (For these awards, all contacts must be two-way in that mode and so indicated on the QSL cards.)

WAZ awards are also issued for various bands: 160 Meters (mixed only, contacts starting January 1, 1975); 80, 40, 20, 15 or 10 meters (any single mode, contacts starting January 1, 1973); 30, 17 or 12 meters (any single mode, contacts starting January 1, 1991); Satellite (mixed only, contacts starting January 1, 1989); and 6 Meters and EME (mixed only, contacts starting January 1, 1973). Applications and cards for Digital, 160 Meters, Satellite, 6 Meters and EME

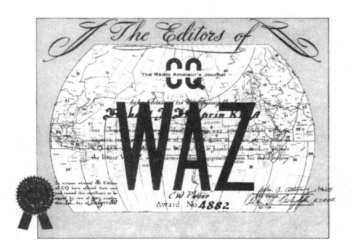

must be submitted directly to the WAZ Manager, not through checkpoints.

The 160 Meter WAZ Award requires that the applicant submit QSL cards from at least 30 zones. Stickers for 35, 36, 37, 38, 39 and 40 zones can be obtained from the WAZ Manager upon submission of the QSL cards and payment of the appropriate fees.

The Satellite and 6 Meter WAZ Awards require that the applicant submit QSL cards from at least 25 zones. Stickers for 30, 35, 36, 37, 38, 39 and 40 zones can be obtained from the WAZ Manager upon submission of the QSL cards and payment of the appropriate fees.

5 Band WAZ

CQ offers a most challenging DX award — 5 Band WAZ. Applicants who succeed in presenting proof of contact with the 40 zones of the world on these five HF bands — 80, 40, 20, 15 and 10 meters (for a total of 200) — will receive a special certificate in recognition of this achievement.

Contacts must be made after January 1, 1979, using any combination of modes (CW, SSB, RTTY). The award is available for Mixed Mode only. The first plateau, where the initial certificate is issued, requires a total of 150 of the possible 200 zones on a combination of the five bands. Applicants should use a separate sheet for each frequency band, using *CQ* Form 1479. Endorsements in increments of 10 are issued until the full 200 zone level is reached. A plaque is available at the 200 zone level.

Initial applications of up to 170 cards may be checked at an authorized checkpoint. Cards for all endorsements must be checked only by the WAZ Award Manager.

A regular WAZ or Single Band WAZ is a prerequisite for a 5 Band WAZ certificate. All applications should show the applicant's WAZ number. All applications should be sent to the WAZ Award Manager. The 5 Band WAZ Award is governed by the same rules as the regular WAZ Award and uses the same zone boundaries.

The *CQ* DX Awards Program

The *CQ* DX Award is issued in three categories: SSB, CW and RTTY. Each award requires proof of contact with 100 or more countries using that mode. All QSOs must be 2× SSB, 2× CW or 2× RTTY. Cross-mode or one-way QSOs are not valid for the *CQ* DX Awards. All contacts must be with licensed land-based amateur stations working in authorized amateur bands. Contacts with ships and aircraft cannot be counted. QSLs must be listed in alphabetical order by prefix, and all QSOs must be dated after November 15, 1945. The application (Form 1067B) and full rules and current fees are available from the *CQ* website, **www.cq-amateur-radio.com**.

QSL cards must be verified by one of the authorized checkpoints for the *CQ* DX Awards or must be included with the application and sent to the Keith Gilbertson, KØKG, *CQ* DX Awards Manager, 21688 Sandy Beach Lane, Rochret, MN 56578. In all cases, include adequate funds for return postage.

Endorsement stickers are issued for 150, 200, 250, 275, 300, 310 and 320 countries. The ARRL DXCC List constitutes the basis for the *CQ* DX Award country status. Deleted countries will not be valid for the *CQ* DX Awards. If a DXCC country is deleted, it will automatically be deleted from *CQ* award records and totals readjusted accordingly. Special endorsement stickers are available for 3.5/7 MHz and 28 MHz (100 countries); 1.8 MHz, QRP, Mobile, SSTV and Satellite (50 countries each).

The *CQ* DX Honor Roll lists all stations with a total of 275 countries or more. Separate Honor Rolls are maintained for SSB and CW. To remain on the Honor Roll, a station's country total must be updated annually.

CQ DX Field Award

The *CQ* DX Field Award rewards contacts with the 324 Maidenhead Grid Fields (10° latitude by 20° longitude rectangles lettered AA through RR). There are four categories — Mixed, CW, SSB and Digital — and 50 confirmed QSOs are required for the initial award. Endorsements are available at various levels up to the full 324 Fields. Special endorsement stickers are available for various bands and modes. Check **www.cq-amateur-radio.com** for details and forms.

CQ WPX Award

The *CQ* WPX Award is for working different Amateur Radio prefixes around the world (NN1, DL7, JA6, 9J2 and so on). For portable stations, the portable designator becomes the prefix. For example, WN5N/7 counts as WN7 and J6/WN5N counts as J6.

Certificates are issued for contacts on HF (160-10 meters) and 6 meters. Awards start at 400 prefixes for Mixed Mode and 300 prefixes for single-mode awards —CW, SSB and Digital. Cross-mode contacts are not eligible for single-mode awards. Endorsements are issued in increments of 50 prefixes.

Band endorsements are available for 1.8 MHz (50 prefixes), 3.5 and 5 MHz (175 prefixes), 7 and 10 MHz (250 prefixes) and 14 – 50 MHz (300 prefixes). Continent endorsements are available as well — North America (160 prefixes), South America (95 prefixes), Europe (160 prefixes), Africa (90 prefixes), Asia (75 prefixes), and Oceania (60 prefixes).

High scoring stations are eligible for the WPX Award of Excellence and for inclusion in the WPX Honor Roll.

As of mid-2012, *CQ* WPX Awards are supported by ARRL's Logbook of The World. LoTW users may track prefix confirmations and request credits toward *CQ* WPX awards. See **www.arrl.org/cq-awards** for details.

Applications (*CQ* form 1051) and appropriate fees should be sent to *CQ* WPX Award Manager Steve Bolia, N8BJQ, PO Box 355, New Carlisle, OH 45344. Complete rules, forms and other resources are available at **www.cq-amateur-radio.com**.

County Hunting: USA-CA Program

The United States of America Counties Award (USA-CA), also sponsored by *CQ*, is issued for confirmed two-way radio contacts with specified numbers of US counties. Full rules, forms and current fees are available from **www.cq-amateur-radio.com**.

The USA-CA is issued in seven different classes. Higher levels are awarded as endorsement seals the basic certificate. Also, special endorsements will be made for all one band or mode operations subject to the rules.

Class	Counties Required	States Required
USA-500	500	Any
USA-1000	1000	25
USA-1500	1500	45
USA-2000	2000	50
USA-2500	2500	50
USA-3000	3000	50
USA 3077	ALL	50

USA-CA is available to all licensed amateurs everywhere in the world. You can accumulate contacts toward the USA-CA Award with any call sign you have held, and from any operating QTHs or dates. All contacts must be confirmed by QSL, and such QSLs must be in your possession for examination by USA-CA officials. QSL cards must not be altered in any way. QSOs via repeaters, satellites, moonbounce and phone patches are not valid for USA-CA. So-called "team" contacts, where one person acknowledges a signal report and another returns a signal report, while both amateur call signs are logged, are not valid for USA-CA. Acceptable contact can be made with only one station at a time.

Unless otherwise indicated on QSL cards, the QTH printed on cards will determine county identity. For mobile and portable operations, the postmark shall identify the county unless other information is stated on QSL card to positively identify the county of operation In the case of cities, parks or reservations not within counties proper, applicants may claim any one of adjoining counties for credit (once).

The USA-CA program is administered by a *CQ* staff member acting as USA-CA Custodian, and all applications and related correspondence should be sent directly to the custodian at his or her QTH. Decisions of the Custodian in administering these rules and their interpretation, including future amendments, are final.

The scope of USA-CA makes it mandatory that special Record Books be used for application. For this purpose, *CQ* provides a 64-page 4.25 × 11-inch Record Book that contains application and certification forms and provides record-log space meeting the conditions of any class award and/or endorsement requested.

A completed USA-CA Record Book constitutes the medium of the basic award application and becomes the property of *CQ* for record purposes. On subsequent applications for either higher classes or for special endorsements, the applicant may use additional Record Books to list required data or may make up his own alphabetical list conforming to requirements. It is recommended that two be obtained, one for application

use and one for personal file copy. See the USA-CA section of the *CQ* website for cost and ordering information.

Make Record Book entries necessary for county identity and enter other log data necessary to satisfy any special endorsements (band-mode) requested. Have the certification form provided signed by two licensed amateurs (General or higher) or an official of a national-level radio organization or affiliated club verifying the QSL cards for all contacts as listed have been seen.

The USA-CA custodian reserves the right to request any specific cards for any reason. In such cases, the applicant should send sufficient postage for return of cards by registered mail. Send the original completed Record Book (not a copy) and certification forms and handling fee to Ted Melinosky, K1BV, 12 Wells Woods Rd, Columbia, CT 06237. For later applications for higher-class seals, send the Record Book or self-prepared list per rules and handling fee. For application for later special endorsements (band/mode) where certificates must be returned for endorsement, send certificate and handling fee.

County hunter activity may be found daily on these frequencies: 14.336 MHz SSB, 14.066.5 MHz CW and 10.122.5 MHz CW.

INFORMATION ON OTHER AWARDS

One of the handiest references for the awards chaser is *The K1BV DX Awards Directory* website at **www.dxawards. com**. As of mid-2012, this online directory contained information for more than 3300 different awards from 110 DXCC countries. *The K1BV DX Awards Website* also features sections with hints and suggestions for both the beginning and advanced collector of awards. This website is updated regularly and also features information on current short duration awards.

LOGBOOK OF THE WORLD (LOTW)

Note: Logbook of The World is an evolving system that is revised and updated on a continuing basis. The information given here was current as of mid-2012 but is subject to change. Please check **www.arrl.org/logbook-of-the-world** *for the latest details and more information.*

By the mid to late 1990s, the electronic transmission of QSO confirmations was a concept whose time had come. In some senses, Internet technology was rendering the time-honored methods of QSLing obsolete. As postage and printing costs rose and delivery difficulties and delays increased, many people were asking "why not the Internet?" At the July 2000 ARRL Board meeting, staff presented a concept for Internet-based QSLing. But the proposal for confirming QSOs went in a direction that many people didn't expect.

When the term "electronic QSL" hit the streets as early as 1998, most people envisioned sending e-mail images of a QSL card to one another. Some even suggested that these e-mail exchanges would include digital signatures to assure the integrity of the information. But the proposal to the Board in 2000 was to create *a depository of QSO information* that would allow participants to submit radio logs containing digitally signed QSO records. Logs from all participants would be collected in a secure, central database, where they could be scanned for matching confirmations. A pair of matching QSO records resulted in a confirmation that could be sent to the appropriate award system, where awards credit for both participants could be automatically recorded. After some discussion, then-Delta Division Director Rick Roderick, K5UR, spoke up and said, "So, this is like a Logbook of the World?" It is, and the name stuck.

Digital security experts, and active DXers/contesters Dick Green, WC1M, and Ted Demopoulos, KT1V, were hired to write the specifications for Logbook of The World (usually called LoTW or just Logbook). After some months pinning down system details, ARRL programmers and volunteers led by then-ARRL Web/Software Development Manager Jon Bloom, KE3Z, began writing the software for this complex and challenging project. Logbook of The World went "live" in September 2003. By mid-2012, the system had more than

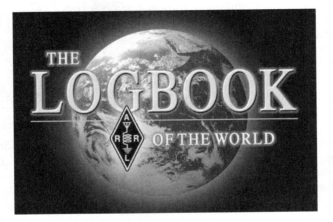

50,000 users worldwide, had received more than 425 *million* QSOs, and had made nearly *60 million* confirmations. Using only QSOs confirmed in LoTW, users had confirmed DXCC on 9 bands and WAS on 10 bands. Some stations have LoTW-only Mixed DXCC totals over 300! Stations from 339 current DXCC countries had submitted LoTW logs.

Trustworthy Data

Logbook of The World is designed to generate QSO confirmations that can be used for awards credits. That is to say, when you submit a log, your data is compared to all of the existing data in the database. If the log data you submit matches that in another station's record, the result is a confirmed QSO record. Either you or the other operator may then apply that confirmed QSO credit to various awards. All of this data is handled electronically, from the submission of the original logs to placement of the credit in an award database.

Creating a paper QSL card based on this electronic QSO data is *not* part of LoTW, although other services could be employed to perform that service. LoTW goes a step or two beyond the concept of a QSL card. A single QSL card is a one-sided request for a confirmation from the other side of the QSO. LoTW begins by verifying that a QSO has occurred between two stations, based on the "signed" data submitted by each.

In order for participants to have confidence in an electronic QSL system, they must be assured that each confirmation submitted to the system is authentic — that it comes from the true owner of the associated call sign. With digital signature technology, it is possible for an amateur to indelibly "mark" QSO data with a signature connected to his/her call sign. The Logbook of The World system uses digital signatures to ensure the authenticity of every QSO record. Digital signatures utilize a technology called *Public Key Infrastructure* or *PKI*. These signatures cannot be forged, and the QSO data cannot be altered without detection. This not only ensures that we know the origin of the data, but also assures us that the data has not been altered anywhere along the way.

A Digital Certificate

In order to be able to submit your log to Logbook of The World, you must obtain a *digital certificate*. A digital certificate ties the identity of a participant to a digital key pair, which allows an electronic message to be signed.

For digital signatures to be trusted, we must be sure of the identity of each person to whom a certificate is assigned. We will need to verify you are who you say you are. The security of the entire system depends heavily on the method used for verifying the user's identity. This process is called *Authentication*. Authentication for US call signs relies on a combination of information in the *FCC license database* and postal mail addresses. Authentication for non-US calls relies on photocopies of a radio license and an official identification document. You can find out more about how to obtain a certificate by visiting the ARRL Logbook of The World website (**www.arrl.org/logbook-of-the-world**).

You'll need to apply for, receive and install the digital certificate on your system to become a registered LoTW user and start submitting QSOs. The program *TQSLCert*, downloadable from the LoTW website, is used for generating requests for digital certificates and storing the resulting digital certificates that you receive from ARRL.

The Hows and Whens

To get started you should visit the LoTW website at **www.arrl.org/ logbook-of-the-world** where you can find directions, updates, news and tips. This system will be "always under construction" as we add software updates, additional capabilities and more user information. Once you have received and installed your digital certificate, another piece of software found on the LoTW website is are key to the process: *TQSL* is the utility program used to prepare log data for submission to LoTW.

Anyone with a suitable computer can submit data to LoTW as soon as they have received a digital certificate from ARRL. LoTW will accept signed logs in either ADIF (Amateur Data Interchange Format) or Cabrillo (contest log) format, which are standard in most commercial logging software. Log files are "signed" using a digital certificate. The signing process is a mathematical operation that will work best on computers with a fast, modern processor, but older computers will work. At present, you need to use a computer with a *Windows*, *Linux* or *Mac OS* operating system to run *TQSL* and *TQSLCert*. Access to an Internet connection is necessary.

You may send in QSO information from your logs as far back in time as 1945. Computer logging really got going only in the late 1980s and early 1990s, so it is not going to be likely that you will find many confirmations for QSOs farther back than that. But many people have typed their old logs into logging programs, so one never knows. You can query the system to determine if a certain station has submitted a log.

Although there may be cases when you will want to use *TQSL's* ability to manually enter a submission for a small group of QSOs (perhaps just the ones you need), the best method will be to submit all of your contacts to give others credit for your QSO even if you have no interest in theirs. The first time, submit your whole log. After that, submit that portion created since you last submitted (resubmitting *all* of your QSOs just slows down the system and is of no benefit to you).

A number of popular logging and contesting programs include built-in support for LoTW. That makes it easier to select a group of QSOs and prepare them for submission. Some logging programs automate the process completely, digitally signing the QSOs with your certificate, generating the appropriate file for submission, and calling up your e-mail program to send the file to ARRL.

How am I going to receive awards credit? Look for links to "Awards" on the LoTW website. Here you can find out what countries or states you have confirmed in the system and follow the directions to select the ones that you would like to use for credit for your DXCC, WAS, VUCC or *CQ* WPX award. (More awards may be supported in the future.) You can also link your existing DXCC or VUCC records to your Logbook account to see what credits you already have and where the new Logbook credits fit in. You can even see which awards you earned while you were busy working the necessary stations!

One very important point: *ARRL will not be the "QSL Manager" for the stations submitting logs to Logbook of the World*. If a contact is not in the log, you will need to work it out with the station involved. We will not search the log for your contact. If you can't submit a match, you won't be able to receive a credit. Broken calls and incorrect QSO information won't be acceptable. A time window will allow some leeway to allow for variations in time keeping, however.

What does it cost? Everyone is invited to submit data — Logbook wants all logs! For this reason, there will be *no charge for submitting logs*. This all takes time and money, of course, and LoTW is being paid for initially by ARRL members, so there is to be a per-QSO charge for each *credit used toward an award*. Check the LoTW website for the current fee schedule — you will be pleasantly surprised to see how much less expensive it is than the cost to print paper cards and exchange them via postal mail. Detailed instructions for using LoTW confirmations for award credit are shown on the website.

While we hope everyone will use and enjoy Logbook of The World, we realize that there will be those who cannot, or will not, use it. ARRL will *always* accept traditional QSL cards for its awards using the same applications and methods now in place. We do anticipate the nature of QSLing will change. We are confident that everyone will find their own "best" way to make use of this new technology. Most people use a combination of Logbook and traditional QSLing methods. Others have started "from scratch" and built credits for awards that in the past would have taken many years and hundreds or thousands of dollars in postage and printing costs to achieve. Some of those who have avoided operating because of the resulting QSL responsibilities have become more active. Will you be one of them?

Chapter 14

References

ALLOCATION OF INTERNATIONAL CALL SIGN SERIES

Call Sign Series	Allocated to
AAA-ALZ	United States of America
AMA-AOZ	Spain
APA-ASZ	Pakistan
ATA-AWZ	India
AXA-AXZ	Australia
AYA-AZZ	Argentina
A2A-A2Z	Botswana
A3A-A3Z	Tonga
A4A-A4Z	Oman
A5A-A5Z	Bhutan
A6A-A6Z	United Arab Emirates
A7A-A7Z	Qatar
A8A-A8Z	Liberia
A9A-A9Z	Bahrain
BAA-BZZ	China (People's Republic of)
CAA-CEZ	Chile
CFA-CKZ	Canada
CLA-CMZ	Cuba
CNA-CNZ	Morocco
COA-COZ	Cuba
CPA-CPZ	Bolivia
CQA-CUZ	Portugal
CVA-CXZ	Uruguay
CYA-CZZ	Canada
C2A-C2Z	Nauru
C3A-C3Z	Andorra
C4A-C4Z	Cyprus
C5A-C5Z	Gambia
C6A-C6Z	Bahamas
C7A-C7Z	World Meteorological Organization
C8A-C9Z	Mozambique
DAA-DRZ	Germany (Federal Rep of)
DSA-DTZ	Korea (Rep of)
DUA-DZZ	Philippines
D2A-D3Z	Angola
D4A-D4Z	Cape Verde
D5A-D5Z	Liberia
D6A-D6Z	Comoros
D7A-D9Z	Korea (Rep of)
EAA-EHZ	Spain
EIA-EJZ	Ireland
EKA-EKZ	Armenia
ELA-ELZ	Liberia
EMA-EOZ	Ukraine
EPA-EQZ	Iran (Islamic Rep of)
ERA-ERZ	Moldova
ESA-ESZ	Estonia
ETA-ETZ	Ethiopia
EUA-EWZ	Belarus
EXA-EXZ	Kyrgyz Republic
EYA-EYZ	Tajikistan
EZA-EZZ	Turkmenistan
E2A-E2Z	Thailand
E3A-E3Z	Eritrea
E4A-E4Z	Palestinian Authority
E5A-E5Z	New Zealand - Cook Islands
E6A-E6Z	Niue
E7A-E7Z	Bosnia and Herzegovina
FAA-FZZ	France
GAA-GZZ	United Kingdom of Great Britain and Northern Ireland
HAA-HAZ	Hungary
HBA-HBZ	Switzerland
HCA-HDZ	Ecuador
HEA-HEZ	Switzerland
HFA-HFZ	Poland
HGA-HGZ	Hungary
HHA-HHZ	Haiti
HIA-HIZ	Dominican Republic
HJA-HKZ	Colombia
HLA-HLZ	Korea (Rep of)
HMA-HMZ	Korea (Dem People's Rep of)
HNA-HNZ	Iraq
HOA-HPZ	Panama
HQA-HRZ	Honduras
HSA-HSZ	Thailand
HTA-HTZ	Nicaragua
HVA-HVZ	Vatican City State
HWA-HYZ	France
HZA-HZZ	Saudi Arabia
H2A-H2Z	Cyprus
H3A-H3Z	Panama
H4A-H4Z	Solomon Islands
H6A-H7Z	Nicaragua
H8A-H9Z	Panama
IAA-IZZ	Italy
JAA-JSZ	Japan
JTA-JVZ	Mongolia
JWA-JXZ	Norway
JYA-JYZ	Jordan
JZA-JZZ	Indonesia
J2A-J2Z	Djibouti
J3A-J3Z	Grenada
J4A-J4Z	Greece
J5A-J5Z	Guinea-Bissau
J6A-J6Z	Saint Lucia
J7A-J7Z	Dominica
J8A-J8Z	St. Vincent and the Grenadines
KAA-KZZ	United States of America
LAA-LNZ	Norway
LOA-LWZ	Argentina
LXA-LXZ	Luxembourg
LYA-LYZ	Lithuania
LZA-LZZ	Bulgaria
L2A-L9Z	Argentina
MAA-MZZ	United Kingdom of Great Britain and Northern Ireland
NAA-NZZ	United States of America
OAA-OCZ	Peru
ODA-ODZ	Lebanon
OEA-OEZ	Austria
OFA-OJZ	Finland
OKA-OLZ	Czech Republic
OMA-OMZ	Slovak Republic
ONA-OTZ	Belgium
OUA-OZZ	Denmark
PAA-PIZ	Netherlands
PJA-PJZ	Netherlands (Caribbean)
PKA-POZ	Indonesia
PPA-PYZ	Brazil
PZA-PZZ	Suriname
P2A-P2Z	Papua New Guinea
P3A-P3Z	Cyprus
P4A-P4Z	Aruba
P5A-P9Z	Korea (Dem People's Rep of)
RAA-RZZ	Russian Federation
SAA-SMZ	Sweden
SNA-SRZ	Poland
SSA-SSM	Egypt (Arab Rep of)
SSN-STZ	Sudan
SUA-SUZ	Egypt (Arab Rep of)
SVA-SZZ	Greece
S2A-S3Z	Bangladesh
S5A-S5Z	Slovenia
S6A-S6Z	Singapore
S7A-S7Z	Seychelles
S8A-S8Z	South Africa (Rep of)
S9A-S9Z	Sao Tome and Principe
TAA-TCZ	Turkey
TDA-TDZ	Guatemala
TEA-TEZ	Costa Rica
TFA-TFZ	Iceland
TGA-TGZ	Guatemala
THA-THZ	France
TIA-TIZ	Costa Rica
TJA-TJZ	Cameroon
TKA-TKZ	France
TLA-TLZ	Central African Rep
TMA-TMZ	France
TNA-TNZ	Congo (Rep of the)
TOA-TQZ	France
TRA-TRZ	Gabon
TSA-TSZ	Tunisia
TTA-TTZ	Chad

Call Sign Series	Allocated to	Call Sign Series	Allocated to
TUA-TUZ	Cote d'Ivoire	3XA-3XZ	Guinea
TVA-TXZ	France	3YA-3YZ	Norway
TYA-TYZ	Benin	3ZA-3ZZ	Poland
TZA-TZZ	Mali	4AA-4CZ	Mexico
T2A-T2Z	Tuvalu	4DA-4IZ	Philippines
T3A-T3Z	Kiribati	4JA-4KZ	Azerbaijani
T4A-T4Z	Cuba	4LA-4LZ	Georgia
T5A-T5Z	Somalia	4MA-4MZ	Venezuela
T6A-T6Z	Afghanistan	4OA-4OZ	Montenegro (Republic of)
T7A-T7Z	San Marino	4PA-4SZ	Sri Lanka
T8A-T8Z	Palau	4TA-4TZ	Peru
T9A-T9Z	Bosnia and Herzegovina	4UA-4UZ	United Nations
UAA-UIZ	Russian Federation	4VA-4VZ	Haiti
UJA-UMZ	Uzbekistan	4WA-4WZ	Timor-Leste
UNA-UQZ	Kazakhstan	4XA-4XZ	Israel
URA-UZZ	Ukraine	4YA-4YZ	International Civil Aviation Organization
VAA-VGZ	Canada	4ZA-4ZZ	Israel
VHA-VNZ	Australia	5AA-5AZ	Libya
VOA-VOZ	Canada	5BA-5BZ	Cyprus
VPA-VSZ	United Kingdom of Great Britain and Northern Ireland	5CA-5GZ	Morocco
VRA-VRZ	China (People's Republic of) - Hong Kong	5HA-5IZ	Tanzania
VSA-VSZ	United Kingdom of Great Britain and Northern Ireland	5JA-5KZ	Colombia
VTA-VWZ	India	5LA-5MZ	Liberia
VXA-VYZ	Canada	5NA-5OZ	Nigeria
VZA-VZZ	Australia	5PA-5QZ	Denmark
V2A-V2Z	Antigua and Barbuda	5RA-5SZ	Madagascar
V3A-V3Z	Belize	5TA-5TZ	Mauritania
V4A-V4Z	Saint Kitts and Nevis	5UA-5UZ	Niger
V5A-V5Z	Namibia	5VA-5VZ	Togolese Rep
V6A-V6Z	Micronesia (Federated States of)	5WA-5WZ	Samoa
V7A-V7Z	Marshall Islands	5XA-5XZ	Uganda
V8A-V8Z	Brunei Darussalam	5YA-5ZZ	Kenya
WAA-WZZ	United States of America	6AA-6BZ	Egypt
XAA-XIZ	Mexico	6CA-6CZ	Syria
XJA-XOZ	Canada	6DA-6JZ	Mexico
XPA-XPZ	Denmark	6KA-6NZ	Korea (Rep of)
XQA-XRZ	Chile	6OA-6OZ	Somalia
XSA-XSZ	China (People's Republic of)	6PA-6SZ	Pakistan
XTA-XTZ	Burkina Faso	6TA-6UZ	Sudan
XUA-XUZ	Cambodia (Kingdom of)	6VA-6WZ	Senegal
XVA-XVZ	Viet Nam	6XA-6XZ	Madagascar
XWA-XWZ	Laos (People's Dem Rep)	6YA-6YZ	Jamaica
XXA-XXZ	China (People's Republic of) - Macao	6ZA-6ZZ	Liberia
XYA-XZZ	Myanmar	7AA-7IZ	Indonesia
YAA-YAZ	Afghanistan	7JA-7NZ	Japan
YBA-YHZ	Indonesia	7OA-7OZ	Yemen
YIA-YIZ	Iraq	7PA-7PZ	Lesotho
YJA-YJZ	Vanuatu	7QA-7QZ	Malawi
YKA-YKZ	Syrian Arab Rep	7RA-7RZ	Algeria
YLA-YLZ	Latvia	7SA-7SZ	Sweden
YMA-YMZ	Turkey	7TA-7YZ	Algeria
YNA-YNZ	Nicaragua	7ZA-7ZZ	Saudi Arabia
YOA-YRZ	Romania	8AA-8IZ	Indonesia
YSA-YSZ	El Salvador	8JA-8NZ	Japan
YTA-YUZ	Serbia (Republic of)	8OA-8OZ	Botswana
YVA-YYZ	Venezuela	8PA-8PZ	Barbados
Y2A-Y9Z	Germany (Federal Rep of)	8QA-8QZ	Maldives
ZAA-ZAZ	Albania	8RA-8RZ	Guyana
ZBA-ZJZ	United Kingdom of Great Britain and Northern Ireland	8SA-8SZ	Sweden
ZKA-ZMZ	New Zealand	8TA-8YZ	India
ZNA-ZOZ	United Kingdom of Great Britain and Northern Ireland	8ZA-8ZZ	Saudi Arabia
ZPA-ZPZ	Paraguay	9AA-9AZ	Croatia
ZQA-ZQZ	United Kingdom of Great Britain and Northern Ireland	9BA-9DZ	Iran
ZRA-ZUZ	South Africa (Rep of)	9EA-9FZ	Ethiopia
ZVA-ZZZ	Brazil	9GA-9GZ	Ghana
Z2A-Z2Z	Zimbabwe	9HA-9HZ	Malta
Z3A-Z3Z	Former Yugoslav Republic of Macedonia	9IA-9JZ	Zambia
2AA-2ZZ	United Kindom of Great Britain and Northern Ireland	9KA-9KZ	Kuwait
3AA-3AZ	Monaco	9LA-9LZ	Sierra Leone
3BA-3BZ	Mauritius	9MA-9MZ	Malaysia
3CA-3CZ	Equatorial Guinea	9NA-9NZ	Nepal
3DA-3DM	Swaziland	9OA-9TZ	Congo (Dem Rep of)
3DN-3DZ	Fiji	9UA-9UZ	Burundi
3EA-3FZ	Panama	9VA-9VZ	Singapore
3GA-3GZ	Chile	9WA-9WZ	Malaysia
3HA-3UZ	China (People's Republic of)	9XA-9XZ	Rwanda
3VA-3VZ	Tunisia	9YZ-9ZZ	Trinidad and Tobago
3WA-3WZ	Viet Nam		

Morse Code Character Set[1]

A	didah	•—
B	dahdididit	—•••
C	dahdidahdit	—•—•
D	dahdidit	—••
E	dit	•
F	dididahdit	••—•
G	dahdahdit	——•
H	didididit	••••
I	didit	••
J	didahdahdah	•———
K	dahdidah	—•—
L	didahdidit	•—••
M	dahdah	——
N	dahdit	—•
O	dahdahdah	———
P	didahdahdit	•——•
Q	dahdahdidah	——•—
R	didahdit	•—•
S	dididit	•••
T	dah	—
U	dididah	••—
V	didididah	•••—
W	didahdah	•——
X	dahdididah	—••—
Y	dahdidahdah	—•——
Z	dahdahdidit	——••
1	didahdahdahdah	•————
2	dididahdahdah	••———
3	didididahdah	•••——
4	dididididah	••••—
5	dididididit	•••••
6	dahdidididit	—••••
7	dahdahdididit	——•••
8	dahdahdahdidit	———••
9	dahdahdahdahdit	————•
0	dahdahdahdahdah	—————

At [@]	didahdahdidahdit	•——•—•	AC
Period [.]:	didahdidahdidah	•—•—•—	AAA
Comma [,]:	dahdahdididahdah	——••——	MIM
Question mark or request for repetition [?]:	dididahdahdidit	••——••	IMI
Error:	dididididididit	••••••••	HH
Hyphen or dash [−]:	dahdididididah	—••••—	DU
Double dash [=]	dahdidididah	—•••—	BT
Colon [:]:	dahdahdahdididit	———•••	OS
Semicolon [;]:	dahdidahdidahdit	—•—•—•	KR
Left parenthesis [(]:	dahdidahdahdit	—•——•	KN
Right parenthesis [)]:	dahdidahdahdidah	—•——•—	KK
Fraction bar [/]:	dahdididahdit	—••—•	DN
Quotation marks ["]:	didahdididahdit	•—••—•	AF
Dollar sign [$]:	dididahdididah	•••—••—	SX
Apostrophe [']:	didahdahdahdahdit	•————•	WG
Paragraph [¶]:	didahdidahdidit	•—•—••	AL
Underline [_]:	dididahdahdidah	••——•—	IQ
Starting signal:	dahdidahdidah	—•—•—	KA
Wait:	didahdididit	•—•••	AS
End of message or cross [+]:	didahdidahdit	•—•—•	AR
Invitation to transmit [K]:	dahdidah	—•—	K
End of work:	dididahdidah	•••—•—	SK
Understood:	dididahdit	•••—•	SN

Notes:

1. Not all Morse characters shown are used in FCC code tests. License applicants are responsible for knowing, and may be tested on, the 26 letters, the numerals 0 to 9, the period, the comma, the question mark, AR, SK, BT and fraction bar [DN].

2. The following letters are used in certain European languages which use the Latin alphabet:

Ä, Ą	didahdidah	•—•—
Á, Å, À, Â	didahdahdidah	•——•—
Ç, Ć	dahdidahdidit	—•—••
É, È, Ę	dididahdidit	••—••
È	didahdididah	•—••—
Ê	didahdididahdit	•—••—•
Ö, Ø, Ó	dahdahdahdit	———•
Ñ	dahdahdidahdah	——•——
Ü	dididahdah	••——
Ź	dahdahdidit	——••
Ż	dahdahdididah	——••—
CH, Ș	dahdahdahdah	————

3. Special Esperanto characters:

Ĉ	dahdidahdidit	—•—••
Ŝ	didididahdit	•••—•
Ĵ	didahdahdahdit	•———•
Ĥ	dahdididahdit	—••—•
Ŭ	dididahdah	••——
Ĝ	dahdahdidahdit	——•—•

4. Signals used in other radio services:

Interrogatory	dididahdidah	••—•—	INT
Emergency silence	dididididahdah	••••——	HM
Executive follows	dididahdididah	••—••—	IX
Break−in signal	dahdahdahdahdah	—————	TTTTT
Emergency signal	dididahdahdahdididit	•••———•••	SOS
Relay of distress	dahdididahdididahdidit	—••—••—••	DDD

Morse Code for Other Languages

Code	Japanese	Korean	Arabic	Hebrew	Russian	Greek
•	he			vav	Е,Э E	E epsilon
—	mu	a		tav	Т T	T tau
••	nigori	ŏ		yod	И I	I iota
•—	i	ya		aleph	А A	A alpha
—•	ta	o	ta	nun	Н N	N nu
——	yo	yo	ya	mem	М M	M mu
•••	ra	m	alif	shin	С S	Σ sigma
••—	u	yŏ	noon	tet	У U	ΟΥ omicron ypsilon
•—•	na	ta	meem	reish	Р R	P rho
•——	ya	yu	seen	dalet	В V	Ω omega
—••	ho	p(b)	ta	chaf	Д D	Δ delta
—•—	wa	-ng	ra	gimmel	К K	K kappa
——•	ri	s	waw	heh	Г G	Γ gamma
———	re	p'	dal	chet	О O	O omicron
••••	nu	u	kaf	feh	Х H	H eta
•••—	ku	r-(-l)	ghain	lamed	Ж J	ΗΥ eta ypsilon
••—•	ti	n	kha	peh	Ф F	Φ phi
••——	no	k(g)	ha	ayen	Ю yu	ΑΥ alpha ypsilon
•—••	ka	ch(j)	dad	bet	Л L	Λ lambda
•—•—	ro	h	fa	samech	Я ya	ΑΙ alpha iota
•——•	tu	t(d)	lam	zain	П P	Π pi
•———	wo	k'	ain	kof	Й Y	ΥΙ ypsilon iota
—•••	ha	ch'	jeem		Б B	B beta
—••—	ma	t'	ba		Ь,Ъ mute	Ξ xi
—•—•	ni	ae	sad		Ц TS	Θ theta
—•——	ke		tha		Ы I	Υ ypsilon
——••	hu		za		З Z	Z zeta
——•—	ne		dhal		Щ SHCH	Ψ psi
———•	so		qaf		Ч CH	ΕΥ epsilon ypsilon
————	ko		zay		Ш SH	X khi
••—••	to		sheen			
••—•—	mi		he			
••——•	han-nigori					
•—•••	o					
•—••—	(w)i					
•—•—•	n					
•—•——	te					
•——••	(w)e					
•——•—	hyphen					
•———•	se					
—•••—	me					
—••—•	mo					
—••——	yu					
—•—••	ki					
—•—•—	sa					
—•——•	ru					
—•———	e					
——••—	hi					
——•—•	si					
——•——	a					
———•—	su					

Arabic: lam-alif

Spanish Phonetics

America	ah-MAIR-ika
Brasil	brah-SIL
Canada	cana-DAH
Dinamarca	dina-MAR-ka
Espana	es-PAHN-yah
Francia	FRAHN-seeah
Grenada	gre-NAH-dah
Holanda	oh-LONN-dah
Italia	i-TAL-eeah
Japon	hop-OWN
Kilowatio	kilo-WAT-eeoh
Lima	LIMA
Mejico	MEH-heeco
Norvega	nor-WAY-gah
Ontario	on-TAR-eeoh
Portugal	portu-GAL
Quito	KEY-toe
Roma	ROW-mah
Santiago	santee-AH-go
Toronto	tor-ON-toe
Uniforme	oonee-FORM-eh
Victoria	vic-TOR-eeah
Washington, Wisky	washingtone, wisky
Xilofono	see-LOW-phono
Yucatan	yuca-TAN
Zelandia	see-LAND-eeah
W	DOE-bleh-vay
0	cero	SEH-roe
1	uno	OO-no
2	dos	DOS
3	tres	TRAYCE
4	cuatro	KWAT-roe
5	cinco	SINK-oh
6	seis	SAYCE
7	siete	see-AY-teh
8	ocho	OCH-oh
9	nueve	new-AY-veh

—John Mason Jr., EA4AXW

A large selection of phonetic alphabets is at
www.w2aee.columbia.edu/phonetic.html

Morse Abbeviated ("Cut") Numbers

Numeral	Long Number			Abbreviated Number		Equivalent Character
1	didahdahdahdah	•————	didah	•—		A
2	dididahdahdah	••———	dididah	••—		U
3	didididahdah	•••——	dididdah	•••—		V
4	dididididah	••••—	dididididah	••••—		4
5	dididididit	•••••	dididididit	••••• or •		5 or E
6	dahdidididit	—••••	dahdidididit	—••••		6
7	dahdahdidididit	——•••	dahdididit	—•••		B
8	dahdahdahdidit	———••	dahdidit	—••		D
9	dahdahdahdahdit	————•	dahdit	—•		N
0	dahdahdahdahdah	—————	dah	—		T

Note: These abbreviated numbers are not legal for use in call signs. They should be used only where there is agreement between operators and when no confusion will result.

DX Operating Code

For W/VE Amateurs

Some DXers have caused considerable confusion and interference in their efforts to work DX stations. The points below, if observed by all W/VE amateurs, will help make DX more enjoyable for all.

1) *Call* DX only after he calls CQ, QRZ? or signs $\overline{SK}$, or voice equivalents thereof. Make your calls short.

2) Do not call a DX station:

  a) On the frequency of the station he is calling until you are sure the QSO is over ($\overline{SK}$).

  b) Because you hear someone else calling him.

  c) When he signs $\overline{KN}$, AR or CL.

  d) Exactly on his frequency.

  e) After he calls a directional CQ, unless of course you are in the right direction or area.

3) Keep within frequency band limits. Some DX stations can get away with working outside, but you cannot.

4) Observe calling instructions given by DX stations. Example: 15U means "call 15 kHz up from my frequency." 15D means down, etc.

5) Give honest reports. Many DX stations depend on W/VE reports for adjustment of station and equipment.

6) Keep your signal clean. Key clicks, ripple, feedback or splatter gives you a bad reputation and may get you a citation from the FCC.

7) *Listen* and call the station you want. Calling CQ DX is not the best assurance that the rare DX will reply.

8) When there are several W or VE stations waiting, avoid asking DX to "listen for a friend." Also avoid engaging him in a ragchew against his wishes.

For Overseas Amateurs

To all overseas amateur stations:

In their eagerness to work you, many W and VE amateurs resort to practices that cause confusion and QRM. Most of this is good-intentioned but ill-advised; some of it is intentional and selfish. The key to the cessation of unethical DX operating practices is in your hands. We believe that your adoption of certain operating habits will increase your enjoyment of Amateur Radio and that of amateurs on this side who are eager to work you. We recommend your adoption of the following principles:

1) Do not answer calls on your own frequency.

2) Answer calls from W/VE stations only when their signals are of good quality.

3) Refuse to answer calls from other stations when you are already in contact with someone, and do not acknowledge calls from amateurs who indicate they wish to be "next."

4) Give *everybody* a break. When many W/VE amateurs are patiently and quietly waiting to work you, avoid complying with requests to "listen for a friend."

5) Tell listeners where to call you by indicating how many kilohertz up (U) or down (D) from your frequency you are listening.

6) Use the ARRL-recommended ending signals, especially $\overline{KN}$ to indicate to impatient listeners the status of the QSO. $\overline{KN}$ means "Go ahead (specific station); all others keep out."

7) Let it be known that you avoid working amateurs who are constant violators of these principles.

ARRL Procedural Signals (Prosigns)

In general, the CW prosigns are used on all data modes as well, although word abbreviations may be spelled out. That is, "CLEAR" might be used rather than "CL" on radioteletype. Additional radioteletype conventions appear at the end of the table.

Situation	CW	Voice
check for a clear frequency	QRL?	Is the frequency in use?
seek contact with any station	CQ	CQ
after call to specific named station or to indicate end of message	AR	over, end of message
invite any station to transmit	K	go
invite a specific named station to transmit	KN	go only
invite receiving station to transmit	BK	back to you
all received correctly	R	received
please stand by	AS	wait, stand by
end of contact (sent before call sign)	SK	clear
going off the air	CL	closing station

Additional RTTY prosigns

SK QRZ—Ending contact, but listening on frequency.
SK KN—Ending contact, but listening for one last transmission from the other station.
SK SZ—Signing off and listening on the frequency for any other calls.

Q Signals

These Q signals most often need to be expressed with brevity and clarity in amateur work. (Q abbreviations take the form of questions only when each is sent followed by a question mark.)

QRA What is the name of your station? The name of your station is _____.

QRG Will you tell me my exact frequency (or that of _____)? Your exact frequency (or that of _____) is _____ kHz.

QRH Does my frequency vary? Your frequency varies.

QRI How is the tone of my transmission? The tone of your transmission is _____ (1. Good; 2. Variable; 3. Bad).

QRJ Are you receiving me badly? I cannot receive you. Your signals are too weak.

QRK What is the intelligibility of my signals (or those of _____)? The intelligibility of your signals (or those of _____) is _____ (1. Bad; 2. Poor; 3. Fair; 4. Good; 5. Excellent).

QRL Are you busy? I am busy (or I am busy with _____). Please do not interfere.

QRM Is my transmission being interfered with? Your transmission is being interfered with (1. Nil; 2. Slightly; 3. Moderately; 4. Severely; 5. Extremely.)

QRN Are you troubled by static? I am troubled by static _____ (1-5 as under QRM).

QRO Shall I increase power? Increase power.

QRP Shall I decrease power? Decrease power.

QRQ Shall I send faster? Send faster (_____ WPM).

QRS Shall I send more slowly? Send more slowly (_____ WPM).

QRT Shall I stop sending? Stop sending.

QRU Have you anything for me? I have nothing for you.

QRV Are you ready? I am ready.

QRW Shall I inform _____ that you are calling on _____ kHz? Please inform _____ that I am calling on _____ kHz.

QRX When will you call me again? I will call you again at _____ hours (on _____ kHz).

QRY What is my turn? Your turn is numbered _____

QRZ Who is calling me? You are being called by _____ (on _____ kHz).

QSA What is the strength of my signals (or those of _____)? The strength of your signals (or those of _____) is _____

(1. Scarcely perceptible; 2. Weak; 3. Fairly good; 4. Good; 5. Very good).

QSB Are my signals fading? Your signals are fading.

QSD Is my keying defective? Your keying is defective.

QSG Shall I send _____ messages at a time? Send _____ messages at a time.

QSK Can you hear me between your signals and if so can I break in on your transmission? I can hear you between my signals; break in on my transmission.

QSL Can you acknowledge receipt? I am acknowledging receipt.

QSM Shall I repeat the last message which I sent you, or some previous message? Repeat the last message which you sent me [or message(s) number(s) _____].

QSN Did you hear me (or _____) on _____ kHz? I did hear you (or _____) on _____ kHz.

QSO Can you communicate with _____ direct or by relay? I can communicate with _____ direct (or by relay through _____).

QSP Will you relay to _____? I will relay to _____

QST General call preceding a message addressed to all amateurs and ARRL members. This is in effect "CQ ARRL."

QSU Shall I send or reply on this frequency (or on _____ kHz)? Send or reply on this frequency (or _____ kHz).

QSV Shall I send a series of Vs on this frequency (or on _____ kHz)? Send a series of Vs on this frequency (or on _____ kHz).

QSW Will you send on this frequency (or on _____ kHz)? I am going to send on this frequency (or on _____ kHz).

QSX Will you listen to _____ on _____ kHz? I am listening to _____ on _____ kHz.

QSY Shall I change to transmission on another frequency? Change to transmission on another frequency (or on _____ kHz).

QSZ Shall I send each word or group more than once? Send each word or group twice (or _____ times).

QTA Shall I cancel message number _____? Cancel message number _____

QTB Do you agree with my counting of words? I do not agree

with your counting of words. I will repeat the first letter or digit of each word or group.

QTC How many messages have you to send? I have _____ messages for you (or for _____).

QTH What is your location? My location is _____

QTR What is the correct time? The correct time is _____

QTV Shall I stand guard for you? Stand guard for me.

QTX Will you keep your station open for further communication with me? Keep your station open for me.

QUA Have you news of _____? I have news of _____.

ARRL QN Signals

QNA* Answer in prearranged order.

QNB* Act as relay between _____ and _____.

QNC All net stations copy. I have a message for all net stations.

QND* Net is Directed (Controlled by net control station.)

QNE* Entire net stand by.

QNF Net is Free (not controlled).

QNG Take over as net control station

QNH Your net frequency is High.

QNI Net stations report in. I am reporting into the net. (Follow with a list of traffic or QRU.)

QNJ Can you copy me?

QNK* Transmit messages for _____ to _____.

QNL Your net frequency is Low.

QNM* You are QRMing the net. Stand by.

QNN Net control station is _____. What station has net control?

QNO Station is leaving the net.

QNP Unable to copy you. Unable to copy _____.

QNQ* Move frequency to _____ and wait for _____ to finish handling traffic. Then send him traffic for _____.

QNR* Answer _____ and Receive traffic.

QNS Following Stations are in the net.* (follow with list.) Request list of stations in the net.

QNT I request permission to leave the net for _____ minutes.

QNU* The net has traffic for *you*. Stand by.

QNV* Establish contact with _____ on this frequency. If successful, move to _____ and send him traffic for _____.

QNW How do I route messages for _____?

QNX You are excused from the net.*

QNY* Shift to another frequency (or to _____ kHz) to clear traffic with _____.

QNZ Zero beat your signal with mine.

**For use only by the Net Control Station.*

Notes on Use of QN Signals

These QN signals are special ARRL signals for use in amateur CW nets *only*. They are not for use in casual amateur conversation. Other meanings that may be used in other services do not apply. Do not use QN signals on phone nets. *Say it with words.* QN signals need not be followed by a question mark, even though the meaning may be interrogatory.

The RST System

Readability

1—Unreadable.
2—Barely readable, occasional words distinguishable.
3—Readable with considerable difficulty.
4—Readable with practically no difficulty.
5—Perfectly readable.

Signal Strength

1—Faint signals, barely perceptible.
2—Very weak signals.
3—Weak signals.
4—Fair signals.
5—Fairly good signals.
6—Good signals.
7—Moderately strong signals.
8—Strong signals.
9—Extremely strong signals.

Tone

1—Sixty-cycle ac or less, very rough and broad.
2—Very rough ac, very harsh and broad.
3—Rough ac tone, rectified but not filtered.
4—Rough note, some trace of filtering.
5—Filtered rectified ac but strongly ripple-modulated.
6—Filtered tone, definite trace of ripple modulation.
7—Near pure tone, trace of ripple modulation.
8—Near perfect tone, slight trace of modulation.
9—Perfect tone, no trace of ripple of modulation of any kind.

If the signal has the characteristic steadiness of crystal control, add the letter X to the RST report. If there is a chirp, add the letter C. Similarly for a click, add K. (See FCC Regulations §97.307, Emissions Standards.) The above reporting system is used on both CW and voice; leave out the "tone" report on voice.

CW Abbreviations

AA	All after	HI	The telegraphic laugh; high	SKED	Schedule
AB	All before	HR	Here, hear	SRI	Sorry
AB	About	HV	Have	SSB	Single sideband
ADR	Address	HW	How	SVC	Service; prefix to service message
AGN	Again	LID	A poor operator		
ANT	Antenna	MA, MILS	Milliamperes	T	Zero
BCI	Broadcast interference	MSG	Message; prefix to radiogram	TFC	Traffic
BCL	Broadcast listener	N	No	TMW	Tomorrow
BK	Break; break me; break in	NCS	Net control station	TNX-TKS	Thanks
BN	All between; been	ND	Nothing doing	TT	That
BUG	Semi-automatic key	NIL	Nothing; I have nothing for you	TU	Thank you
B4	Before	NM	No more	TVI	Television interference
C	Yes	NR	Number	TX	Transmitter
CFM	Confirm; I confirm	NW	Now; I resume transmission	TXT	Text
CK	Check	OB	Old boy	UR-URS	Your; you're; yours
CL	I am closing my station; call	OC	Old chap	VFO	Variable-frequency oscillator
CLD-CLG	Called; calling	OM	Old man	VY	Very
CQ	Calling any station	OP-OPR	Operator	WA	Word after
CUD	Could	OT	Old timer; old top	WB	Word before
CUL	See you later	PBL	Preamble	WD-WDS	Word; words
CW	Continuous wave (i.e., radio-telegraph)	PSE	Please	WKD-WKG	Worked; working
		PWR	Power	WL	Well; will
DE	From	PX	Press	WUD	Would
DLD-DLVD	Delivered	R	Received as transmitted; are	WX	Weather
DR	Dear	RCD	Received	XCVR	Transceiver
DX	Distance, foreign countries	RCVR (RX)	Receiver	XMTR (TX)	Transmitter
ES	And, &	REF	Refer to; referring to; reference	XTAL	Crystal
FB	Fine business, excellent	RFI	Radio Frequency Interference	XYL (YF)	Wife
FM	Frequency modulation	RIG	Station equipment	YL	Young lady
GA	Go ahead (or resume sending)	RPT	Repeat; I repeat; report	73	Best regards
GB	Good-by	RTTY	Radioteletype	88	Love and Kisses
GBA	Give better address	RX	Receiver		
GE	Good evening	SASE	Self-addressed, stamped envelope		
GG	Going				
GM	Good morning	SED	Said		
GN	Good night	SIG	Signature; signal		
GND	Ground	SINE	Operator's personal initials or nickname		
GUD	Good				

Although abbreviations help to cut down unnecessary transmission, make it a rule not to abbreviate unnecessarily when working an operator of unknown experience.

ITU Recommended Phonetics

A — Alfa (**AL** FAH)
B — Bravo (**BRAH** VOH)
C — Charlie (**CHAR** LEE OR **SHAR** LEE)
D — Delta (**DELL** TAH)
E — Echo (**ECK** OH)
F — Foxtrot (**FOKS** TROT)
G — Golf (**GOLF**)
H — Hotel (HOH **TELL**)
I — India (**IN** DEE AH)
J — Juliet (**JEW** LEE ETT)
K — Kilo (**KEY** LOH)
L — Lima (**LEE** MAH)
M — Mike (**MIKE**)
N — November (NO **VEM** BER)
O — Oscar (**OSS** CAH)
P — Papa (PAH **PAH**)

Q — Quebec (KEH **BECK**)
R — Romeo (**ROW** ME OH)
S — Sierra (SEE *AIR* RAH)
T — Tango (**TANG** GO)
U — Uniform (**YOU** NEE FORM or **OO** NEE FORM)
V — Victor (**VIK** TAH)
W — Whiskey (**WISS** KEY)
X — X-Ray (**ECKS** RAY)
Y — Yankee (**YANG** KEY)
Z — Zulu (**ZOO** LOO)

Note: The **Boldfaced** syllables are emphasized. The pronunciations shown in the table were designed for speakers from all international languages. The pronunciations given for "Oscar" and "Victor" may seem awkward to English-speaking people in the U.S.

ARRL NUMBERED RADIOGRAMS

Group One—For Possible "Relief Emergency" Use

ONE	Everyone safe here. Please don't worry.
TWO	Coming home as soon as possible.
THREE	Am in _____ hospital. Receiving excellent care and recovering fine.
FOUR	Only slight property damage here. Do not be concerned about disaster reports.
FIVE	Am moving to new location. Send no further mail or communication. Will inform you of new address when relocated.
SIX	Will contact you as soon as possible.
SEVEN	Please reply by Amateur Radio through the amateur delivering this message. This is a free public service.
EIGHT	Need additional _____ mobile or portable equipment for immediate emergency use.
NINE	Additional _____ radio operators needed to assist with emergency at this location.
TEN	Please contact _____. Advise to standby and provide further emergency information, instructions or assistance.
ELEVEN	Establish Amateur Radio emergency communications with _____ on _____ MHz.
TWELVE	Anxious to hear from you. No word in some time. Please contact me as soon as possible.
THIRTEEN	Medical emergency situation exits here.
FOURTEEN	Situation here becoming critical. Losses and damage from _____ increasing.
FIFTEEN	Please advise your condition and what help is needed.
SIXTEEN	Property damage very severe in this area.
SEVENTEEN	REACT communications services also available. Establish REACT communication with _____ on channel _____.
EIGHTEEN	Please contact me as soon as possible at _____.
NINETEEN	Request health and welfare report on _____ . (State name, address and telephone number.)
TWENTY	Temporarily stranded. Will need some assistance. Please contact me at _____.
TWENTY ONE	Search and Rescue assistance is needed by local authorities here. Advise availability.
TWENTY TWO	Need accurate information on the extent and type of conditions now existing at your location. Please furnish this information and reply without delay.
TWENTY THREE	Report at once the accessibility and best way to reach your location.
TWENTY FOUR	Evacuation of residents from this area urgently needed. Advise plans for help.
TWENTY FIVE	Furnish as soon as possible the weather conditions at your location.
TWENTY SIX	Help and care for evacuation of sick and injured from this location needed at once.

Emergency/priority messages originating from official sources must carry the signature of the originating official.

Group Two—Routine Messages

FORTY SIX	Greetings on your birthday and best wishes for many more to come.
FORTY SEVEN	Reference your message number _____ to _____ delivered on _____ at _____ UTC.
FIFTY	Greetings by Amateur Radio.
FIFTY ONE	Greetings by Amateur Radio. This message is sent as a free public service by ham radio operators at _____. Am having a wonderful time.
FIFTY TWO	Really enjoyed being with you. Looking forward to getting together again.
FIFTY THREE	Received your _____. It's appreciated; many thanks.
FIFTY FOUR	Many thanks for your good wishes.
FIFTY FIVE	Good news is always welcome. Very delighted to hear about yours.
FIFTY SIX	Congratulations on your _____, a most worthy and deserved achievement.
FIFTY SEVEN	Wish we could be together.
FIFTY EIGHT	Have a wonderful time. Let us know when you return.
FIFTY NINE	Congratulations on the new arrival. Hope mother and child are well.
*SIXTY	Wishing you the best of everything on _____.
SIXTY ONE	Wishing you a very Merry Christmas and a Happy New Year.
*SIXTY TWO	Greetings and best wishes to you for a pleasant _____ holiday season.
SIXTY THREE	Victory or defeat, our best wishes are with you. Hope you win.
SIXTY FOUR	Arrived safely at _____.
SIXTY FIVE	Arriving _____ on _____. Please arrange to meet me there.
SIXTY SIX	DX QSLs are on hand for you at the _____ QSL Bureau. Send _____ self addressed envelopes.
SIXTY SEVEN	Your message number _____ undeliverable because of _____. Please advise.
SIXTY EIGHT	Sorry to hear you are ill. Best wishes for a speedy recovery.
SIXTY NINE	Welcome to the _____. We are glad to have you with us and hope you will enjoy the fun and fellowship of the organization.

*Can be used for all holidays.
Note: ARL numbers should be spelled out at all times.

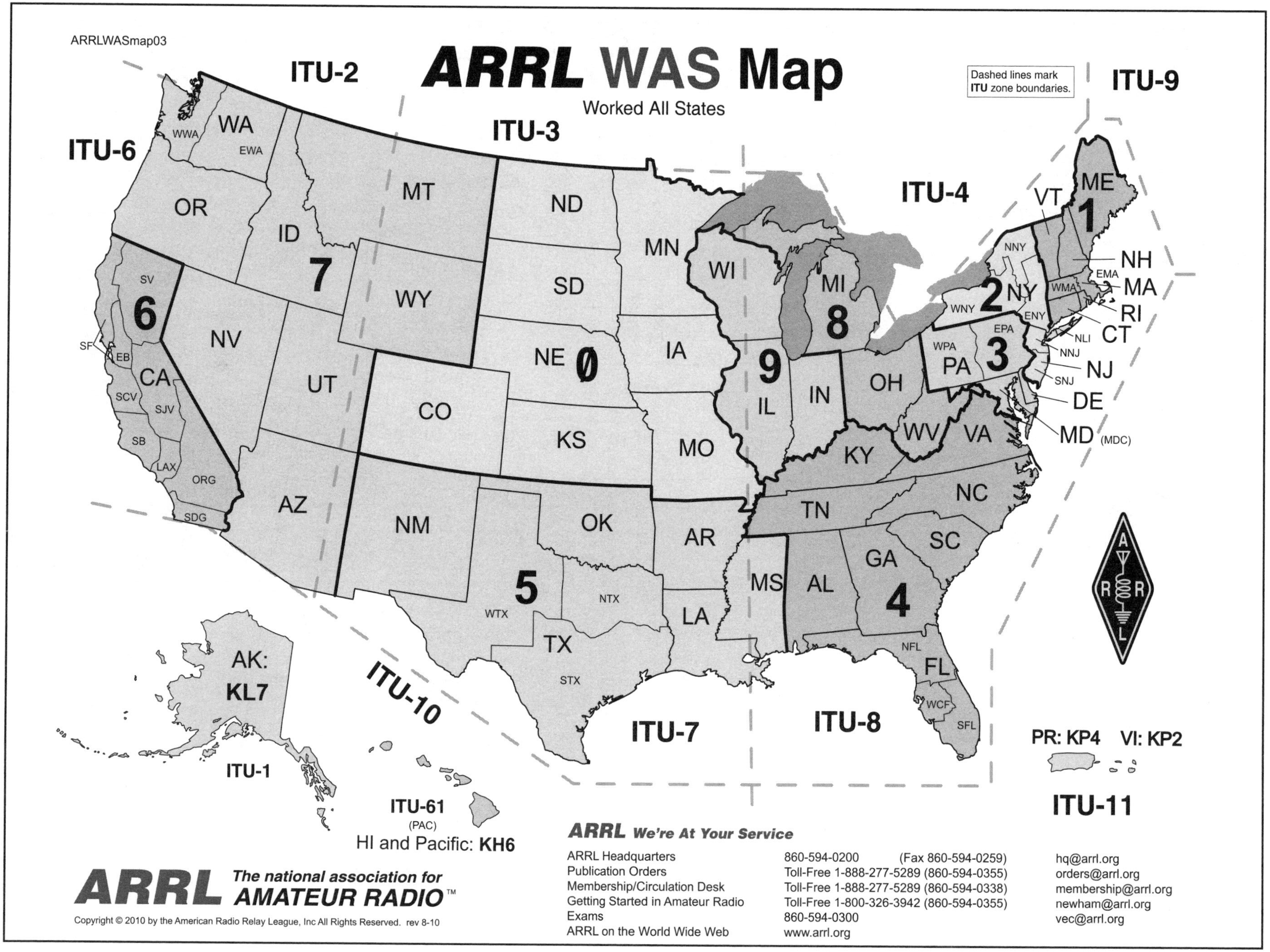
ARRLWASmap03
ARRL WAS Map
Worked All States
Dashed lines mark ITU zone boundaries.
ITU-2
ITU-3
ITU-4
ITU-6
ITU-9
ITU-1
ITU-10
ITU-7
ITU-8
ITU-11
ITU-61
(PAC)
HI and Pacific: KH6
AK: KL7
PR: KP4 VI: KP2
WA WWA EWA
OR
ID
MT
WY
ND
SD
MN
WI
MI
NV
CA SV SF EB SCV SJV SB LAX ORG SDG
UT
CO
NE
KS
IA
MO
IL
IN
OH
AZ
NM
OK
TX WTX NTX STX
AR
LA
MS
AL
TN
KY
WV
VA
NC
SC
GA
FL NFL WCF SFL
NY NNY WNY ENY NLI
PA WPA EPA
NJ NNJ SNJ
DE
MD (MDC)
ME
VT
NH
MA WMA EMA
RI
CT
1
2
3
4
5
6
7
8
9
Ø
ARRL We're At Your Service
ARRL Headquarters 860-594-0200 (Fax 860-594-0259) hq@arrl.org
Publication Orders Toll-Free 1-888-277-5289 (860-594-0355) orders@arrl.org
Membership/Circulation Desk Toll-Free 1-888-277-5289 (860-594-0338) membership@arrl.org
Getting Started in Amateur Radio Toll-Free 1-800-326-3942 (860-594-0355) newham@arrl.org
Exams 860-594-0300 vec@arrl.org
ARRL on the World Wide Web www.arrl.org
ARRL The national association for AMATEUR RADIO™
Copyright © 2010 by the American Radio Relay League, Inc All Rights Reserved. rev 8-10

A map showing US states, ARRL Sections and ITU zones

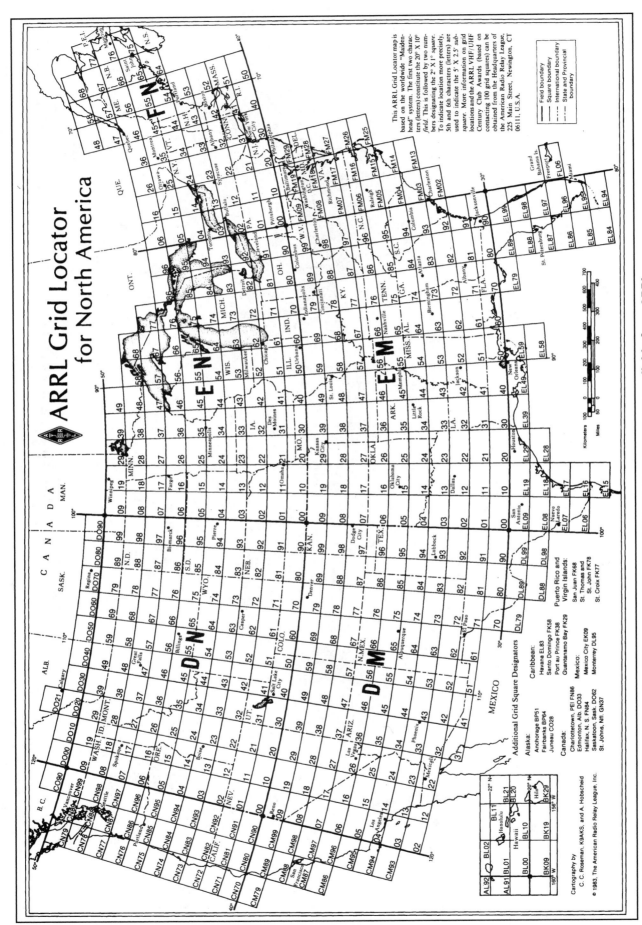

ARRL Grid Locator Map for North America. This map and the World Grid Locator Map are available from ARRL.

Index

The letters "ff" after a page number indicate coverage of the indexed topic on succeeding pages.

Notes

Notes

Notes

Notes

Notes

Notes

Notes

Notes

F E E D B A C K

Please use this form to give us your comments on this book and what you'd like to see in future editions, or e-mail us at **pubsfdbk@arrl.org** (publications feedback). If you use e-mail, please include your name, call, e-mail address and the book title, edition and printing in the body of your message. Also indicate whether or not you are an ARRL member.

Where did you purchase this book?   ☐ From ARRL directly   ☐ From an ARRL dealer

Is there a dealer who carries ARRL publications within:

☐ 5 miles   ☐ 15 miles   ☐ 30 miles   of your location?   ☐ Not sure.

License class:

☐ Novice   ☐ Technician   ☐ Technician with code   ☐ General   ☐ Advanced   ☐ Amateur Extra

Name _____   ARRL member? ☐ Yes ☐ No

_____   Call Sign _____

Address _____

City, State/Province, ZIP/Postal Code _____

Daytime Phone (   ) _____   Age _____

If licensed, how long? _____

Other hobbies _____   E-mail _____

Occupation _____

For ARRL use only	OPMAN
Edition	10 11 12
Printing	3 4 5 6 7 8 9 10 11 12

From _____

_____

_____

EDITOR, THE ARRL OPERATING MANUAL
ARRL—THE NATIONAL ASSOCIATION FOR AMATEUR RADIO
225 MAIN STREET
NEWINGTON CT 06111-1494

please fold and tape